INTRODUCTION TO
SOLID STATE PHYSICS

CHARLES KITTEL

PROFESSOR OF PHYSICS
UNIVERSITY OF CALIFORNIA
BERKELEY, CALIFORNIA

SECOND EDITION

New York · JOHN WILEY & SONS, Inc.

London

Library of Congress Catalog Card Number: 56-9822

Printed in the United States of America

Foreword

Brought about largely through the application of quantum mechanics, kinetic theory, and the theory of defect structures, great strides have been made recently in our understanding of the structure, properties, and behavior of materials. Scientists and engineers now use the tools of solid state physics and modern chemistry to investigate, develop, and apply metals, ceramics, glass, semiconductors, and polymers. In addition, but perhaps less obviously, research in atomic energy and electronics has catalyzed advances in the technology of these same materials. Developments in these fields have been stimulated by the demand for new materials with improved properties and for new properties in old materials.

The general plan of this series of books is to present the science and technology underlying the behavior and the manufacture and the technical use of all important solid materials. Serious overlapping will be avoided by having available to all authors the current state of development of the whole series so that each book can be better integrated with others related to it. The series is designed so that the books will meet the needs of university students, younger scientists and engineers, as well as the more experienced people who may not have had the benefit of the formal courses now coming into university curricula. It is proposed, furthermore, to serve these needs by presenting the material from a fundamental point of view so that the books will have lasting interest and importance.

In several volumes of the series the physics and chemistry of solids will be described. Other books will be concerned with the behavior of metals, ceramics, glass, semiconductors, and polymers. It is hoped that the series will be an extensive one, fully describing the science, technology, and engineering of materials. The scientific description of the behavior of these materials is the physics of solids. Dr. Kittel's first edition of this book is an admirable introduction and review of this subject.   The new edition, with its critical revision and new material, not only is the keystone of the series but also initiates it with a thoroughness and stature which the editor hopes to maintain.

JOHN H. HOLLOMON

Preface to the Second Edition

This volume is intended as an introductory textbook in solid state physics for students of physics, chemistry, and engineering. My object has been to write an elementary and short account of representative aspects of the physics of solids. The level of presentation supposes that the reader will have a good general familiarity with modern atomic physics to the extent of the undergraduate courses offered under this title in many universities. A course in quantum mechanics is not prerequisite to understanding most of the book, but the reader should be familiar with the Planck radiation law, the de Broglie relation, the Bohr theory of the hydrogen atom, the Zeeman effect, and the wave equation for free particles. Several advanced topics requiring a formal background of quantum mechanics are developed in appendices.

Solid state physics is a very wide field. It is concerned with the physical properties of solids, particularly the special properties exhibited by atoms and molecules because of their association and regular periodic arrangement in crystals. The existence of powerful theoretical methods and concepts applicable to a wide range of problems has been an important unifying influence in the field. It is quite natural therefore that an introductory textbook should emphasize the elementary theory of simple models of solids. In the selection of material I have frankly favored those areas which may be discussed in terms of simple, concrete, and well-developed models. One should remember, however, that real solids are almost always more complicated than the models we invent.

The second edition is longer than the first edition by about 200 pages. Half of the increase in length is brought about by fuller explanations of the basic concepts, particularly in the areas of crystal symmetry and energy band theory. The other half represents the addition of new material on alloys, semiconductors, photoconductivity, luminescence, and imperfections in solids. I have been assisted in the preparation of the second edition by the responses made to a survey by the publishers among teachers using the earlier edition as a textbook; it is a pleasure to thank collectively the many persons who thus gave me the benefit of their experience.

   This book is not intended to be a general reference book. Several active and important branches of solid state physics have not been mentioned at all. Among the topics omitted are internal friction, thermoelectric effects, phase transformations, oxide cathodes, surface physics, piezoelectricity, liquid and solid helium, plastics, and molecular crystals. As nearly every chapter is the subject of separate monographs by other authors, it is inevitable that the treatment of the subjects which have been included should be incomplete. In all chapters the references to the literature are intended only to be representative of some of the reviews and the classical papers, along with enough of a selection from recent work to enable the reader to get an impression of the nature of the current activity. The selection of citations from such a wealth of excellent work is more random than calculated. I extend apologies for those omitted through the action of the laws of chance.

   Problem sets are included at the end of every chapter, with problems of considerable length or difficulty marked by an asterisk. A very brief summary of relevant parts of thermodynamics and statistical mechanics is given in Appendix R. Gaussian cgs units are used except where otherwise noted. The value of e, the charge on the electron, is taken as negative in sign: $e = -4.80 \times 10^{-10}$ esu for the electron.

   The preface to the first edition included the following statement of acknowledgments: "I am greatly indebted to my students who have checked over parts of the volume: E. Abrahams, M. Cohen, H. Kaplan, F. Keffer, J. Tessman, and Y. Yafet. I wish to thank J. Bardeen for reviewing the chapters on superconductivity and semiconductors, and F. Seitz for reviewing the chapters dealing with imperfections in solids; K. K. Darrow has kindly reviewed several chapters. It is a pleasure to thank R. T. Birge for assistance in connection with the values of fundamental physical constants; N. Bloembergen for the suggestion of a number of problems; Sir Lawrence Bragg and W. M. Lomer for a photograph of a dislocation model; A. von Hippel and P. W. Forsbergh, Jr., for a photograph of ferroelectric domains; H. F. Kay and B. J. Applebe for a photograph of crystal growth pattern; A. F. Kip and M. Tinkham for a hyperfine structure photograph; E. R. Parker for a photograph of a low angle grain boundary; H. J. Williams for a ferromagnetic domain photograph; and W. H. Zachariasen for tables of ionic radii.   I wish also to acknowledge help and suggestions from W. Brattain, E. Fermi, C. Herring, A. N. Holden, Miss U. Martius, J. Weymouth, and Mrs. E. A. Wood.   Mrs. C. E. Thornhill has very kindly assisted in the preparation of the indexes."

The second edition was kindly checked throughout by R. E. Behringer.   The chapter on dislocations was almost entirely rewritten by John Fisher, to whom I am greatly indebted for his charitable help and authoritative discussion.   I am grateful to F. Stein for checking the proofs.   It is a pleasure to thank W. Shockley for numerous suggestions; F. Keffer and A. M. Portis for the suggestion of a number of problems; P. H. Keesom and N. Pearlman for a tabulation of values of the Debye temperature; D. S. McClure for a photograph of an exciton spectrum; J. B. Newkirk for photographs of crystal growth; A. L. Schawlow for a photograph of the domain structure of a superconductor; A. H. White for a photograph of transistors; W. J. Merz and R. Pepinsky for tabulations of data on ferroelectrics; M. Tinkham for assistance in the preparation of the subject index; J. C. Kendrew and R. G. Parrish for a Buerger precession camera x-ray photograph; F. L. Vogel, Jr., for a photograph of dislocation etch pits; Mrs. J. M. Joliffe for a powder camera photograph; J. Washburn for a Laue photograph; C. A. Fowler, Jr., for a photograph of domain patterns; R. L. Steere for an electron microscope photograph of a virus crystal; C. S. Barrett for x-ray photographs of the order-disorder transformation in Cu_3Au; C. J. Kriessman for a graph of values of the magnetic susceptibility of metals; S. Brenner and Miss D. Kontoleon for photographs of metal whiskers; J. W. Mitchell for a photograph of dislocation networks; H. Brooks for values of effective masses; Cyril S. Smith for a photograph of a dislocation grain boundary; and W. Knight for a susceptibility compilation.   I have profited particularly from a lecture series given at Berkeley by F. Seitz.   I wish also to acknowledge help and suggestions from R. H. Bube, M. Lampert, J. H. Hollomon, H. W. Lewis, R. Smoluchowski, J. E. Goldman, and W. D. Knight.   Longmans, Green and Company, the publishers of *Introduction to crystallography* by F. C. Phillips, have kindly given permission to reproduce a considerable number of figures used there.   I am grateful to A. F. Kip for discussions of his experience in teaching a course based on the book. Without the help of Mrs. C. E. Thornhill this edition could never have appeared.

C. KITTEL

Berkeley, California
August, 1956

Contents

spin resonance absorption. Macroscopic equations. Line width.
Zero field electronic splitting. Further remarks. Note on units.

absolute zero. Gyromagnetic and spin resonance experiments. Gyromagnetic experiments. Ferromagnetic resonance absorption. Ferromagnetic domains. Origin of domains. Coercive force and hysteresis. Reversible permeability. Magnetic materials. Anisotropy energy. Magnetostriction. The Bloch wall. Domain dimensions. Antiferromagnetism. Two-sublattice model. Susceptibility below the Curie point. Antiferromagnetic resonance. Determination of spin lattices by neutron diffraction. Magnetic properties of ferrites.

paramagnetic salts.   I. Perturbation of nearly free electrons by a periodic potential.   J. Tight binding approximation for metallic electrons.   K. Electrical conductivity at low temperatures.   L. Mobility in intrinsic semiconductors.   M. Derivation of the Conwell-Weisskopf formula.   N. Fermi level and the chemical potential.   O. Semiclassical discussion of ferromagnetic spin waves. P. The Bloch theorem.   Q. Important conversion factors.   R. Summary of results of thermodynamics and statistical mechanics. S. Values of general physical constants.

General References

Crystallography

F. C. Phillips, *An introduction to crystallography*, Longmans, London, 1946.
M. J. Buerger, *Elementary crystallography*, John Wiley & Sons, New York, 1956.

Atomic physics background

Max Born, *Atomic physics*, Hafner, New York, 5th ed., 1951.
F. K. Richtmyer and E. H. Kennard, *Introduction to modern physics*, McGraw-Hill Book Co., New York, 4th ed., 1947.

Elementary texts

F. O. Rice and E. Teller, *Structure of matter*, John Wiley & Sons, New York, 1949.
J. C. Slater, *Introduction to chemical physics*, McGraw-Hill Book Co., New York, 1939.
J. C. Slater, *Quantum theory of matter*, McGraw-Hill Book Co., New York, 1951.

Advanced texts

N. F. Mott and H. Jones, *Theory of the properties of metals and alloys*, Clarendon Press, Oxford, 1936.
F. Seitz, *Modern theory of solids*, McGraw-Hill Book Co., New York, 1940.
F. Seitz and D. Turnbull, *Solid state physics, advances in research and applications*, Academic Press, New York.
A. H. Wilson, *Theory of metals*, Cambridge University Press, Cambridge, 2nd ed., 1953.
R. E. Peierls, *Quantum theory of solids*, Clarendon Press, Oxford, 1955.
Handbuch der Physik, Springer, numerous volumes.

Data collections and bibliographical aids

Chemical Abstracts (especially the decennial indices).
Gmelins *Handbuch der anorganischen Chemie*.
Landolt-Börnstein *Physikalisch-chemische Tabellen*, J. Springer, Berlin, 5th ed., 1935; 6th ed., 1952.
C. J. Smithells, *Metals reference book*, Butterworths Scientific Publications, London, 1949.

xvii

1

The Description of Crystal Structures†

We are concerned first with the geometrical properties of perfect crystals. A perfect crystal is considered to be constructed by the infinite regular repetition in space of identical structural units or building blocks. We give in this chapter an introductory discussion of the essential symmetry properties of crystal structures. It is impossible to give a full discussion here; the interested reader is referred to the specialized textbooks listed at the end of the chapter. The properties of periodic arrangements of atoms are of central importance in solid state physics; in this chapter our task is to analyze and describe the geometrical properties of the possible periodic arrangements.

TRANSLATION GROUP

We define an ideal crystal as a body composed of atoms arranged in a lattice such that there exist three fundamental translation vectors $\mathbf{a}$, $\mathbf{b}$, $\mathbf{c}$, with the property that the atomic arrangement looks the same in every respect when viewed from any point $\mathbf{r}$ as when viewed from the point

$$(1.1) \qquad \mathbf{r}' = \mathbf{r} + n_1\mathbf{a} + n_2\mathbf{b} + n_3\mathbf{c},$$

where n_1, n_2, n_3 are arbitrary integers. The fundamental translation vectors are *primitive* if any two points $\mathbf{r}$, $\mathbf{r}'$ from which the atomic arrangement looks the same always satisfy (1.1) with a suitable choice of the integers n_1, n_2, n_3. We shall consider frequently the primitive translation vectors as defining the *crystal axes* $\mathbf{a}$, $\mathbf{b}$, $\mathbf{c}$, although other (non-primitive) choices of crystal axes will be employed also.

The operation of displacing a crystal parallel to itself by

$$(1.2) \qquad \mathbf{T} = n_1\mathbf{a} + n_2\mathbf{b} + n_3\mathbf{c}$$

is called a *translation operation*. The totality of such operations, for all values of the integers n_1, n_2, n_3, is known as the *translation group* of the crystal. The most important descriptive characteristics of crys-

---

† Most of this chapter is fairly difficult and may be postponed until a second reading.

tal structures are the symmetry operations[1] associated with the structure. The discussion of the symmetry of crystals in three dimensions can become rather tedious, and instead we shall treat fairly completely the theory of crystals in two dimensions, with a discussion of only a few important examples of structures in three dimensions.

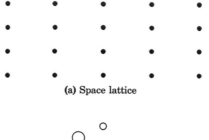

(a) Space lattice

(b) Basis, containing two different ions

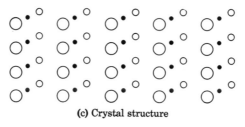

(c) Crystal structure

Fig. 1.1.   The crystal structure (c) may be considered to be formed by the addition of the basis (b) to every lattice point of the space lattice (a).

A parallel net-like arrangement of points is by definition a *lattice*, provided the environment about any particular point is in every way the same as about any other point.   It is essential to distinguish a lattice from a crystal structure: a crystal structure is formed by associating with every lattice point a unit assembly, or *basis*, of atoms identical in composition, arrangement, and orientation.   The distinction is illustrated in Fig. 1.1.   All lattice points are connected, as we would expect, by the translation operations **T** defined by Eq. (1.2) above.

[1] The present discussion of crystal symmetry follows generally the treatment by F. Seitz, Z. Krist. **88,** 433 (1934); **90,** 289 (1935); **91,** 336 (1935); **94,** 100 (1936); and Vol. 1 of *International tables for x-ray crystallography*, Kynoch Press, Birmingham, 1952.   A particularly readable discussion of space groups is given by F. C. Phillips, *An introduction to crystallography*, Longmans, London, 1946, pp. 221–272.

TWO-DIMENSIONAL CRYSTALS

The general two-dimensional lattice shown in Fig. 1.2 is an infinite array of points. The points obey the lattice condition that every point should have the same environment in the same orientation. It is apparent that **a, b** indicated in the figure are a possible choice for the primitive translation vectors of the lattice. The general parallelogram defined by primitive **a, b** forms a *primitive cell*, which is a type of *unit cell*. We shall later discuss unit cells in detail, but it will suffice now to state that the crystal translation operations applied to a unit cell will cover all points of the plane. A unit cell which contains lattice points at corners only is called a *primitive cell*.

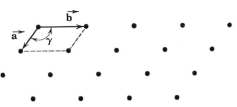

Fig. 1.2. General oblique lattice in two dimensions, showing a choice of the fundamental translation vectors **a, b** and a unit cell.

It is useful to introduce special relations connecting the primitive vectors **a, b.** The relations will define four special lattices with symmetry properties not present in the general oblique lattice, Fig. 1.2. To understand the special lattices, we must first discuss the symmetry operations associated with two-dimensional point groups.

TWO-DIMENSIONAL POINT GROUPS

A point group is a collection of symmetry operations applied about a point which leave the body invariant. The body may be, for example, a molecule, a group of atoms, a lattice, or a crystal structure. The symmetry operations in the two-dimensional crystallographic point groups are the one-, two-, three-, four-, and six-fold rotations about a point and mirror reflection across a line. The rotations are denoted by number, and the mirror reflection by the symbol m. For a planar molecule, any rotation $2\pi/n$, where n is an integer, may in principle be a symmetry operation. For a lattice, we shall now show that only values $n = 1, 2, 3, 4,$ and 6 are compatible with the translational symmetry requirement, Eq. (1.1).

An example of an excluded rotation is $2\pi/5$. A lattice does not exist which can be brought into coincidence with itself by a rotation of $2\pi/5$ about an axis through a lattice point. The proof of this particular statement is left as Problem 1.1, although the general result derived immediately below is sufficient to exclude such a rotation.

We have seen that the lattice is invariant under the translations

$$(1.3) \qquad \mathbf{T} = n_1\mathbf{a} + n_2\mathbf{b},$$

in two dimensions. As we shall see, this requirement puts restrictions on the allowed rotations and on the translations compatible with a given rotation. We also wish to study lattices which are invariant under more general conditions: under a rotation about a lattice point combined with a translation.

Referred to a fixed Cartesian coordinate system, the rotation of a point x, y through an angle ϕ (about the origin) to the point x', y' is represented by the equations

$$x' = x \cos \phi - y \sin \phi;$$
$$y' = x \sin \phi + y \cos \phi.$$

We assume that $\mathbf{a}$ is the shortest non-vanishing translation in the translation group. We choose coordinate axes so that $\mathbf{a}$ is parallel to the x axis. If now we rotate $\mathbf{a}$ by an angle ϕ, we get a new vector $\mathbf{a}'$ with components

$$a_x' = a \cos \phi;$$
$$a_y' = a \sin \phi.$$

If the lattice is invariant under the rotation ϕ, the vector $\mathbf{a}' - \mathbf{a}$ must be of the form $\mathbf{T}$, as in Eq. (1.3). The vector $\mathbf{a}' - \mathbf{a}$ has the components

$$a_x' - a_x = a(\cos \phi - 1);$$
$$a_y' - a_y = a \sin \phi;$$
and so

$$(1.4) \qquad |\mathbf{a}' - \mathbf{a}|^2 = a^2(2 - 2 \cos \phi).$$

Now we must have $|\mathbf{a}' - \mathbf{a}|^2 \geq a^2$, because $\mathbf{a}' - \mathbf{a}$ is a vector $\mathbf{T}$, and $\mathbf{a}$ is the shortest vector of this type. Thus, from (1.4), $2 - 2 \cos \phi \geq 1$, or $\cos \phi \leq \frac{1}{2}$, so that

$$(1.5) \qquad \frac{\pi}{3} \leq \phi \leq \frac{5\pi}{3}.$$

This is one condition on the acceptable range of ϕ. The rotation $\phi = 0$ is obviously also allowed, for we may take $\mathbf{a'} = \mathbf{a}$, so that $\mathbf{T} = 0$.

Another restriction is obtained in considering that the vector $\mathbf{a'} + \mathbf{a}$ must also be of the form $\mathbf{T}$ and not smaller in magnitude than $\mathbf{a}$. Thus we must have $2 + 2 \cos \phi \geq 1$, or $\cos \phi \geq -\frac{1}{2}$, so that

$$(1.6) \qquad -\frac{2\pi}{3} \leq \phi \leq \frac{2\pi}{3}.$$

This is the second condition on the acceptable range of ϕ. The rotation of $\phi = \pi$ is allowed, however, for we may take $\mathbf{a'} = -\mathbf{a}$, so that $\mathbf{T} = 0$.

The final restriction results when the inverse rotation $-\phi$ is applied to $\mathbf{a}$, giving a new vector $\mathbf{a''}$ with components

$$a_x'' = a \cos \phi;$$

$$a_y'' = -a \sin \phi.$$

The vector $\mathbf{a'} + \mathbf{a''}$ has components

$$a_x' + a_x'' = 2a \cos \phi;$$

$$a_y' + a_y'' = 0;$$

and so

$$(1.7) \qquad |\mathbf{a'} + \mathbf{a''}|^2 = 4a^2 \cos^2 \phi.$$

We must have, by the above argument, $4 \cos^2 \phi \geq 1$, or

$$(1.8) \qquad -\frac{\pi}{3} \leq \phi \leq \frac{\pi}{3}; \qquad \frac{2\pi}{3} \leq \phi \leq \frac{4\pi}{3}.$$

In addition, the values $\pi/2$, $3\pi/2$ are allowed, as we might have $\mathbf{a'} + \mathbf{a''} = 0$.

This completes the enumeration of conditions on ϕ. We see from Eqs. (1.5), (1.6), (1.8) and the accompanying remarks that ϕ may take on *only* the values

$$0, \pi/3, \pi/2, 2\pi/3, \pi, 4\pi/3, 3\pi/2, 5\pi/3.$$

The permissible rotations are therefore multiples of $2\pi/n$, where $n = 1$, 2, 3, 4, or 6. This is the result that we set out to prove.

ENUMERATION OF TWO-DIMENSIONAL CRYSTALLOGRAPHIC POINT GROUPS

The various combinations of allowed rotation and reflection operations are found to give rise to 10 different two-dimensional point groups permissible in a crystal. The point groups are denoted as follows:

$$1, 2, 1m, 2mm, 4, 4mm, 3, 3m, 6, 6mm.$$

The first position refers to the rotation about the point: thus the point group 4 contains 4-fold rotations. The second position refers to a mirror line normal to the x-axis, and it refers also to other mirror lines related to this by a rotation operation. The third position refers to the presence of other mirror lines related among themselves by symmetry, but not contained in the first set of mirror lines. Crystals having any particular point-group symmetry are said to belong to a particular crystal *class*.

The graphical symbols for symmetry operations are:

1	None	The graphical symbols for the point groups are built
2	●	up from those for the symmetry operations. The
		point-group symbols are shown in Fig. 1.3. Posi-
3	▲	tions of equivalent points are also shown; the
		symmetry operations of the group carry one point
4	■	into all the equivalent positions. The points them-
		selves should not be thought of as possessing sym-
6	⬢	metry elements; they should rather be thought of as
		scalene triangles, figures with no symmetry elements.

TWO-DIMENSIONAL BRAVAIS LATTICES

Mirror line ▬

The requirement that a lattice should be invariant under a rotation operation $2\pi/n$, where $n = 1, 2, 3, 4$, or 6, or under the mirror operation, places restrictions on the primitive translation vectors $\mathbf{a}$, $\mathbf{b}$, except for the point operations 1 and 2. The general oblique lattice, Fig. 1.2, is invariant under the point operations 1 and 2 without further restriction. All operations are always considered to be applied through a lattice point.

The point operation 4 obviously requires a square lattice, Fig. 1.4a. The point operations 3 and 6 require a hexagonal lattice, Fig. 1.4b. It is easily seen that this is invariant under a rotation $2\pi/6$ about an axis through a lattice point and normal to the plane.

The mirror reflection m is a little more interesting. We write the primitive translation vectors $\mathbf{a}$, $\mathbf{b}$ in terms of the unit vectors $\mathbf{i}$, $\mathbf{j}$ along the x, y axes:

$$(1.9) \qquad \begin{aligned} \mathbf{a} &= a_x\mathbf{i} + a_y\mathbf{j}; \\ \mathbf{b} &= b_x\mathbf{i} + b_y\mathbf{j}. \end{aligned}$$

If the primitive vectors are mirrored in the x axis, we have after the

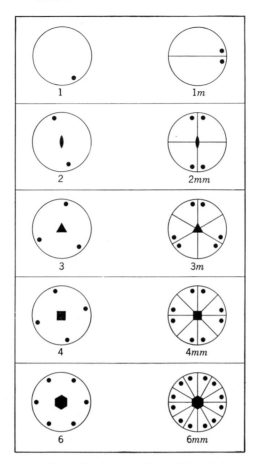

Fig. 1.3. The ten two-dimensional crystallographic point groups. Equivalent points are shown.

reflection operation

$$\mathbf{a}' = a_x\mathbf{i} - a_y\mathbf{j};$$

(1.10)

$$\mathbf{b}' = b_x\mathbf{i} - b_y\mathbf{j}.$$

We wish $\mathbf{a}'$, $\mathbf{b}'$ to be lattice vectors. One possible choice of $\mathbf{a}$, $\mathbf{b}$ to accomplish this is

$$\mathbf{a} = a\mathbf{i};$$

(1.11)

$$\mathbf{b} = b\mathbf{j};$$

the resulting lattice is rectangular, Fig. 1.4c.

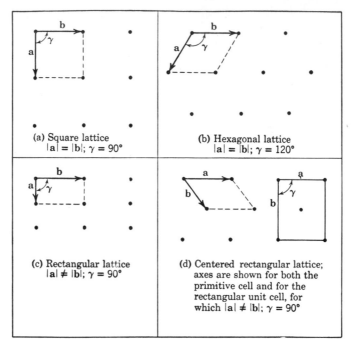

Fig. 1.4.   Special two-dimensional lattices.   These four, together with the oblique lattice (Fig. 1.2) form the five two-dimensional Bravais lattices.   The restrictions on the primitive translation vectors are given below each lattice.   Primitive cells are shown, completed by broken lines.

There is a second possibility, as $\mathbf{b}'$ will be a lattice vector if

$$\mathbf{b}' = \mathbf{a} - \mathbf{b},$$

or, by using (1.9) and (1.10),

(1.12)
$$b_x' = a_x - b_x = b_x;$$
$$b_y' = a_y - b_y = -b_y.$$

We have a solution if $a_y = 0$; $a_x = 2b_x$; thus another possible choice of primitive translation vectors is

(1.13)
$$\mathbf{a} = a\mathbf{i};$$
$$\mathbf{b} = \tfrac{1}{2}a\mathbf{i} + b_y\mathbf{j}.$$

This choice gives a *centered* rectangular lattice, Fig. 1.4d.   A centered lattice is denoted by c, and a primitive lattice is denoted by p.

We have now exhausted the two-dimensional lattices which are required by the point-group operations applied to lattice points.   Such lattices are called Bravais or space lattices.   The five possibilities are

summarized in Table 1.1.   The term *system* used there is a classification referring to the axial relations in an obvious way.

TABLE 1.1.   THE FIVE TWO-DIMENSIONAL BRAVAIS LATTICES

Lattice	Conventional Unit Cell	Corresponding Axes	Corresponding System	Point-Group Symmetry about Lattice Points
Oblique	Parallelogram	$a \neq b, \gamma \neq 90°$	Oblique	1, 2
Primitive rectangular	Rectangle	$a \neq b, \gamma = 90°$	Rectangular	$1m, 2mm$
Centered rectangular				
Square	Square	$a = b, \gamma = 90°$	Square	$4, 4mm$
Hexagonal	60° rhombus	$a = b, \gamma = 120°$	Hexagonal	$3, 3m, 6, 6mm$

TWO-DIMENSIONAL SPACE GROUPS

We remarked earlier in connection with Fig. 1.1 that a crystal structure is formed by associating with every lattice point (of a Bravais
lattice) a unit assembly or basis of atoms.   If the basis consists only
of a single atom at the lattice point (for this purpose atoms are usually
considered spherical in form), little more needs to be said.   The resulting crystal structure will have the highest point-group symmetry compatible with the lattice system, as tabulated.   These crystal point

System	Highest Symmetry Crystal Point Group
Oblique	2
Rectangular	$2mm$
Square	$4mm$
Hexagonal	$6mm$

groups are known as the *holohedral* point groups.

Suppose, however, that the basis
consists of a single molecule which has
itself no point-group symmetry; that is,
the point group is 1.   We naturally
would expect such a molecule to crystallize in the oblique system, as shown
in Fig. 1.5.   If there were two similar
molecules in the basis arranged with
point-group symmetry 2 about the
center of the line connecting the molecules, the crystal would be expected to
fall also in the oblique system, as
shown in Fig. 1.6.   In Fig. 1.6a, the
most obvious symmetry elements are the two-fold axes at the cor-

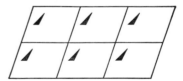

Fig. 1.5.   Oblique lattice with a
basis of one molecule of point-
group symmetry 1, as represented
by a scalene triangle.   The associated space group is denoted
by $p1$; that is, the lattice is
primitive and the only point
group is 1.

ners of a unit cell, but it is clear that other two-fold axes are implicit in the pattern. The pattern of symmetry elements is known as a *space group*, and a plan of a unit of the complete space group *p2* (short symbol) is shown in Fig. 1.6b.

A space group is a repetitive pattern of symmetry elements. It is not a crystal structure. For a crystal structure to be characterized by a given space group, the structure must display all the symmetry elements of the space group, and only these. The symmetry of a crystal structure is specified completely when the space group is known. The space group is characterized by the Bravais lattice and by the type

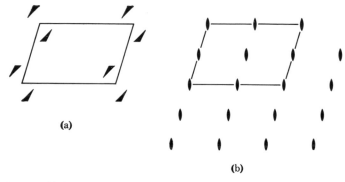

(a)

(b)

Fig. 1.6. (a) Oblique lattice with a basis of two identical molecules, the basis having point-group symmetry 2. (b) A unit of the associated space group. The short symbol for this space group is *p2*, and the long symbol is *p211*. The point-group elements are two-fold rotations.

and location of the point group and other symmetry elements within a unit cell. The space group, through its symmetry elements, determines the positions of equivalent points within the unit cell. For a crystal structure to be characterized by a particular space group, if any one point in a cell is occupied, it is necessary that all equivalent points be occupied by identical atoms or molecules.

There are seventeen distinct space groups in two dimensions. Of these, thirteen are obtained simply by locating the elements of one of the ten two-dimensional point groups at the lattice points of the appropriate Bravais lattices. From Table 1.1 it would appear that twelve space groups are obtained in this way, but the thirteenth possibility arises because the mirror plane in the point group *3m* can be oriented in two different ways relative to a hexagonal lattice.

The four remaining two-dimensional space groups utilize what is called a compound operation, the glide line of symmetry, combining a reflection and a translation. The glide line is denoted by the printed

TABLE 1.2. TWO-DIMENSIONAL LATTICES, POINT GROUPS, AND SPACE GROUPS

System and Lattice Symbol	Point Group	Space-Group Symbols		Space-Group Number
		Full	Short	
Oblique	1	$p1$	$p1$	1
p (primitive)	2	$p211$	$p2$	2
Rectangular p and c (centered)	m	$p1m1$	pm	3
		$p1g1$	pg	4
		$c1m1$	cm	5
	$2mm$	$p2mm$	pmm	6
		$p2mg$	pmg	7
		$p2gg$	pgg	8
		$c2mm$	cmm	9
Square	4	$p4$	$p4$	10
p	$4mm$	$p4mm$	$p4m$	11
		$p4gm$	$p4g$	13
Hexagonal	3	$p3$	$p3$	13
p	$3m$	$p3m1$	$p3m1$	14
		$p31m$	$p31m$	15
	6	$p6$	$p6$	16
	$6mm$	$p6mm$	$p6m$	17

Note. The two distinct space groups $p3m1$ and $p31m$ correspond to different orientations of the point group relative to the lattice. This possibility does not lead to distinct groups in any other case.

symbol g and the graphical symbol — — — — —. The operation consists of a reflection in the line followed by a translation of one-half the repeat distance along the line. In the space group $p1g1$ shown as No. 4 in the accompanying figures, the only symmetry operation is the glide line. This requires a rectangular lattice. A reflection in the glide line followed by a translation of one-half the repeat distance parallel to the line is seen to carry the arrangement into itself.

Table 1.2 shows the relations between the two-dimensional lattices, point groups, and space groups. The accompanying figures illustrate the symmetry properties of the seventeen two-dimensional space groups, as given in the *International tables for x-ray crystallography*.

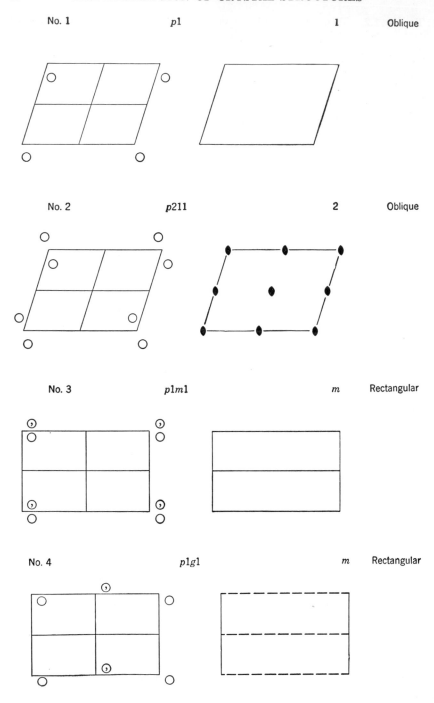

No. 1   *p*1   1   Oblique

No. 2   *p*211   2   Oblique

No. 3   *p*1*m*1   *m*   Rectangular

No. 4   *p*1*g*1   *m*   Rectangular

No. 5   *c1m1*   *m*   Rectangular

No. 6   *p2mm*   *mm*   Rectangular

No. 7   *p2mg*   *mm*   Rectangular

No. 8   *p2gg*   *mm*   Rectangular

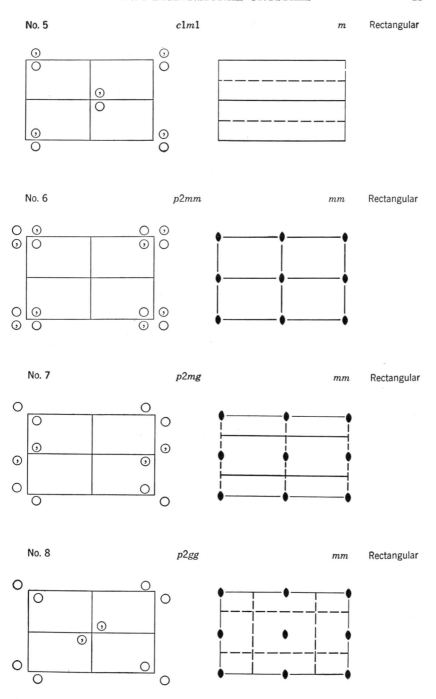

No. 9   *c2mm*   *mm*   Rectangular

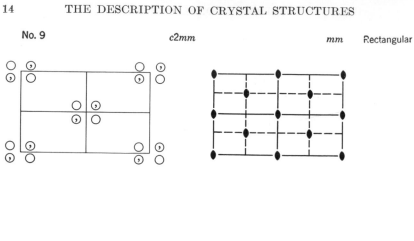

No. 10   *p4*   4   Square

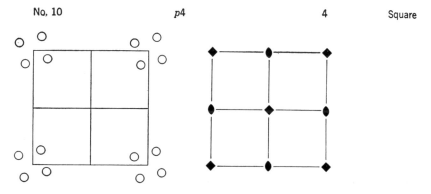

No. 11   *p4mm*   *4mm*   Square

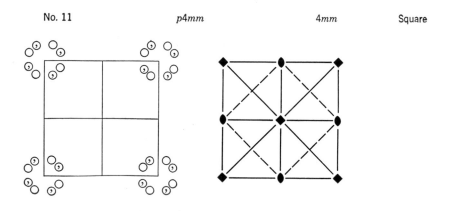

No. 12   *p4gm*   4*mm*   Square

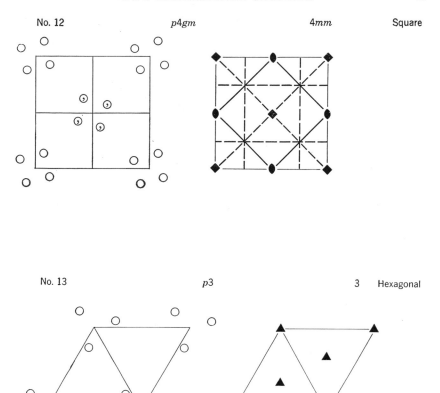

No. 13   *p3*   3   Hexagonal

No. 14   *p3m*1   3*m*   Hexagonal

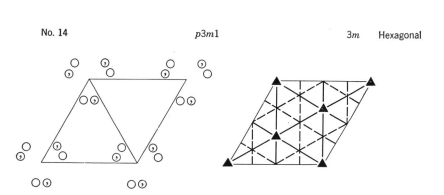

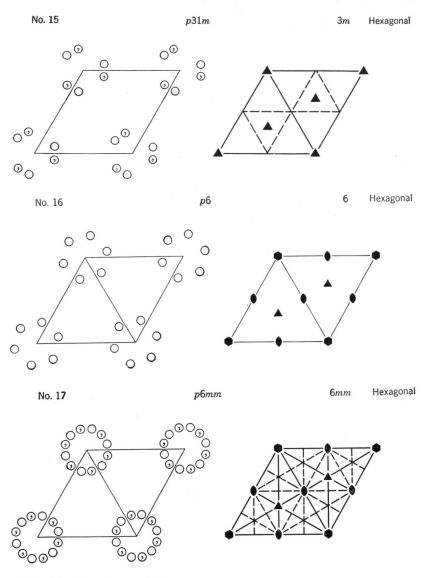

No. 15   p31m   3m   Hexagonal

No. 16   p6   6   Hexagonal

No. 17   p6mm   6mm   Hexagonal

The headings for each figure are:

Number   Space-Group Symbol   Point-Group Symbol   System

The left-hand diagram shows the equivalent general positions of the space group, that is, the complete set of positions produced by the operation of the symmetry elements of the space group upon one position chosen at random.   Points marked ⊙ are in a mirror relationship to points marked ○. The right-hand diagram shows the space group, that is, the position and type of the symmetry elements. The space-group symbol is given in the "long" form for completeness, although this form sometimes contains superfluous entries. The number of the space group is in accord with that in the International Tables, but the number is not intended to be used to identify the space group. The space-group symbol is intended for identification.

THREE-DIMENSIONAL CRYSTALS

THREE-DIMENSIONAL POINT GROUPS

It is possible to show,[2] by employing arguments similar to those developed for two-dimensional crystals, that there are thirty-two different three-dimensional point groups permissible in a three-dimensional crystal. We discuss first the symmetry elements associated with the three-dimensional crystal point groups:

Rotation axes. One-, two-, three-, four-, and six-fold rotation axes are permissible, corresponding to rotations by 360°, 180°, 120°, 90°, and 60°. The rotation axes are denoted by the symbols 1, 2, 3, 4, and 6. The axes 2, 3, 4, and 6 are often referred to as diad, triad, tetrad, and hexad axes, respectively.

Reflection plane. Mirror reflection is in a plane through the lattice point. A reflection plane is denoted by m.

Inversion center. A crystal structure possesses a center of inversion if the structure is brought into self-coincidence by the operation $r \rightarrow -r$, where r is the vector position of an arbitrary point in the crystal referred to the lattice point. An inversion center is denoted by $\bar{1}$.

Rotation-inversion axes. A crystal structure has a rotation-inversion axis if it is brought into self-coincidence by rotation followed by inversion. Crystals can possess one-, two-, three-, four-, and six-fold rotation-inversion axes. A combined rotation-inversion operation is known also as an improper rotation. The rotation-inversion axes are denoted by the symbols $\bar{1}$, $\bar{2}$ ($\equiv m$), $\bar{3}$, $\bar{4}$, $\bar{6}$. The symmetry operations for the last three are represented by the accompanying devices. We note that $\bar{3} \equiv 3$ plus center of inversion; $\bar{6} \equiv 3$ plus normal mirror plane.

$\bar{3}$

$\bar{4}$

$\bar{6}$

The thirty-two permitted crystal point groups may be arranged into seven systems according to the set of Bravais lattices on which they operate. The international point-group notation follows, where the symbol X stands for the order of rotation symmetry:

[2] A concise treatment is given by F. Seitz, Z. Krist. **90**, 289 (1935).

Rotation axis: X

Rotation-inversion axis: $\bar{X}$

Rotation axis with mirror plane normal to it: X/m or $\dfrac{X}{m}$

Rotation axis with diad axis (axes) normal to it: $X2$

Rotation axis with mirror plane (planes) parallel to it: Xm

Rotation-inversion axis with diad axis (axes) normal to it: $\bar{X}2$

Rotation-inversion axis with mirror plane (planes) parallel to it: $\bar{X}m$

Rotation axis with a mirror plane normal to it and mirror planes parallel to it: X/mm or $\dfrac{X}{m}\,m$

The crystal point groups are listed in Table 1.3, with their short and full international symbols and also with their Schoenflies symbol. The Schoenflies notation is commonly used in molecular spectroscopy but will not be employed in this text. The holohedral (highest symmetry) class for each system is the last entry under the particular system.

Pauling has suggested that the structures of some alloys with very large numbers of atoms in a unit cell can be understood as an attempt to incorporate in a crystal icosahedral groups of atoms with a *local* five-fold rotation symmetry. The most complex metal structure known, $Mg_{32}(Zn, Al)_{49}$ is of this type.

Stereograms of the thirty-two three-dimensional point groups are presented in Fig. 1.7. The general equivalent directions and symmetry elements are shown. The principal n-fold axis is represented by the n-sided figure in the center of the diagrams. Reflection planes are indicated by heavy lines. If there is present a reflection plane normal to the principal axis, the outer circle is heavy on the symmetry element stereogram. Symmetry axes perpendicular to the principal axis are denoted by the appropriate symbol placed at the ends of the line through the center of the circle. The symbol · represents a point above the plane of the paper; the symbol ○ represents a point below the plane of the paper. All the points shown can be obtained from any one of them by application of the several symmetry operations.

As an example in the use of the stereograms, we consider the group $4mm$, which is illustrated in detail in Fig. 1.8. The square in the center represents the four-fold axis. Starting with the point 1, we can obtain the points 3, 5, and 7 by applying successive rotations of $2\pi/4$. By reflection of point 1 in the mirror plane a, we obtain point 2; from this point, we obtain the points 4, 6, and 8 by rotations. The eight equivalent points are all that can be obtained from a single point by combinations of 4-fold rotations and reflection in a plane parallel to the rotation axis. From the diagram, we see that the set of equivalent points also possesses the reflection planes b, c, and d.

TABLE 1.3. THE THIRTY-TWO CRYSTAL POINT GROUPS

System	International Symbol Short	Full	Schoenflies Symbol
Triclinic	1	1	C_1
	$\bar{1}$	$\bar{1}$	$C_i(S_2)$
Monoclinic	2	2	C_2
	m	m	$C_s(C_{1h})$
	$2/m$	$\dfrac{2}{m}$	C_{2h}
Orthorhombic	222	222	$D_2(V)$
	$mm2$	$mm2$	C_{2v}
	mmm	$\dfrac{2}{m}\dfrac{2}{m}\dfrac{2}{m}$	$D_{2h}(V_h)$
Tetragonal	4	4	C_4
	$\bar{4}$	$\bar{4}$	S_4
	$4/m$	$\dfrac{4}{m}$	C_{4h}
	422	422	D_4
	$4mm$	$4mm$	C_{4v}
	$\bar{4}2m$	$\bar{4}2m$	$D_{2d}(V_d)$
	$4/mmm$	$\dfrac{4}{m}\dfrac{2}{m}\dfrac{2}{m}$	D_{4h}
Trigonal	3	3	C_3
	$\bar{3}$	$\bar{3}$	$C_{3i}(S_6)$
	32	32	D_3
	$3m$	$3m$	C_{3v}
	$\bar{3}m$	$\bar{3}\dfrac{2}{m}$	D_{3d}
Hexagonal	6	6	C_6
	$\bar{6}$	$\bar{6}$	C_{3h}
	$6/m$	$\dfrac{6}{m}$	C_{6h}
	622	622	D_6
	$6mm$	$6mm$	C_{6v}
	$\bar{6}m2$	$\bar{6}m2$	D_{3h}
	$6/mmm$	$\dfrac{6}{m}\dfrac{2}{m}\dfrac{2}{m}$	D_{6h}
Cubic	23	23	T
	$m3$	$\dfrac{2}{m}\bar{3}$	T_h
	432	432	O
	$\bar{4}3m$	$\bar{4}3m$	T_d
	$m3m$	$\dfrac{4}{m}\bar{3}\dfrac{2}{m}$	O_h

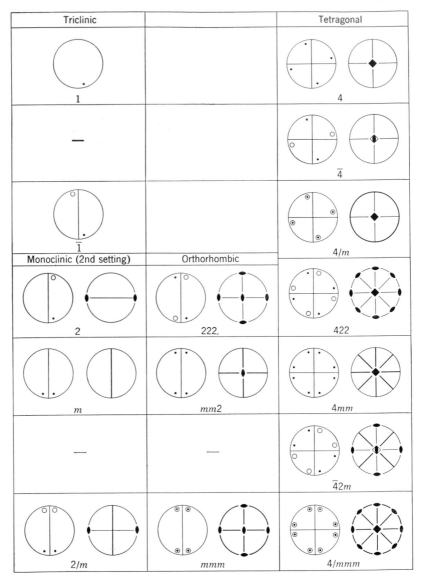

Fig. 1.7.   Stereograms of the 32 three-dimensional point groups.   The z axis is normal to the paper.   (From *International tables for x-ray crystallography*.)

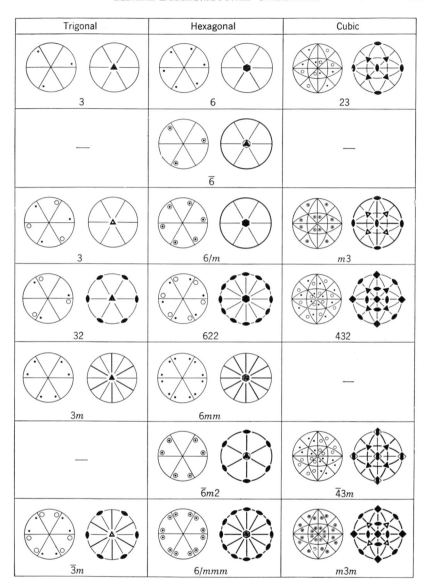

Fig. 1.7. (*Continued*).

The symmetry elements of a cube are shown in detail in Fig. 1.9. The inversion element is not indicated. The reader will benefit by identifying the elements of the point group $m3m$ shown in Fig. 1.7 with those shown in Fig. 1.9. In interpreting the elements of $m3m$ in Fig. 1.7, we recall that the stereogram shows the projection on an equatorial plane of the intersection of a symmetry element with the surface of a sphere drawn about the reference point.

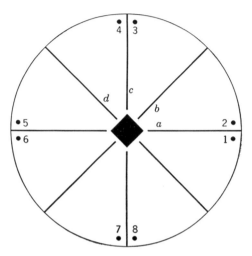

Fig. 1.8.   Stereogram of the point group $4mm$, showing equivalent points, four-fold rotation axis, and two sets of mirror planes.

Schiff[3] has shown how to construct paper representations of the non-cubic crystal classes. The representations exhibit the full symmetries of the point group and are useful in the classroom.

THREE-DIMENSIONAL BRAVAIS LATTICES

We saw in two dimensions that the ten permissible point groups were associated with five different Bravais lattices. In three dimensions it turns out by parallel arguments that the thirty-two permissible point groups require fourteen different Bravais or space lattices. The three-dimensional Bravais lattices are listed in Table 1.4. The lattices are grouped into seven systems: triclinic, monoclinic, orthorhombic, tetragonal, cubic, trigonal, and hexagonal. The division into systems is summarized conveniently in terms of the axial relations for the conventional unit cells. The axes a, b, c and angles α, β, γ are shown in Fig. 1.10. The fourteen space lattices are illustrated in

[3] L. I. Schiff, Am. J. Phys. **22**, 621 (1954).

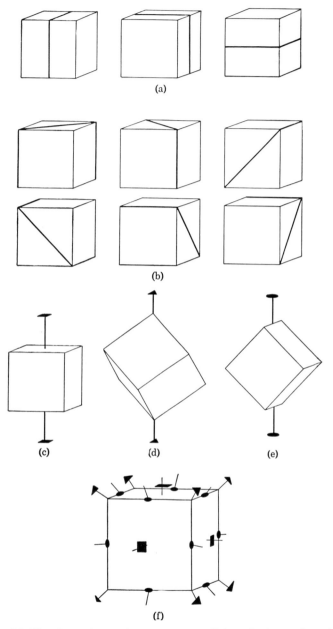

Fig. 1.9.   (a) The three planes of symmetry parallel to the faces of a cube.   (b) The six diagonal planes of symmetry in a cube.   (c) One of the tetrad axes of a cube.   (d) One of the triad axes of a cube.   (e) One of the diad axes of a cube.   (f) The thirteen axes of symmetry shown by a cube.   (After Phillips.)

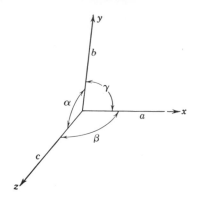

Fig. 1.10. Crystal axes.

TABLE 1.4. THE FOURTEEN BRAVAIS LATTICES AND CONVENTIONAL UNIT CELLS

System	Number of Lattices in System	Lattice Symbols	Nature of Unit-Cell Axes and Angles	Lengths and Angles to Be Specified	Symmetry of Lattice
Triclinic	1	P	$a \neq b \neq c$ $\alpha \neq \beta \neq \gamma$	a, b, c α, β, γ	$\bar{1}$
Monoclinic	2	P C	$a \neq b \neq c$ $\alpha = \gamma = 90° \neq \beta$	a, b, c β	$2/m$
Orthorhombic	4	P C I F	$a \neq b \neq c$ $\alpha = \beta = \gamma = 90°$	a, b, c	mmm
Tetragonal	2	P I	$a = b \neq c$ $\alpha = \beta = \gamma = 90°$	a, c	$4/mmm$
Cubic	3	P I F	$a = b = c$ $\alpha = \beta = \gamma = 90°$	a	$m3m$
Trigonal	1	R	$a = b = c$ $\alpha = \beta = \gamma$ $< 120°, \neq 90°$	a α	$\bar{3}m$
Hexagonal	1	P	$a = b \neq c$ $\alpha = \beta = 90°$ $\gamma = 120°$	a, c	$6/mmm$

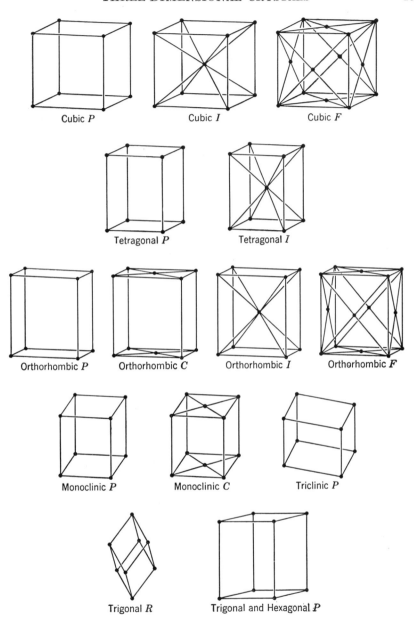

Cubic *P* Cubic *I* Cubic *F*

Tetragonal *P* Tetragonal *I*

Orthorhombic *P* Orthorhombic *C* Orthorhombic *I* Orthorhombic *F*

Monoclinic *P* Monoclinic *C* Triclinic *P*

Trigonal *R* Trigonal and Hexagonal *P*

Fig. 1.11. The fourteen Bravais or space lattices.

Fig. 1.11 by a conventional unit cell of each. The conventional cells are not always primitive, as sometimes a multiply primitive cell has a closer connection with the symmetry elements than has a primitive cell.

In the triclinic system the single space lattice has a primitive (*P*) unit cell, with three axes of unequal lengths and unequal angles. The symmetry of the lattice is $\bar{1}$, all space lattices being invariant under inversion.

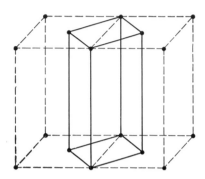

Fig. 1.12.   The primitive cell (heavy lines) of a monoclinic *C* space lattice.

In the monoclinic system there are two space lattices, one with a primitive (*P*) unit cell and the other (*C*) with a conventional cell which is base-centered (non-primitive), with lattice points at the face centers of the cell faces normal to the *c* axis. The corresponding primitive cell of the monoclinic *C* space lattice is shown in Fig. 1.12; the primitive cell is an oblique rhombic prism.

In the orthorhombic system there are four space lattices: one lattice (*P*) has a primitive cell; one lattice is base-centered (*C*); one is body-centered (*I* = German *Innenzentrierte*); and one is face-centered (*F*).

In the tetragonal system the simplest unit is a right square prism; this is a primitive cell and is associated with a tetragonal *P* space lattice. A second tetragonal lattice *I* is body-centered.

TABLE 1.5.   CHARACTERISTICS OF CUBIC LATTICES

	Simple	Body-Centered	Face-Centered
Unit cell volume	a^3	a^3	a^3
Lattice points per cell	1	2	4
Lattice points per unit volume	$1/a^3$	$2/a^3$	$4/a^3$
Nearest neighbor distance	a	$3^{1/2}a/2$	$a/2^{1/2}$
Number of nearest neighbors	6	8	12
Second neighbor distance	$2^{1/2}a$	a	a
Number of second neighbors	12	6	6

In the cubic system there are three space lattices: the simple cubic *P* lattice which is primitive; the body-centered *I* lattice; and the face-centered *F* lattice. The characteristics of the three cubic space lattices are summarized in Table 1.5. The primitive translation vectors of the body-centered cubic *I* lattice are shown in Fig. 1.13 and of the face-centered *F* lattice in Fig. 1.14*a*. In Fig. 1.14*b* we show for

variety an electron microscope photograph of an actual crystal structure. Each molecule shown is a tobacco ring spot virus particle.
This is one of the few crystals whose structures have been photographed
directly with the electron microscope.

In the trigonal system a rhombohedron is usually chosen as the unit
cell. The lattice is primitive, but it is usually denoted by R, rather
than P, so that we speak of the trigonal R space lattice.

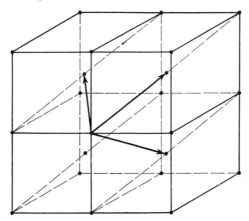

Fig. 1.13. Primitive translation vectors of the body-centered cubic I lattice; the
primitive cell is obtained on completing the rhombohedron.

In the hexagonal system the unit cell conventionally chosen is a
right prism based on a rhombus with an angle of 60°. The lattice is
primitive. The relation of the above cell with a hexagonal prism is
shown in Fig. 1.15. This cell is used sometimes also for trigonal
lattices.

THREE-DIMENSIONAL SPACE GROUPS

The fourteen space lattices exhibit the full (holohedral) symmetry
of the crystal systems to which they belong. The point-group symmetry of the various systems is given in the last column in Table 1.4.
We recall that a space group is an infinite array of symmetry elements
arranged on a space lattice. There are 230 distinct space groups;
that is, there are 230 basically different repetitive patterns in which
symmetry elements may be arranged. The possible symmetry elements include not only the point-group operations which leave the
space lattice invariant but also the screw axis and glide-plane operations to be described.

A *screw axis* combines rotation with translation parallel to the axis.
For example, the external macroscopic symmetry of the properties of

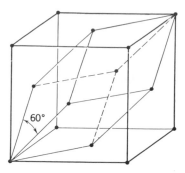

Fig. 1.14a.   The rhombohedral primitive cell of the face-centered cubic F lattice.

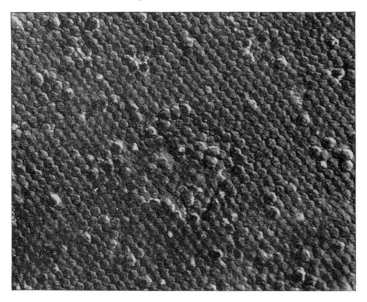

Fig. 1.14b.   Electron microscope photograph of a crystal plane of tobacco ring spot virus.   Each virus may be considered to be a large molecule.   The plane exposed may be a (111) plane.   The apparent diameter of a virus particle here is 260 A.   (Courtesy of R. L. Steere.)

a crystal may show that a two-fold symmetry axis exists.   We may suppose therefore that a two-fold regularity exists in the structure. This regularity may be simple, as in Fig. 1.16a, where the atomic arrangement itself possesses a two-fold or rotation diad axis.   Another kind of two-fold regularity is also possible, as shown in Fig. 1.16b, where a rotation through π together with a translation along the axis by half the repeat distance produces a repetitive two-fold arrangement. Such an axis is called a screw diad axis; it is denoted by 2_1.   Similar

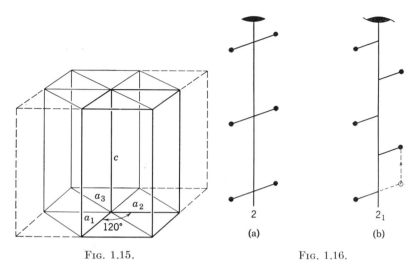

FIG. 1.15.   FIG. 1.16.

Fig. 1.15.   Relation of the primitive cell in the hexagonal system (heavy lines) to a prism of hexagonal symmetry.   (By permission from *Structure of metals*, by C. S. Barrett.   Copyright 1943.   McGraw-Hill Book Co.)

Fig. 1.16.   The operations of axes 2 and 2_1.   (After Phillips.)

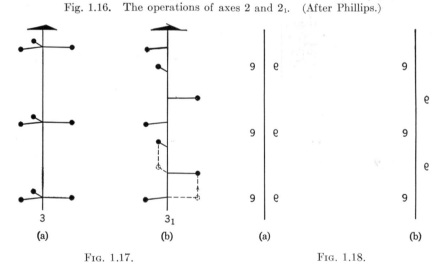

FIG. 1.17.   FIG. 1.18.

Fig. 1.17.   The operations of the axes 3 and 3_1.   (After Phillips.)

Fig. 1.18.   (a) Mirror reflection; (b) glide reflection.

operations are possible with other rotation elements; the symbols and descriptions of the permissible operations are given in Table 1.6.   The operations of the rotation triad axis 3 and the screw triad axis 3_1 are shown in Fig. 1.17.   With the axis 3_1 each rotation through $2\pi/3$ is combined with a translation upwards by one-third the repeat distance.

The axis 3_2 is equivalent to 3_1, except that the sense in 3_2 is that of a left-hand screw and in 3_1 of a right-hand screw.

A *glide plane* combines a reflection plane with a translation parallel to the plane. Figure 1.18 contrasts mirror reflection and glide reflection. The symbols which denote the several types of symmetry planes are shown in Table 1.7. The notation in the last column is explained in the next section.

TABLE 1.6. SYMBOLS OF SYMMETRY AXES

Symbol	Symmetry Axis	Graphical Symbol	Nature of Right-Handed Screw Translation along the Axis	Symbol	Symmetry Axis	Graphical Symbol (normal to plane of paper)	Nature of Right-Handed Screw Translation along the Axis
1	Rotation monad	None	None	4	Rotation tetrad		None
$\bar{1}$	Inversion monad	o	None	4_1	Screw tetrads		$c/4$
2	Rotation diad	(normal to paper)	None	4_2			$2c/4$
		(parallel to paper)		4_3			$3c/4$
				$\bar{4}$	Inversion tetrad		None
2_1	Screw diad	(normal to paper)	$c/2$	6	Rotation hexad		None
		(parallel to paper)	Either $a/2$ or $b/2$	6_1	Screw hexads		$c/6$
		Normal to paper		6_2			$2c/6$
3	Rotation triad	▲	None	6_3			$3c/6$
3_1	Screw triads		$c/3$	6_4			$4c/6$
3_2			$2c/3$	6_5			$5c/6$
$\bar{3}$	Inversion triad		None	$\bar{6}$	Inversion hexad		None

There are only two space groups in the triclinic system. We discuss these as simple illustrations of space groups. Space group $P1$ with point-group symmetry 1 is shown in Fig. 1.19. Space group $P\bar{1}$ with point-group symmetry $\bar{1}$ is shown in Fig. 1.20, where each of the lattice points has an inversion center (also called a center of symmetry). A unit atomic group is inverted across each lattice point, as indicated by

TABLE 1.7. SYMBOLS OF SYMMETRY PLANES

Symbol	Symmetry Plane	Graphical Symbol		Nature of Glide Translation
		Normal to Plane of Projection	Parallel to Plane of Projection	
m	Reflection plane (mirror)			None. (NOTE. If the plane is at $z = \frac{1}{4}$ this is shown by printing $\frac{1}{4}$ beside the symbol.)
a, b	Axial glide plane			$a/2$ along [100] or $b/2$ along [010]; or along $\langle 100 \rangle$.
c			None	$c/2$ along z-axis; or $(a + b + c)/2$ along [111] on rhombohedral axes.
n	Diagonal glide plane (net)			$(a + b)/2$ or $(b + c)/2$ or $(c + a)/2$; or $(a + b + c)/2$ (tetragonal and cubic).
d	"Diamond" glide plane			$(a \pm b)/4$ or $(b \pm c)/4$ or $(c \pm a)/4$; or $(a \pm b \pm c)/4$ (tetragonal and cubic). The glide planes are at $z = \frac{1}{8}$ and $\frac{3}{8}$ as shown.

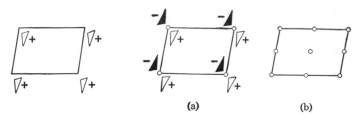

FIG. 1.19.   FIG. 1.20.

Fig. 1.19.   Structure of a crystal based on space group $P\,1$.   A unit of the structure is represented by the scalene triangle, which is repeated throughout the
structure.   The unit is at some height, as indicated by $+$, above the base of the
cell.   (After Phillips.)

Fig. 1.20.   (a) Structure based on space group $P\bar{1}$; (b) Plan of a unit of the space
group $P\bar{1}$.   (After Phillips.)

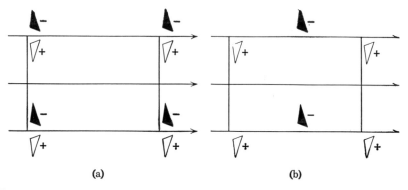

(a)   (b)

Fig. 1.21.   (a) Portion of a structure based on the space group $P2$; (b) portion of a
structure based on the space group $P2_1$.   Horizontal screw axes are shown with
single-barbed arrows.   (After Phillips.)

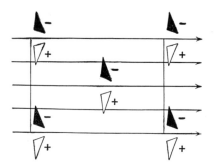

Fig. 1.22.   Portion of a structure based on the space group $C2$.   (After Phillips.)

the scalene triangles in the figure.   The top surface (unshaded) of a triangle above ($+$) the figure is replaced by the bottom surface (solid) of the triangle below ($-$) the figure.   The operation of centers of symmetry at the corners of the unit cell shown in Fig. 1.20a call forth other inversion centers, and a complete plan of a unit of the space group $P\bar{1}$ is shown in Fig. 1.20b.

There are thirteen monoclinic space groups; we illustrate only four of them: $P2$, containing a rotation diad axis, is shown in Fig. 1.21a;

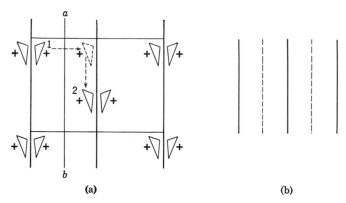

(a)   (b)

Fig. 1.23.   (a) A portion of a structure based on the space group Cm; (b) a portion of the space group Cm.

$P2_1$, containing a screw diad axis, is shown in Fig. 1.21b; $C2$, with a centered monoclinic space lattice and a rotation diad axis, is shown in Fig. 1.22.   Figure 1.23a shows a portion of a structure based on the space group Cm.   Planes of glide reflection, such as the one marked ab, occur as extra symmetry elements arising automatically.

Detailed descriptions of all 230 space groups will be found under reference 1 above.

MILLER INDICES

The position and orientation of a crystal plane is determined by giving the coordinates of three non-colinear atoms lying in the plane. If each of the atoms lies on a crystal axis, the plane may be specified by giving the positions of the atoms along the axes in terms of the lattice constants.   If, for example, the atoms determining the plane have coordinates $(4, 0, 0)$; $(0, 1, 0)$; $(0, 0, 2)$ relative to the axis vectors from some origin, the plane may be specified by the three numbers 4, 1, 2.

It turns out to be more useful to specify the orientation of a plane by *Miller indices*, which are determined as follows:

(1) Find the intercepts on the three basis axes in terms of the lattice constants.

(2) Take the reciprocals of these numbers and reduce to the smallest three integers having the same ratio. The result is enclosed in parentheses: (hkl).

For the plane whose intercepts are 4, 1, 2 the reciprocals are $\frac{1}{4}$, 1, $\frac{1}{2}$, and the Miller indices are (142). If an intercept is at infinity, the corresponding index is zero. The Miller indices of some important planes in a cubic crystal are illustrated by Fig. 1.24.

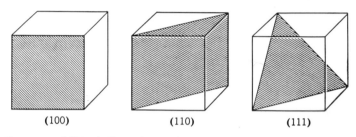

(100)   (110)   (111)

Fig. 1.24. Miller indices of some important planes in a cubic crystal.

The indices (hkl) denote a single plane or a set of parallel planes. If a plane cuts an axis on the negative side of the origin, the corresponding index is negative and is indicated by placing a minus sign above the index: $(h\bar{k}l)$. The cube faces of a cubic crystal are (100); (010); (001); $(\bar{1}00)$; $(0\bar{1}0)$; and $(00\bar{1})$. Planes equivalent by symmetry are denoted by curly brackets (braces) around Miller indices; the cube faces are $\{100\}$.

The indices of a direction in a crystal are expressed as the set of the smallest integers which have the same ratios as the components of a vector in the desired direction referred to the axis vectors. The integers are written between square brackets, $[uvw]$. The x axis is the [100] direction; the $-y$ axis is the $[0\bar{1}0]$ direction. A full set of equivalent directions is denoted this way: $\langle uvw \rangle$. In cubic crystals a direction $[uvw]$ is perpendicular to a plane (uvw) having the same indices, but this is not generally true in other crystal systems.

The positions of points in a unit cell are specified in terms of lattice coordinates, in which each coordinate is a fraction of the axial length, a, b, or c, in the direction of the coordinate, with the origin taken at the corner of a unit cell. Thus the coordinates of the central point of a cell are $\frac{1}{2}\frac{1}{2}\frac{1}{2}$, and the face-center positions are $\frac{1}{2}\frac{1}{2}0$; $0\frac{1}{2}\frac{1}{2}$; $\frac{1}{2}0\frac{1}{2}$.

In terms of the Miller indices the law of rational indices states that the indices of crystal faces are three small whole numbers. The law of rational indices is a natural consequence of the atomic nature of crystals.

In the hexagonal space lattice one often uses hexagonal indices with the four axes a_1, a_2, a_3, c, as shown in Fig. 1.15. In this notation the c axis is the [0001] direction.

SIMPLE CRYSTAL STRUCTURES

We discuss briefly a small number of simple crystal structures of general interest, including the hexagonal close-packed, diamond, cubic zinc sulfide, sodium chloride, cesium chloride, and fluorite structures. The perovskite structure is discussed in Chapter 7 and the spinel structure in Chapter 15.

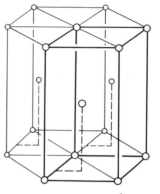

HEXAGONAL CLOSE-PACKED STRUCTURE (hcp)

There are two ways of arranging equivalent spheres to minimize the interstitial volume. One way leads to a structure with cubic symmetry and is the face-centered cubic (cubic close-packed) structure; the other has hexagonal symmetry and is called the *hexagonal close-packed structure* (Fig. 1.25). Spheres may be arranged in a single closest-packed layer by placing each sphere in contact with six others. A second similar layer may be packed on top of this by placing each sphere in contact with three spheres of the bottom layer. A third layer can be added in two ways: in the cubic structure the spheres in the third layer are placed over the holes in the first layer not occupied by the second layer; in the hexagonal structure the spheres in the third

Fig. 1.25. The hexagonal close-packed structure. The atom positions in this structure do not constitute a space lattice. The space lattice is *simple hexagonal* with two atoms $(000; \frac{2}{3} \frac{1}{3} \frac{1}{2})$ associated with each lattice point. (By permission from *Structure of metals*, by C. S. Barrett. Copyright 1943. McGraw-Hill Book Co.)

layer are placed directly over the spheres of the first layer. The two possibilities are illustrated in Fig. 1.26. The c/a ratio for hexagonal closest-packing of spheres is $(\frac{8}{3})^{\frac{1}{2}} = 1.633$. By convention we refer to crystals as hcp even if the actual c/a ratio departs somewhat from the theoretical value. Thus zinc with $c/a = 1.85$ ($a = 2.66$ A; $c = 4.94$ A) is referred to commonly as hcp, although the interatomic bond angles are quite different from the ideal hcp structure. The unit cell of the hcp structure is the hexagonal primitive cell; the basis contains two atoms, as shown in Fig. 1.25.

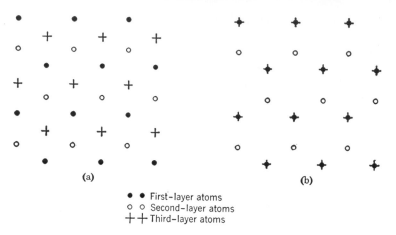

(a)   (b)

● ● First-layer atoms
○ ○ Second-layer atoms
+ + Third-layer atoms

Fig. 1.26. Modes of superposition of close-packed layers of spheres in (a) cubic
close-packing and (b) hexagonal close-packing.

DIAMOND STRUCTURE

The space lattice of diamond is face-centered cubic with a basis of two atoms at $000; \frac{1}{4}\frac{1}{4}\frac{1}{4}$ associated with each lattice point, as shown in Fig. 1.27.   The tetrahedral bonding of the diamond structure is exhibited in Fig. 1.28.   Each atom has four nearest neighbors and twelve next-nearest neighbors.   There are eight atoms in a unit cube.   The diamond lattice is relatively empty; the maximum proportion of the available volume which may be filled by hard spheres is only 0.34, or about 46 percent of the filling factor for a closest-packed structure.   Carbon, silicon, germanium, and gray tin crystallize in the diamond structure, with lattice constants 3.56, 5.43, 5.65, and 6.46A, respectively.

ZINC BLENDE STRUCTURE

We have seen that the diamond structure is composed of two fcc lattices displaced from each other by one-quarter of a body diagonal. The cubic zinc sulfide structure results from the diamond structure when Zn atoms are placed on one fcc lattice and S atoms on the other fcc lattice.   The coordinates of the Zn atoms are $000; 0\frac{1}{2}\frac{1}{2}; \frac{1}{2}0\frac{1}{2}; \frac{1}{2}\frac{1}{2}0$; the coordinates of the S atoms are $\frac{1}{4}\frac{1}{4}\frac{1}{4}; \frac{1}{4}\frac{3}{4}\frac{3}{4}; \frac{3}{4}\frac{1}{4}\frac{3}{4}; \frac{3}{4}\frac{3}{4}\frac{1}{4}$. There are four molecules of ZnS per unit cell.   Each atom has about it four equally distant atoms of the opposite kind arranged at the corners of a regular tetrahedron.   The diamond structure possesses a center of symmetry at the midpoint of each line connecting nearest-neighbor atoms; the ZnS structure does not have inversion symmetry.

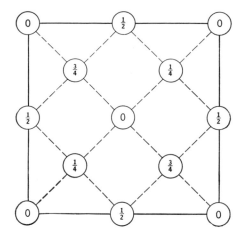

Fig. 1.27. Atomic positions in the unit cell of the diamond structure projected on a cube face; fractions denote height above base in units of a cube edge. The points at 0 and $\frac{1}{2}$ are on the fcc lattice; those at $\frac{1}{4}$ and $\frac{3}{4}$ are on a similar lattice displaced along the body diagonal by one-fourth of its length.

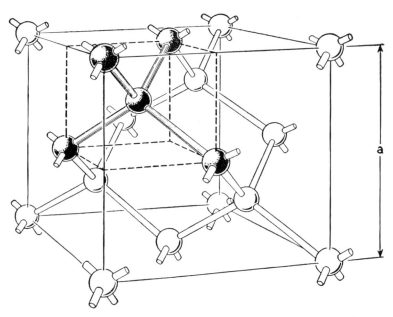

Fig. 1.28. Crystal structure of diamond, showing the tetrahedral bond arrangement. (After W. Shockley, *Electrons and holes in semiconductors.* Copyright 1950. Van Nostrand.)

This is particularly evident if we look at the arrangement of atoms along a body diagonal. In diamond the order is CC···CC···CC, where the dots represent vacancies. In ZnS the order is ZnS···ZnS···ZnS, which is not invariant under inversion. Examples of the cubic zinc sulfide structure are listed in the immediately following table.

Crystal	a	Crystal	a
CuF	4.26 A	CdS	5.82 A
CuCl	5.41	InAs	6.04
AgI	6.47	InSb	6.46
ZnS	5.41	SiC	4.35
ZnSe	5.65	AlP	5.42

It is thought that the tetrahedral bond arrangement of the ZnS structure is a sign of covalent bonding, as discussed in Chapter 3; ionic bonds would tend as we shall see later to favor structures with a higher number of nearest neighbors (coordination number).

SODIUM CHLORIDE STRUCTURE

The sodium chloride structure is shown in Fig. 1.29a. The space lattice is face-centered cubic, with a basis of one Na atom and one Cl

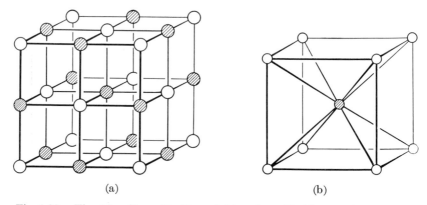

(a)   (b)

Fig. 1.29. The (a) sodium chloride and (b) cesium chloride crystal structures

atom separated by one-half the body diagonal of a unit cube. There are four molecules in a unit cube, with atoms in the positions:

$$\text{Na}: 000; \tfrac{1}{2}\tfrac{1}{2}0; \tfrac{1}{2}0\tfrac{1}{2}; 0\tfrac{1}{2}\tfrac{1}{2}.$$

$$\text{Cl}: \tfrac{1}{2}\tfrac{1}{2}\tfrac{1}{2}; 00\tfrac{1}{2}; 0\tfrac{1}{2}0; \tfrac{1}{2}00.$$

Each atom has as nearest neighbors six atoms of the opposite kind, so that the coordination number is 6.

Representative crystals having the NaCl arrangement include those in the immediately following table.

Crystal	a	Crystal	a
LiH	4.08 A	NH_4I	7.24 A
NaCl	5.63	AgBr	5.77
KBr	6.59	MgO	4.20
RbI	7.33	MnO	4.43
PbS	5.92	UO	4.92

CESIUM CHLORIDE STRUCTURE

The cesium chloride structure is shown in Fig. 1.29b. There is one molecule per unit cell, with atoms in the body-centered positions:

$$Cs: 000 \quad \text{and} \quad Cl: \tfrac{1}{2}\tfrac{1}{2}\tfrac{1}{2}.$$

The space lattice is simple cubic. Each atom is at the center of a cube of atoms of the opposite kind, so that the coordination number is 8. Representative crystals having the CsCl arrangement include those in the immediately following table.

Crystal	a	Crystal	a
CsCl	4.11 A	CuZn (β-brass)	2.94 A
TlBr	3.97	AgMg	3.28
TlI	4.20	LiHg	3.29
NH_4Cl	3.87	AlNi	2.88
RbCl(190°C)	3.74	BeCu	2.70

CALCIUM FLUORIDE (FLUORITE) STRUCTURE

The cubic calcium fluoride CaF_2 structure is shown in Fig. 1.30. The space lattice is fcc; the basis has a Ca atom at 000, one F atom at

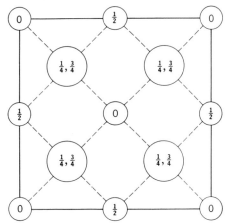

Fig. 1.30.   Atom positions with the unit cell of fluorite projected on a cube face; small circles are Ca atoms, large circles F atoms.

TABLE 1.8. COMMON CRYSTAL STRUCTURES OF SELECTED ELEMENTS

Element	Structure	Density 20°C g/cm^3	Lattice Constants (at Room Temperature) (Angstroms)		Atomic Volume (cm^3/mole)	Nearest Neighbor Distance (A)
			a	c or Axial Angle		
Aluminum	fcc	2.70	4.04		9.99	2.86
Argon	fcc		5.43(20°K)			3.83
Barium	bcc	3.5	5.01		39	4.34
Beryllium	hcp	1.82	2.27	3.59	4.96	2.22
Bismuth	rhombo-hedral	9.80	4.74	$\alpha = 57°41'$	21.3	3.10
Boron	complex	2.3			4.7	
Cadmium	hcp	8.65	2.97	5.61	13.0	2.97
Calcium	fcc	1.55	5.56		25.9	3.93
Carbon	diamond	3.51	3.56			1.54
Cerium	fcc	6.9	5.14		20	3.64
Cesium	bcc	1.9	6.05(92°K)		70	5.24
Chromium	bcc	7.19	2.88		7.23	2.49
Cobalt	hcp	8.9	2.51	4.07	6.6	2.50
Copper	fcc	8.96	3.61		7.09	2.55
Gadolinium	hcp	7.95	3.62	5.75	19.7	3.55
Germanium	diamond	5.36	5.65		13.5	2.44
Gold	fcc	19.32	4.07		10.2	2.88
Helium	hcp		3.57(2°K)	5.83		3.57
Iron (α)	bcc	7.87	2.86		7.1	2.48
Lanthanum	fcc	6.15	5.29			3.73
Lead	fcc	11.34	4.94		18.27	3.49
Lithium	bcc	0.53	3.50		13	3.03
Magnesium	hcp	1.74	3.20	5.20	14.0	3.19
Manganese	complex	7.43			7.39	2.24
Molybdenum	bcc	10.2	3.14		9.41	2.72
Neon	fcc		4.52(20°K)			3.20
Nickel	fcc	8.90	3.52		6.59	2.49
Niobium	bcc	8.57	3.29		10.8	2.85
Palladium	fcc	12.0	3.88		8.89	2.74
Platinum	fcc	21.45	3.92		9.10	2.77
Potassium	bcc	0.86	5.33		45	4.62
Rubidium	bcc	1.53	5.62(92°K)		55.9	4.87
Silicon	diamond	2.33	5.43		12.0	2.35
Silver	fcc	10.49	4.08		10.28	2.88
Sodium	bcc	0.97	4.28		24	3.71
Strontium	fcc	2.6	6.05		34	4.30
Tantalum	bcc	16.6	3.30		10.9	2.85
Thalium	hcp	11.85	3.45	5.51	17.24	3.40
Tin (gray)	diamond	5.75	6.46			

TABLE 1.8. *(Continued)*

Element	Structure	Density 20°C g/cm^3	Lattice Constants (at Room Temperature) (Angstroms)		Atomic Volume (cm^3/mole)	Nearest Neighbor Distance (A)
			a	c or Axial Angle		
Titanium	hcp	4.54	2.95	4.73	10.6	2.91
Tungsten	bcc	19.3	3.16		9.53	2.73
Uranium	complex	18.7			12.7	2.76
Vanadium	bcc	6.0	3.03		8.5	2.63
Xenon	fcc		6.24(92°K)			4.41
Zinc	hcp	7.13	2.66	4.94	9.17	2.66
Zirconium	bcc	6.5	3.61(850°C)		14	3.16

$\frac{1}{4} \frac{1}{4} \frac{1}{4}$ and the other F atom at $\frac{3}{4} \frac{3}{4} \frac{3}{4}$. Each Ca atom is at the center of eight F atoms at the corners of a surrounding cube, and each F atom is at the center of a tetrahedron of Ca atoms. Representative crystals having the CaF_2 arrangement include those in the immediately following table.

Crystal	a	Crystal	a
CaF_2	5.45 A	Ir_2P	5.54 A
BaF_2	6.19	$AuAl_2$	6.00
UO_2	5.47	$PbMg_2$	6.84
K_2O	6.44	$SiMg_2$	6.39
Li_2Te	6.50	$PtGa_2$	5.91

COLLECTIONS OF CRYSTAL STRUCTURE DATA

The reader who wishes to look up the crystal structure of a substance may profitably consult the loose-leaf compilation by Wyckoff.[4] The *Strukturbericht* and *Structure Reports* are also valuable aids. The principal journals in the field are *Acta Crystallographica* and *Zeitschrift für Kristallographie*.

In Table 1.8 we list for convenience common crystal structures of a number of elements, and their lattice constants at room temperature. Hume-Rothery[5] has given a useful series of tables of crystal structures of elements arranged according to the groups in the periodic table.

[4] R. W. G. Wyckoff, *Crystal structures*, Interscience Publishers, New York, 1948.
[5] W. Hume-Rothery, *Structure of metals and alloys*, Institute of Metals, London, 1947, pp. 47–55.

PROBLEMS

1.1. (a) A lattice cannot have five-fold rotational symmetry. Prove this statement by considering a vector **a** taken to be the smallest non-vanishing translation of the lattice, and show that the vector $\mathbf{a}'' - \mathbf{a}'$ would be shorter than **a**, where $\mathbf{a}'$, $\mathbf{a}''$ are vectors obtained from **a** by rotations of $\pm 2\pi/5$.

(b) Prove that a lattice cannot have seven-fold rotational symmetry.

1.2. (a) Discuss the symmetry elements of the two-dimensional space group $p4mm$; explain how each symmetry element occurs.

(b) Do the same for $p3m1$.

1.3. (a) Draw a pattern of a structure based on the three-dimensional space group $C2/m$; draw a portion of the space group itself.

(b) Do the same for $I4$.

1.4.* Show with a full discussion that the space group of the diamond structure is $F4_1/d\bar{3}2/m$. Find the space group of the cubic ZnS (zinc blende) structure.

1.5. Show that the maximum proportion of the available volume which may be filled by hard spheres arranged in various structures is

Simple cubic	$\pi/6$ ($= 0.52$)
Body-centered cubic	$\pi 3^{1/2}/8$ ($= 0.68$)
Face-centered cubic	$\pi 2^{1/2}/6$ ($= 0.74$)
Hexagonal close-packed	$\pi 2^{1/2}/6$ ($= 0.74$)
Diamond	$\pi 3^{1/2}/16$ ($= 0.34$)

We may note that by experiment [O. K. Rice, J. Chem. Phys. **12**, 1 (1944)] it is found that the volume of an arrangement of spheres packed at random into a container exceeds that of the cubic and hexagonal close-packed arrangements by 15 to 20 percent. For further details on the packing of spheres, see A. H. Boerdijk, Philips Research Repts. **7**, 303 (1952), and references cited therein.

1.6. Show that the c/a ratio for an ideal hexagonal close-packed structure is $(\frac{8}{3})^{1/2} = 1.633$. Compare this with the experimental values of the ratios for twelve metals possessing hcp structures.

1.7. Hard spheres of radius b are arranged in contact in simple cubic, body-centered cubic, and face-centered cubic structures. Find the radius s of the largest sphere which can fit into the largest interstice in the several structures.

1.8. Describe and discuss the crystal structures of ZnO, NiAs, TiO_2, and α-quartz.

1.9. What point group describes the symmetry of the interatomic force acting on (a) a carbon atom in a diamond lattice; (b) a zinc atom in a wurtzite lattice; (c) a boron atom in BN?

1.10. Show that a bcc lattice may be decomposed into two sc lattices A, B with the property that none of the nearest neighbor lattice points to a lattice point on A lie on A, and similarly for the B lattice. Show that to obtain the same property a sc lattice is decomposed into two fcc lattices, and a fcc lattice into four sc lattices. These considerations are of interest for antiferromagnetism, Chapter 15.

1.11. Show that among the nearest neighbor sites in a fcc lattice there are groups of three sites such that each site is a vertex of an equilateral triangle.

1.12. Prove that in a cubic crystal a direction $[uvw]$ is perpendicular to a plane (uvw) having the same indices.

1.13. Define the following terms, distinguishing carefully between them: point group, translation group, crystal class, space lattice, Bravais lattice, space group, crystal system.

1.14. Bring to class a crystal you have grown of any salt; what would you do to grow a larger crystal?

REFERENCES

S. Bhagavantam and T. Venkatarayudu, *Theory of groups and its application to physical problems*, Andhara University, Waltair, 2nd ed., 1951.

W. L. Bragg, *The crystalline state*, Vol. I., G. Bell and Sons, Ltd., London, 1933.

M. J. Buerger, *Elementary crystallography*, John Wiley & Sons, New York, 1956.

C. W. Bunn, *Chemical crystallography*, Clarendon Press, Oxford, 1945.

P. H. Groth, *Chemische Krystallographie*, 5 volumes, W. Engelmann, Leipzig, 1906.

W. Hume-Rothery, *The structure of metals and alloys*, Institute of Metals, London, 1947.

International tables for x-ray crystallography, Kynoch Press, Birmingham, 1952.

Internationale Tabellen zur Bestimmung von Kristallstrukturen, Borntraeger, Berlin, 1935.

R. W. James, *The optical principles of the diffraction of x-rays*, G. Bell and Sons, Ltd., London, 1948.

K. Lonsdale, *Crystals and x-rays*, G. Bell and Sons, Ltd., London, 1948.

C. Palache, H. Berman, and C. Frondel, *Dana's system of mineralogy*, Vols. I and II, John Wiley & Sons, New York, 7th ed., 1944, 1951.

L. Pauling, *Nature of the chemical bond*, Cornell University Press, Ithaca, 1945.

F. C. Phillips, *An introduction to crystallography*, Longmans, London, 1946.

A. Schoenflies, *Theorie der Kristallstruktur*, Borntraeger, Berlin, 1923.

F. Seitz, "A matrix-algebraic development of the crystallographic groups," Z. Krist. **88**, 433 (1934); **90**, 289 (1935); **91**, 336 (1935); **94**, 100 (1936).

Strukturbericht, 7 vols.; Akademische Verlagsgesellschaft, Leipzig, 1913–1939; continued as *Structure Reports*, published by the International Union of Crystallography.

W. Voigt, *Lehrbuch der Kristallphysik*, Teubner, Leipzig and Berlin, 1910.

W. A. Wooster, *A textbook on crystal physics*, Cambridge University Press, Cambridge, 1938.

R. W. G. Wyckoff, *Crystal structures*, Interscience Publishers, New York, 1948.

W. H. Zachariasen, *Theory of x-ray diffraction in crystals*, John Wiley & Sons, New York, 1945.

* Problems of unusual length or difficulty are marked with an asterisk.

2

Diffraction of X-Rays by Crystals

To explore the structure of crystals we require waves which interact with atoms and which have a wavelength comparable with the interatomic spacing in crystals; that is, we require a wavelength of the order of 1 A ($= 10^{-8}$ cm). Radiation of longer wavelength generally cannot resolve the details of structure on an atomic scale, and radiation of much shorter wavelength is diffracted through only very small angles, as seen from Eq. (2.1) below, although crystal spectrometers for gamma rays have been operated successfully. The interaction of the radiation with the atoms should be weak enough so that the wave can penetrate in a coherent fashion into the crystal for a distance of the order of perhaps 1000 lattice constants, to obtain good resolution. The most convenient waves suitable for general purposes are those associated with x-rays, while the waves associated with neutrons and electrons have found important applications. A wavelength of 1 A requires energies of the order of 10^4, 10^2, and 10^{-1} ev for x-rays, electrons, and neutrons, respectively. The reader may verify these values from the relations $\lambda = hc/E$ for x-rays and $\lambda = h/(2ME)^{\frac{1}{2}}$ for neutrons and electrons, where E is the energy and M is the particle mass. The discussion below is formulated explicitly for x-ray diffraction, although many of the results are applicable also to neutron and electron diffraction.

The present chapter serves as an introduction to the concepts and methods relating to the propagation of waves in a periodic structure, a problem of central importance in solid state physics. We shall be concerned in this book with three types of waves: electromagnetic waves (photons), elastic waves (phonons), and electron waves.

When an atom is exposed to electromagnetic radiation, the atomic electrons are accelerated, and they radiate at the frequency of the incident radiation. At optical frequencies the superposition of the waves scattered by individual atoms in a crystal results in the ordinary optical refraction. If the wavelength of the radiation is comparable with or smaller than the lattice constant, we shall also have diffraction of the incident beam under certain conditions.   At optical frequencies ($\sim 10^{15}$ cps) only refraction occurs; at x-ray frequencies ($\sim 10^{18}$ cps) diffraction is important.   In this chapter we discuss some of the principles and methods used in the investigation of crystal structure by x-ray diffraction.

BRAGG'S LAW

W. L. Bragg[1] found that one could account for the position of the diffracted beams produced by a crystal in an x-ray beam by a simple

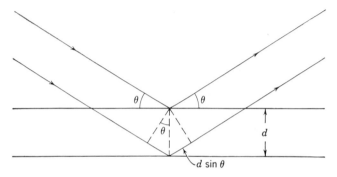

Fig. 2.1.   Derivation of the Bragg equation $2d \sin \theta = n\lambda$; here d is the spacing of parallel atomic planes and $2n\pi$ is the difference in phase between reflections from successive planes.

model which assumes that x-rays are reflected specularly from the various planes of atoms in the crystal.   The diffracted beams are found only for special situations in which the reflections from parallel planes of atoms interfere constructively.   The original derivation of the Bragg law is indicated in Fig. 2.1.

We consider in the crystal a series of atomic planes which are considered to be partly reflecting for radiation of wavelength λ and which are spaced equal distances d apart.   The radiation is incident in the plane of the paper.   The path difference for rays reflected from adjacent planes is $2d \sin \theta$.   Reinforcement of the radiation reflected from successive planes will occur when the path difference is an integral number n of wavelengths.   The condition for constructive reflection is that

(2.1) $$2d \sin \theta = n\lambda.$$

This is the Bragg law.   We shall derive this relation below in a more sophisticated manner, considering in detail the atomic nature of the

[1] W. L. Bragg, Proc. Cambridge Phil. Soc. **17**, 43 (1913).

crystal. It should be emphasized that the Bragg equation results from the fundamental periodicity of the structure, and the equation does not refer to the actual composition or arrangement of the atoms associated with the reflecting planes. The latter considerations will be seen below to affect the intensity of the diffracted radiation and to determine the relative intensity of the various orders n of diffraction. An important consequence of (2.1) is that wavelengths $\lambda \leq 2d$ are essential if Bragg reflection is to occur.

We may get an idea of the magnitude of the diffraction angle θ by considering $CuK\alpha_1$ radiation incident on a cubic crystal with a lattice constant of 4.00 A. The wavelength of the $CuK\alpha_1$ line is 1.54 A. In the first order ($n = 1$) reflection from (100) planes, $\theta = \sin^{-1}(1.54/8.00) = 11.1°$. As the wavelength is decreased, the angle is decreased: for gamma-rays glancing angles must be used.

LAUE DIFFRACTION EQUATIONS

The Laue equations are derived from a simple static atomic model of a crystal structure. They illustrate effectively the conditions for

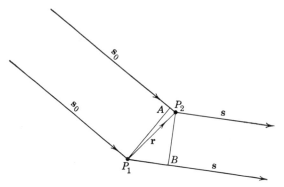

Fig. 2.2.   Calculation of the phase difference of the waves scattered from two
lattice points.

the formation of a diffracted beam. The Bragg equation (2.1) will be derived as a direct consequence of the Laue equations.

We consider the nature of the x-ray diffraction pattern produced by identical scattering centers located at the lattice points of a space lattice. We first look at the scattering from any two lattice points, P_1 and P_2 in Fig. 2.2, separated by the vector $\mathbf{r}$. The unit incident wave normal is $\mathbf{s}_0$, and the unit scattered wave normal is $\mathbf{s}$. We examine at a point a long distance away the difference in phase of the radiation scattered by P_1 and P_2.

If P_2A and P_1B are the projections of $\mathbf{r}$ on the incident and scattered wave directions, the path difference between the two scattered waves is

(2.2) $$P_2A - P_1B = \mathbf{r} \cdot \mathbf{s}_0 - \mathbf{r} \cdot \mathbf{s} = \mathbf{r} \cdot (\mathbf{s}_0 - \mathbf{s}).$$

The vector $\mathbf{s}_0 - \mathbf{s} = \mathbf{S}$ has a simple interpretation (Fig. 2.3) as the direction of the normal to a plane that would reflect the incident direction into the scattering direction. This plane is a useful mathematical construction and may be spoken of as the *reflecting plane*. If 2θ is the angle $\mathbf{s}$ makes with $\mathbf{s}_0$, then θ is the angle of incidence, and from the figure we see that $|S| = 2 \sin \theta$, as $\mathbf{s}$ and $\mathbf{s}_0$ are unit vectors.

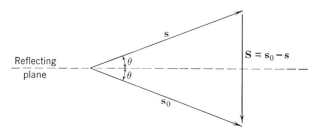

Fig. 2.3.   Construction of the normal to the reflecting plane.

The phase difference ϕ is $2\pi/\lambda$ times the path difference between the waves scattered between the two lattice points. That is, if the path difference is a whole wavelength λ, the phase difference is 2π. We have

(2.3) $$\phi = (2\pi/\lambda)(\mathbf{r} \cdot \mathbf{S}).$$

The amplitude of the scattered wave is a maximum in a direction such that the contributions from each lattice point differ in phase only by integral multiples of 2π. For this condition, the separate scattered amplitudes add up constructively and the intensity in the diffracted beam is a maximum. If $\mathbf{a}$, $\mathbf{b}$, $\mathbf{c}$ are the primitive translation vectors, we must have for the diffraction maxima

(2.4)
$$\phi_a = (2\pi/\lambda)(\mathbf{a} \cdot \mathbf{S}) = 2\pi h;$$
$$\phi_b = (2\pi/\lambda)(\mathbf{b} \cdot \mathbf{S}) = 2\pi k;$$
$$\phi_c = (2\pi/\lambda)(\mathbf{c} \cdot \mathbf{S}) = 2\pi l;$$

where h, k, l are integers. If α, β, γ are the direction cosines of $\mathbf{S}$ with respect to $\mathbf{a}$, $\mathbf{b}$, $\mathbf{c}$, we have

(2.5)
$$\mathbf{a} \cdot \mathbf{S} = 2a\alpha \sin \theta = h\lambda;$$
$$\mathbf{b} \cdot \mathbf{S} = 2b\beta \sin \theta = k\lambda;$$
$$\mathbf{c} \cdot \mathbf{S} = 2c\gamma \sin \theta = l\lambda.$$

These are the Laue equations. They have solutions only for special values of θ and the wavelength λ.

The Laue equations (2.5) have a direct geometrical interpretation, which the reader may establish with a little contemplation. We recall that α, β, γ are the direction cosines of **S**, the normal to the reflecting plane, referred to the basis vectors **a**, **b**, **c**. The Laue equations state that in a diffraction direction the direction cosines are proportional to h/a, k/b, l/c, respectively. Now the adjacent lattice planes (hkl) intersect the axes at intervals a/h, b/k, c/l, by the definition of the Miller indices h, k, l in Chapter 1. By elementary plane geometry the direction cosines of the normal to (hkl) are proportional to h/a, k/b, l/c. Therefore the lattice planes (hkl) must be parallel to the reflecting plane, and the diffraction maxima occur when the scattering direction may be derived from the incident direction by reflection in a lattice plane.

If $d(hkl)$ is the spacing between two adjacent planes of a set (hkl), we have by projection

$$(2.6) \qquad d(hkl) = a\alpha/h = b\beta/k = c\gamma/l.$$

Then, from (2.5), we have

$$(2.7) \qquad 2d(hkl) \sin \theta = \lambda.$$

Now the integers, h, k, l of the Laue equations are not necessarily identical with the Miller indices of an actual crystal plane, as the h, k, l of the Laue equations may contain a common integral factor n, while in the Miller indices the common factor n has been eliminated. We may then write

$$(2.8) \qquad 2d \sin \theta = n\lambda,$$

where d is the spacing between adjacent planes with Miller indices $(h/n, k/n, l/n)$. This is the *Bragg equation* (2.1), and we have derived it here from the Laue equations. The integer n is called the order of reflection.

We may interpret (2.7) by giving an extended meaning to the spacing $d(hkl)$ when h, k, l have a common factor n: the diffracted wave actually arises from the nth order reflection from the true lattice planes, but, as a mathematical device, we may think of the diffracted wave as a first order reflection from a set of planes parallel to the true lattice planes but with a spacing $d(hkl)$ equal to $1/n$ of the true spacing.

It is useful to discuss the interference conditions in terms of a mathematical transformation known as the reciprocal lattice. This method is developed in the section below.

INTERFERENCE CONDITIONS AND THE RECIPROCAL LATTICE[2]

The conditions for an x-ray beam to be diffracted by a crystal may be expressed in an elegant form with the help of the reciprocal lattice transformation. The reciprocal lattice is very widely used in x-ray crystallography and in the quantum theory of metals. We let $\mathbf{a}$, $\mathbf{b}$, $\mathbf{c}$ be the primitive translations of the crystal lattice. We define the primitive translations $\mathbf{a}^*$, $\mathbf{b}^*$, $\mathbf{c}^*$ of the reciprocal lattice by the relations

$$(2.9) \qquad \mathbf{a}^* \cdot \mathbf{a} = \mathbf{b}^* \cdot \mathbf{b} = \mathbf{c}^* \cdot \mathbf{c} = 1;$$
$$\mathbf{a}^* \cdot \mathbf{b} = \mathbf{a}^* \cdot \mathbf{c} = \mathbf{b}^* \cdot \mathbf{c} = \mathbf{b}^* \cdot \mathbf{a} = \mathbf{c}^* \cdot \mathbf{a} = \mathbf{c}^* \cdot \mathbf{b} = 0.$$

Equations (2.9) define the magnitude and direction of $\mathbf{a}^*$, $\mathbf{b}^*$, $\mathbf{c}^*$. The directions are such that, for example, $\mathbf{a}^*$ is perpendicular to the plane $\mathbf{b}$ and $\mathbf{c}$, and in fact is given by

$$(2.10) \qquad \mathbf{a}^* = \frac{\mathbf{b} \times \mathbf{c}}{\mathbf{a} \cdot [\mathbf{b} \times \mathbf{c}]}.$$

Similar expressions obtain for the other vectors. The reciprocal lattice has a definite orientation relative to the crystal lattice.

The properties of the reciprocal lattice that make it of value in diffraction problems are: (1) The vector $\mathbf{r}^*(hkl)$ from the origin to the point (h, k, l) of the reciprocal lattice is normal to the (hkl) plane of the crystal lattice. (2) The length of the vector $\mathbf{r}^*(hkl)$ is equal to the reciprocal of the spacing of the planes (hkl) of the crystal lattice. As proof of (1) we note that $(\mathbf{a}/h) - (\mathbf{b}/k)$ is a vector in the (hkl) plane. Then

$$\mathbf{r}^*(hkl) \cdot \left(\frac{\mathbf{a}}{h} - \frac{\mathbf{b}}{k}\right) = (h\mathbf{a}^* + k\mathbf{b}^* + l\mathbf{c}^*) \cdot \left(\frac{\mathbf{a}}{h} - \frac{\mathbf{b}}{k}\right) = 0.$$

We can do the same thing for a second vector in the plane, say $(\mathbf{a}/h) - (\mathbf{c}/l)$, proving the first result. Furthermore, if $\mathbf{n}$ is the unit normal to the plane, $\mathbf{a} \cdot \mathbf{n}/h$ is the interplanar spacing, and, as $\mathbf{n} = \mathbf{r}^*/|r^*|$,

$$(2.11) \qquad d(hkl) = \mathbf{n} \cdot \mathbf{a}/h = (\mathbf{r}^* \cdot \mathbf{a})/h|r^*| = 1/|r^*|,$$

using (2.9). This proves the second result.

It is efficacious to write the Bragg equation in the form $2d(hkl) \sin \theta = \lambda$. If h, k, l have a common factor n, the diffracted ray may be considered either as an nth order reflection from lattice planes with their true spacing, or else as a first order reflection from a set of planes

[2] This section follows closely the development given by R. W. James, *Optical principles of the diffraction of x-rays*, G. Bell and Sons, Ltd., London, 1948. For an elementary discussion see M. J. Buerger, *X-ray crystallography*, John Wiley & Sons, New York, 1942.

parallel to the true lattice planes but with a spacing $d(hkl)$ equal to
$1/n$ of the true spacing. The vector $\mathbf{r}^*$ (hkl) in the reciprocal lattice
is in the same direction but n times as long as the vector corresponding
to the true crystal plane. That is, the nth point from the origin in a
given row in the reciprocal lattice corresponds to the nth order reflection from the associated crystal planes. Every point in the reciprocal
lattice corresponds to a possible reflection from the crystal lattice.

The Bragg equation has a simple geometrical significance in the
reciprocal lattice. In Fig. 2.4 we draw AO as a vector of length $1/\lambda$

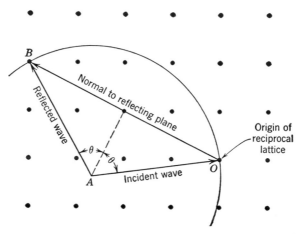

Fig. 2.4.   Ewald's construction in the reciprocal lattice.

in the direction of the incident radiation and terminating at the origin
of the reciprocal lattice. Following Ewald, we draw a sphere of radius
$1/\lambda$ about A as center; then the possible directions of the diffracted
rays for this incident ray are determined by the intersections of the
sphere with the points of the reciprocal lattice. That is, the direction
AB is the direction of a diffraction maximum; here B is a point of the
reciprocal lattice.

We prove the Ewald result by noting that OB is normal to one of the
lattice planes (hkl) and of length $1/d(hkl)$; it is also equal in length
to $(2/\lambda) \sin \theta$, where θ is the glancing angle between the planes (hkl)
and the incident and reflected rays. Therefore $2d(hkl) \sin \theta = \lambda$, which
is just the Bragg condition. This result may be written in vector form.
If $\mathbf{G}$ is 2π times the vector from the origin to a lattice point in the
reciprocal lattice, and $\mathbf{k}$ is the propagation vector (of magnitude $2\pi/\lambda$)
of the incident x-ray, then the condition for Bragg reflection is, from
Fig. 2.4,

$$(\mathbf{k} + \mathbf{G})^2 = k^2,$$

or

(2.12) $$2\mathbf{k} \cdot \mathbf{G} + G^2 = 0.$$

We shall encounter the condition (2.12) again in later chapters in connection with the study of Brillouin zones.

As an example we show that a fcc lattice has as its reciprocal a bcc lattice. In the direct fcc lattice the distance between lattice planes in each cube edge direction is $a/2$, where a is the lattice constant; thus there are points in the reciprocal lattice along the x, y, z axes at $2/a$ from the origin. There is only one set of planes in the direct lattice separated by a distance greater than $a/2$, namely, the planes normal to the direction of the body diagonal. The separation of these planes is $a/3^{1/2}$, as is evident from Fig. 2.5. These planes in the direct lattice are represented in the reciprocal lattice by a point in the [111] direction at a distance $3^{1/2}/a$ from

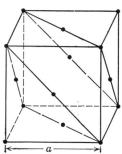

Fig. 2.5. A pair of parallel adjacent (111) planes in a face-centered cubic lattice; the spacing is $a/3^{1/2}$.

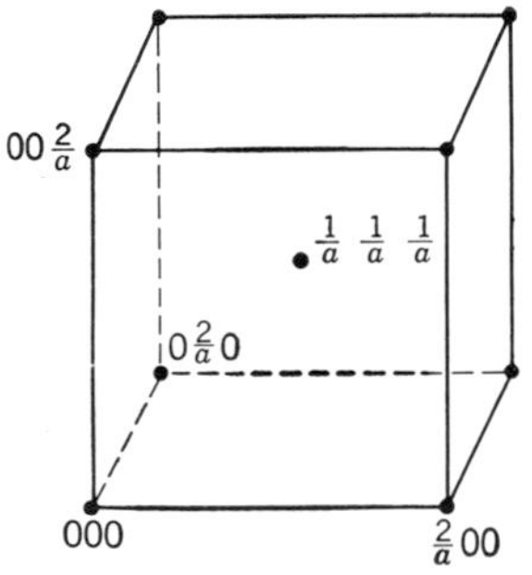

the origin at a cube corner. The distance is actually one-half the length of the body diagonal of the unit cube in the reciprocal lattice, so the reciprocal lattice point lies at the body center. The unit cell in the reciprocal lattice is shown in Fig. 2.6. It is left to Problem 2.3 to show that a body-centered cubic lattice has as its reciprocal a face-centered cubic lattice.

Fig. 2.6. Body-centered cubic cell reciprocal to the face-centered cubic cell in the direct lattice as shown in Fig. 2.5. The two largest interplanar spacings in the direct lattice are represented in the reciprocal lattice by the points shown here.

ATOMIC SCATTERING FACTOR

The intensity of a given diffracted wave depends on a number of factors. One of these is the atomic scattering factor, which describes the result of interference effects within the scattering atoms arising from the finite extent of the atoms in relation to the wavelength. We give below an approximate classical calculation of the coherent atomic scattering factor.

We arrange the coordinate system in Fig. 2.7 so that the incident and reflected wave normals make equal angles with the vertical axis, corresponding to Bragg reflection from the horizontal plane at angle θ. The difference in phase between the radiation scattered by an element of charge at (r, ϕ) and the radiation which would be scattered by the same amount of charge located at the center of the atom is $\phi = (2\pi/\lambda)\,(\mathbf{r} \cdot \mathbf{S})$, according to (2.3). Then the amplitude scattered by one electron in the actual atom referred to the amplitude which would be scattered by an electron at the center of

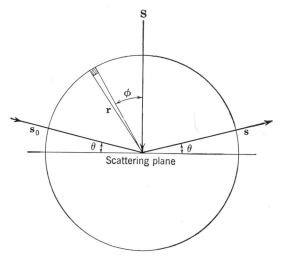

Fig. 2.7.   Calculation of the atomic scattering factor f.   The normal to the scattering plane is $\mathbf{S}$.

the atom is, by superposition,

$$(2.13) \qquad\qquad f = \int \rho(\mathbf{r})e^{i(2\pi/\lambda)\,(\mathbf{r}\cdot\mathbf{S})}\,d\tau,$$

where $\rho(\mathbf{r})\,d\tau$ is the probability of finding the electron in the element of volume $d\tau$ at $\mathbf{r}$.

If $\mathbf{r}$ makes an angle ϕ with $\mathbf{S}$, then

$$(2\pi/\lambda)(\mathbf{S} \cdot \mathbf{r}) = (4\pi/\lambda) \sin \theta r \cos \phi = \mu r \cos \phi,$$

where $\mu = 4\pi(\sin \theta)/\lambda$.   If the charge density is spherically symmetric,

$$f = \int \rho(r)e^{i\mu r \cos \phi}\, 2\pi r^2 \sin \phi\, dr\, d\phi$$

$$= \int_0^\infty 4\pi r^2 \rho(r)\, \frac{\sin \mu r}{\mu r}\, dr.$$

Writing $U(r)\,dr = 4\pi r^2 \rho(r)\,dr$ as the probability that an electron lies between radii r and $r + dr$, we have

$$(2.14) \qquad\qquad f = \int_0^\infty U(r)\, \frac{\sin \mu r}{\mu r}\, dr$$

for the *atomic scattering factor*. It is the ratio of the radiation amplitude scattered by the charge distribution in an atom to that scattered
by a point electron. Tables of atomic scattering factors calculated by
the Hartree and Thomas-Fermi methods have been published.[3] The
results for sodium are plotted in Fig. 2.8. At $\theta = 0$ our calculation
gives $f = Z$, the number of atomic electrons.

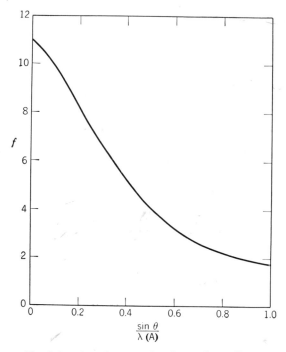

Fig. 2.8. Atomic scattering factor for sodium.

GEOMETRICAL STRUCTURE FACTOR

The Laue and Bragg equations determine the reflections (hkl) which
are possible for a given crystal lattice, but the relative intensities of
the various reflections depend on the contents of the unit cell, that is,
on the number, type, and distribution of atoms in the cell. We must
now determine the amplitude of the wave scattered in a given direction
by all the atoms in the unit cell. The *structure amplitude* $|F(hkl)|$ for
a given hkl reflection is the reflection amplitude divided by the amplitude of the wave scattered by a single point electron for the same
wavelength.

[3] *International tables for the determination of crystal structure*, Borntraeger,
Berlin, 1935.

The value of $F(hkl)$ will be given by

$$(2.15) \qquad F(hkl) = \sum_i f_i e^{i\phi_i} = \sum_i f_i e^{i(2\pi/\lambda)(\mathbf{r}_i \cdot \mathbf{S})},$$

where the sum is extended over all atoms in a unit cell; ϕ_i is the phase of the wave scattered by the ith atom referred to that of the origin, $\mathbf{r}_i$ is the vector from the origin to the ith atom; f_i is the atomic structure factor of the ith atom.

$$(2.16) \qquad \mathbf{r}_i = u_i \mathbf{a} + v_i \mathbf{b} + w_i \mathbf{c}.$$

By the Laue equations

$$(2.17) \qquad (\mathbf{r}_i \cdot \mathbf{S}) = \lambda(hu_i + kv_i + lw_i),$$

so that

$$(2.18) \qquad F(hkl) = \sum_i f_i e^{i2\pi(hu_i + kv_i + lw_i)},$$

and

$$(2.19) \quad |F|^2 = [\Sigma\, f_i \cos 2\pi(hu_i + kv_i + lw_i)]^2 \\ + [\Sigma\, f_i \sin 2\pi(hu_i + kv_i + lw_i)]^2.$$

When all the atoms are identical we have, from (2.18), $F(hkl) = f\mathcal{S}$, where $\mathcal{S}$ is called the geometrical structure factor and is given by

$$(2.20) \qquad \mathcal{S} = \Sigma\, e^{i2\pi(hu_i + kv_i + lw_i)}.$$

The usual basis of a body-centered cubic structure of identical atoms has atoms at 000 and $\frac{1}{2}\frac{1}{2}\frac{1}{2}$. We find

$$(2.21) \qquad \mathcal{S} = 1 + e^{i\pi(h+k+l)}.$$

When $h + k + l$ is odd, $\mathcal{S} = 0$, and the intensities of all spectra for which (hkl) satisfy this condition are zero. For example, metallic sodium has a bcc structure; its diffraction spectrum does not contain lines such as (100), (300), (111), or (221), but lines such as (200), (110), and (222) will be present; here the planes are referred to a cubic unit cell. For each of the possible space groups there are characteristic absences of reflections, and from these the space group is determined.

There is a simple physical interpretation of the result that, in particular, the (100) reflection vanishes for the body-centered cubic lattice. The (100) reflection normally occurs when the reflections from the first and third planes in Fig. 2.9 are out of phase by 2π. However, in the bcc lattice there is an intervening plane of atoms, labeled the second plane in the figure, which is equal in scattering power to the other planes and which, situated midway between them, gives a reflection out of phase by π, thereby canceling the contribution from another plane. The cancellation of the (100) reflection occurs only if the various planes are identical in composition; thus, in the CsCl structure (Fig. 1.29b) the cancellation does not occur, as the planes of Cs and Cl atoms alternate.

This discussion has assumed that the crystal is large and perfect. The effect of thermal motion on the structure factors may be quite

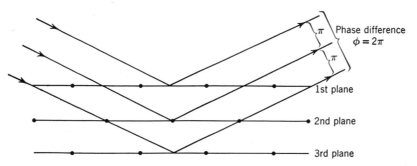

Fig. 2.9.   Explanation of the absence of a (100) reflection from a body-centered cubic lattice.

important, as well as the effect of the mosaic or block structure of actual crystals.

EXPERIMENTAL X-RAY DIFFRACTION METHODS

The Bragg law,

$$2d \sin \theta = n\lambda,$$

for x-ray diffraction requires that θ and λ be matched; that is, x-rays of wavelength λ striking a crystal at an arbitrary angle of incidence in general will not be reflected. To satisfy the Bragg law it is necessary to provide experimentally for a continuous range of values of either λ or θ. The standard methods of diffraction used in crystal structure analysis accomplish this.

Laue method.   A single crystal is held stationary in a beam of continuous wavelength x-ray radiation. The crystal selects out and diffracts the discrete values of λ for which planes exist of spacing d and incidence angle θ satisfying the Bragg law.

Rotating-crystal method.   A single crystal is rotated about a fixed axis in a beam of monochromatic x-rays.   The variation in θ brings different atomic planes into position for reflection.

Powder method (Debye-Scherrer-Hull method).   A powdered sample of crystalline material is placed in a fixed position in a monochromatic beam.   Among the distribution of crystallite orientations there will be some for which the angle of incidence satisfies the Bragg law.

All three of the above methods are employed, sometimes with modifications, in current research.   The Laue method is convenient for the rapid determination of crystal orientation and symmetry and also for studying the extent of crystalline imperfection under mechanical and thermal treatment.   The rotating-crystal method is the principal method used for structure determination when a single crystal specimen is available.   The powder method is convenient in applied and in metallurgical work because single crystals are not required.   Accounts of the essential features of these methods are given below.

LAUE METHOD

A Laue camera is illustrated schematically in Fig. 2.10.   A source is used which produces a beam of x-rays over a wide range of wave-

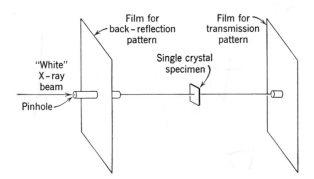

Fig. 2.10.   Arrangement of a camera for Laue patterns.

lengths, perhaps from 0.2 A to 2 A; a pinhole arrangement is employed to produce a well-collimated beam.   The dimensions of the single crystal specimen need not be greater than 1 mm.   Flat film is placed to receive either the transmitted diffracted lines or the reflected diffracted lines.   The diffraction pattern consists of a series of spots, as shown for a silicon crystal in Fig. 2.11.

Each reflecting plane in the crystal selects from the incident beam a wavelength satisfying the Bragg equation $2d \sin \theta = n\lambda$. The pattern must show the symmetry of the crystal in the orientation used; thus, if a cubic crystal is oriented with a body-diagonal or [111] direction parallel to the beam, then the Laue pattern will show the three-fold symmetry appropriate to the [111] axis. This feature makes the

Fig. 2.11.   Laue pattern of a silicon crystal in approximately the [100] orientation.
(Courtesy of J. Washburn.)

Laue pattern particularly convenient for checking the orientation of crystals in solid state experiments.

The Laue method has certain disadvantages for crystal structure determination.   Because of the wide range of wavelengths, it is possible for several wavelengths to reflect in different orders from a single plane, and different orders of reflection may superpose on a single spot. This feature makes the determination of reflected intensity difficult.

ROTATING-CRYSTAL METHOD

A simple rotating-crystal camera is shown in Fig. 2.12. The film is mounted with cylindrical geometry concentric with a rotating spindle on which the single crystal specimen is mounted. The dimensions of the crystal are usually less than 1 mm. The incident monochromatic beam is diffracted from a given crystal plane of interplanar spacing d whenever in the course of rotation the value of θ satisfies the Bragg equation. In particular, all planes parallel to the rotation axis

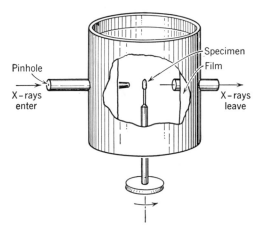

Fig. 2.12. A rotating-crystal camera. (By permission from *Structure of metals*, by C. S. Barrett. Copyright 1943. McGraw-Hill Book Co.)

will reflect in the horizontal plane. Planes with other orientations will reflect in layers above and below the horizontal plane.

Several variations of the rotating-crystal method are in common use. In *oscillating-crystal* photographs the crystal is oscillated through a limited angular range, instead of being rotated through 360°. The limited range reduces the possibility of overlapping reflections. The *Weissenberg goniometer* shifts the film in synchronism with the oscillation of the crystal. This procedure eliminates overlapping reflections and is also convenient for analytical reasons. For details of the moving-film methods, which are now widely applied in structure-determination problems, the reader is referred to the book by Buerger listed at the end of the chapter. In the *Bragg spectrometer* an ionization chamber is used to detect the diffracted radiation; it is well suited for absolute intensity measurements. A precession camera photograph for a fairly complicated crystal, sperm whale myoglobin type A, is shown in Fig. 2.13.

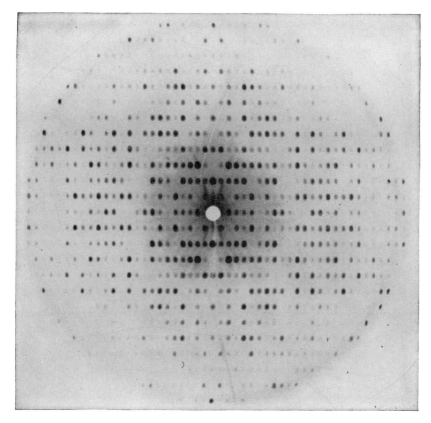

Fig. 2.13.   Precession camera photograph for sperm whale myoglobin type A
crystals.   (After J. C. Kendrew and R. G. Parrish.)

POWDER METHOD

In the powder method illustrated in Fig. 2.14 the incident monochromatic radiation strikes a finely powdered specimen or a fine-
grained polycrystalline specimen contained in a thin-walled capillary
tube.   Diffracted rays go out from individual crystallites which happen to be oriented with planes making an incident angle θ with the
beam satisfying the Bragg equation.   An example of a powder-
pattern photograph is given in Fig. 2.15.   Diffracted rays leave the
specimen along the generators of cones concentric with the original
beam.   The generators make an angle 2θ with the direction of the
original beam, where θ is the Bragg angle.   The cones intercept the
film in a series of concentric rings.

An important use of the powder method is in the study of phase diagrams of alloy systems. Special cameras are constructed to permit the specimen to be at an elevated temperature, up to 1000°C or more.

Cameras for precision studies of lattice parameters (unit cell dimensions) usually make use of the fact that diffraction lines are more sensitive at large angles θ than at small angles to small changes in the interplanar spacing d. *Back-reflection* is a term applied to x-ray work

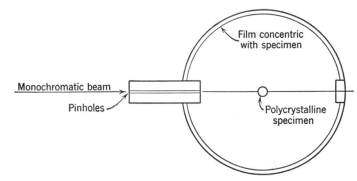

Fig. 2.14.   Schematic arrangement of a powder camera.

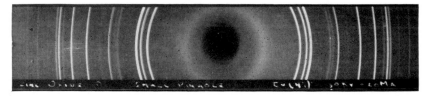

Fig. 2.15.   Powder pattern for ZnO.   (Courtesy of J. M. Jolliffe.)

at large angles. From the Bragg equation we have, at constant λ,

$$\Delta(d \sin \theta) = (\Delta d) \sin \theta + d \cos \theta (\Delta \theta) = 0,$$

or

$$\frac{\Delta \theta}{\Delta d} = -\frac{\tan \theta}{d}.$$

Thus the variation in θ for a given variation Δd in d is larger when θ approaches 90°. The reflected lines occur at 2θ from the incident beam, so that the maximum sensitivity is in the backward direction.

SOLID STATE AND METALLURGICAL APPLICATIONS

Unfortunately we do not have space in this book to go into the many interesting and important applications of x-ray methods to solid state and metallurgical problems. The applications, which go considerably beyond the formal problems of crystal structure determination, are treated at length in the book by Barrett listed at the end of the chapter and also in the papers by Barrett, Guinier, and Warren and Averbach in the symposium volume entitled *Imperfections in nearly perfect crystals.*

PROBLEMS

2.1. Show that the perpendicular distance between adjacent planes of a set (hkl) in a simple cubic lattice of lattice constant a is

$$d(hkl) = a/(h^2 + k^2 + l^2)^{1/2}.$$

Hint: If one plane of the set passes through the origin, the equation of the nearest plane parallel to this plane is $xh + yk + zl = a$.

2.2. Design on paper a rotating-crystal experiment to determine the crystal structure of a single crystal specimen of NaBr. Consider voltage, target material, distances, spacing of different reflections, and other relevant experimental factors.

2.3. Show that a body-centered cubic lattice has as its reciprocal a face-centered cubic lattice.

2.4. Show that the geometrical structure factor for a face-centered cubic lattice referred to a cubic unit cell is

$$\mathbb{S} = 1 + e^{i\pi(h+k)} + e^{i\pi(h+l)} + e^{i\pi(l+k)}.$$

Show that no reflections can occur for which the indices are partly even and partly odd.

2.5. Discuss the major experimental differences between x-ray, electron, and neutron diffraction from the standpoint of the observed diffraction patterns [see for example, C. G. Shull and E. O. Wollan, Science **108**, 69 (1948)].

2.6. Discuss several of the principal methods of growing inorganic and metal single crystals in the laboratory. [Reference: H. E. Buckley, *Crystal growth*, John Wiley & Sons, New York, 1951.]

2.7. The electron charge density $\rho(\mathbf{r})$ in a crystal may be expressed as a Fourier series

$$\rho(\mathbf{r}) = \sum_{\mathbf{k}} \rho_{\mathbf{k}} e^{i\mathbf{k}\cdot\mathbf{r}}.$$

If we write $\mathbf{k}$ in terms of the primitive translations of the reciprocal lattice, as follows:

$$\mathbf{k} = k_1\mathbf{a}^* + k_2\mathbf{b}^* + k_3\mathbf{c}^*,$$

show that the requirement that $\rho(\mathbf{r})$ be invariant under all translations by lattice vectors of the form

$$\mathbf{T} = n_1\mathbf{a} + n_2\mathbf{b} + n_3\mathbf{c}$$

may be satisfied by setting k_1, k_2, k_3 equal to integral multiples of 2π. Thus, if we write

$$\mathbf{r} = u\mathbf{a} + v\mathbf{b} + w\mathbf{c}$$

and, taking h, k, l as integers,

$$\mathbf{k} = 2\pi(h\mathbf{a}^* + k\mathbf{b}^* + l\mathbf{c}^*),$$

we have

$$\rho = \sum_{hkl} \rho(hkl) e^{2\pi i(hu+kv+lw)}.$$

We note that the values of **k** which occur in the Fourier series are equal to 2π times the vectors from the origin to the lattice points of the reciprocal lattice.

REFERENCES

Most of the references listed at the end of Chapter 1 are pertinent also to the present chapter.

G. E. Bacon, *Neutron diffraction*, Clarendon Press, Oxford, 1955.

C. S. Barrett, *Structure of metals*, McGraw-Hill, New York, 2nd ed., 1952.

J. Bouman, editor, *Selected topics in x-ray crystallography*, North-Holland, Amsterdam, 1951.

L. Brillouin, *Wave propagation in periodic structures*, McGraw-Hill, New York, 1946.

M. J. Buerger, *X-ray crystallography*, John Wiley & Sons, New York, 1942.

A. H. Compton and S. K. Allison, *X-rays in theory and experiment*, Van Nostrand, New York, 1935.

H. Lipson and W. Cochran, *The determination of crystal structures*, G. Bell, London, 1953.

Shockley, Hollomon, Maurer, and Seitz, editors, *Imperfections in nearly perfect crystals*, John Wiley & Sons, New York, 1952.

3

Classification of Solids; Lattice Energy of Ionic Crystals

We discuss first in this chapter the approximate classification of crystals in terms of the dominant type of chemical binding force keeping the atoms together. We then discuss in some detail the classical theory of ionic crystals, as in some (but not all) respects ionic crystals are the simplest solids to understand. It should be emphasized here that the periodic nature of crystalline solids is often an essential factor in the determination of the equilibrium structure. Periodicity may be required to make complicated units fit together snugly, to make chemical bonds match at suitable spacings and angles, to minimize the electrostatic energy of an ionic system, and for other, more subtle, reasons.

EMPIRICAL CLASSIFICATION OF CRYSTAL BINDING

It is useful to make an approximate qualitative classification of crystals in terms of the dominant type of chemical binding displayed. It may not be possible or sensible to classify some solids, whereas with others it may be possible[1] to make an approximate quantitative assessment of the contribution of the various types of binding to the total binding energy. The principal types of binding are given in Table 3.1.

The static forces binding atoms and molecules in solids are almost entirely electrostatic in nature, with only insignificant contributions from magnetic interactions. There are also important kinetic effects on the binding energy, arising from the motion of the atomic electrons. By and large, the important differences among the several types of crystal bonds may be attributed to qualitative differences in the distribution of electrons around the atoms and molecules. If it were

---

[1] See, for example, L. Pauling, *Nature of the chemical bond,* Cornell University Press, Ithaca, 2nd ed., 1945. For the application of molecular beam and microwave spectroscopy to this problem, see C. H. Townes and B. P. Dailey, J. Chem. Phys. **17,** 782 (1949).

easier to prepare maps showing the distribution of electrons in the interior of crystals, we should be able to define the character of the binding by more quantitative criteria than are at present available.

There is an extraordinary and beautiful diversity in the structural composition of solid materials, ranging from the bare simplicity of the structure of diamond, the alkali halides, and monovalent metals through glasses, fibers, plastics, intermetallic compounds, organic crystals, and complex silicates of geological significance to the intricacies of biological substances. X-ray crystallography has made great progress in understanding structures over this broad spectrum. Solid state physics, however, is concerned at present largely with substances having simple structures and binding chracteristics. The complexity of the observable phenomena in even the simple structures suggests that it would be most profitable to try to understand these first. Accordingly, in this book we inquire principally into the properties of the simpler ionic, covalent, and metallic crystals.

TABLE 3.1. CLASSIFICATION OF CRYSTAL TYPES

The binding energy is the energy necessary to dissociate the solid into separated atoms, molecules, or ions, as appropriate. The binding energy is taken at room temperature, except for the molecular crystals where it is taken at the melting point. Note that 1 ev/molecule = 23.05 kcal/mole.

Crystal Type	Examples	Binding Energy (kcal/mole)	Characteristics of Type
Ionic	NaCl	180	Strong absorption in far infrared; low electrical conductivity at low temperatures; good conductivity by ions at high temperatures.
	LiF	240	
Covalent	Diamond	~170	Great hardness; low conductivity at low temperatures when specimens are pure.
	SiC	283	
Metallic	Na	26	High electrical conductivity.
	Fe	94	
Molecular	A	1.8	Low melting and boiling points; very compressible.
	CH_4	2.4	
Hydrogen-bonded	H_2O (ice)	12	Tendency to polymerize (that is, to form groups of many molecules); increased binding energy of molecules in comparison with similar molecules without hydrogen bonds.
	HF	7	

IONIC CRYSTALS

In ionic crystals electrons are transferred from atoms of one type to atoms of a second type, so that the crystal is made up of positive and negative ions. The ions arrange themselves so the Coulomb attraction between ions of opposite sign is stronger than the Coulomb repulsion between ions of the same sign. The *ionic bond* is thus essentially the bond resulting from the electrostatic interaction of oppositely charged ions. Two common crystal structures found for ionic crystals, the sodium chloride and the cesium chloride structures, are shown in Fig. 1.29.

The degree of ionization of the constituent atoms of an ionic crystal is often such that the electronic configurations of all ions correspond to closed electronic shells, as in the inert gas atoms. In lithium fluoride the configuration[2] of the neutral atoms are, according to Table 3.2,

$$\text{Li:} \quad 1s^2 2s,$$
$$\text{F:} \quad 1s^2 2s^2 2p^5,$$

while the singly charged ions have the configurations

$$\text{Li}^+: \quad 1s^2,$$
$$\text{F}^-: \quad 1s^2 2s^2 2p^6,$$

as for helium and neon, respectively. The inert gas atoms have closed shells, and the charge distributions are spherically symmetric. We may expect accordingly that the charge distributions on each ion in an ionic crystal may have approximately spherical symmetry, with some distortion near the region of contact with neighboring atoms.

COVALENT CRYSTALS

When a covalent bond is formed we imagine that an electron from each atom is transferred to the region between the two atoms joined by the bond.

In an ionic bond it is a good approximation to think of the valence electrons as attached to definite atoms. The Pauli principle applied to ions with filled electronic shells ensures a low electron density in the region between the two ions where the charge shells make contact. Ions with filled shells do not generally form covalent bonds. In a

---

[2] The notation used to describe the electronic configuration of atoms and ions is discussed in all textbooks of introductory atomic physics. The letters s, p, d, $\cdots$ signify electrons having orbital angular momentum 0, 1, 2, $\cdots$ in units $\hbar$; the number to the left of the letter denotes the principal quantum number of one orbit, and the superscript to the right denotes the number of electrons in the orbit.

TABLE 3.2.   PERIODIC TABLE, WITH THE OUTER ELECTRON CONFIGURATIONS OF NEUTRAL ATOMS IN THEIR GROUND STATES

(Configuration assignments for the rare earth and actinide elements are somewhat uncertain.)

1 H $1s$	3 Li $2s$	11 Na $2p^6 3s$	19 K $3p^6 4s$	37 Rb $4p^6 5s$	55 Cs $5p^6 6s$	87 Fr $6p^6 7s$
2 He $1s^2$	4 Be $2s^2$	12 Mg $2p^6 3s^2$	20 Ca $3p^6 4s^2$	38 Sr $4p^6 5s^2$	56 Ba $5p^6 6s^2$	88 Ra $6p^6 7s^2$
	5 B $2s^2 2p$	13 Al $3s^2 3p$	21 Sc $3d 4s^2$	39 Y $4d 5s^2$	57 La $5p^5 5d 6s^2$	89 Ac $6d 7s^2$
	6 C $2s^2 2p^2$	14 Si $3s^2 3p^2$	22 Ti $3d^2 4s^2$	40 Zr $4d^2 5s^2$	58 Ce $4f^2 6s^2$	90 Th $6d^2 7s^2$
	7 N $2s^2 2p^3$	15 P $3s^2 3p^3$	23 V $3d^3 4s^2$	41 Nb $4d^4 5s$	59 Pr $4f^3 6s^2$	91 Pa $5f^2 6d 7s^2$
	8 O $2s^2 2p^4$	16 S $3s^2 3p^4$	24 Cr $3d^5 4s$	42 Mo $4d^5 5s$	60 Nd $4f^4 6s^2$	92 U $5f^3 6d 7s^2$
	9 F $2s^2 2p^5$	17 Cl $3s^2 3p^5$	25 Mn $3d^5 4s^2$	43 Tc $4d^6 5s$	61 Pm $4f^5 6s^2$	93 Np $5f^5 7s^2$
	10 Ne $2s^2 2p^6$	18 A $3s^2 3p^6$	26 Fe $3d^6 4s^2$	44 Ru $4d^7 5s$	62 Sm $4f^6 6s^2$	94 Pu $5f^6 7s^2$
			27 Co $3d^7 4s^2$	45 Rh $4d^8 5s$	63 Eu $4f^7 6s^2$	95 Am $5f^7 7s^2$
			28 Ni $3d^8 4s^2$	46 Pd $4d^{10}$	64 Gd $4f^7 5d 6s^2$	96 Cm $5f^7 6d 7s^2$
			29 Cu $3d^{10} 4s$	47 Ag $4d^{10} 5s$	65 Tb $4f^8 5d 6s^2$	97 Bk $5f^8 6d 7s^2$
			30 Zn $3d^{10} 4s^2$	48 Cd $4d^{10} 5s^2$	66 Dy $4f^{10} 6s^2$	98 Cf $5f^9 6d 7s^2$
			31 Ga $4s^2 4p$	49 In $5s^2 5p$	67 Ho $4f^{11} 6s^2$	
			32 Ge $4s^2 4p^2$	50 Sn $5s^2 5p^2$	68 Er $4f^{12} 6s^2$	
			33 As $4s^2 4p^3$	51 Sb $5s^2 5p^3$	69 Tm $4f^{13} 6s^2$	
			34 Se $4s^2 4p^4$	52 Te $5s^2 5p^4$	70 Yb $4f^{14} 6s^2$	
			35 Br $4s^2 4p^5$	53 I $5s^2 5p^5$	71 Lu $4f^{14} 5d 6s^2$	
			36 Kr $4s^2 4p^6$	54 Xe $5s^2 5p^6$	72 Hf $5d^2 6s^2$	
					73 Ta $5d^3 6s^2$	
					74 W $5d^4 6s^2$	
					75 Re $5d^5 6s^2$	
					76 Os $5d^6 6s^2$	
					77 Ir $5d^9$	
					78 Pt $5d^9 6s$	
					79 Au $5d^{10} 6s$	
					80 Hg $5d^{10} 6s^2$	
					81 Tl $6s^2 6p$	
					82 Pb $6s^2 6p^2$	
					83 Bi $6s^2 6p^3$	
					84 Po $6s^2 6p^4$	
					85 At $6s^2 6p^5$	
					86 Rn $6s^2 6p^6$	

covalent or homopolar bond the charge density between the two atoms may be rather high,[3] and the valence electrons are to an appreciable extent shared between two atoms.   The covalent bond is the normal electron-pair bond of chemistry, encountered particularly in organic chemistry.   It is characterized by a high density of electrons between

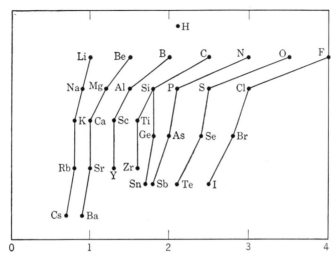

Fig. 3.1.   The electronegativity scale of the elements, showing relation to the periodic table.   The electronegativities are plotted against the horizontal scale, and different columns of the periodic table are separated vertically.   (After L. Pauling, *Nature of the chemical bond*, Cornell University Press.)

the ions and also by marked directional properties.   The carbon bond is a good example of the directional properties of the covalent bond: carbon atoms often prefer to join onto each other or to other atoms by four bonds making tetrahedral angles with each other.   That is, each carbon atom will be at the center of the tetrahedron formed by the nearest neighbor atoms.   Diamond (Figs. 1.27 and 1.28) and methane, CH_4, are typical examples of the tetrahedral covalent bond.   The diamond structure is loosely packed in a geometrical sense: the tetrahedral bond allows only four nearest neighbors, while a closest-packed structure would require twelve nearest neighbor atoms.   The covalent

[3] Compare the electron distribution maps obtained by x-ray analysis of diamond and sodium chloride, in Figs. 53 and 66 of Y. K. Syrkin and M. E. Dyatkina, *Structure of molecules and the chemical bond*, Butterworths Scientific Publications, London, 1950.   R. Brill, Acta Cryst. **3**, 333 (1950), has found by x-ray methods that the change a carbon atom suffers in forming a covalent bond in diamond consists in concentrating about 0.5 to 0.7 of an electron (of the outer shell) in every chemical bond.

bond is usually formed from two electrons, one from each atom participating in the bond. The spins of the two electrons in the bond are antiparallel. The carbon atom $(2s^2 2p^2)$ tends, in a sense, to fill up the $2p^6$ electron shell by sharing electrons with four neighbors.

There is apparently a continuous range of crystals between the ionic and the covalent limits. It is often of importance to estimate the extent to which a given bond is ionic or covalent, but this may be difficult to do with any confidence. We think of NaF as an ionic

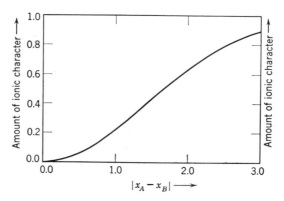

Fig. 3.2. Curve relating amount of ionic character of a bond A—B to the difference in electronegativity $x_A - x_B$ of the atoms. (After L. Pauling, *Nature of the chemical bond*, Cornell University Press.)

crystal, and perhaps of InSb as largely covalent, but it is at present difficult to know what to say about the nature of the bonding of ZnS or PbS, for example. Pauling[1] has formulated (Fig. 3.1) on a semi-empirical basis an electronegativity scale of some of the elements. Electronegativity is a chemical term meaning the power of an atom in a molecule to attract electrons to itself. The electronegativity is approximately proportional to the sum of the ionization energy and the electron affinity of the atom. A suggested empirical connection between the ionic character of a bond and the difference in electronegativity of the atoms being joined is shown in Fig. 3.2. Atoms with nearly filled shells (Na, Cl) tend to be ionic, whereas atoms not close in the periodic table to the inert gases tend to be covalent (C, Ge, Si, Te).

METAL CRYSTALS

Metals are characterized by high electrical conductivity, and so a portion of the electrons in a metal must be free to move about. The electrons available to participate in the conductivity are called conduction electrons. In some metals such as the alkali metals the interaction of the ion cores with the conduction electrons is largely responsible for the binding energy. We may think of an alkali metal crystal as an array of positive ions embedded in a more-or-less uniform sea of negative charge. In some metals such as the transition metals it has been suggested that there may also be binding effects from covalent-type bonds among the inner electron shells. Transition group elements have incomplete d-electron shells and are characterized by high binding energy (Table 4.3).

The binding energy of an alkali metal crystal is seen from Table 3.1 to be very considerably less than that of an alkali halide crystal, so the bond formed by a quasi-free conduction electron is not very strong. Part of the explanation is that the interatomic distances are relatively large in the alkali metals because the kinetic energy of the conduction electrons favors large interatomic distances, leading thus to weak binding. In the transition metals such as iron and tungsten the inner electronic shells make a substantial contribution to the binding. The binding energy of tungsten, for example, is 201 kcal/mole.

MOLECULAR CRYSTALS

Inert gas atoms and saturated molecules are bound together in the solid phase by weak electrostatic forces known as van der Waals forces.[4] These forces arise in the following way: even in an atom or molecule which has on the average an electric dipole moment of zero there will be a fluctuating dipole moment associated with the instantaneous position of the electrons in the atom. The instantaneous electric field associated with the moment will induce a dipole moment in neighboring atoms. The average interaction of the original moment and the induced moment gives rise to an attractive force between the atoms. Forces of this origin are also called dispersion forces. Many organic solids are held together by van der Waals forces.

Molecular crystals are characterized by weak binding, with low melting and boiling points. The crystal structures are often those with dense packing. The inert gas crystals crystallize with cubic close packing.

HYDROGEN-BONDED CRYSTALS

As neutral hydrogen has only one electron, it should form a covalent bond with only one other atom. It is known, however, that under certain conditions an atom of hydrogen is attracted by rather strong

---

[4] An elementary discussion of the theory of van der Waals forces is given in M. Born, *Atomic physics*, Hafner, New York, 5th ed., 1951.

forces to two atoms, thus forming what is called a *hydrogen bond* between them, with a bond energy of about 5 kcal/mole. It is believed that the hydrogen bond[5] is largely ionic in character, being formed only between the most electronegative atoms. The hydrogen atom loses its electron to one of the other atoms in the molecule; the proton forms the hydrogen bond. The small size of the proton permits only two nearest neighbor atoms because they are so close that more than two of them would get in each other's way; thus the hydrogen bond connects only two atoms.

The hydrogen bond is an important interaction between H_2O molecules and is responsible, together with the electrostatic attraction of the electric dipole moments, for the striking physical properties of water and ice. The hydrogen bond restrains protein molecules to their normal geometrical arrangements. It is also responsible for the polymerization of hydrogen fluoride and formic acid, for example. It is important in certain ferroelectric crystals, such as potassium dihydrogen phosphate.

LATTICE ENERGY OF IONIC CRYSTALS

When we speak of ionic crystals we mean substances such as lithium fluoride and sodium chloride. These are perhaps as simple as any chemical compound existing in nature, and for this reason they have been the subject of a great deal of theoretical calculation, and many of their physical properties have been investigated experimentally over a wide range of temperature. The idealized model of an ionic crystal supposes that the constituents are positive and negative ions bearing charges which are multiples of the electronic charge, with the charge distributed with spherical symmetry on each ion as in the rare gas atoms. The interactions between ions are assumed to be primarily the electrostatic interactions between spherical charge distributions.

It is reasonable to ask how well our assumptions are satisfied in actual crystals. This question is not easy to answer, as in the absence of complete x-ray maps of the electron distribution in the crystal there is no physical method available at present which can determine the quantitative deviation from the ideal ionic state. Pauling's estimates were discussed above. It appears that the binding in many of the alkali halides may be largely ionic, while the binding may be less completely ionic, for example, in substances containing oxygen or sulfur ions.

A short estimate suggests that we are not misguided in looking to electrostatic or Coulomb interactions for a large part of the binding

[5] For a discussion of the hydrogen bond, see L. Pauling, reference 1.

energy of an ionic crystal. The distance between a positive ion and the nearest negative ion in sodium chloride is known to be 2.81×10^{-8} cm, so that the attractive part of the potential energy of the two ions by themselves is

$$e^2/r_0 = (4.8 \times 10^{-10})^2/(2.8 \times 10^{-8}) = 8 \times 10^{-12} \text{ ergs},$$

which is about 5 ev. This value may be compared with the known value 183 kcal/mole, or about 8 ev/molecule, of the heat of formation of the crystal starting with ions at infinite separation. The order of magnitude agreement between the values of 5 and 8 ev/molecule is quite suggestive and leads us to calculate more closely the lattice energy of sodium chloride.

LATTICE ENERGY OF SODIUM CHLORIDE

Sodium chloride crystallizes in the structure shown in Fig. 3.3. The space lattice is fcc with one Na^+ and one Cl^- ion with each lattice point. We construct the sodium chloride crystal structure by arranging alternately Na^+ and Cl^- ions at the lattice points of a simple cubic lattice. In the crystal each ion is surrounded by six nearest neighbors of the opposite charge and twelve next nearest neighbors of the same charge as the reference ion. We suppose that the Na^+ ion carries a single positive charge, so that the electronic configuration is identical with neon, and that the Cl^- ion carries a single negative charge (argon configuration).

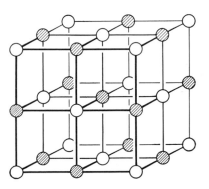

Fig. 3.3.   The sodium chloride structure.

If ϕ_{ij} is the interaction energy between ions i and j, the total energy of any one ion i is

$$\phi_i = {\sum_j}' \phi_{ij},$$

where the prime indicates that the summation is to include all ions except $j = i$. We suppose that ϕ_{ij} may be written as the sum of a central field repulsive potential varying as $r_{ij}{}^n$ and a Coulomb potential:

(3.1)
$$\phi_{ij} = \frac{\lambda}{r_{ij}{}^n} \pm \frac{e^2}{r_{ij}},$$

where the $+$ sign is to be taken for like charges and the $-$ sign for unlike charges. The repulsive term describes the fact that the ion cores act as if they are fairly hard, and each resists overlapping with the electron distributions of neighboring ion cores. We shall regard λ and n as constants to be determined from observed values of the lattice constant and compressibility. It is actually possible to do somewhat better than this and to compute the repulsive interaction from approximate solutions of the quantum-mechanical problem, but the classical ionic crystal theory we give here is a quite good approximation to the facts.

The value of ϕ_i does not depend on whether the reference ion i is a positive or a negative ion, and as the sum can be made to converge rapidly its value will not depend on the particular location of the reference ion in the crystal as long as it is not near the surface. Neglecting surface effects, we may write the total lattice energy U_0 of a crystal composed of $2N$ ions as

$$U_0 = N\phi,$$

where N, rather than $2N$, occurs because in taking the total lattice energy we must count each *pair* of interactions only once. The total lattice energy is the energy required to separate the crystal into individual ions at an infinite distance apart.

It is convenient to introduce quantities p_{ij} such that

$$r_{ij} = p_{ij}R,$$

where R is the nearest neighbor separation in the crystal; then

$$\phi_{ij} = \frac{1}{p_{ij}{}^n}\frac{\lambda}{R^n} \pm \frac{1}{p_{ij}}\frac{e^2}{R}$$

and

(3.2)
$$\phi = \frac{\lambda A_n}{R^n} - \frac{\alpha e^2}{R}.$$

Here

$$A_n = \sum_j{}' p_{ij}{}^{-n};$$

(3.3)
$$\alpha = \sum_j{}' (\mp)p_{ij}{}^{-1}.$$

The quantity α is known as the *Madelung constant* and is a property of the crystal structure. The Madelung constant is of central importance in the theory of ionic crystals, and methods for the calculation of the constants will be discussed.   The sum A_n converges rapidly, as n is usually large, often of the order of 10.   We need not, however, attempt to calculate the product λA_n, which involves through λ the quantum-mechanical solution of the repulsive potential problem, if we are content to substitute in our theory the observed value of the lattice constant.   The variation of ϕ with R is illustrated in Fig. 3.4.

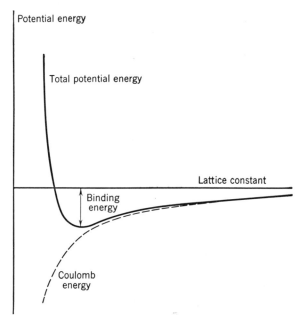

Fig. 3.4.   Dependence of potential energy of an ionic crystal on the value of the lattice constant.

At the equilibrium separation $\partial\phi/\partial R = 0$, so that

(3.4)
$$-\frac{nA_n\lambda}{R_0^{n+1}} + \frac{\alpha e^2}{R_0^2} = 0.$$

We use this relation to eliminate λA_n from Eq. (3.2), obtaining

$$\phi = -\frac{\alpha e^2}{R_0}\left(1 - \frac{1}{n}\right).$$

The total lattice energy of the crystal of $2N$ ions at their equilibrium separation is then

(3.5)
$$U_0 = -\frac{N\alpha e^2}{R_0}\left(1 - \frac{1}{n}\right).$$

The total binding energy may be attributed almost entirely to the Coulomb energy, as we shall find that n is of the order of 10.

EVALUATION OF THE MADELUNG CONSTANT

The first calculation of the Coulomb energy constant α was made by Madelung.[6] A powerful general method for lattice sum calculations was developed by Ewald,[7] and Evjen[8] has given a rather simple method which arranges the counting in a rapidly convergent way.

The definition of the Madelung constant α is, from Eq. (3.3),

$$\alpha = \sum_{j}' (\pm)p_{ij}^{-1},$$

where now, if we take the reference ion as a negative charge, the plus sign will be used for positive ions and the minus sign for negative ions. An equivalent definition is

(3.6)
$$\frac{\alpha}{R_0} = \sum_{j}' \frac{(\pm)}{r_j}$$

where r_j is the distance of the jth ion from the reference ion and is always to be taken as positive.

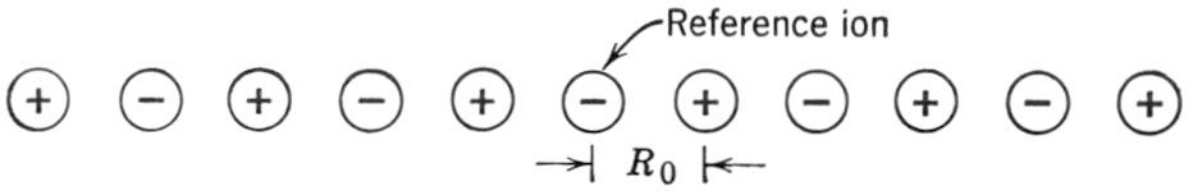

Fig. 3.5. Line of ions of alternating signs with distance R_0 between ions.

We shall first compute the value of the Madelung constant for an infinite line of ions of alternating sign, as shown in Fig. 3.5. We pick a negative ion as reference ion, and let R_0 denote the distance between adjacent ions. We have

$$\frac{\alpha}{R_0} = 2\left[\frac{1}{R_0} - \frac{1}{2R_0} + \frac{1}{3R_0} - \frac{1}{4R_0} + \cdots\right],$$

or
$$\alpha = 2\left[1 - \frac{1}{2} + \frac{1}{3} - \frac{1}{4} + \cdots\right];$$

[6] E. Madelung, Physik. Z. 19, 524 (1918).
[7] P. P. Ewald, Ann. Physik 64, 253 (1921).
[8] H. M. Evjen, Phys. Rev. 39, 675 (1932); see also K. Højendahl, Kgl. Danske Videnskab. Selskab, Math.-fys. Medd. 16 (2), 133 (1938); E. J. W. Verwey and J. E. Asscher, Rec. trav. chim. 65, 521 (1946); F. C. Frank, Phil. Mag. 41, 1287 (1950); S. K. Roy, Can. J. Phys. 32, 509 (1954); J. Kanamori, T. Moriya, K. Motizuki, and T. Nagamiya, J. Phys. Soc. Japan 10, 93 (1955).

the factor 2 occurs because there are two ions, one to the right and one to the left, at each distance r_j.   We may conveniently sum this expression by recalling the series expansion

$$\ln (1 + x) = x - \frac{x^2}{2} + \frac{x^3}{3} - \frac{x^4}{4} + \cdots ,$$

and so for the one-dimensional chain

$$\alpha = 2 \ln 2.$$

There was no special difficulty about carrying out this calculation for the one-dimensional lattice.   However, in three dimensions the series does present greater difficulty.   It is not possible to write down the successive terms by a casual inspection, nor is it possible to sum the series conveniently.   It is important so to arrange the terms in the series that the contributions from the positive and negative terms nearly cancel, or else the series will not converge.

In the sodium chloride structure there are six positive ions (the nearest neighbors to the negative reference ion) at $p = 1$, giving a positive contribution to α of $\frac{6}{1}$; there are twelve negative ions at $p = 2^{1/2}$, giving $-12/2^{1/2}$; eight positive ions at $p = 3^{1/2}$, giving $8/3^{1/2}$; six negative ions at $p = 2$, giving $-\frac{6}{2}$; etc., and so

$$\alpha = \frac{6}{1} - \frac{12}{2^{1/2}} + \frac{8}{3^{1/2}} - \frac{6}{2} + \cdots$$

$$= 6.000 - 8.485 + 4.620 - 3.000 + \cdots .$$

The convergence is obviously poor.

We may improve the convergence by arranging the counting according to the schemes of Evjen and others.   We work with groups of ions which are more or less neutral, if necessary taking fractional charges.   The physical motivation for working with neutral groups is that the potential of a neutral assembly of ions falls off faster at a distance from the assembly than if the assembly has an excess of charge.   We obtain in the sodium chloride structure nearly neutral groups by considering the charges on cubes, with the understanding that charges on cube faces are to be treated as shared between two cells, on edges between four cells, and on corners between eight.

A simple method of counting is illustrated for a two-dimensional lattice by Fig. 3.6.   In the actual sodium chloride structure the first cube surrounding a negative reference ion intercepts six positive charges on cube faces, twelve negative charges on cube edges, and eight positive charges at cube corners—a resultant of one positive

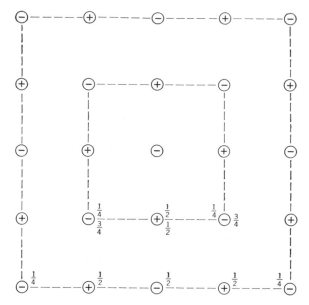

Fig. 3.6. Illustration of the Evjen method applied to a two-dimensional lattice. The weight attached to several charges is indicated. The boundary of the inner square has a net charge $4(\frac{1}{2}) - 4(\frac{1}{4}) = 1$; the outer strip has $4(\frac{1}{2}) - 4(\frac{3}{4}) - 4(\frac{1}{2})$
$$+ 8(\frac{1}{2}) - 4(\frac{1}{4}) = 0.$$

charge according to the present scheme of counting fractional charges. The contribution to α from the first cube is

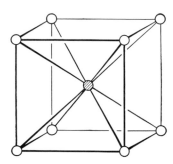

Fig. 3.7. The cesium chloride crystal structure.

$$\frac{6/2}{1} - \frac{12/4}{2^{1/2}} + \frac{8/8}{3^{1/2}} = 1.45.$$

On taking into account in similar fashion the ions in the next larger cube enclosing the original cube, we get in this approximation $\alpha = 1.75$, which is close to the accurate value $\alpha = 1.747558$ which has been worked out for the sodium chloride structure by the Ewald method.

The Ewald method is derived and discussed in Appendix A. Values of Madelung constants for many different crystal structures are tabulated by Sherman[9] in a review article. Typical values of α are listed below, based on unit charges and referred to the nearest neighbor distance.

[9] J. Sherman, Chem. Revs. **11**, 93 (1932).

Structure	α
Sodium chloride, NaCl	1.747558
Cesium chloride, CsCl	1.762670
Zinc blende, ZnS	1.6381
Wurtzite, ZnS	1.641

The cesium chloride lattice is body-centered cubic and may be easily visualized. We consider (Fig. 3.7) cesium ions placed at the lattice points of a simple cubic lattice. At the center of each cube we place a chlorine ion; this is the desired structure. It will be seen that the chlorine ions when arranged in the prescribed way also form a simple cubic lattice by themselves. Each ion is at the center of a cube formed by eight ions of the opposite charge. As the number of nearest neighbors is eight, we say that the *coordination number* is eight; the coordination number of the sodium chloride lattice is six.

For the same nearest neighbor distance the cesium chloride structure has a slightly ($\sim 1\%$) higher Coulomb energy than the sodium chloride structure, as the value of the Madelung constant α is higher for cesium chloride; however, each ion has eight nearest neighbors contributing to the repulsive energy, while there are only six in sodium chloride. As the repulsive energy is about 10% of the total energy, we might expect the 2% or 3% difference in repulsive energy to outweigh the Coulomb energy difference and thus to favor the sodium chloride structure by a small amount. It is indeed the case that many more ionic crystals are known with the sodium chloride structure than with the cesium chloride structure, but as the differences in binding energy are small we can often only decide at a given temperature which will be stable for a particular salt by a consideration of second order contributions to the energy. A detailed discussion of the stability of the two lattices is given by May.[10]

CALCULATION OF THE REPULSIVE POTENTIAL EXPONENT n

We may make a very rough estimate of the value of the exponent n in the repulsive term in the potential energy. We compare the calculated Coulomb energy with the observed total binding energy, and then estimate n on the basis of Eq. (3.5).

Substance	U (Coulomb) (kcal/mole)	U_0 (observed) (kcal/mole)
NaCl	206	183
NaBr	195	173
NaI	180	166
KCl	185	164

[10] A. May, Phys. Rev. **52**, 339 (1937). For a discussion of transformations observed under high pressure, see P. W. Bridgman, *Physics of high pressure*. Macmillan Co., New York, 2nd ed., 1950.

We see that the Coulomb energy is of the order of 10% higher than the observed total energy, so that if the repulsive energy were the only additional contribution to be considered we should have to suppose the value of n to be of the order of 10. We must remark that the Coulomb interaction by itself accounts remarkably well for the binding energy, suggesting that our basic assumption about the ionic nature of the compounds has considerable merit.

It is possible to calculate n from independent data. It is convenient to work with the observed values of the compressibility K, defined as

(3.7)
$$K = -\frac{1}{V}\frac{dV}{dp}.$$

At very low temperatures we may neglect thermal effects and write, from the first law of thermodynamics,

$$dU = -p\,dV$$

so that $dp/dV = -d^2U/dV^2$, and (at $0°$K)

(3.8)
$$\frac{1}{K} = V\frac{d^2U}{dV^2}.$$

For the sodium chloride structure, $V = 2NR^3$, where N is the total number of molecules and R is the nearest neighbor distance. We have

$$dU/dV = (dU/dR)(dR/dV);$$

$$d^2U/dV^2 = (dU/dR)(d^2R/dV^2) + (d^2U/dR^2)(dR/dV)^2.$$

At the equilibrium separation, $R = R_0$ and dU/dR is zero, so that

(3.9)
$$\frac{1}{K} = \frac{1}{18NR_0}\left(\frac{d^2U}{dR^2}\right)_{R_0},$$

using

(3.10)
$$(dR/dV)^2 = 1/36N^2R^4.$$

From Eq. (3.2) we have

$$U = N\left[\frac{\lambda A_n}{R^n} - \frac{\alpha e^2}{R}\right],$$

so that

$$\frac{d^2U}{dR^2} = N\left[\frac{n(n+1)A_n\lambda}{R^{n+2}} - \frac{2\alpha e^2}{R^3}\right].$$

At equilibrium, using Eq. (3.4) to eliminate $A_n \lambda$, we have

$$\left(\frac{d^2 U}{dR^2}\right)_{R_0} = \frac{N(n-1)\alpha e^2}{R_0{}^3}$$

so that

(3.11)
$$\frac{1}{K} = \frac{(n-1)e^2 \alpha}{18 R_0{}^4}.$$

We may use this relation to calculate n, as we may measure K, e, and R_0, and we have calculated the Madelung constant α. The compressibility of sodium chloride has been measured by Slater,[11] and he has estimated the extrapolation to absolute zero temperature as $K = 3.3 \times 10^{-12}$ cm^2/dyne. We have then

(3.12)
$$n = 1 + \frac{18 R_0{}^4}{K e^2 \alpha} = 9.4,$$

which is of the magnitude we expected.

Table 3.3 gives a comparison of the observed binding energies of a number of ionic crystals with the calculated values of Slater obtained by using values of n derived from compressibility data. The results of rather more refined calculations by Mayer and collaborators are also given. For a discussion of the methods by which the experimental values are obtained from thermochemical data, and the use of the Born-Haber cycle in this connection, the reader is referred to the review article by Sherman.[12]

Pauling in the book cited at the end of the chapter discusses the structures of complex ionic crystals of geological importance.

LATER WORK

The classical theory of ionic crystals is discussed quite fully in a book by Born,[13] and references to much of the work since that time are given by Seitz,[14] who considers the Born-Mayer theory and the work of Mayer and his collaborators in detail. The latter work is motivated by quantum mechanics, but does not represent a complete quantum-mechanical calculation. A number of correction terms are discussed in detail. A modern treatment of the general theory is given in the book by Born and Huang cited at the end of the chapter. The most thorough quantum-mechanical discussion of the binding energy of

[11] J. C. Slater, Phys. Rev. **23**, 488 (1924).
[12] J. Sherman, Chem. Revs. **11**, 93 (1932).
[13] M. Born, *Atomtheorie des festen Zustandes*, Teubner, Leipzig, 1923.
[14] F. Seitz, *Modern theory of solids*, McGraw-Hill Book Co., New York, 1940.

TABLE 3.3. THEORETICAL AND EXPERIMENTAL LATTICE ENERGIES
AT ROOM TEMPERATURE

Crystal	Lattice Constant (A)	Lattice Energy (kcal/mole)		
		Theoretical (Mayer et al.)	Theoretical (Slater) (0°K)	Experimental
LiF	4.02	240.1	231	
LiCl	5.13	199.2	189	198.1
LiBr	5.49	188.3	180	189.3
LiI	6.00	174.1		181.1
NaF	4.62	213.4		
NaCl	5.63	183.1	178	182.8
NaBr	5.96	174.6	169	173.3
NaI	6.46	163.9		166.4
KF	5.34	189.7	182	
KCl	6.28	165.4	164	164.4
KBr	6.59	159.3	157	156.2
KI	7.05	150.8	148	151.5
RbF	5.64	181.6		
RbCl	6.54	160.7		160.5
RbBr	6.85	153.5	152	153.3
RbI	7.33	145.3	147	149.0
CsF	6.01	173.7		
CsCl†	4.11	152.2		155.1
CsBr†	4.29	146.3		148.6
CsI†	4.56	139.1		145.3
AgF	4.92	219		217.7
AgCl	5.55	203		205.7
AgBr	5.77	197		201.8
AgI‡	6.47	190		199.2
TlCl†	3.83	167		170.1
TlBr†	3.97	164		165.6
TlI†	4.20	159		160.8
MgO	4.20	939		
CaO	4.80	831		
SrO	5.14	766		
BaO	5.52	727		
MgS	5.19	800		
CaS	5.68	737		
SrS	5.87	686		
BaS	6.35	647		
CuCl‡	5.41	216		221.9
CuBr‡	5.68	208		216.0
CuI‡	6.04	199		213.4

Structures are similar to NaCl except when marked as follows:

† CsCl structure
‡ Zinc blende structure

The theoretical lattice energies are from the calculations of Mayer and collaborators as summarized in the Landolt-Börnstein tables; most of the experimental values are taken from Table XXIV in F. Seitz, *Modern theory of solids*, McGraw-Hill Book Co., New York, 1940.

TABLE 3.4. COMPARISON OF LÖWDIN'S CALCULATIONS WITH EXPERIMENTAL
RESULTS EXTRAPOLATED TO 0°K

	NaCl		KCl	
	Theo-retical	Experi-mental	Theo-retical	Experi-mental
Lattice constant (A)	5.50	5.58	6.17	6.23
Lattice energy (kcal/mole)	183.2	182.8	163.9	164.4
Compressibility (10^{-12} cm^2/dyne)	4.6	3.3	6.0	4.8

TABLE 3.5. IONIC CRYSTAL RADII ACCORDING TO ZACHARIASEN

(Unpublished)

The interionic distance D is represented by $D_N = R_C + R_A + \Delta_N$, for ionic
crystals, where N is the coordination number of the cation, R_C and R_A are
the standard radii of the cation and anion, and Δ_N is a correction for coordination number. Room temperature.

(a)

N	Δ_N (A)	N	Δ_N (A)	N	Δ_N (A)
1	-0.50	5	-0.05	9	$+0.11$
2	-0.31	6	0	10	$+0.14$
3	-0.19	7	$+0.04$	11	$+0.17$
4	-0.11	8	$+0.08$	12	$+0.19$

(b) *Standard Radii (in A) for Ions with Inert Gas Configurations*

-2		O 1.46	S 1.90	Se 2.02	Te 2.22	Po 2.30
-1		F 1.33	Cl 1.81	Br 1.96	I 2.19	At 2.27
$+1$	Li 0.68	Na 0.98	K 1.33	Rb 1.48	Cs 1.67	Fr 1.75
$+2$	Be 0.30	Mg 0.65	Ca 0.94	Sr 1.10	Ba 1.29	Ra 1.37
$+3$	B 0.16	Al 0.45	Sc 0.68	Y 0.88	La 1.04	Ac 1.11
$+4$		Si 0.38	Ti 0.60	Zr 0.77	Ce 0.92	Th 0.99
$+5$				Nb 0.67		Pa 0.90
$+6$						U 0.83

(c) *Actinide Ions*

	Ac	Th	Pa	U	Np	Pu	Am
$+3$	1.11	1.08	1.05	1.03	1.01	1.00	0.99
$+4$		0.99	0.96	0.93	0.92	0.90	0.89
$+5$			0.90	0.89	0.88	0.87	0.86
$+6$				0.83	0.82	0.81	0.80

ionic crystals has been made by Löwdin,[15] who starts with radial wave
functions of the free ions in the approximation of self-consistent fields
with exchange; he computes from these wave functions alone the lattice energy, lattice constant, and various elastic properties. No empirical data are introduced except values of the fundamental physical

[15] Per-Olov Löwdin, Thesis, Uppsala, 1948; Ark. Mat. Astron. Fysik **35A**,
Nos. 9, 30 (1947).

constants e, m, h, etc. Some of the results at $0°K$ for sodium chloride and potassium chloride are given in Table 3.4, as taken from Löwdin's thesis.

IONIC RADII

It is found that the interatomic distances in the alkali halides are approximately additive, so that to a certain extent the ions may be regarded as rigid spheres. The distance at which the ions come into contact is the equilibrium interionic distance. The approximate validity of the ionic radius concept is a consequence of the very strong dependence of the repulsive forces on interionic distance.

The tailing-off of the radial wave functions according to quantum mechanics tells us that no absolute significance may be attached to a table of ionic radii, but for many purposes a set of radii, such as those in Tables 3.5 and 3.6, may be of value. It is necessary to assign one

TABLE 3.6. IONIC CRYSTAL RADII ACCORDING TO PAULING, IN ANGSTROMS

(L. Pauling, *Nature of the chemical bond*, Cornell University Press, Ithaca, 1945, p. 346.)

			H^-		Li^+	Be^{2+}	B^{3+}	C^{4+}	N^{5+}	O^{6+}	F^{7+}
			2.08		0.60	0.32	0.20	0.15	0.11	0.09	0.07
C^{4-}	N^{3-}	O^{2-}	F^-		Na^+	Mg^{2+}	Al^{3+}	Si^{4+}	P^{5+}	S^{6+}	Cl^{7+}
2.60	1.71	1.40	1.36		0.95	0.65	0.50	0.41	0.34	0.29	0.26
Si^{4-}	P^{3-}	S^{2-}	Cl^-		K^+	Ca^{2+}	Sc^{3+}	Ti^{4+}	V^{5+}	Cr^{6+}	Mn^{7+}
2.71	2.12	1.84	1.81		1.33	0.99	0.81	0.68	0.59	0.52	0.46
					Cu^+	Zn^{2+}	Ga^{3+}	Ge^{4+}	As^{5+}	Se^{6+}	Br^{7+}
					0.96	0.74	0.62	0.53	0.47	0.42	0.39
Ge^{4-}	As^{3-}	Se^{2-}	Br^-		Rb^+	Sr^{2+}	Y^{3+}	Zr^{4+}	Nb^{5+}	Mo^{6+}	
2.72	2.22	1.98	1.95		1.48	1.13	0.93	0.80	0.70	0.62	
					Ag^+	Cd^{2+}	In^{3+}	Sn^{4+}	Sb^{5+}	Te^{6+}	I^{7+}
					1.26	0.97	0.81	0.71	0.62	0.56	0.50
Sn^{4-}	Sb^{3-}	Te^{2-}	I^-		Cs^+	Ba^{2+}	La^{3+}	Ce^{4+}			
2.94	2.45	2.21	2.16		1.69	1.35	1.15	1.01			
					Au^+	Hg^{2+}	Tl^{3+}	Pb^{4+}	Bi^{5+}		
					1.37	1.10	0.95	0.84	0.74		

radius somewhat arbitrarily in constructing a table, as a constant distance may be added to the cations and subtracted from the anions without changing the observed lattice constants in diatomic structures. It is usual in empirical treatments to take the radius of F^- as 1.33 A, when the coordination number (number of nearest neighbors) is 6. The radii in Table 3.6 were calculated theoretically by Pauling with the help of certain empirical data. Empirical radii values for other ions, based on $O^{2-} = 1.40$ A, are given in Table 3.7.

TABLE 3.7. EMPIRICAL IONIC RADII

(After Pauling)

NH$_4^+$	1.48 A	Mn^{2+}	0.80 A	Ti^{3+}	0.69 A
Tl$^+$	1.44 A	Fe^{2+}	0.75 A	V^{3+}	0.66 A
		Co^{2+}	0.72 A	Cr^{3+}	0.64 A
		Ni^{2+}	0.70 A	Mn^{3+}	0.62 A
				Fe^{3+}	0.60 A

Trivalent rare earth ions, 0.90 ± 0.05 A

As an example of the use of the tables, we consider BaTiO$_3$ (Fig. 8.1), with a measured average lattice constant of 4.004 A at room temperature. If we suppose that the structure is determined by the Ba-O contacts, we have, from Table 3.5, $D_{12} = 1.29 + 1.46 + 0.19 = 2.94$ A, or $a = 4.16$ A; if the Ti-O contact determines the structure, we have $D_6 = 0.60 + 1.46 = 2.06$, or $a = 4.12$ A. The fact that the actual lattice constant is appreciably smaller than the estimates may perhaps suggest that the bonding is not purely ionic, but is partly covalent. For sodium chloride, which is probably principally ionic, we have $D_6 = 0.98 + 1.81 = 2.79$, or $a = 5.58$ A, while 5.63 A is observed at room temperature.

PROBLEMS

3.1. Show that the constant A_n in Eq. (3.2) has the value 6.42(6) for the sodium chloride lattice for $n = 10$. Values of A_n are tabulated by J. E. Lennard-Jones and A. E. Ingham, Proc. Roy. Soc. 107A, 636 (1925).

3.2. Calculate the value of λ in Eq. (3.1) for sodium chloride, taking $n = 10$; $A_{10} = 6.43$; and $R_0 = 2.81 \times 10^{-8}$ cm. Ans. $\lambda = 0.7 \times 10^{-88}$ ergs cm^{10}.

3.3. Show for the sodium chloride structure that $\alpha \cong 1.75$; use the Evjen method as discussed in the text, carrying the enumeration out to the cube whose faces are distant $2R_0$ from the central atom, where R_0 is the nearest neighbor distance. It will be found convenient to set out the enumeration in a systematic form, expressing atomic positions in terms of the integers n_1, n_2, n_3, where $x = n_1 R_0$, $y = n_2 R_0$, $z = n_3 R_0$ give the coordinates relative to Cartesian coordinate axes along the crystal axes. In this notation the distance of the ion at n_1, n_2, n_3 from the origin is $R_0[n_1{}^2 + n_2{}^2 + n_3{}^2]^{1/2}$. We must also know the number of sites at the same distance from the origin. Such sites arise from the same set of numerical values n_1, n_2, n_3, but arranged in all possible orders and with all possible combinations of sign. There are in general six orders and eight combinations of sign, making forty-eight equivalent positions. If one of the n's is zero, there are twenty-four equivalent positions. If two n's are equal in magnitude but different from zero, there are twenty-four equivalent positions. If all three n's are equal in magnitude there are eight equivalent positions, corresponding to the corners of a cube. Other similar relations are easily established.

3.4. Discuss quantitatively the probable effect of doubling the ionic charges on the lattice constant, compressibility, and binding energy of sodium chloride; the repulsive potential is to be taken as unchanged.

3.5.* Calculate by the Ewald method given in Appendix A the value of the Madelung constant for the cesium chloride lattice.

84 CLASSIFICATION OF SOLIDS

3.6.* Using the theory developed in this chapter, calculate for sodium chloride the value of the pressure coefficient of compressibility $(dK/dp)/K$ at zero pressure and at $0°K$, using appropriate numerical data. *Ans.* -1.8×10^{-11} cm^2/dyne.

3.7. Suppose that it were possible to permeate the space between ions in an ionic crystal with a homogeneous fluid of dielectric constant ϵ without affecting the equation for the repulsive interactions between ions, but reducing the Coulomb interaction by a factor $1/\epsilon$. Calculate the lattice constant and binding energy of sodium chloride in this situation, taking $\epsilon = 81$ as for water. This is to a certain extent the explanation of the solvent properties of water and other dipolar liquids. Compare the binding energy per atom with the approximate thermal energy kT per atom at room temperature, where k is the Boltzmann constant. A high dielectric constant is to a certain extent responsible for the solvent properties of water and other dipolar liquids, such as NH_3, HF, HCN.

3.8. Check the Zachariasen radii (Table 3.5) against observed lattice constants for ten crystals chosen from various sections of Wyckoff's compilation or elsewhere.

3.9. Replacing the repulsive potential λr_{ij}^{-n} over all ions by the potential $Ae^{-r/\rho}$ over only nearest neighbor ions, find values of A and ρ for sodium chloride. The exponential potential is suggested by quantum theory and is used in most recent work in the field.

REFERENCES

M. Born, *Atomtheorie des festen Zustandes*, Teubner, Leipzig, 1923.

M. Born and M. Göppert-Mayer, *Handbuch der Physik* **24/2**, 623–794, Springer, Berlin, 1933.

M. Born and K. Huang, *Dynamical theory of crystal lattices*, Clarendon Press, Oxford, 1954.

W. Kleber, *Angewandte Gitterphysik*, W. de Gruyter and Co., Berlin, 2nd ed., 1949.

L. Pauling, *Nature of the chemical bond*, Cornell University Press, Ithaca, 2nd ed., 1945; see especially Chapter 10.

F. Seitz, *Modern theory of solids*, McGraw-Hill Book Co., New York, 1940.

4

Elastic Constants of Crystals

This chapter is concerned with the elastic constants of single crystals. The elastic constants are of interest because of the insight they give into the nature of the binding forces in solids, and they are also of importance for the thermal properties of solids. We give first a review of the formal phenomenology of elastic constants of single crystals, for small deformations. Polycrystalline specimens may have isotropic elastic properties and may be described approximately by fewer elastic constants than a single crystal, but the values of the constants for single crystals are of fundamental significance.

We shall see that the elastic properties of a crystal are generally anisotropic. Even in a cubic crystal, the connection between stress and strain depends on the orientation of the crystal axes relative to the stress system. Anisotropic properties of crystals are often called tensor properties.

In the early development of the present chapter we treat the crystal as homogeneous; no reference is made at this point to the fact that the crystal is actually composed of discrete atoms. The discussion of elastic waves is limited therefore to wavelengths much longer than a lattice constant. In Chapter 5 we shall consider the extension of the theory to shorter wavelengths, and we shall see there that the periodic nature of the lattice causes effects on the propagation of elastic waves somewhat similar to the effects, such as Bragg reflection, on x-radiation.

ANALYSIS OF ELASTIC STRAINS AND STRESSES

The local elastic strain of a body may be specified by six numbers. If α, β, γ are the angles between the unit cell axes $\mathbf{a}$, $\mathbf{b}$, $\mathbf{c}$, the strain may be specified by the changes $\Delta\alpha$, $\Delta\beta$, $\Delta\gamma$; Δa, Δb, Δc resulting from the deformation. This is a good physical specification of strain, but for non-orthogonal axes it leads to mathematical complications. It is usual instead to specify the strain in terms of the six components e_{xx}, e_{yy}, e_{zz}, e_{xy}, e_{yz}, e_{zx} which are defined below.

We imagine that three *orthogonal* axes $\mathbf{f}$, $\mathbf{g}$, $\mathbf{h}$ of *unit length* are embedded securely in the unstrained solid, as shown in Fig. 4.1. We suppose that after a small uniform deformation has taken place the axes, which we now label $\mathbf{f}'$, $\mathbf{g}'$, $\mathbf{h}'$, are distorted in orientation and in length, so that with the same atom as origin we may write.

$$\mathbf{f}' = (1 + \varepsilon_{xx})\mathbf{f} + \varepsilon_{xy}\mathbf{g} + \varepsilon_{xz}\mathbf{h};$$

(4.1)
$$\mathbf{g}' = \varepsilon_{yx}\mathbf{f} + (1 + \varepsilon_{yy})\mathbf{g} + \varepsilon_{yz}\mathbf{h};$$

$$\mathbf{h}' = \varepsilon_{zx}\mathbf{f} + \varepsilon_{zy}\mathbf{g} + (1 + \varepsilon_{zz})\mathbf{h}.$$

The fractional changes of length of the $\mathbf{f}$, $\mathbf{g}$, and $\mathbf{h}$ axes are ε_{xx}, ε_{yy}, ε_{zz}, respectively, to the first order. We define the strain components

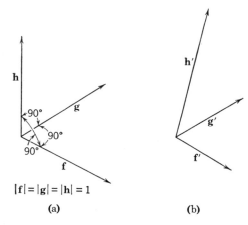

$$|\mathbf{f}| = |\mathbf{g}| = |\mathbf{h}| = 1$$

(a)   (b)

Fig. 4.1.   Coordinate axes for the description of the state of strain; the orthogonal unit axes in the unstrained state (a) are deformed in the strained state (b).

e_{xx}, e_{yy}, e_{zz} by the relations

(4.2) $e_{xx} = \varepsilon_{xx}$; $e_{yy} = \varepsilon_{yy}$; $e_{zz} = \varepsilon_{zz}$.

The strain components e_{xy}, e_{yz}, e_{zx} may be defined as the changes in angle between the axes, so that to the first order

$$e_{xy} = \mathbf{f}' \cdot \mathbf{g}' = \varepsilon_{yx} + \varepsilon_{xy};$$

(4.3)
$$e_{yz} = \mathbf{g}' \cdot \mathbf{h}' = \varepsilon_{zy} + \varepsilon_{yz};$$

$$e_{zx} = \mathbf{h}' \cdot \mathbf{f}' = \varepsilon_{zx} + \varepsilon_{xz}.$$

This completes the definition of the six strain components. A deformation is *uniform* if the values of the strain components are independent of the choice of origin.

We note that merely rotating the axes does not change the angle between them. Using (4.3) we see that for a pure rotation $\varepsilon_{yx} = -\varepsilon_{xy}$;

$\varepsilon_{zy} = -\varepsilon_{yz}$; $\varepsilon_{zx} = -\varepsilon_{xz}$. If we exclude pure rotations as not being of interest here, we may without further loss of generality take $\varepsilon_{yx} = \varepsilon_{xy}$; $\varepsilon_{zy} = \varepsilon_{yz}$; $\varepsilon_{zx} = \varepsilon_{xz}$, so that in terms of the strain components we have

$$\mathbf{f}' - \mathbf{f} = e_{xx}\mathbf{f} + \tfrac{1}{2}e_{xy}\mathbf{g} + \tfrac{1}{2}e_{zx}\mathbf{h};$$

(4.4)
$$\mathbf{g}' - \mathbf{g} = \tfrac{1}{2}e_{xy}\mathbf{f} + e_{yy}\mathbf{g} + \tfrac{1}{2}e_{yz}\mathbf{h};$$

$$\mathbf{h}' - \mathbf{h} = \tfrac{1}{2}e_{zx}\mathbf{f} + \tfrac{1}{2}e_{yz}\mathbf{g} + e_{zz}\mathbf{h}.$$

We consider under a deformation which is substantially uniform near the origin a particle originally at the position

(4.5)
$$\mathbf{r} = x\mathbf{f} + y\mathbf{g} + z\mathbf{h}.$$

After deformation the particle is at

(4.6)
$$\mathbf{r}' = x\mathbf{f}' + y\mathbf{g}' + z\mathbf{h}',$$

so that the displacement is given by

(4.7)
$$\boldsymbol{\varrho} = \mathbf{r}' - \mathbf{r} = x(\mathbf{f}' - \mathbf{f}) + y(\mathbf{g}' - \mathbf{g}) + z(\mathbf{h}' - \mathbf{h}).$$

If we write the displacement as

(4.8)
$$\boldsymbol{\varrho} = u\mathbf{f} + v\mathbf{g} + w\mathbf{h},$$

we have from (4.4) and (4.7) the following expressions for the strain components:

(4.9)
$$e_{xx} = \frac{\partial u}{\partial x}; \qquad e_{yy} = \frac{\partial v}{\partial y}; \qquad e_{zz} = \frac{\partial w}{\partial z};$$

$$e_{xy} = \frac{\partial v}{\partial x} + \frac{\partial u}{\partial y}; \qquad e_{yz} = \frac{\partial w}{\partial y} + \frac{\partial v}{\partial z}; \qquad e_{zx} = \frac{\partial u}{\partial z} + \frac{\partial w}{\partial x}.$$

We have written derivatives for application to non-uniform strain. The expressions (4.9) are frequently used in the literature to define the strain components. Occasionally definitions of e_{xy}, e_{yz}, and e_{zx} are given which differ by a factor $\frac{1}{2}$ from those given here.   For a uniform deformation the displacement $\boldsymbol{\varrho}$ has the components

(4.10)
$$u = e_{xx}x + \tfrac{1}{2}e_{xy}y + \tfrac{1}{2}e_{zx}z;$$

$$v = \tfrac{1}{2}e_{xy}x + e_{yy}y + \tfrac{1}{2}e_{yz}z;$$

$$w = \tfrac{1}{2}e_{zx}x + \tfrac{1}{2}e_{yz}y + e_{zz}z.$$

DILATION

The fractional increment of volume caused by a deformation is called the *dilation*. The unit cube of edges $\mathbf{f}$, $\mathbf{g}$, $\mathbf{h}$ after deformation has a volume

(4.11) $$V' = \mathbf{f}' \cdot \mathbf{g}' \times \mathbf{h}' \cong 1 + e_{xx} + e_{yy} + e_{zz},$$

where squares and products of strain components are neglected. Thus the dilation is

(4.12) $$\delta = \Delta V / V' = e_{xx} + e_{yy} + e_{zz}.$$

SHEARING STRAIN

We may interpret the strain components of the type

$$e_{xy} = \frac{\partial v}{\partial x} + \frac{\partial u}{\partial y}$$

as made up of two simple shears. In one of the shears, planes of the material normal to the x axis slide in the y direction; in the other shear, planes normal to y slide in the x direction.

STRESS COMPONENTS

The force acting on a unit area in the solid is defined as the stress. There are nine stress components: X_x, X_y, X_z, Y_x, Y_y, Y_z, Z_x, Z_y, Z_z.

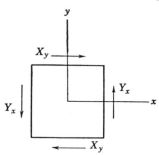

Fig. 4.2. Demonstration that $Y_x = X_y$ in order that the body may be in equilibrium.

The capital letter indicates the direction of the force, and the subscript indicates the normal to the plane to which the force is applied. Thus the stress component X_x represents a force applied in the x direction to a unit area of a plane whose normal lies in the x direction; the stress component X_y represents a force applied in the x direction to a unit area of a plane whose normal lies in the y direction. The number of independent stress components is reduced to six by applying to an elementary cube as in Fig. 4.2 the condition that the angular acceleration vanish, and hence that the total torque must be zero. It follows that

$$Y_z = Z_y; \qquad Z_x = X_z; \qquad X_y = Y_x,$$

and the independent stress components may be taken as X_x, Y_y, Z_z, Y_z, Z_x, X_y.

ELASTIC COMPLIANCE AND STIFFNESS CONSTANTS

Hooke's law states that for small deformations the strain is proportional to the stress, so that the strain components are linear functions of the stress components:

$$
\begin{aligned}
e_{xx} &= s_{11}X_x + s_{12}Y_y + s_{13}Z_z + s_{14}Y_z + s_{15}Z_x + s_{16}X_y; \\
e_{yy} &= s_{21}X_x + s_{22}Y_y + s_{23}Z_z + s_{24}Y_z + s_{25}Z_x + s_{26}X_y; \\
e_{zz} &= s_{31}X_x + s_{32}Y_y + s_{33}Z_z + s_{34}Y_z + s_{35}Z_x + s_{36}X_y; \\
e_{yz} &= s_{41}X_x + s_{42}Y_y + s_{43}Z_z + s_{44}Y_z + s_{45}Z_x + s_{46}X_y; \\
e_{zx} &= s_{51}X_x + s_{52}Y_y + s_{53}Z_z + s_{54}Y_z + s_{55}Z_x + s_{56}X_y; \\
e_{xy} &= s_{61}X_x + s_{62}Y_y + s_{63}Z_z + s_{64}Y_z + s_{65}Z_x + s_{66}X_y.
\end{aligned}
$$

(4.13)

Conversely, the stress components are linear functions of the strain components:

$$
\begin{aligned}
X_x &= c_{11}e_{xx} + c_{12}e_{yy} + c_{13}e_{zz} + c_{14}e_{yz} + c_{15}e_{zx} + c_{16}e_{xy}; \\
Y_y &= c_{21}e_{xx} + c_{22}e_{yy} + c_{23}e_{zz} + c_{24}e_{yz} + c_{25}e_{zx} + c_{26}e_{xy}; \\
Z_z &= c_{31}e_{xx} + c_{32}e_{yy} + c_{33}e_{zz} + c_{34}e_{yz} + c_{35}e_{zx} + c_{36}e_{xy}; \\
Y_z &= c_{41}e_{xx} + c_{42}e_{yy} + c_{43}e_{zz} + c_{44}e_{yz} + c_{45}e_{zx} + c_{46}e_{xy}; \\
Z_x &= c_{51}e_{xx} + c_{52}e_{yy} + c_{53}e_{zz} + c_{54}e_{yz} + c_{55}e_{zx} + c_{56}e_{xy}; \\
X_y &= c_{61}e_{xx} + c_{62}e_{yy} + c_{63}e_{zz} + c_{64}e_{yz} + c_{65}e_{zx} + c_{66}e_{xy}.
\end{aligned}
$$

(4.14)

The quantities s_{11}, s_{12}, $\cdots$ are called the *elastic constants* or *elastic compliance constants;* the quantities c_{11}, c_{12}, $\cdots$ are called the *elastic stiffness constants* or *moduli of elasticity.* Other names are also current.

ENERGY DENSITY

We calculate the increment of work δW done by the stress system in straining a small cube of side L, with the origin at one corner of the cube and the coordinate axes parallel to the cube edges. We have

(4.15) $$\delta W = \mathbf{F} \cdot \delta \boldsymbol{\varrho}$$

where $\mathbf{F}$ is the applied force and, from (4.8),

(4.16) $$\delta \boldsymbol{\varrho} = \mathbf{f}\, \delta u + \mathbf{g}\, \delta v + \mathbf{h}\, \delta w$$

is the displacement. If X, Y, Z denote the components of $\mathbf{F}$ per unit area, then

(4.17) $$\delta W = L^2(X\, \delta u + Y\, \delta v + Z\, \delta w).$$

We note that the displacement of the three cube faces containing the origin is zero, so that the forces all act at a distance L from the origin. Now by definition of the strain components

(4.18) $$\delta u = L(\delta e_{xx} + \tfrac{1}{2}\delta e_{xy} + \tfrac{1}{2}\delta e_{zx}),$$

etc., so that

$$\delta W = L^3(X_x\,\delta e_{xx} + Y_y\,\delta e_{yy} + Z_z\,\delta e_{zz} + Y_z\,\delta e_{yz} + Z_x\,\delta e_{zx} + X_y\,\delta e_{xy}).$$

The increment δU of elastic energy per unit volume is

(4.19) $$\delta U = X_x\,\delta e_{xx} + Y_y\,\delta e_{yy} + Z_z\,\delta e_{zz}$$
$$+ Y_z\,\delta e_{yz} + Z_x\,\delta e_{zx} + X_y\,\delta e_{xy}.$$

We have $\partial U/\partial e_{xx} = X_x$ and $\partial U/\partial e_{yy} = Y_y$, and on further differentiation

$$\partial X_x/\partial e_{yy} = \partial Y_y/\partial e_{xx}.$$

This leads from (4.14) to the relation

$$c_{12} = c_{21};$$

and in general we have

(4.20) $$c_{ij} = c_{ji},$$

giving fifteen relations among the thirty non-diagonal terms of the matrix of the c's. The thirty-six elastic stiffness constants are in this way reduced to twenty-one coefficients. Similar relations hold among the elastic compliances. The matrix of the c's or s's is therefore symmetrical.

CUBIC CRYSTALS

The number of independent elastic stiffness constants is usually reduced if the crystal possesses symmetry elements, and in the important case of cubic crystals there are only three independent stiffness constants, as we now show. We suppose that the coordinate axes are chosen parallel to the cube edges. It is apparent that the three axes are equivalent since the cube possesses a four-fold axis normal to each face. We therefore have, from (4.14),

$$c_{11} = c_{22} = c_{33}; \qquad c_{44} = c_{55} = c_{66}.$$

In addition there is a mirror plane normal to each axis; hence reversing the direction of one of the coordinate axes must leave the stress unaltered. Applying these two restrictions and noting the further restriction imposed by (4.20), we have

$$c_{14} = c_{25} = c_{36} = c_{63} = c_{52} = c_{41} = 0,$$

$$c_{45} = c_{56} = c_{64} = c_{46} = c_{65} = c_{54} = 0,$$

$$c_{15} = c_{26} = c_{34} = c_{43} = c_{62} = c_{51} = c_{16}$$
$$= c_{24} = c_{35} = c_{53} = c_{42} = c_{61} = 0.$$

The type of elementary symmetry arguments employed here finds wide application in connection with other anisotropic properties of crystals.

The array of values of the elastic stiffness constant is therefore reduced for a cubic crystal to the matrix

$$(4.21) \qquad \|c_{ij}\| = \begin{Vmatrix} c_{11} & c_{12} & c_{12} & 0 & 0 & 0 \\ c_{12} & c_{11} & c_{12} & 0 & 0 & 0 \\ c_{12} & c_{12} & c_{11} & 0 & 0 & 0 \\ 0 & 0 & 0 & c_{44} & 0 & 0 \\ 0 & 0 & 0 & 0 & c_{44} & 0 \\ 0 & 0 & 0 & 0 & 0 & c_{44} \end{Vmatrix}$$

It is readily seen that for a cubic crystal

$$(4.22) \quad U = \tfrac{1}{2}c_{11}(e_{xx}^2 + e_{yy}^2 + e_{zz}^2) + c_{12}(e_{yy}e_{zz} + e_{zz}e_{xx}$$
$$+ e_{xx}e_{yy}) + \tfrac{1}{2}c_{44}(e_{yz}^2 + e_{zx}^2 + e_{xy}^2)$$

satisfies the condition (4.19) for the elastic energy density function. For example,

$$\partial U/\partial e_{yy} = c_{11}e_{yy} + c_{12}e_{zz} + c_{12}e_{xx} = Y_y,$$

by (4.21).

For cubic crystals the compliance and stiffness constants are related by

$$(4.23) \quad \begin{aligned} c_{11} &= (s_{11} + s_{12})/(s_{11} - s_{12})(s_{11} + 2s_{12}); \\ c_{12} &= -s_{12}/(s_{11} - s_{12})(s_{11} + 2s_{12}); \\ c_{44} &= 1/s_{44}; \\ s_{11} &= (c_{11} + c_{12})/(c_{11} - c_{12})(c_{11} + 2c_{12}); \\ s_{12} &= -c_{12}/(c_{11} - c_{12})(c_{11} + 2c_{12}); \\ s_{44} &= 1/c_{44}. \end{aligned}$$

Values of elastic data for various cubic crystals are tabulated in Table 4.1. The values refer to room temperature. A general review of elastic constant data and of relationships among various coefficients for the crystal classes has been given by Hearmon.[1] In Fig. 4.3 the experimental values of the elastic constants of sodium chloride are plotted over a wide temperature range. The theory of the temperature dependence of the elastic constants has been considered by Born[2] and by Fürth.[3]

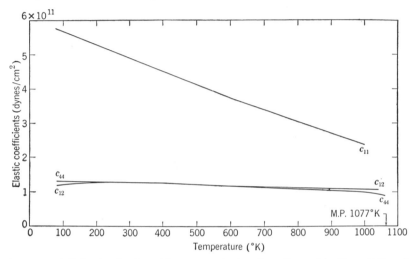

Fig. 4.3. Adiabatic elastic stiffness constants of sodium chloride. [After L. Hunter and S. Siegel, Phys. Rev. **61**, 84 (1942); F. C. Rose, Phys. Rev. **49**, 50 (1936).]

EXPERIMENTAL DETERMINATION OF ELASTIC CONSTANTS

The classic methods for the measurement of the elastic constants of crystals are described in the review by Hearmon just cited. Since his review the use of the ultrasonic pulse method has become widespread[4] because of its convenience and adaptability to a wide range of experimental conditions. In this method an ultrasonic pulse generated by a quartz transducer is transmitted through the test crystal and reflected from the rear surface of the crystal back to the transducer. The elapsed time between initiation and receipt of the pulse is measured by standard electronic methods. The velocity is obtained by dividing

[1] R. F. S. Hearmon, Revs. Modern Phys. **18**, 409 (1946); see also S. Bhagavantam, Proc. Indian Acad. Sci. **A41**, 72 (1955); for ionic crystals see S. O. Lundqvist, Arkiv för Fysik **6**, 25 (1953).

[2] M. Born, J. Chem. Phys. **7**, 591 (1939).

[3] R. Fürth, Proc. Cambridge Phil. Soc. **37**, 34 (1941).

[4] See, for example, H. Huntington, Phys. Rev. **72**, 321 (1947); J. K. Galt, Phys. Rev. **73**, 1460 (1948).

the round trip distance by the elapsed time. In a representative arrangement the experimental frequency may be 15 mc, and the pulse length 1 μsec. The wavelength is of the order of 3×10^{-2} cm. The crystal specimen may be of the order of 1 cm in length.

The elastic stiffness constants c_{11}, c_{12}, c_{44} of a cubic crystal may be determined from the velocities of three waves. A longitudinal wave propagates along a cube axis with velocity $(c_{11}/\rho_0)^{1/2}$, where ρ_0 is the

TABLE 4.1. ELASTIC STIFFNESS CONSTANTS OF CUBIC CRYSTALS
(AT ROOM TEMPERATURE UNLESS OTHERWISE STATED)

Stiffness Constants in 10^{12} dyne/cm^2

Crystal	c_{11}	c_{12}	c_{44}
Na(210°K)	0.055	0.042	0.049
K	0.046	0.037	0.026
Fe	2.37	1.41	1.16
Ni(demag)	2.50	1.60	1.185
W	5.01	1.98	1.15
Cu	1.684	1.214	0.754
Cu(10°K)	1.762	1.249	0.818
Diamond	10.76	1.25	5.76
Si	1.66	0.64	0.79
Ge	1.29	0.48	0.67
Al	1.08	0.62	0.28
Pb	0.48	0.41	0.14
LiF	1.19	0.54	0.53
NaCl	0.486	0.127	0.128
KCl	0.40	0.062	0.062
NaBr	0.33	0.13	0.13
KBr	0.35	0.058	0.050
KI	0.27	0.043	0.042
AgCl	0.60	0.36	0.062
AgBr	0.56	0.33	0.073

density. A shear wave propagates along a cube axis with velocity $(c_{44}/\rho_0)^{1/2}$, while a shear wave with particle motion along a $1\bar{1}0$ direction propagates along a 110 direction with velocity $[(c_{11} - c_{12})/2\rho_0]^{1/2}$. The first two results are derived below, and the latter result is the basis of a problem at the end of the chapter.

ELASTIC WAVES IN CUBIC CRYSTALS

By considering the forces acting on an element of volume in the crystal we find for the equation of motion in the x direction

(4.24)
$$\rho_0 \ddot{u} = \frac{\partial X_x}{\partial x} + \frac{\partial X_y}{\partial y} + \frac{\partial X_z}{\partial z},$$

with similar equations for the y and z directions; ρ_0 is the density. From (4.21) it follows, taking the cube edges as the x, y, z directions, that

$$\rho_0 \ddot{u} = c_{11} \frac{\partial e_{xx}}{\partial x} + c_{12} \left(\frac{\partial e_{yy}}{\partial x} + \frac{\partial e_{zz}}{\partial x} \right) + c_{44} \left(\frac{\partial e_{xy}}{\partial y} + \frac{\partial e_{xz}}{\partial z} \right),$$

which reduces, using (4.9), to

$$(4.25) \quad \rho_0 \ddot{u} = c_{11} \frac{\partial^2 u}{\partial x^2} + c_{44} \left(\frac{\partial^2 u}{\partial y^2} + \frac{\partial^2 u}{\partial z^2} \right)$$

$$+ (c_{12} + c_{44}) \left(\frac{\partial^2 v}{\partial x \, \partial y} + \frac{\partial^2 w}{\partial x \, \partial z} \right).$$

One solution is given by a longitudinal wave,

$$u = u_0 e^{i(\omega t - kx)},$$

moving along the x cube edge; from (4.25)

$$-\omega^2 \rho_0 = -k^2 c_{11},$$

so that the velocity is

$$(4.26) \qquad v = \omega/k = (c_{11}/\rho_0)^{1/2}.$$

Another solution is given by a transverse or shear wave moving along the y cube edge, with the particle motion in the x direction:

$$u = u_0 e^{i(\omega t - ky)},$$

which gives, on substitution in (4.25),

$$-\omega^2 \rho_0 = -k^2 c_{44},$$

so that

$$(4.27) \qquad v = (c_{44}/\rho_0)^{1/2}.$$

There is also a solution given by a shear wave moving in the z direction with particle motion in the x direction. In general there are three types of wave motion for a given direction of propagation in the crystal, but only for a few special directions can the waves be classified as pure longitudinal or pure transverse. Further details are given by Mueller,[5] and the general problem has been treated by Schaefer and co-workers.[6]

[5] H. Mueller, Z. Krist. **99**, 122 (1938).

[6] C. Schaefer, L. Bergmann, E. Fues, and H. Ludloff, Akad. Wiss. Berlin, Sitzberichte Phys.-Math. Kl. **14**, 22 (1935).

ELASTIC ISOTROPY

By minor manipulations we may rewrite (4.25) as

$$(4.28) \quad \rho_0 \ddot{u} = (c_{11} - c_{12} - 2c_{44}) \frac{\partial^2 u}{\partial x^2} + c_{44} \nabla^2 u + (c_{12} + c_{44}) \frac{\partial}{\partial x} \text{ div } \varrho,$$

where the displacement $\varrho = u\mathbf{i} + v\mathbf{j} + w\mathbf{k}$ is not to be confused with the density ρ_0. If

$$(4.29) \qquad\qquad c_{11} - c_{12} = 2c_{44},$$

the first term on the right in (4.28) drops out, and we can write on summing with the equations for the y and z motions:

$$(4.30) \qquad\qquad \rho_0 \ddot{\varrho} = c_{11} \text{ grad div } \varrho - c_{44} \text{ curl curl } \varrho.$$

This equation has the important property that it is invariant under rotations of the reference axes, as each term in the equation is an invariant. Thus the relation (4.29) is the condition that the crystal should be elastically isotropic; that is, that waves should propagate in all directions with equal velocities. However, the longitudinal wave velocity is not necessarily equal to the transverse wave velocity. The term in grad div gives rise to a longitudinal wave, that is, with particle displacement ϱ in the direction of the propagation vector $\mathbf{k}$. The term in curl curl gives rise to two independent orthogonal transverse waves of equal frequency; the particle displacements are in a plane normal to the propagation vector.

The anisotropy factor A in a cubic crystal is defined as the square of the ratio of velocities of the shear waves propagating in the [100] and [110] directions:

$$(4.31) \qquad\qquad A = 2c_{44}/(c_{11} - c_{12})$$

and is unity for elastic isotropy. Values of A for representative metals at room temperature follow:

Fe 2.4;   K 6.3;   W 1.0;   Al 1.2;   Cu 3.3;   Pb 3.9.

CAUCHY RELATIONS

If certain conditions are satisfied, there exist among the elastic stiffness constants relations first obtained by Cauchy. The relations reduce to

$$(4.32) \qquad\qquad c_{12} = c_{44}$$

in a crystal of cubic symmetry. If this is satisfied, the isotropy condition (4.29) becomes $c_{11} = 3c_{44}$. If then a cubic crystal were elastically isotropic *and* the Cauchy relation satisfied, the velocity of the transverse waves would be equal to $(\frac{1}{3})^{\frac{1}{2}}$ the velocity of the longitudinal waves.

The conditions[7] for the validity of the Cauchy relations are:

1. All forces must be central, i.e., act along lines joining the centers of the atoms. This is not generally true of covalent binding forces, nor of metallic binding forces.

2. Every atom must be at a center of symmetry; that is, replacing every interatomic vector $\mathbf{r}_{jk}$ by $-\mathbf{r}_{jk}$ should not change the structure.

3. The crystal should be initially under no stress.

In metallic lattices the nature of the binding is not such that we would expect the Cauchy relation to work out well, and this is the case, as shown in Table 4.1. In ionic crystals the electrostatic interaction of the ions is the principal interaction and is central in nature. It is not surprising that the Cauchy relation is moderately well satisfied in the alkali halides, as shown also by the table.

LATTICE THEORY OF ELASTIC COEFFICIENTS

In this section we indicate the type of connection which exists between the macroscopic elastic constants and the forces between pairs of atoms in the structure. We suppose that two nearby atoms 1, 2 are displaced from equilibrium by ϱ_1, ϱ_2. If $|\varrho_2 - \varrho_1|$ is small in comparison with the lattice constant, the displacement energy may be written in a Hooke's law approximation

$$\frac{\alpha}{2}(u_2 - u_1)^2 + \frac{\beta}{2}[(v_2 - v_1)^2 + (w_2 - w_1)^2],$$

where the pair of atoms are supposed to have been initially along the x axis. If the forces between the atoms are central, we would have $\beta = 0$.

For a monatomic simple cubic lattice with only nearest neighbor interactions the energy is

$$(4.33) \quad \frac{\alpha}{2}\sum_{lmn}[(u_{l+1,m,n} - u_{l,m,n})^2 + (v_{l,m+1,n} - v_{l,m,n})^2$$

$$+ (w_{l,m,n+1} - w_{l,m,n})^2] + \frac{\beta}{2}\sum_{lmn}[(v_{l+1,m,n} - v_{l,m,n})^2$$

$$+ (v_{l,m,n+1} - v_{l,m,n})^2 + \cdots + (u_{l,m,n+1} - u_{l,m,n})^2].$$

[7] C. Zener, Phys. Rev. **71**, 323 (1947); G. Leibfried, Z. Physik **129**, 307 (1951).

If a is the nearest neighbor distance, we may write for the energy density for a homogeneous pure strain

$$U = \frac{N\alpha a^2}{2}(e_{xx}^2 + e_{yy}^2 + e_{zz}^2) + \frac{N\beta a^2}{4}(e_{yz}^2 + e_{zx}^2 + e_{xy}^2),$$

where N is the atomic concentration. On comparison with (4.22) we see that our model leads to the following expressions for the elastic coefficients:

(4.34) $c_{11} = \alpha/a;$ $c_{12} = 0;$ $c_{44} = \beta/2a.$

We note that with only nearest neighbor forces on the central force assumption ($\beta = 0$) the simple cubic lattice does not possess any

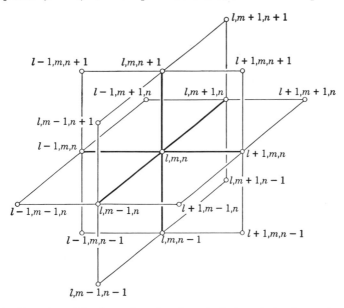

Fig. 4.4. Location of lattice points for the calculation of elastic constants with interactions out to second nearest neighbor atoms.

resistance to shear. It is apparent, however, that the addition of next nearest neighbor forces will result in resistance to shear by providing force connections along the face diagonals. Following Born and von Kármán,[8] we consider the elastic constants of a monatomic simple cubic lattice counting interactions out to second nearest neighbors, as shown in Fig. 4.4. The force $X(l, m, n)$ in the x direction on the atom at lattice point l, m, n is given by

[8] M. Born and T. von Kármán, Physik. Z. **13**, 297 (1912).

(4.35) $\quad X(l, m, n) = \alpha[u(l + 1, m, n) + u(l - 1, m, n)$
$- 2u(l, m, n)] + \beta[u(l, m + 1, n) + u(l, - 1, n)$
$+ u(l, m, n + 1) + u(l, m, n - 1) - 4u(l, m, n)]$
$+ \gamma[u(l + 1, m, n + 1) + u(l + 1, m + 1, n) + u(l + 1, m, n - 1)$
$+ u(l + 1, m - 1, n) + u(l - 1, m + 1, n) + u(l - 1, m, n - 1)$
$+ u(l - 1, m - 1, n) + u(l - 1, m, n + 1) - 8u(l, m, n)]$
$+ \delta[u(l, m + 1, n + 1) + u(l, m - 1, n + 1) + u(l, m + 1, n - 1)$
$+ u(l, m - 1, n - 1) - 4u(l, m, n)] + \kappa[v(l + 1, m + 1, n)$
$+ v(l - 1, m - 1, n) - v(l + 1, m - 1, n) - v(l - 1, m + 1, n)$
$+ w(l + 1, m, n + 1) + w(l - 1, m, n - 1)$
$$- w(l + 1, m, n - 1) - w(l - 1, m, n + 1)].$$

The terms in α and β refer to nearest neighbor interactions, those in γ, δ, κ to next nearest neighbor interactions. For central forces $\beta = 0$; $\delta = 0$; $\gamma = \kappa$. On passing from the difference equation (4.35) to a differential equation we find, taking the lattice constant as a,

(4.36) $\quad a^{-3}X(l, m, n) = \rho\ddot{u} = \dfrac{\alpha}{a}\dfrac{\partial^2 u}{\partial x^2} + \dfrac{\beta}{a}\left(\dfrac{\partial^2 u}{\partial y^2} + \dfrac{\partial^2 u}{\partial z^2}\right)$

$$+ \dfrac{2\gamma}{a}\left(2\dfrac{\partial^2 u}{\partial x^2} + \dfrac{\partial^2 u}{\partial y^2} + \dfrac{\partial^2 u}{\partial z^2}\right) + \dfrac{2\delta}{a}\left(\dfrac{\partial^2 u}{\partial y^2} + \dfrac{\partial^2 u}{\partial z^2}\right)$$

$$+ \dfrac{4\kappa}{a}\left(\dfrac{\partial^2 v}{\partial x\,\partial y} + \dfrac{\partial^2 w}{\partial x\,\partial z}\right).$$

On comparing (4.36) with (4.25) we find that the two equations are equivalent if we set

$$c_{11} = (\alpha + 4\gamma)/a;$$

(4.37) $\qquad\qquad c_{44} = (\beta + 2\gamma + 2\delta)/a;$

$$c_{12} + c_{44} = 4\kappa/a.$$

There are not enough independent elastic constants to determine the five atomic force constants. For central forces

$$c_{11} = (\alpha + 4\gamma)/a;$$

(4.38) $\qquad\qquad c_{44} = 2\gamma/a;$

$$c_{12} = 2\gamma/a.$$

We note that in this instance the Cauchy relation is valid.

CALCULATIONS FOR METALS

The elastic constants of metals have been calculated by Jones,[9] Fuchs, Zener, and others, with reasonable success. We mention here a

[9] A review of the theory is given by H. Jones, Physica **15**, 13–22 (1949).

TABLE 4.2. COMPRESSIBILITY $K = -(1/V)(dV/dp)$ OF METALS NEAR ROOM TEMPERATURE, IN 10^7 CM^2/KG

(These values $\times 10^{-13}$ give, approximately, cm^2/dyne)

Li 87	Be 7.8														
Na 156	Mg 29.5											Al 13.4			
K 357	Ca 57	Sc	Ti 8.0	V 6.1	Cr 6.1	Mn 7.9	Fe 5.9	Co 5.4	Ni 5.3	Cu 7.2	Zn 16.9	Ga 20	Ge 13.8	As 44	Se 11.8
Rb 520	Sr 82	Y	Zr 11.0	Nb 5.7	Mo 3.6	Tc	Ru 3.4	Rh 3.6	Pd 5.3	Ag 9.9	Cd 22.5	In 25.0	Sn 18.8	Sb 27.0	Te 50.8
Cs 700	Ba 102	La 35	Hf 9.0	Ta 4.8	W 3.2	Re	Os	Ir 2.7	Pt 3.6	Au 5.8	Hg 37	Tl 34.8	Pb 23.7	Bi 29.2	Po

TABLE 4.3. COHESIVE ENERGY OF METALS, IN KCAL/MOLE AT ROOM TEMPERATURE

Li 36.5	Be 76.6														
Na 26.0	Mg 36											Al 74.4			
K 22.6	Ca 46	Sc 93	Ti 112	V 120	Cr 80	Mn 68	Fe 97	Co 105	Ni 101	Cu 81	Zn 31	Ga 66	Ge 78	As 61	Se 48
Rb 18.9	Sr 39	Y 103	Zr 125	Nb 184	Mo 155	Tc	Ru 160	Rh 138	Pd 93	Ag 69	Cd 27	In 58	Sn 72	Sb 60	Te 48
Cs 18.8	Ba 42	La 88	Hf (>72)	Ta 185	W 201	Re 189	Os 174	Ir 165	Pt 122	Au 82	Hg 15	Tl 43	Pb 46	Bi 50	Po

TABLE 4.4. MELTING POINTS OF METALS (°C)

Li 180	Be 1278														
Na 97.7	Mg 650										Al 660				
K 63.6	Ca 850	Sc 1200	Ti 1690	V 1900	Cr 1550	Mn 1250	Fe 1530	Co 1490	Ni 1452	Cu 1083	Zn 419.5	Ga 30.2	Ge 958.5	As 817	Se 217
Rb 39.0	Sr 800	Y 1452	Zr 1830	Nb 2415	Mo 2600	Tc (2700)	Ru 2400	Rh 1970	Pd 1553	Ag 960.5	Cd 320.5	In 155	Sn 231.9	Sb 630.5	Te 453
Cs 28.5	Ba 710	La 826	Hf 2230	Ta 3027	W 3390	Re 3167	Os 2700	Ir 2454	Pt 1771	Au 1063	Hg −38.9	Tl 303.5	Pb 327	Bi 271	Po

TABLE 4.5. REPRESENTATIVE VALUES OF THE VELOCITY OF ELASTIC WAVES IN METALS AT ROOM TEMPERATURE

Metal	Density (g/cm^3)	Longitudinal Wave (infinite medium) (m/sec)	Transverse Wave (m/sec)
Ag	10.5	3600	1590
Al	2.7	6260	3080
Au	19.3	3240	1200
Cd	8.6	2780	1500
Cu	8.9	4700	2260
Fe	7.9	5850	3230
Ni	8.9	5630	2960
Pb	11.4	2160	700
Pt	21.4	3960	1670
Sn	7.3	3320	1670
W	19.3	5460	2620
Zn	7.1	4170	2410

related theory, due to Zener,[10] of the proclivity of bcc structures to instability at low temperatures.   Results obtained by Barrett[11] are in agreement with Zener's predictions; Barrett finds in bcc lithium a transformation to fcc or to hcp with stacking faults can be induced if the metal is plastically deformed in the vicinity of 77°K.   Zener pointed out that a homogeneous shear of 0.35 in a bcc structure in the (110) plane and the [1$\bar{1}$0] direction will produce an atomic arrangement very nearly fcc.   The stiffness constant for this deformation is $\frac{1}{2}(c_{11} - c_{12})$ which is very small (in comparison with c_{44}) for metals and alloys of bcc structure that have filled inner shells of electrons.   (See Problem 4.7.)   For example, the value of the anisotropy constant A defined by (4.31) is 18.7 for β-brass (bcc) and only 4.0 for α-brass (fcc).   Thermal vibration amplitudes in the [1$\bar{1}$0] direction should accordingly be very large.   At high temperatures, because of free energy considerations, a structure permitting large amplitude vibrations will occur, other factors being equal, in preference to a structure permitting only low amplitude vibrations.   At low temperatures the vibrations are not important, the internal energy then being the major influence in the free energy $F = U - TS$.   We may accordingly expect to find metals which are fcc at low temperatures and which transform to bcc at high temperatures.   Lithium is an example of this behavior.   Barrett[12] has found a similar transformation in sodium at low temperature.

The compressibilities of a number of metals are given in Table 4.2; for comparison and reference, values of the cohesive energy are given in Table 4.3, melting points in Table 4.4, and elastic wave velocities in Table 4.5.

PROBLEMS

4.1. Show that the strain

$$2\omega_z = \frac{\partial v}{\partial x} - \frac{\partial u}{\partial y}$$

represents a rigid rotation about the z-axis by a small angle ω_z.   Note that

$$x' = x - \omega_z y;$$

$$y' = y + \omega_z x.$$

4.2. Show that the stresses acting on a plane whose normal makes direction cosines α, β, γ with the coordinate axes may be expressed in terms of the usual stress components by the equations

[10] C. Zener, Phys. Rev. **71**, 846 (1947).

[11] C. S. Barrett, Phys. Rev. **72**, 245 (1947).

[12] C. S. Barrett (private communication); see also D. L. Martin, Phys. Rev. Let. **1**, 447 (1958).

$$X_n = \alpha X_x + \beta X_y + \gamma X_z;$$

$$Y_n = \alpha Y_x + \beta Y_y + \gamma Y_z;$$

$$Z_n = \alpha Z_x + \beta Z_y + \gamma Z_z.$$

4.3. Show that the bulk modulus $B = -V\,(dp/dV)$ in cubic crystals is given by

$$B = \frac{c_{11} + 2c_{12}}{3}.$$

4.4. A cubic crystal is subject to tension in the [100] direction. Find expressions for Young's modulus and Poisson's ratio in terms of the elastic compliances or stiffnesses.

4.5. Show that the velocity of propagation of a shear wave moving along a [110] direction with particle motion along a [1$\bar{1}$0] direction in a cubic crystal is

$$v = [(c_{11} - c_{12})/2\rho_0]^{1/2}.$$

4.6. Show that in a cubic crystal the condition for a longitudinal wave in the [111] direction to have the same velocity as a longitudinal wave in the [110] direction is that $c_{11} - c_{12} = 2c_{44}$.

4.7. Show that in a cubic crystal the effective compliance constant for a shear across the (110) plane in the [1$\bar{1}$0] direction is equal to $2(s_{11} - s_{12})$ and the stiffness constant is $\frac{1}{2}(c_{11} - c_{12})$, while in the [001] direction in the same plane the effective compliance constant is s_{44}.

4.8. Make a table comparing the linear compressibility coefficients $(1/l)(dl/dp)$ of hexagonal metal crystals parallel and perpendicular to the axis as a function of the c/a ratio.

4.9.* Write down the equations for v and w similar to Eq. (4.25) for u. Find the determinantal equation which expresses the condition that

$$\varrho = \varepsilon e^{i(\omega t - \mathbf{k}\cdot\mathbf{r})}$$

be a solution of the elastic wave equations in a cubic crystal, where ε is a constant polarization vector. A. E. Fein and C. S. Smith, J. Appl. Phys. **23**, 1212 (1952), have given instructive graphs of the polarization angle between the direction of particle motion and the propagation direction, with nickel used as a numerical example. The polarization angles do not deviate by more than 11° from the angles for isotropic conditions.

REFERENCES

"Discussion on elastic constants of metals," Nature **170**, 527 (1952).

R. F. S. Hearmon, "Elastic constants of anisotropic materials," Revs. Modern Phys. **18**, 409–440 (1946).

K. F. Herzfeld, *Handbuch der Experimentalphysik*. Akademische Verlagsgesellschaft, Leipzig, 1928, vol. 7/2.

A. E. H. Love, *A treatise on the mathematical theory of elasticity*, Dover Publications, New York, 1944.

W. Voigt, *Lehrbuch der Kristallphysik*, Teubner, Berlin, 1928.

W. A. Wooster, *A textbook on crystal physics*, Cambridge University Press, Cambridge, 1938.

C. Zener, *Elasticity and anelasticity of metals*, University of Chicago Press, Chicago, 1948.

5

Lattice Vibrations

In this chapter we discuss the elastic vibrations of crystals. We extend the discussion of the preceding chapter to the short wavelength range, where the wavelength of the lattice wave is comparable with the lattice constant of the crystal. We shall see that the periodic quality of the crystal structure causes for elastic waves a behavior like that of Bragg reflection for x-rays. We shall also discuss the spectrum, or frequency distribution, of the lattice vibrations. The spectrum is important in connection with optical absorption by crystals and in connection with the theory of the heat capacity of solids, as treated in Chapter 6. The spectrum of the lattice vibrations is also important in problems which involve the interaction of electrons and photons with the crystal lattice, as in electrical resistivity, infrared absorption, dielectric breakdown, and x-ray diffraction broadening. We use here in a loose sense the term *lattice*, where strictly we should write *structure*, but in the present context the use of lattice is sanctioned by convention.

VIBRATIONS OF HOMOGENEOUS LINE IN ONE DIMENSION

Although elastic waves in a homogeneous solid were treated in some generality in Chapter 4, it is instructive to rederive the theory here for a quite simple problem. We treat a homogeneous elastic line, and suppose that the motion of each element of the line is constrained to be parallel to the line itself; that is, we admit only longitudinal waves. For the present we exclude from consideration transverse waves, which are waves in which the direction of particle motion is perpendicular to the direction of propagation of the wave. Let x denote the positional coordinate of a particular element of the line, and let u denote the displacement of the element from its equilibrium position; then the value of the strain e, defined as the fractional change of length, is

$$(5.1) \qquad\qquad e = \partial u/\partial x.$$

If F is the force producing the strain, we define the elastic stiffness c

by the equation

(5.2) $F/e = c.$

We study then the propagation of longitudinal waves on a homogeneous line of linear density ρ and elastic stiffness c. We consider the forces acting on an element of length Δx. At one end of the element the strain is $e(x)$, and at the other end it is $e(x + \Delta x) = e(x) + (\partial e/\partial x)\, \Delta x = e(x) + (\partial^2 u/\partial x^2)\, \Delta x$, and so the resultant force acting on the element is $c(\partial^2 u/\partial x^2)\, \Delta x$. Setting the force equal to the mass of the element $\rho\, \Delta x$ times the acceleration $\partial^2 u/\partial t^2$, we have the wave equation

(5.3) $$\frac{\partial^2 u}{\partial x^2} = \left(\frac{\rho_0}{c}\right)\frac{\partial^2 u}{\partial t^2},$$

with velocity

(5.4) $v_0 = (c/\rho_0)^{1/2},$

independent of frequency. It is plausible that the velocity should increase with the stiffness and decrease with the density. The solutions are of the form $e^{i(\omega t \pm kx)}$, where $\omega = kv_0$. The quantity k is equal to $2\pi/\lambda$ if λ is the wavelength; k is usually called the *wave vector*.

WAVE MOTION ON A LINE OF SIMILAR ATOMS

The behavior of elastic waves on a line of similar atoms is not different from that of elastic waves on a homogeneous line, provided the

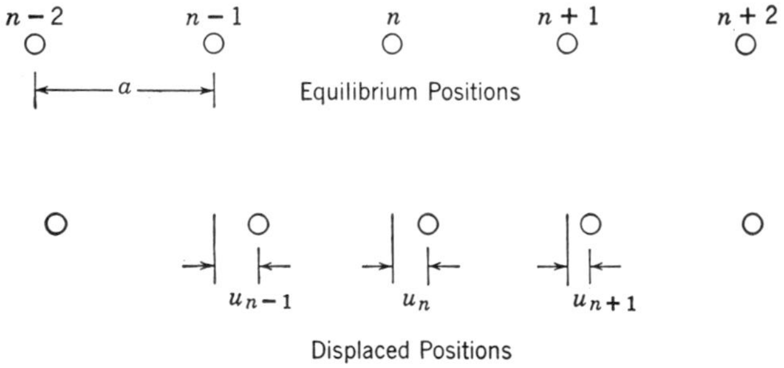

Fig. 5.1. Coordinates describing the deformation of a linear monatomic lattice of lattice constant a.

wavelength is long in comparison with the interatomic spacing. It is interesting to see what happens on the line of atoms as the wavelength is made shorter. We consider a line of similar atoms of mass M spaced with lattice constant a as shown in Fig. 5.1, and let u_n denote the displacement of the nth atom from its equilibrium position. If we have to deal with nearest neighbor interactions alone, the force F_n acting on the nth atom may be written

(5.5) $$F_n = \beta(u_{n+1} - u_n) - \beta(u_n - u_{n-1}),$$

the first term in parentheses on the right being the increase in length of the bond between atoms n and $n + 1$, the second term being the increase in length of the bond between atoms n and $n - 1$. If both bonds increase in length, the two forces on atom n will be oppositely directed. Here β is the force constant. Looked at on a macroscopic scale, the line has a linear density $\rho = M/a$, as there are $1/a$ atoms per unit length, and an elastic stiffness $c = \beta a$. The latter result follows as the force required to stretch a single bond is

$$F = \beta(u_n - u_{n-1}) = \beta a e,$$

and by the definition of the elastic stiffness must be equal to ce, so that $c = \beta a$.

We now examine the propagation of waves along the line of particles; we expect to find that as long as the wavelength is much longer than the particle spacing, the waves propagate in the manner prescribed by the macroscopic wave equation (5.3), but for very short wavelengths new features may enter the problem.

The equation of motion of the nth atom is, using (5.5),

(5.6) $$M\ddot{u}_n = \beta(u_{n+1} + u_{n-1} - 2u_n),$$

where β is the force constant and M the atomic mass. We look for solutions having the form of a traveling wave,

(5.7) $$u_n = \xi e^{i(\omega t + kna)},$$

as na is the quantity most similar to the line variable x in the continuum, a being the nearest neighbor distance and n the running index. On substituting this trial function in the equation of motion we find that it is a solution if

$$-\omega^2 M = \beta(e^{ika} + e^{-ika} - 2).$$

Now

$$e^{ika} + e^{-ika} - 2 = (e^{ika/2} - e^{-ika/2})^2 = -4 \sin^2 (ka/2),$$

and so we have a solution if

(5.8) $$\omega = \pm (4\beta/M)^{\frac{1}{2}} \sin (ka/2).$$

This relation, connecting ω and k, is the dispersion relation for the problem. The dependence of ω on k for the positive branch of the curve is shown in Fig. 5.2.

It is seen that the maximum frequency which can be propagated in the lattice is $\omega_m = (4\beta/M)^{\frac{1}{2}}$, corresponding to the values $k_m = \pm\pi/a$. Values of k outside these limits do not give us anything new: for example, the motions of two successive particles in the chain are described by the ratio $u_n/u_{n+1} = e^{-ika}$, which reduces to -1 for $k = k_m$, so

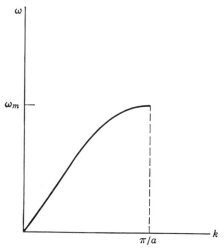

Fig. 5.2. Plot of frequency ω vs. wave number k for a monatomic linear lattice.

that here the particles move 180° out of phase with each other. Larger values of k merely reproduce motions already described by values of k within the limits $\pm k_m$. If we should encounter a value of k outside these limits, we handle it by subtracting the appropriate integral multiple of $2\pi/a$ which will carry k back inside the limits. The region between $\pm k_m$ is sometimes called the first Brillouin zone, for reasons which will emerge presently.

We note that at the limiting frequency ω_m the solution does not represent a traveling wave, as in (5.7), but rather a standing wave, as

$$u_n = \xi e^{i\omega t} e^{in\pi} = \xi e^{i\omega t} \cos n\pi.$$

This situation is exactly equivalent to that found for Bragg reflection of x-rays: when the Bragg condition is satisfied a traveling wave cannot propagate in a lattice, but through successive Bragg reflections back and forth a standing wave is set up. The critical value $k_m = \pm\pi/a$ found here satisfies the Bragg condition $2d \sin \theta = n\lambda$, as we let $\theta = \frac{1}{2}\pi$, $d = a$, $k = 2\pi/\lambda$, $n = \pm1$.

For low k or long wavelengths, (5.8) reduces, on setting sin $(ka/2) \cong ka/2$, to

(5.9) $$\omega \cong (\beta/M)^{\frac{1}{2}}ka = (c/\rho_0)^{\frac{1}{2}}k = v_0 k,$$

where $v_0 = (c/\rho_0)^{\frac{1}{2}}$ is, according to (5.4), exactly the wave velocity on the equivalent homogeneous line. The actual atomic nature of the line affects the propagation when k becomes comparable with k_m. The phase velocity is a function of the wave number and is

(5.10) $$v = \frac{\omega}{k} = v_0 \left[\frac{\sin (ka/2)}{ka/2} \right].$$

In actual substances the order of magnitude of the limit on k is

$$|k_m| = \frac{\pi}{a} \approx 10^8 \text{ cm}^{-1},$$

and because sound velocities in solids are of the order of magnitude of 3×10^5 cm/sec the cut-off frequency is

$$\omega_m = v_m k_m = 2v_0 k_m/\pi \approx 2 \times 10^{13} \text{ rad/sec.}$$

The cut-off frequency lies in the infrared region. The highest ultrasonic frequency yet generated in the laboratory is 10^9 in quartz, and this is very considerably below the limiting frequency. Estimates of elastic constants and frequency distribution of normal modes at frequencies of 10^{11} to 10^{14} cps may be made by the study of non-Bragg diffuse x-ray reflections.[1] The lattice waves modulate the crystal to make possible reflections in directions not coinciding with those occurring in the unperturbed lattice.

ENUMERATION OF NORMAL MODES FOR FINITE LINE

One is often concerned, as in calculating the heat capacity, with the distribution of normal modes in a crystal. As a simple illustration of the method of analysis used in determining the distribution, we consider the case of a one-dimensional line of length L carrying $N + 1$ particles at separation a. We suppose that the particles $n = 0$ and $n = N$ at the ends of the line are held fixed; the normal modes, which are constructed by taking linear combinations of the running wave solutions $u_n = \xi e^{i(\omega t + kna)}$ of the previous section, are then of the form

(5.11) $$u_{k,n} = C_k e^{i\omega_k t} \sin kna;$$

[1] See, for example, G. N. Ramachandran and W. A. Wooster, Acta Cryst. **4**, 335, 431 (1951); P. Olmer, Acta Cryst. **1**, 57 (1948); E. H. Jacobsen, Phys. Rev. **97**, 654 (1955); H. Cole, J. Appl. Phys. **24**, 482 (1953).

here k is restricted by the boundary conditions to the values

(5.12) $k = \pi/L,\ 2\pi/L,\ 3\pi/L,\ \cdots,\ N\pi/L,$

and C_k is an arbitrary complex number determining the amplitude and phase of the motion.

The solution for $k = \pi/L$ has $u \propto \sin n\pi a/L$ and vanishes for $n = 0$ and $n = N$ as required, with a maximum for $n = N/2$. The solution for $k = N\pi/L = \pi/a = k_m$ has $u \propto \sin n\pi$, permitting no motion at all, because $\sin n\pi$ vanishes at each particle. There are $N - 1$ allowed values (eigenvalues) of k. This number is equal to the number of particles allowed to move. Each allowed value of k is associated with a solution (eigenfunction) of the form (5.11). These features of the one-dimensional problem are characteristic also of the lattice vibration problems in two and three dimensions.

We sometimes wish to know the number of modes per unit range of k. We shall denote this quantity by $w(k)$; it is sometimes called the density of states in k-space. For our one-dimensional line there is one mode for each interval $\Delta k = \pi/L$, so that

(5.13) $w(k) = L/\pi.$

Another method of enumerating states which is often used is to consider the medium unbounded, but to impose the physically reasonable requirement that the solutions should be periodic over some sufficiently large distance L, so that $u(na) = u(na + L)$. This may be required without changing the physical nature of the problem in any essential respect. This is the method of *periodic boundary conditions*. Then, in (5.7),

$$k = \pm 2\pi/L,\ \pm 4\pi/L,\ \pm 6\pi/L,\ \cdots,\ \pm N\pi/L.$$

This method of enumeration gives essentially the same number of states as given by (5.12), but we have now both plus and minus values of k, while doubling the interval between successive states. The smoothed density of states interpreted in terms of a unit range of $|k|$ is unchanged.

Later, in connection with the heat capacity of solids, we shall need to know the frequency distribution of the normal modes, that is, the number of states per unit frequency range. In terms of the number of states $w(k)$ per unit wave vector range, the number of states $C(\omega)\,d\omega$ in $d\omega$ at ω is given by

(5.14) $C(\omega)\,d\omega = w(k)(dk/d\omega)\,d\omega,$

and so we need to know $dk/d\omega$. For the line of similar atoms we have, from (5.8),

$$(5.15) \qquad k = (2/a) \sin^{-1}(\omega/\omega_m),$$

where $\omega_m = (4\beta/M)^{\frac{1}{2}}$, and so

$$(5.16) \qquad \frac{dk}{d\omega} = \frac{2}{a(\omega_m{}^2 - \omega^2)^{\frac{1}{2}}},$$

which has a singularity at $\pm\omega_m$. In our one-dimensional problem above, $w(k) = L/2\pi$, with periodic boundary conditions.

In two- and three-dimensions the problem of determining the frequency distribution is quite difficult. A good bibliography of work in the field, with particular reference to the existence of non-analytic points in the distributions, is given by Rosenstock.[2]

ONE-DIMENSIONAL CRYSTAL WITH TWO KINDS OF ATOMS

With two kinds of atoms, as in an ionic crystal, or in general with two (or more) atoms per primitive cell, the results show new features. The dispersion relation ω vs. k develops two branches, known as the acoustical and optical branches. The optical branch is active in infrared absorption. We consider a one-dimensional crystal with two kinds of atoms, spaced a apart. Atoms of mass M are located at the odd-numbered lattice points $2n - 1$, $2n + 1$, $\cdots$; atoms of mass m are located at the even-numbered lattice points $2n$, $2n + 2$, $\cdots$. The equations of motion under the assumption of nearest neighbor interactions are

$$(5.17) \qquad \begin{aligned} m\ddot{u}_{2n} &= \beta(u_{2n+1} + u_{2n-1} - 2u_{2n}); \\ M\ddot{u}_{2n+1} &= \beta(u_{2n+2} + u_{2n} - 2u_{2n+1}). \end{aligned}$$

We look for solutions of the form

$$(5.18) \qquad \begin{aligned} u_{2n} &= \xi e^{i(\omega t + 2nka)}, \\ u_{2n+1} &= \eta e^{i(\omega t + [2n+1]ka)}, \end{aligned}$$

which lead, on substitution in the equations of motion, to

$$(5.19) \qquad \begin{aligned} -\omega^2 m\xi &= \beta\eta(e^{ika} + e^{-ika}) - 2\beta\xi; \\ -\omega^2 M\eta &= \beta\xi(e^{ika} + e^{-ika}) - 2\beta\eta. \end{aligned}$$

[2] H. B. Rosenstock, Phys. Rev. **97**, 290 (1955); see also L. Van Hove, Phys. Rev. **89**, 1189 (1953).

This set of homogeneous equations has a non-trivial solution only if the determinant of the coefficients of the unknowns ξ, η vanishes:

(5.20)
$$\begin{vmatrix} 2\beta - m\omega^2 & -2\beta \cos ka \\ -2\beta \cos ka & 2\beta - M\omega^2 \end{vmatrix} = 0$$

or

(5.21)
$$\omega^2 = \beta \left(\frac{1}{m} + \frac{1}{M} \right) \pm \beta \left[\left(\frac{1}{m} + \frac{1}{M} \right)^2 - \frac{4 \sin^2 ka}{Mm} \right]^{1/2}$$

For small k the two roots are

(5.22)
$$\omega^2 = 2\beta \left(\frac{1}{m} + \frac{1}{M} \right),$$

and

(5.23)
$$\omega^2 = \frac{2\beta}{M + m} k^2 a^2.$$

For $k = \pi/2a$, the roots are

(5.24)
$$\omega^2 = 2\beta/m,$$

and

(5.25)
$$\omega^2 = 2\beta/M.$$

The variation of ω with k as given by (5.21) is shown in Fig. 5.3 for the case $m > M$. It is seen that the dispersion relation has two branches, one called the *acoustical branch* and the other the *optical branch*.

We may understand the nature of the two branches by considering the motions of the two types of atoms, as shown for transverse waves in Fig. 5.4. The ratio of the amplitudes is ξ/η, and for small k in the optical branch we find, from (5.19) and (5.22),

(5.26)
$$\xi/\eta = -M/m,$$

which shows that the atoms vibrate against each other in such a way that the center of mass of the cell is fixed. If the ions are oppositely charged, we may excite a motion of this type with electric fields, as, for example, by a light wave; for this reason the branch is called the optical branch. We should qualify this discussion by saying that the only vibrations excited in the optical branch by light (usually in the infrared) have small k in comparison with the limit $\pi/2a$. The reason is that the light itself has only a small value of the wave vector $2\pi/\lambda$, and it turns out that it is only possible to excite crystal vibrations of nearly the same wave vector as that of the light.

We note from Fig. 5.3 that wave-like solutions do not exist for frequencies between $(2\beta/m)^{\frac{1}{2}}$ and $(2\beta/M)^{\frac{1}{2}}$. This is an example of a forbidden band, such as we shall encounter later in the electron theory of metals. In the language of electron theory, there is a frequency

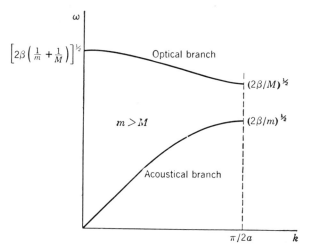

Fig. 5.3. Optical and acoustical branches of the frequency vs. wave number relation for a diatomic linear lattice, showing the limiting frequencies.

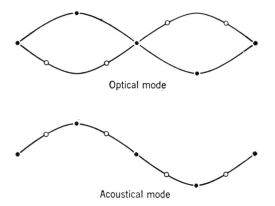

Fig. 5.4. Nature of the optical and acoustical modes illustrated by the particle amplitudes for the two modes at the same wavelength. The drawing is for transverse waves.

gap at the boundary $k = \pi/2a$ of the first Brillouin zone, that is, at the k-value for which Bragg reflection occurs. The propagation constant k for frequencies in the forbidden gap is complex, indicating that the wave is damped. An excellent discussion of wave propagation in a diatomic lattice is given in Chapter 4 of the book by Brillouin cited at the end of the chapter.

The other solution for small k is

$$(5.27) \qquad\qquad\qquad \xi = \eta;$$

the atoms (and their center of mass) move together, as in acoustical vibrations; hence the term acoustical branch. The division of the dispersion relation into acoustical and optical branches occurs also with diatomic lattices in two and three dimensions.

VIBRATIONS OF TWO- AND THREE-DIMENSIONAL LATTICES

There is usually no particular problem in setting up the equations of motion, analogous to (5.6), for two- and three-dimensional lattices. The equation of motions in three dimensions were first written down and the solutions indicated by Born and von Kármán.[3] The solutions are readily found in terms of plane waves of the form exp $i(\omega t - \mathbf{k} \cdot \mathbf{r}_j)$. The enumeration of the states of the system offers greater difficulties than in one dimension; for references to the considerable literature on this problem the paper by Bowers and Rosenstock[4] may be consulted. Some of the results will be discussed in the next chapter.

INFRARED ABSORPTION

We consider now the response of the diatomic linear crystal to electromagnetic radiation in the infrared part of the spectrum, for example at a wavelength of 100 μ (10^{-2} cm) and a frequency of 3×10^{12} cps. The wave vector of the radiation field is $k = 2\pi/\lambda \approx 600$ cm^{-1}, and this is very much smaller than the cut-off of the lattice vibrations, which is $k_m = \pi/2a \approx 10^8$ cm^{-1}. We may therefore, in dealing with electromagnetic excitation of the optical branch, suppose that the wave vector of the excited mode is essentially zero. This assumption simplifies the discussion considerably.

In this limit the equations of motion (5.19) of the two types of ions in a field $E = E_0 e^{i\omega t}$ reduce to, on adding a force term $\pm eE_0$,

$$-\omega^2 m\xi = 2\beta(\eta - \xi) - eE_0;$$

$$-\omega^2 M\eta = -2\beta(\eta - \xi) + eE_0;$$

where E_0 is the amplitude of the electric intensity of the radiation field and $\pm e$ is the ionic charge. We solve these equations for ξ and η,

[3] M. Born and T. von Kármán, Physik. Z. **13**, 297 (1912).

[4] W. A. Bowers and H. B. Rosenstock, J. Chem. Phys. **18**, 1056 (1950); see also W. A. Nierenberg, J. Chem. Phys. **19**, 659 (1951); H. B. Rosenstock, Phys. Rev. **97**, 290 (1955); E. W. Montroll, Am. Math. Monthly **61**, 46 (1954).

obtaining

(5.28)
$$\eta = \frac{(e/M)E_0}{\omega_0{}^2 - \omega^2};$$

(5.29)
$$\xi = \frac{-(e/m)E_0}{\omega_0{}^2 - \omega^2};$$

where

(5.30)
$$\omega_0{}^2 = 2\beta\left(\frac{1}{m} + \frac{1}{M}\right),$$

corresponding to the $k = 0$ limit of the optical branch. We may, according to (5.28) and (5.29), expect the infrared absorption to go through a maximum near the frequency ω_0.

We have seen earlier in this chapter that the force constant β is related to the elastic stiffness c of the line by the relation $c = \beta a$, where a is the interatomic separation. As in a three-dimensional crystal there will be of the order of $1/a^2$ lines per unit area, the force constant will be of the order of $\beta \approx ac_{11}$, where c_{11} is one of the usual elastic stiffness constants and is approximately 5×10^{11} dynes/cm^2, for sodium chloride. Therefore $\beta \approx (3 \times 10^{-8})(5 \times 10^{11}) = 1.5 \times 10^4$ dynes/cm, which leads to the rough estimate for sodium chloride:

$$\omega_0{}^2 \approx 2(1.5 \times 10^4)\left(\frac{1}{35.5} + \frac{1}{23.0}\right)\frac{1}{1.67 \times 10^{-24}},$$

or $\omega_0 \approx 3.6 \times 10^{13}$ rad/sec and $\lambda_0 \approx 50 \ \mu$, in satisfactory order-of-magnitude agreement with the observed absorption maximum at $\lambda_0 = 61 \ \mu$.

It is characteristic of ionic crystals that they have an absorption maximum in the infrared associated with the motion of charges of opposite sign toward each other. There is also a maximum in the intensity reflected from the surface of a crystal, and the position of this maximum is close[5] to the wavelength for which the absorption is a maximum. The wavelength at maximum reflection is known as the residual ray or *Reststrahl* wavelength, and the selective reflection has been employed experimentally to obtain narrow bands of radiation in the far infrared. Positions of the absorption and reflection maxima are given in Table 5.1, and the transmission through a thin film of

[5] T. H. Havelock, Proc. Roy. Soc. (London) **A86**, 1 (1912). The separation of the two maxima occurs because the reflection and absorption coefficients involve the real and imaginary parts of the refractive index in different ways.

TABLE 5.1. WAVELENGTHS OF MAXIMUM ABSORPTION AND REFLECTION

Crystal	Absorption (μ)	Reflection (μ)
NaCl	61.1	52.0
KCl	70.7	63.4
KBr	88.3	82.0
KI	102.0	94.0
RbCl	84.8	73.8
CsCl	102.0	. . . . .
RbI	129.5	. . . . .
AgCl	. . . . .	81.5
AgBr	. . . . .	112.7
TlCl	117.0	91.9
TlI	. . . . .	151.8
ZnS	33	30.9

sodium chloride is shown in Fig. 5.5. We shall return to the theory of the Reststrahl absorption in Chapter 7. The symbol μ denotes 1 micron $\equiv 10^{-4}$ cm.

The dispersive properties of the Reststrahl motion in ionic crystals are applied in prisms in infrared spectroscopy. The absorption coefficients and refractive indices of a number of crystals in the infrared are

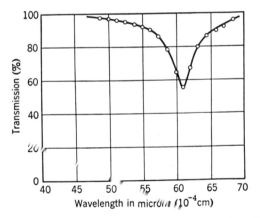

Fig. 5.5. Transmission of infrared radiation through a thin (0.17 μ) sodium chloride film. [After R. B. Barnes, Z. Physik **75**, 723 (1932).]

shown in Figs. 5.6 and 5.7. Large single crystals are produced commercially for use in prisms, and also for use as windows and lens elements. For some purposes, such as for infrared windows, it is desired to have the Reststrahl reflection occur at as long wavelengths as possible. Reference to Eq. (5.30) suggests that the masses of the constituent atoms should be as heavy as practical. A mixed thallium bromide-thallium iodide crystal known as KRS-5 is widely used

which may be written as

$$M\omega^2 = 2\alpha(2 - \cos k_x a - \cos k_y a),$$

where a is the lattice constant, and

$$k_x = p\pi/[a(N + 1)]; \qquad k_y = q\pi/[a(N + 1)].$$

We note that the region of k-space for which solutions are defined is a square of side approximately π/a; this region is called the first Brillouin zone. Show that the k values marking the boundary are associated with the maximum wavelength for which Bragg reflection can occur in the structure.

5.5. Discuss the principal experimental methods used in the spectroscopy of the far infrared region, with particular reference to the spectra of solids.

5.6.* Discuss the behavior of a diatomic periodic lattice for frequencies in the forbidden gap.

5.7.* Discuss the analogy between electrical waves in a periodic filter circuit and elastic waves in a diatomic periodic lattice.

REFERENCES

M. Born and K. Huang, *Dynamical theory of crystal lattices*, Clarendon Press, Oxford, 1954.

L. Brillouin, *Wave propagation in periodic structures*, McGraw-Hill Book Co., New York, 1946.

C. Schaefer and F. Matossi, *Das ultrarote Spektrum*, J. Springer, Berlin, 1930.

Thermal Properties of Solids

We discuss first the classical, the Einstein, and the Debye approximations to the heat capacity associated with the lattice vibrations of crystals; the features of exact calculations are indicated. Electronic contributions to the heat capacity are summarized. We discuss the principal features of the thermal conductivity of metals and insulators; other anharmonic effects are treated in relation to the heat capacity at high temperatures and to thermal expansion and the Grüneisen relation.

REVIEW OF CLASSICAL STATISTICAL MECHANICS

The elementary result which we remember from the theory of the ideal gas and from classical statistics is that the average energy of a classical system is equal to $\frac{1}{2}kT$ per degree of freedom; here k is the Boltzmann constant and has the value 1.38×10^{-16} ergs/°K; T is the temperature. This result is correct, within the limits of classical theory, for a system of free particles. It is easy to extend the result to particles interacting with harmonic forces, by which we mean forces that vary according to Hooke's law directly as the relative displacement. It turns out that the average kinetic energy, $\frac{1}{2}kT$ per degree of freedom, remains unchanged, and the average potential energy is just equal to the average kinetic energy. We have the result that for particles with harmonic interactions the average total energy is kT per degree of freedom. This result and the appropriate extensions to more general interactions may be derived from one theorem. The theorem, which we may look upon as the central result of classical statistical mechanics, states that in thermal equilibrium the average value $\bar{A}$ of any quantity $A(\mathbf{p}, \mathbf{q})$ which is a function of the coordinates $\mathbf{q}$ and conjugate momenta $\mathbf{p}$ of a system is given by

(6.1) $$\bar{A} = \frac{\int A(\mathbf{p}, \mathbf{q})e^{-E(\mathbf{p},\,\mathbf{q})/kT}\,d\mathbf{p}\,d\mathbf{q}}{\int e^{-E(\mathbf{p},\,\mathbf{q})/kT}\,d\mathbf{p}\,d\mathbf{q}}.$$

Here $E(\mathbf{p}, \mathbf{q})$ is the energy; the symbols $\mathbf{p}$, $\mathbf{q}$ denote the set of all momenta and coordinates for the system. If there are N particles and we use Cartesian coordinates, we have

$$\mathbf{p} \equiv (p_{x1}, p_{y1}, p_{z1}, p_{x2}, p_{y2}, p_{z2}, \cdots, p_{xN}, p_{yN}, p_{zN});$$

$$\mathbf{q} \equiv (x_1, y_1, z_1, x_2, y_2, z_2 \cdots, x_N, y_N, z_N).$$

Furthermore, $p_{xi} = M_i\, dx_i/dt$, etc., where M_i is the mass of the ith particle. The integrals are to be taken over the entire region of variation of each independent variable, usually from $-\infty$ to $+\infty$.

The reader may recognize the theorem (6.1) as a statement of the Boltzmann distribution law. It may be more familiar in the form

(6.2)
$$\frac{n_1}{n_2} = \frac{g_1 e^{-E_1/kT}}{g_2 e^{-E_2/kT}},$$

which gives the equilibrium ratio of the number of systems n_1, n_2 in the states 1, 2 of statistical weight g_1, g_2 as a function of the energies E_1, E_2. Derivations of the Boltzmann law are readily accessible.[1]

It is instructive to consider several familiar consequences of (6.1). For N free particles, all of mass M, the expression for the energy is

(6.3)
$$E = \frac{1}{2M} \sum_{i=1}^{N} (p_{xi}^2 + p_{yi}^2 + p_{zi}^2).$$

In thermal equilibrium at temperature T the internal energy $U \equiv E$ of the system is

(6.4)
$$U = \frac{\dfrac{1}{2M} \displaystyle\sum_{\alpha=1}^{3N} \int_{-\infty}^{\infty} p_\alpha^2 \prod_{\beta=1}^{3N} e^{-p_\beta^2/2MkT}\, d\mathbf{p}}{\displaystyle\int_{-\infty}^{\infty} \prod_{\beta=1}^{3N} e^{-p_\beta^2/2MkT}\, d\mathbf{p}};$$

the integrals over $d\mathbf{q}$ cancel in numerator and denominator as the energy is independent of $\mathbf{q}$. Through further cancellations we see that the expression for U is just the sum of $3N$ terms, each of which is equal to

$$\frac{\dfrac{1}{2M} \displaystyle\int_{-\infty}^{\infty} p_\alpha^2 e^{-p_\alpha^2/2MkT}\, dp_\alpha}{\displaystyle\int_{-\infty}^{\infty} e^{-p_\alpha^2/2MkT}\, dp_\alpha} = kT \frac{\displaystyle\int_{-\infty}^{\infty} y^2 e^{-y^2}\, dy}{\displaystyle\int_{-\infty}^{\infty} e^{-y^2}\, dy} = \frac{1}{2} kT,$$

[1] For a good introduction, see J. C. Slater, *Introduction to chemical physics*, McGraw-Hill, New York, 1939, pp. 32–64; also M. Born, *Atomic physics*, Hafner, New York, 5th ed., 1951, Chapter I; a full account is given by R. C. Tolman, *Principles of statistical mechanics*, Oxford University Press, London, 1938.

using the definite integrals

$$\int_{-\infty}^{\infty} y^2 e^{-y^2}\, dy = \tfrac{1}{2}\pi^{\frac{1}{2}}; \qquad \int_{-\infty}^{\infty} e^{-y^2}\, dy = \pi^{\frac{1}{2}}.$$

Thus we have

(6.5) $U = \tfrac{3}{2}NkT,$

in agreement with our earlier statement that the average energy is $\tfrac{1}{2}kT$ per degree of freedom, there being $3N$ degrees of freedom in the present problem of N atoms in three-dimensional space.

The energy of a harmonic oscillator of frequency ω is, in one dimension,

(6.6) $E = \dfrac{1}{2M}\, p^2 + \dfrac{1}{2}\, M\omega^2 q^2.$

The average energy of the oscillator in thermal equilibrium is

$$\bar{E} = \frac{\dfrac{1}{2M}\displaystyle\int_{-\infty}^{\infty} p^2 e^{-p^2/2MkT}\, dp}{\displaystyle\int_{-\infty}^{\infty} e^{-p^2/2MkT}\, dp} + \frac{\dfrac{M\omega^2}{2}\displaystyle\int_{-\infty}^{\infty} q^2 e^{-M\omega^2 q^2/2kT}\, dq}{\displaystyle\int_{-\infty}^{\infty} e^{-M\omega^2 q^2/2kT}\, dq},$$

as the other terms cancel, numerator against denominator. The first term on the right is equal to $\tfrac{1}{2}kT$, according to our earlier result. If we let $y^2 = M\omega^2 q^2/2kT$, the second term becomes

$$kT \cdot \frac{\displaystyle\int_{-\infty}^{\infty} y^2 e^{-y^2}\, dy}{\displaystyle\int_{-\infty}^{\infty} e^{-y^2}\, dy} = \frac{1}{2}\, kT,$$

and so

(6.7) $\bar{E} = kT$

for the simple harmonic oscillator in one dimension.

The internal energy of N harmonic oscillators in three dimensions is seen to be

(6.8) $U = 3NkT,$

or, for a mole of substance,

(6.9) $U_M = 3RT.$

The gas constant $R = Lk$, where L is Avogadro's number, 6.025×10^{23}.

If we may consider that the atoms in a solid behave as harmonic oscillators about their equilibrium positions, we see that classical theory predicts the lattice contribution to the molar heat capacity at constant volume

$$(6.10) \qquad C_v = \left(\frac{\partial U_M}{\partial T}\right)_v$$

of a solid should be, for a mole of atoms,

$$(6.11) \qquad C_v = 3R \cong 6 \text{ calories/deg mole.}$$

This value, which is known as the Dulong and Petit value, is in quite good agreement with the observed total heat capacity of many solids,

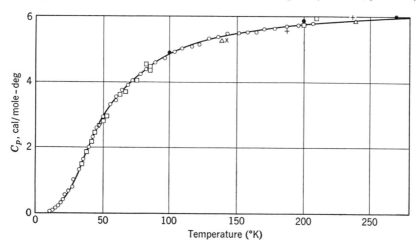

Fig. 6.1. Heat capacity of metallic silver as a function of temperature. The heat capacity at constant pressure, C_p, is the quantity measured, but for solids below room temperature the difference between C_p and C_v is small and usually may be neglected.

including metals, at somewhat elevated temperatures, and often down to room temperature, but the agreement fails at low temperatures. As shown for silver in Fig. 6.1, the heat capacity falls drastically at low temperatures.   It is in fact found that the heat capacity of typical non-metallic crystals approaches zero as T^3, as $T \rightarrow 0$.   The heat capacity of typical metals approaches zero as T, as $T \rightarrow 0$.   It is in fact found experimentally that a T^3 approach is characteristic of lattice vibrations in cubic and near-cubic crystals, while a T approach is characteristic of that part of the heat capacity associated with conduction electrons.   We shall find in due course explanations of these facts.

EINSTEIN MODEL OF THE LATTICE HEAT CAPACITY

Einstein[2] developed a simple model to account for the tendency of the lattice heat capacity to decrease at low temperatures below the value $3R$ per mole which obtains at elevated temperatures. He treats the thermal properties of the vibrations of a lattice of N atoms as a set of $3N$ independent harmonic oscillators in one dimension, each oscillator having the identical frequency ν. He then quantizes the energies of the oscillators according to the prescription developed earlier by Planck in connection with the theory of black body radiation.

We recall that Planck[3] was faced with a critical failure of classical theory as applied to electromagnetic radiation in thermal equilibrium with matter. Classical theory predicted too much energy in the radiation spectrum at high frequencies. The departure of the observed radiation spectrum from the classical prediction occurred at lower and lower frequencies as the temperature was lowered, so that in some respects the failure at low temperature of the classical theory of heat capacity is reminiscent of the earlier difficulties with the black-body-radiation law.

The radiation problem is usually formulated by treating the light waves as equivalent to a set of oscillators. Planck was led to the correct law for the distribution of energy among the oscillators by postulating that the energy of an oscillator of frequency ν was quantized in discrete units $h\nu$. This was the first revolutionary step in the formulation of quantum mechanics, the set of physical laws and principles governing the behavior of atoms, molecules, and solids. In classical theory an oscillator can have any arbitrary amplitude of oscillation and hence any arbitrary energy. According to Planck the energy E may have only the values

$$(6.12) \qquad E = nh\nu, \quad n = 0, 1, 2, \cdots ,$$

where n is any positive integer; ν is the frequency; and h is an experimental constant known as Planck's constant. The value of h has been determined to be 6.624×10^{-27} erg-sec. In modern work one often sees the relation (6.12) written as

$$(6.13) \qquad E = n(h/2\pi)(2\pi\nu) = n\hbar\omega,$$

[2] A. Einstein, Ann. d. Physik **22**, 180 (1907); **34**, 170 (1911).

[3] For a detailed discussion of the Planck radiation law the reader may consult any textbook on modern atomic physics or on heat and thermodynamics. We mention a few examples of such textbooks: F. K. Richtmeyer and E. H. Kennard, *Introduction to modern physics*, McGraw-Hill, New York, 1947, 4th ed., pp. 178–183; M. Born, *Atomic physics*, Hafner, New York, 5th ed., 1951, Chapter VIII.

where ω is the angular frequency, and $\hbar$ (pronounced h-bar) has the value 1.054×10^{-27} erg-sec. An energy level is labeled by the value of the integer n, called the quantum number.

The expression for the average energy of an oscillator on quantum theory is different from the average energy kT on classical theory. According to the Boltzmann distribution law the ratio of the populations in thermal equilibrium of two adjacent ($n' = n + 1$) energy levels is $e^{-(E_{n'}-E_n)/kT} = e^{-\hbar\omega/kT}$. The average energy is readily seen to be given by

$$(6.14) \qquad \bar{E} = \frac{\displaystyle\sum_{n=0}^{\infty} n\hbar\omega e^{-n\hbar\omega/kT}}{\displaystyle\sum_{n=0}^{\infty} e^{-n\hbar\omega/kT}}$$

$$= \frac{\hbar\omega(e^{-\hbar\omega/kT} + 2e^{-2\hbar\omega/kT} + \cdots)}{(1 + e^{-\hbar\omega/kT} + e^{-2\hbar\omega/kT} + \cdots)},$$

where the denominator ensures that the normalization is correct. Writing $x = -\hbar\omega/kT$, we have after a little rearrangement

$$\bar{E} = \hbar\omega \frac{d}{dx} \log (1 + e^x + e^{2x} + \cdots)$$

$$= \hbar\omega \frac{d}{dx} \log \frac{1}{1 - e^x} = \frac{\hbar\omega}{e^{-x} - 1},$$

or, finally,

$$(6.15) \qquad \bar{E} = \frac{\hbar\omega}{e^{\hbar\omega/kT} - 1}.$$

We note that at high temperatures ($kT \gg \hbar\omega$) the denominator can be expanded as

$$e^{\hbar\omega/kT} - 1 = 1 + (\hbar\omega/kT) + \cdots - 1 \cong \hbar\omega/kT,$$

and so $\bar{E} \cong kT$. That is, at high temperatures the average energy using the Planck-Einstein distribution law (6.15) for the harmonic oscillator approaches the classical average energy kT. The new feature is introduced at low temperatures ($kT \ll \hbar\omega$), as here $e^{\hbar\omega/kT} \gg 1$ and

$$(6.16) \qquad \bar{E} \cong \hbar\omega e^{-\hbar\omega/kT},$$

and so as $T \to$ zero the heat capacity approaches zero as

$$(6.17) \qquad C_v \cong Nk(\hbar\omega/kT)^2 e^{-\hbar\omega/kT}.$$

The exponential factor is dominant in the limit, and so the low-temperature limiting variation of the heat capacity on the Einstein model is as $e^{-\hbar\omega/kT}$. Experimentally the variation for the lattice contribution at low temperatures is not exponential, but as T^3. The Debye model, shortly to be discussed, gives a satisfactory account of the T^3 variation.

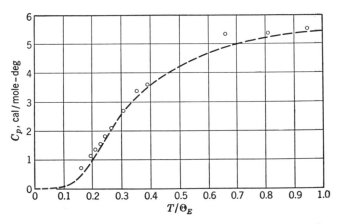

Fig. 6.2. Comparison of experimental values of the heat capacity of diamond and values calculated on the Einstein model, using $\Theta_E = 1320°\text{K}$. [After A. Einstein, Ann. Physik **22**, 180 (1907).]

The Einstein model does, however, give a fairly good representation of the drop in heat capacity at low temperatures, provided that we make an appropriate choice of the oscillator frequency ω. It is convenient to discuss results in terms of a characteristic temperature Θ_E (called the Einstein temperature) defined by

$$(6.18) \qquad \hbar\omega = k\Theta_E.$$

For many solids Θ_E is in the range 100–300°K, although instances are known which fall above or below this range. When we say Θ_E has a particular value, we mean that the heat capacity

$$(6.19) \qquad C = \frac{\partial U}{\partial T} = \frac{\partial(N\bar{E})}{\partial T} = Nk(\hbar\omega/kT)^2 \frac{e^{\hbar\omega/kT}}{(e^{\hbar\omega/kT} - 1)^2}$$

$$= Nk(\Theta_E/T)^2 \frac{e^{\Theta_E/T}}{(e^{\Theta_E/T} - 1)^2}$$

gives a moderately good fit (for that value of Θ_E) to the experimental values over a wide range of temperature in which the heat capacity is varying appreciably with temperature. A theoretical fit to the observations of Weber on diamond is shown in Fig. 6.2, taken from Einstein's original paper.

If Θ_E is expressed in degrees and ω in radians/sec, we have $\omega \approx 10^{11}$ Θ_E. For $\Theta_E = 300°K$, the characteristic frequency $\nu = \omega/2\pi$ is of the order of 5×10^{12} cps. This is a reasonable magnitude for a characteristic atomic oscillation frequency: it is of the order of the Reststrahl frequencies discussed in the last chapter, and also of the order of the frequency associated with an acoustical wavelength of an interatomic distance.

DEBYE MODEL OF THE LATTICE HEAT CAPACITY

The Einstein model does not give an adequate representation of the thermal motion of the lattice at very low temperatures. The situation is evident from a study of Table 6.1. On the Einstein model each atom is treated as an independent oscillator which executes harmonic motion about a fixed point in space. Actually, as we have seen in the last chapter, the atoms oscillate relative to their neighbors in the lattice. For long wavelengths relative to the lattice spacing the motions of adjacent atoms are hardly independent, but large regions of the crystal move together coherently. It is obvious that it is an oversimplification to assign to all $3N$ oscillations the identical frequency—for example, the long wavelength motions may have quite low frequencies. The long wavelength motions are particularly important at low temperatures, as there will always be modes of vibration in an infinite crystal for which $\hbar\omega \ll kT$, even though we may have $T \ll \Theta_E$. Thus even at low temperatures some degrees of freedom of the crystal will behave classically, and each such mode will make an approximate contribution kT to the energy, so that the total energy need not approach zero exponentially, as on the Einstein model.

Let us set up the problem in full, as was first done by Born and von Kármán.[4] We suppose that of the $3N$ normal modes of vibration of the crystal there are $C(\omega) \, d\omega$ modes in the frequency range $d\omega$ at ω. Then the total lattice energy is (on the assumption that the specimen is large enough to permit using an integral instead of a discrete sum over modes)

(6.20)
$$U = \int \frac{\hbar\omega C(\omega) \, d\omega}{e^{\hbar\omega/kT} - 1},$$

[4] M. Born and T. von Kármán, Physik Z. **13**, 297 (1912).

using (6.15) for the energy of a single oscillator of frequency ω.   The problem of finding for a given lattice and set of force constants the frequency spectrum, $C(\omega)$, is quite difficult and tedious in the actual three-dimensional crystals.   References to work in this field were given

TABLE 6.1.   HEAT CAPACITY OF SILVER AT DIFFERENT TEMPERATURES

Temperatures (°K)	C_v (obs) (Cal/mole – deg^2)	C_v Calculated		Θ Calculated from T^3 Law	Θ Calculated from Debye Function
		Einstein	Debye		
1.35	0.000254	8.76×10^{-49}		165	
2	0.000626	1.39×10^{-32}		181	
3	0.00157	6.16×10^{-20}		200	
4	0.00303	5.92×10^{-15}		214	
5	0.00509	1.62×10^{-11}		225	
6	0.00891	3.24×10^{-9}		224	
7	0.0151	1.30×10^{-7}	0.0172	219	
8	0.0236	2.00×10^{-6}	0.0257	216	
10	0.0475	1.27×10^{-4}	0.0502	214	
12	0.0830	0.0010	0.0870	213	
14	0.1336	0.0052	0.137	212	
16	0.2020	0.0180	0.207	211	
20	0.3995	0.0945	0.394	209	
28.56	1.027	0.579	1.014		209
36.16	1.694	1.252	1.69		210
47.09	2.582	2.272	2.60		211
55.88	3.186	2.946	3.22		212
65.19	3.673	3.521	3.73		214
74.56	4.039	3.976	4.13		217
83.91	4.326	4.309	4.45		220
103.14	4.797	4.795	4.86		220
124.20	5.084	5.124	5.17		225
144.38	5.373	5.323	5.37		210
166.78	5.463	5.476	5.51		222
190.17	5.578	5.581	5.61		220
205.30	5.605	5.633	5.66		226

in the preceding chapter.   It is quite easy to find the internal energy U for the monatomic lattice in one dimension considered in Chapter 5. The expression for the density of states found there is

$$(6.21) \qquad C(\omega) = (L/\pi)(2/a)(\omega_m{}^2 - \omega^2)^{-\frac{1}{2}},$$

using Eqs. (5.13), (5.14), and (5.16); here L is the length of the line; a is the lattice spacing, and ω_m is the limiting frequency.   Thus, from (6.20)

$$(6.22) \qquad U = \frac{2\hbar L}{\pi a} \int_0^{\omega_m} \frac{\omega \, d\omega}{(e^{\hbar\omega/kT} - 1)(\omega_m{}^2 - \omega^2)^{1/2}}.$$

The cut-off frequency ω_m was found directly following Eq. (5.10) to be given by $\omega_m = 2v_0/a$, where v_0 is the sound velocity at low frequencies. The heat capacity is obtained on differentiating (6.22) with respect to temperature.

It is quite difficult to find the heat capacity in this way for actual crystals of interest, because the frequency spectrum is difficult to calculate even if all the force constants [such as α, β, γ, δ, κ in Eq. (4.35)] are known, which they are not, and it is also somewhat tedious to calculate the internal energy as a function of temperature for a general form of the frequency distribution. Because of these several difficulties it is usual to discuss the lattice heat capacity in terms of a simple and useful model due to Debye.[5]

Debye assumes that the acoustical spectrum of a monatomic solid may be treated as if the solid were a homogeneous medium, except that the total number of independent elastic waves is cut off at $3N$, to agree with the number of degrees of freedom of N atoms. Debye assumes that the ordinary velocity of sound observed in a crystal at radio frequencies will hold approximately up to the cut-off frequency. It is usual to consider that the solid is elastically isotropic, so that the velocities v_l, v_t of longitudinal and transverse waves are independent of propagation direction relative to the crystal axes.

Our first task is to determine $w(k)$, the number of modes between k and $k + dk$. Here k denotes $|\mathbf{k}|$. We apply the method of periodic boundary conditions, as in Chapter 5, requiring that the vibrational wave $e^{i\mathbf{k}\cdot\mathbf{r}}$ be periodic at the boundaries of a cube of side L. Then $k_x L$, $k_y L$, $k_z L$ must be multiples of 2π, so the allowed values of k may be represented by the points of a simple cubic lattice in k space, with lattice constant $2\pi/L$. The number of modes with wave number less than k is then given closely by the volume, measured in units $2\pi/L$, of the sphere of radius k, which is

$$(4\pi/3)k^3/(2\pi/L)^3.$$

Per unit volume of sample, the number of modes is then

$$(4\pi/3)k^3/(2\pi)^3$$

for each of the three possible polarizations—one longitudinal and two transverse; thus the total number of modes with the magnitude of the

[5] P. Debye, Ann. Physik **39**, 789 (1912).

wave vector less than k is $k^3/2\pi^2$, per unit volume of sample. The number of modes with wave vector in dk at k is

$$(6.23) \qquad w(k)\,dk = d(k^3/2\pi^2) = (3k^2/2\pi^2)\,dk.$$

We recall from (5.14) that the number of modes having angular frequency in $d\omega$ at ω may be written

$$C(\omega)\,d\omega = w(k)(dk/d\omega)\,d\omega.$$

If for all modes the velocity were equal to v_0, we should have $\omega = v_0 k$ and $dk/d\omega = 1/v_0$, so that

$$(6.24) \qquad C(\omega) = 3k^2/2\pi^2 v_0 = 3\omega^2/2\pi^2 v_0^3.$$

If we were to treat longitudinal and transverse modes separately, it is readily seen that

$$(6.25) \qquad C(\omega) = \frac{\omega^2}{2\pi^2}\left(\frac{1}{v_l^3} + \frac{2}{v_t^3}\right).$$

In the interest of brevity we shall use (6.24), rather than (6.25), but this specialization is easily eliminated by induction at the end of the calculation.

Using (6.20) and (6.24), we have for the internal energy

$$(6.26) \qquad U = \frac{3\hbar}{2\pi^2 v_0^3} \int_0^{\omega_m} \frac{\omega^3\,d\omega}{e^{\hbar\omega/kT} - 1}.$$

The upper limit ω_m is determined by the condition that the total number of modes be equal to $3N$, where N is the number of atoms per unit volume. We have seen above that there are $k^3/2\pi^2$ modes per unit volume having wave vector less than k, so that the maximum k_m appropriate to $3N$ modes is given by

$$k_m^3/2\pi^2 = 3N,$$

or

$$(6.27) \qquad k_m = (6\pi^2 N)^{1/3}.$$

In terms of the maximum or cut-off frequency ω_m,

$$(6.28) \qquad \omega_m = v_0(6\pi^2 N)^{1/3}.$$

If we set

$$x = \hbar\omega/kT,$$

we have

$$(6.29) \qquad U = \frac{3k^4 T^4}{2\pi^2 \hbar^3 v_0^3} \int_0^{x_m} \frac{x^3\,dx}{e^x - 1},$$

where

(6.30)

$$x_m = \hbar\omega_m/kT = \hbar k_m v_0/kT$$

$$= (\hbar v_0/kT)(6\pi^2 N)^{\frac{1}{3}} = \Theta/T,$$

this being the definition of the Debye characteristic temperature Θ. The heat capacity is given by differentiating (6.26) or (6.29) with respect to temperature:

(6.31)

$$C_v = 9Nk(T/\Theta)^3 \int_0^{x_m} \frac{e^x x^4 \, dx}{(e^x - 1)^2}.$$

Tables have been calculated for U, C_v, and other quantities on the Debye theory and are given in the Landolt-Börnstein tables, Eg. I,

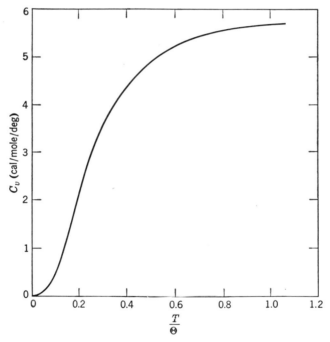

Fig. 6.3. Heat capacity of a solid (in three dimensions), according to the Debye approximation.

p. 702. The heat capacity is plotted in Fig. 6.3. At $T \gg \Theta$ the heat capacity (6.31) approaches the classical Dulong and Petit value of $3R$ per mole, which is found to hold quite well. A comparison of observed and calculated values for aluminum and copper as given in the original paper by Debye is reproduced in Fig. 6.4.

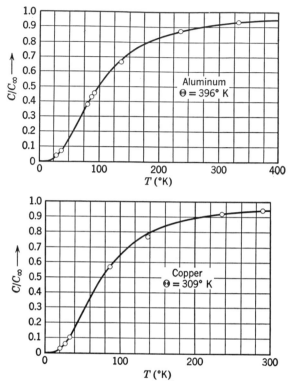

Fig. 6.4.   Observed values, and curves calculated on the Debye model, of the heat capacity of aluminum and copper, taking $\Theta = 396°K$ and $309°K$, respectively. [After P. Debye, Ann. Physik **39**, 789 (1912).]

At very low temperatures we may approximate (6.29) by letting the upper limit go to infinity. We have[6]

$$\int_0^\infty \frac{x^3\,dx}{e^x - 1} = 6\varsigma(4) = 6\sum_1^\infty \frac{1}{n^4} = \frac{\pi^4}{15},$$

where $\varsigma(4)$ is the Riemann zeta function. Thus, for $T \ll \Theta$,

$$U = 3\pi^4 NkT^4/5\Theta^3,$$

and from $C_v = dU/dT$,

(6.32) $C_v = (12\pi^4 Nk/5)(T/\Theta)^3 = 234Nk(T/\Theta)^3,$

exhibiting the Debye T^3 approximation. For sufficiently low temperatures the Debye approximation should be quite good, as here only

[6] E. T. Whittaker and G. N. Watson, *Modern analysis*, Cambridge University Press, Cambridge, 4th ed., 1935, pp. 265–266.

long wavelength acoustic waves are excited, and these are just the waves which may be treated as in an elastic continuum having macroscopic elastic constants.

We can understand the T^3 region qualitatively by a simple argument. It is reasonable to suppose that only those lattice modes having $\hbar\omega \leq kT$ will be excited to any appreciable extent at a low temperature T and, further, the excitation of these modes will be approximately classical—that is, each mode defined as "excited" will have an energy close to kT. Now we know from (6.22) and the relation $\omega = v_0 k$ that the number of "excited" modes is approximately $(T/\Theta)^3$ of the total number of modes $3N$. Thus, there are of the order of $N(T/\Theta)^3$ excited modes, each having energy kT. This gives rise to an internal energy of the order of $NkT(T/\Theta)^3$ and a heat capacity of the order of $Nk(T/\Theta)^3$. However, attention is called to the large numerical factor, 234, in (6.32). In the present paragraph k is used both for the Boltzmann constant and for the magnitude of the wave vector.

TABLE 6.2. VARIATION OF DEBYE Θ WITH TEMPERATURE

Θ as determined at temperature

Substance	$T \approx \Theta$ (°K)	$T \approx \Theta/6$ (°K)	$T \approx \Theta/12$ (°K)
Au	180	172	162
Ag	220	210	209
Cu	315	317	319
Pb	88	87	85
Li	430	379	356
Na	150	159	. . .
K	99	98	. . .
W	310	305	337
KCl	230	225	218

A discussion of methods for the determination of a suitable average sound velocity v_0 to be used in calculating Θ has been published by Blackman,[7] who also emphasizes that the temperatures at which the T^3 approximation holds for actual lattices are considerably lower than one might have thought necessary on the Debye theory; it may be necessary to go below $T = \Theta/50$ to get reasonably pure T^3 behavior. It is customary to test the applicability of the Debye approximation by calculating Θ as a function of temperature by fitting a Debye curve to the experimental heat capacity curve at various temperatures. If the Debye approximation were strictly valid, Θ as determined in this way would be independent of temperature. Results assembled by Blackman[7] are given in Table 6.2.

[7] M. Blackman, Repts. Prog. Phys. **8**, 11 (1941).

The values of Θ obtained from thermal data at low temperatures are in quite good agreement with values of Θ calculated from elastic data when a suitable averaging over possible propagation directions is carried out:

	T (°K)	Θ (thermal) (°K)	Θ (elastic) (°K)
NaCl	10	308	320
KCl	3	230	246
Ag	4	225	216
Zn	4	308	305

Representative values of the Debye characteristic temperature for a number of substances are given in Table 6.3. These data are quite useful in solid state problems, as Θ enters into a number of different phenomena, including electrical resistivity, thermal conductivity, and x-ray diffraction intensity.

TABLE 6.3. REPRESENTATIVE VALUES OF THE DEBYE Θ

Compiled by P. H. Keesom and N. Pearlman

Substance	(°K)	Substance	(°K)	Substance	(°K)
Be	1160	Fe	467	Al	418
Mg	406	Co	445	In	109
Ca	(219)	Ni	456	Tl	89
La	132	Pd	275	C (diamond)	(2000)
Ti	278	Pt	229	Si	658
Zr	270	Cu	339	Ge	366
V	273	Ag	225	Sn (gray)	212
Nb	252	Au	165	Sn (white)	189
Ta	231	Zn	308	Pb	94.5
Cr	402	Cd	300	Bi	117
Mo	425	Hg	(60–90)		
W	(379)				

DIATOMIC LATTICE

One can obtain an exact expression for the heat capacity of a diatomic lattice in one dimension, and Blackman has given numerical results for several values of the mass ratio. If the mass ratio m/M is $\gg 1$, however, the total spread in frequency of the optical branch becomes quite small; this fact suggests a simple approximation to the heat capacity. If the total number of atoms is $2N$, we treat the N normal modes of the optical branch as equivalent to N simple harmonic oscillators of frequency (Eq. 5.22):

$$\omega_0 \cong \left[2\beta \left(\frac{1}{m} + \frac{1}{M} \right) \right]^{1/2} \cong [2\beta/M]^{1/2}.$$

We may then use the Einstein model for the optical modes, and treat the N degrees of freedom of the acoustical branch in the Debye approximation, (6.31).

REVIEW OF THE DEBYE THEORY

It is useful to restate some of the ideas in the theory of the lattice heat capacity before going on to other matters. In developing the theory we first note that we may label the normal vibrations of a lattice by the components of the wave vector $\mathbf{k}$. With periodic boundary conditions over a cube of side L, the allowed values of $\mathbf{k}$ are

$$k_x, k_x, k_z = \pm \frac{2\pi}{L}, \pm \frac{4\pi}{L}, \pm \frac{6\pi}{L}, \cdots$$

If there are N particles, there will be N independent values of $\mathbf{k}$. Each value has associated with it three different modes, having different and orthogonal polarization directions. There are thus a total of $3N$ independent lattice modes associated with N atoms, if we neglect the six degrees of freedom of the body as a whole.

Having enumerated the states, we next want to solve the equations of motion of the lattice, obtaining the $3N$ frequencies $\omega_\mathbf{k}$ associated with the $3N$ values of $\mathbf{k}$. The energy of each mode is quantized: $E_\mathbf{k} = n_\mathbf{k}\hbar\omega_\mathbf{k}$, where $n_\mathbf{k}$ is an integer. Just as the word *photon* is useful in the description of a quantum of energy in the electromagnetic radiation field, so the word *phonon* is used to describe a quantized elastic wave or lattice vibration; in both cases the quantum of energy is equal to $\hbar\omega$. In the Debye approximation we relate $\omega_\mathbf{k}$ and $\mathbf{k}$ not by the equations of atomic lattice dynamics, but rather by the solution of the equations of motion of the macroscopic crystal; it is customary to simplify the problem further by treating the crystal as elastically isotropic.

We then calculate the thermal equilibrium number of quanta excited with each $\omega_\mathbf{k}$. From (6.15) we see that

(6.33)
$$\bar{n}_\mathbf{k} = \frac{1}{e^{\hbar\omega_\mathbf{k}/kT} - 1}.$$

Finally, the total internal energy of the system is found by taking the sum of the equilibrium energies of the individual oscillators:

$$U = \sum_\mathbf{k} \bar{n}_\mathbf{k}\hbar\omega_\mathbf{k} = \int \bar{n}(\omega)\hbar\omega C(\omega) \, d\omega,$$

where $C(\omega)$ is the frequency distribution function.

In Fig. 6.5 we show the results of a theoretical calculation of the frequency spectrum of metallic sodium.   It is seen that the spectrum is quite complex, peaking at a number of intermediate frequencies. On the Debye theory the distribution curves would be parabolic, one curve for longitudinal waves and another for transverse waves.   Each curve would be cut off abruptly at the appropriate maximum frequency, corresponding to a total of N modes for the longitudinal waves

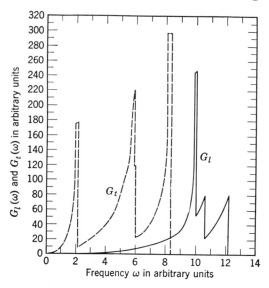

Fig. 6.5.   The frequency spectrum of lattice vibrations in sodium. [According to calculations by A. B. Bhatia, Phys. Rev. **97**, 363 (1955).]   The distribution functions $G_l(\omega)$ and $G_t(\omega)$ are predominantly associated with longitudinal and transverse waves, respectively.

and $2N$ modes for the transverse waves.   The initial curvatures at low ω may be expected to coincide with those obtained from a detailed lattice calculation, as the lattice solutions in the limit of long wavelengths (small k) must approach the usual solutions for elastic waves in the homogeneous solid.

It is not possible in practice to draw from experimental heat capacity data reliable inferences regarding the detailed form of the frequency distribution, as the heat capacity tends to smooth out the individual features of the frequency distribution.

HEAT CAPACITY OF CONDUCTION ELECTRONS IN METALS

When atoms are assembled to make a metal, the valence electrons of the atoms become the conduction electrons of the metal.   In a certain sense the conduction electrons are free to move through the metal, and they may be accelerated by an applied electric field, leading to a flow of electric current. If the conduction electrons behaved as free classical particles, they would make a contribution $C(el) = \frac{3}{2}Nk$ to the heat capacity, where N is the number of conduction electrons per unit volume. That is, one would be led to expect (for $T \gg \Theta$) a total heat capacity of $3R$ per mole for insulators and $(3 + \frac{3}{2})R = 9R/2$ per mole for metals. In fact the heat capacity of metals at high temperatures usually is not particularly different from that of insulators. There is no evidence that the electrons contribute to the heat capacity to anything like the extent envisaged by classical statistics.

The actual thermal behavior of the conduction electron gas in metals is affected profoundly by the Pauli exclusion principle, which expresses the prohibition against two electrons occupying the same quantum state. We shall develop these matters at considerable length in a later chapter on the free electron theory of metals, Chapter 10. It is useful to anticipate the result for the heat capacity here, in order that we may employ it in the discussion of thermal conductivity which follows directly.

For free electrons of mass m, the quantum theory result is that the electronic heat capacity at low temperatures is given by

$$(6.34) \qquad C_v(el) = \gamma T; \qquad \gamma = \pi^2 N^{1/3} km/(3\pi^2)^{2/3}\hbar^2;$$

according to (10.90) and (10.43). For normal metals the definition of a low temperature for the present purpose is by comparison with a temperature of the order of perhaps 30,000°K. We note especially that $C_v(el)$ is linear in the temperature; the numerical value of γ is often of the order of 10^{-4} cal/mole-deg^2, so that at room temperature the electronic contribution is only of the order of 3×10^{-2} cal/mole-deg, quite small in comparison with the Dulong and Petit value for the lattice heat capacity, 6 cal/mole-deg.

At sufficiently low temperatures, usually below 4°K, the electronic contribution to the heat capacity becomes larger than the lattice contribution: the electronic term decreases as T, while at low temperatures the lattice term decreases as T^3, so that if we go low enough in temperature the electronic term will always be dominant in metals. Therefore it is possible to determine the coefficient γ in (6.34) by measurements at low temperatures. We observe that, for $T \ll \Theta$,

$$(6.35) \qquad C_v = C_v(\text{lattice}) + C_v(\text{electronic}) = \alpha T^3 + \gamma T,$$

where α is a constant defined by reference to Eq. (6.32). If we plot (C_v/T) vs. T^2:

$$(6.36) \qquad C_v/T = \gamma + \alpha T^2,$$

we should have a straight line with the property that the extrapolated intercept on the vertical axis at $T = 0$ gives the value of γ, while the slope of the line gives α and therefore the value of the Debye Θ. A plot of this kind for silver is shown in Fig. 6.6.

A short table of experimental values of γ is given in Table 6.4; additional data are given in Table 10.4. It is found experimentally that

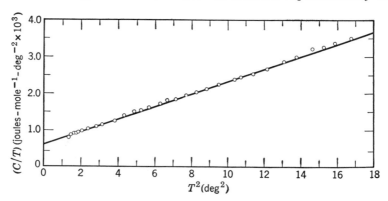

Fig. 6.6.   Heat capacity of metallic silver. [According to Corak, Garfunkel, Satterthwaite, and Wexler.]

the temperature dependence of the conduction electron heat capacity is actually linear in T for most metals; however, the coefficient γ may have values quite different from those calculated from (6.34).

TABLE 6.4.   SELECTED VALUES OF THE ELECTRONIC
HEAT CAPACITY COEFFICIENT

(For more complete data see Table 10.4)

Metal	$\gamma \times 10^4$ (cal/mole-deg^2)
Cu	1.65
Ag	1.46
Au	1.78
α-Mn	33
α-Fe	12
Co	12
Ni	17
Cd	1.7
Zn	1.3

HEAT CAPACITY ASSOCIATED WITH INTERNAL DEGREES OF FREEDOM

One sometimes observes contributions to the heat capacity from other degrees of freedom of the system than those considered above. In particular, paramagnetic salts may exhibit heat capacities at low temperatures ($\sim 1°K$) which are enormous in comparison with the lattice contribution. The physics of paramagnetism is considered in Chapter 9, but we can indicate here by a simple example the nature of the thermal effects which occur when spin systems interact with internal crystalline electric fields.

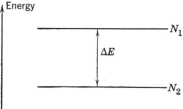

Let us suppose that we have a system of N atoms each of which can be oriented independently relative to some fixed direction in two ways, parallel or antiparallel. We suppose further that the energy of an atom when it is directed in one of the orientations is higher by an amount ΔE than when directed in the opposite orientation. We have then the

Fig. 6.7. Two-level systems with populations N_1, N_2.

simple energy level system indicated in Fig. 6.7. In thermal equilibrium the ratio of the number of atoms N_1 in the upper energy state to the number in the lower energy state is given simply by the Boltzmann factor

(6.37)
$$\frac{N_1}{N_2} = e^{-\Delta E/kT},$$

giving

(6.38)
$$N_1 = \frac{N}{1 + e^{\Delta E/kT}},$$

where $N = N_1 + N_2$. The internal energy of the system is

(6.39)
$$U = N_1 \, \Delta E = N \, \Delta E/(1 + e^{\Delta E/kT}).$$

The heat capacity is

(6.40)
$$C = \frac{\partial U}{\partial T} = Nk \frac{(\Delta E/kT)^2 e^{\Delta E/kT}}{(1 + e^{\Delta E/kT})^2}.$$

Plots of N_1 and C as functions of the parameter $x = kT/\Delta E$ are given in Fig. 6.8. Peaks of this type in the heat capacity are often known as Schottky anomalies.

It is evident, if ΔE corresponds to a temperature very much less than the Debye temperature, that the peak value of the heat capacity considered here may be completely dominant in comparison with the lattice heat capacity. For example, if ΔE corresponds to a temperature of $\sim 0.01\Theta$, we have from (6.32) that $C(\text{lattice}) \approx 10^{-4} Nk$, whereas at the peak $C(\text{internal}) \approx Nk$, a factor of the order of 10^4

greater.   If the maximum of the internal effect occurs at 0.001Θ, the factor is 10^6, a figure which suggests the observation that at $0.1°K$ the heat capacity of 1 gm of a suitable paramagnetic salt may be comparable with that of 1 ton of a non-magnetic salt.   It is obvious that paramagnetic impurities must be carefully guarded against in thermal measurements at low temperatures.

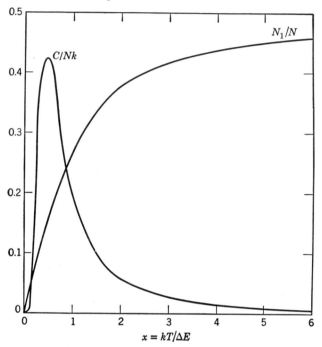

Fig. 6.8.   Plots of the heat capacity C in units of Nk and of the fractional population N_1/N in the upper state as functions of $kT/\Delta E$ for a two-level system.

Internal effects have been observed arising from the thermal ionization of impurities in semiconductor crystals; the energy level schemes will be discussed in Chapter 13.   In molecular crystals there also may be effects associated with the onset of internal rotation or hindered rotation of molecules.   Crystallographic phase transformations are usually accompanied by thermal effects.

THERMAL CONDUCTIVITY OF SOLIDS

The thermal conductivity coefficient K of a solid is most easily defined with respect to the steady state flow of heat down a long rod within which there exists a temperature gradient $\partial T/\partial x$:

$$(6.41) \qquad\qquad Q = K\,\partial T/\partial x,$$

where Q is the flux of thermal energy (energy transmitted across unit area per unit time); K is often expressed in units cal/cm-sec-deg or watts/cm-deg. To convert to watts/cm-deg, multiply K in cal/cm-sec-deg by 4.186.

The form of the equation (6.41) defining the conductivity implies that the process of thermal energy transfer is a random process. The energy does not simply enter one end of the specimen and proceed directly in a straight path to the other end, but the energy diffuses through the specimen, suffering frequent collisions. If the energy were propagated directly through the specimen without deflection, then the expression for the thermal flux would not depend on the temperature gradient, but only on the difference in temperature ΔT between the ends of the specimen, regardless of the length of the specimen. It is the random nature of the conductivity process that brings the temperature gradient into the expression for the thermal flux.

In gas-kinetic theory one finds in a certain approximation the following expression for the thermal conductivity:

$$(6.42) \qquad\qquad K = \tfrac{1}{3}Cu\Lambda,$$

where C is the heat capacity per unit volume, u is the average particle velocity, and Λ is the mean free path of a particle between collisions. This result is derived in the following section.   The result was applied first by Debye to describe thermal conductivity in dielectric solids, C being the heat capacity of the lattice waves or phonons, u the velocity of sound, and Λ the mean free path of the phonons.   Several representative values of the mean free path are given in Table 6.5.

TABLE 6.5. PHONON MEAN FREE PATH VALUES

[Calculated from (6.42), taking $u = 5 \times 10^5$ cm/sec as the average sound velocity]

Crystal	$T(°C)$	$C(\text{cal/cm}^3\text{-deg})$	$K(\text{cal/cm-deg-sec})$	$\Lambda(\text{cm})$
Quartz†	0	0.48	0.03	40×10^{-8}
	−190	0.13	0.12	540×10^{-8}
NaCl	0	0.45	0.17	23×10^{-8}
	−190	0.24	0.064	100×10^{-8}

† Parallel to optic axis.

CALCULATION OF THERMAL CONDUCTIVITY

We give now the kinetic theory calculation of the thermal conductivity of a classical electron gas. We consider the transfer of energy by electrons crossing the xy plane; the temperature gradient is along the z axis. An electron traveling a distance equal to the mean free path Λ and striking the plane at a polar angle θ has a mean energy

$$E(0) + (\Lambda \cos \theta) \frac{\partial E}{\partial z},$$

where $E(0)$ is the mean energy at the plane $z = 0$. By a well-known kinetic theory[8] result the number of molecules which cross unit area of the plane in a direction making an angle between $\theta + d\theta$ with the z axis per second is

$$\tfrac{1}{2}Nu \cos \theta \sin \theta \, d\theta,$$

where N is the concentration and u is the average velocity. The net energy flux is

$$(6.43) \qquad \frac{1}{2} Nu \frac{\partial E}{\partial z} \int_0^\pi \Lambda \cos^2 \theta \sin \theta \, d\theta = \frac{1}{3} Nu\Lambda \frac{\partial E}{\partial z},$$

which, by the definition of the thermal conductivity K, must be equal to $K(\partial T/\partial z)$. Now

$$(6.44) \qquad N(\partial E/\partial z) = N(\partial E/\partial T)(\partial T/\partial z) = C(\partial T/\partial z),$$

where C is the heat capacity of the electron gas per unit volume. Thus, from (6.43) and (6.44)

$$(6.45) \qquad K = \tfrac{1}{3}Cu\Lambda.$$

The corresponding result for Fermi-Dirac statistics (Chapter 10) is obtained by using (10.88) for the heat capacity and writing $\tfrac{1}{2}mu_F^2 = kT_F$, giving

$$(6.46) \qquad C = \pi^2 Nk^2 T/mu_F^2.$$

On substitution in (6.42) we have

$$(6.47) \qquad K = \frac{\pi^2}{3} \frac{Nk^2 T\Lambda}{mu_F} = \frac{\pi^2}{3} \frac{Nk^2 T\tau}{m},$$

where we have introduced the relaxation time $\tau = \Lambda/u_F$, as discussed in Chapter 10.

It is instructive to bring out the random nature of the conductivity process. The usual heat conduction equation for the flux of thermal energy in a linear specimen is

$$(6.48) \qquad Q = K(T_1 - T_2)/L.$$

Here Q = heat transfer across unit area per unit time; $T_1 - T_2$ = temperature drop between ends; L = length of specimen. On sub-

[8] See L. B. Loeb, *Kinetic theory of gases*, McGraw-Hill, New York, 1934.

stituting for K the expression given by (6.45), we have

$$(6.49) \qquad Q = \tfrac{1}{3}C(T_1 - T_2)(\Lambda u/L).$$

In this form the equation may be interpreted very simply: $C(T_1 - T_2)$ is the excess energy density at one end of the specimen with respect to the other end; this excess is propagated down the specimen with an effective transport velocity which is just the carrier velocity reduced by the ratio of the mean free path to the length of the specimen.[9]

PHONON MEAN FREE PATHS IN DIELECTRIC CRYSTALS

The phonon mean free path Λ is determined principally by two processes, geometrical scattering and scattering by other phonons. If the forces between atoms were purely harmonic, there would be no mechanism for collisions between different phonons, and the mean free path would be limited solely by collisions of a phonon with the crystal boundary, and by lattice imperfections. There are situations to be discussed below where these effects are dominant. With anharmonic lattice interactions there is a coupling between different phonons which limits the value of the mean free path.

The theory of the effect of anharmonic coupling on thermal conductivity is one of the most complicated problems in solid state physics. An approximate calculation has been given by Debye,[10] and Peierls[11] has considered the problem in great detail. They both show that Λ is proportional to $1/T$ at high temperatures, in agreement with many experiments. We can understand this dependence in terms of the number of phonons with which a given phonon can interact: at high temperature the excitation of phonons is proportional to T.

At low temperatures Peierls finds Λ approximately proportional to $e^{\Theta/2T}$, where Θ is the Debye temperature. This relation has been approximately verified in an appropriate temperature range by Berman, Simon, and Wilks,[12] as shown in Fig. 6.9. In addition to being

[9] This result for the transport velocity is expected from statistical considerations. It may be noted that the effective transport velocity which obtains in the problem of the one-dimensional random walk is proportional to $\Lambda u/L$, where Λ is now the length of a unit step. One verifies this by calculating $u = \int_0^\infty (L/t)\, q(L;t)\, dt$, where $q(L;t)$ is the distribution function Eq. (32) in S. Chandrasekhar, Revs. Modern Phys. **15**, 1 (1943).

[10] P. Debye, in *Vorträge über die kinetische Theorie der Materie und Elektrizität*, by M. Planck *et al.*, Teubner, Leipzig, 1914.

[11] R. Peierls, Ann. Physik **3**, 1055 (1929); see also C. Herring, Phys. Rev. **95**, 954 (1954).

[12] Berman, Simon, and Wilks, Nature **168**, 277 (1951).

an important mechanism in determining the mean free path, anharmonic interaction is the only mechanism in solids whereby the frequency distribution of phonons may be brought into thermal equilibrium. In thermal conductivity one needs not only a way of limiting the mean free path, but also a way of establishing an equilibrium distribution of phonons at a given temperature.

We may state qualitatively the reasoning which led Peierls to predict $\Lambda \propto e^{\Theta/2T}$ at low temperatures. In a solid treated as a continuum we have to deal with collision processes among phonons in which the total wave vector of the phonons is conserved, as in the collision

(6.50) $$\mathbf{k}_1 + \mathbf{k}_2 = \mathbf{k}_3,$$

two phonons 1 and 2 colliding to give rise to a single phonon 3. Collisions of this type do not change the direction of energy flow. In a discrete lattice Peierls showed that one may also have collisions of the form

(6.51) $$\mathbf{k}_1 + \mathbf{k}_2 = \mathbf{k}_3 + \mathbf{G},$$

where $\mathbf{G}$ is 2π times a reciprocal lattice vector, as defined in Chapter 2. This type of collision, which Peierls called an Umklapp process, gives rise to thermal resistance.

The energy associated with suitable phonons $\mathbf{k}_1$, $\mathbf{k}_2$ has been estimated by Peierls to be of the order of $k\Theta/2$; this is not unreasonable, as roughly speaking each of the phonons 1 and 2 must have wave vectors of the order of $\mathbf{G}/2$ in order for the collision (6.51) to occur and give rise at low temperatures to a cool or low energy phonon 3. However, at low temperatures the number of suitable phonons of the high energy $k\Theta/2$ required may be expected to vary roughly as $e^{-\Theta/2T}$, according to the Boltzmann factor. Figure 6.9 shows that the exponential form is in good agreement with experiment; if we write the exponent as Θ/bT, the results suggest $b = 2.3$ for solid helium, 2.7 for diamond, and 2.1 for sapphire.

Geometrical effects may also be important in limiting the mean free path. We must consider scattering by crystal boundaries, lattice imperfections, and amorphous structures. When Λ becomes comparable with the width of the test specimen, the value of Λ is limited by the width, and the thermal conductivity becomes a function of the dimensions of the specimen. This effect was discovered by de Haas and Biermasz,[13] and the explanation was suggested by Peierls and

[13] W. J. de Haas and T. Biermasz, Physica **2**, 673 (1935); **4**, 752 (1937); **5**, 47, 320, 619 (1938); see also R. Berman, Proc. Roy. Soc. (London) **A208**, 90 (1951).

worked out by Casimir;[14] results of measurements on potassium chloride crystals are given in Fig. 6.10.   The abrupt decrease in thermal conductivity of pure crystals at low temperatures is caused by the size effect.   At low temperatures the Umklapp process becomes ineffective in limiting the thermal conductivity, and the size effect becomes dominant as shown in Fig. 6.11.   One would expect then the phonon

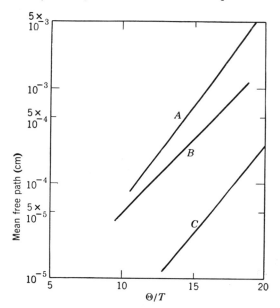

Fig. 6.9.   Phonon mean free paths plotted on a logarithmic scale against Θ/T. A, synthetic sapphire ($\Theta \simeq 980°K$); B, diamond ($\Theta \simeq 1840$); C, solid helium ($\Theta \simeq 22$–35).   (After Berman, Simon, and Wilks.)

mean free path would be constant and of the order of the diameter d of the specimen, so that

(6.52) $K \approx \tfrac{1}{3}Cud.$

The only temperature dependent term on the right is C, the heat capacity, which varies as T^3 at low temperatures.   We may therefore expect the thermal conductivity to vary as T^3 at low temperatures.   The experimental situation, which is reviewed in detail by Berman,[15] suggests that the general features of boundary scattering are seen in the experimental results, but the exponent of T is often between 2 and 2.5,

[14] H. B. G. Casimir, Physica 5, 495 (1938); R. E. B. Makinson, Proc. Cambridge Phil. Soc. 34, 474 (1938).
[15] R. Berman, Advances in Physics, 2, 103 (1953).

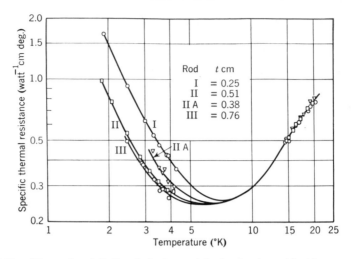

Fig. 6.10.   Thermal resistivity of single crystal of potassium chloride as measured by Biermasz and de Haas.   Below 5°K the resistivity is a function of the crystal thickness t.

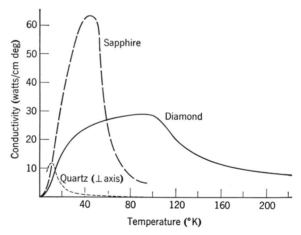

Fig. 6.11.   Thermal conductivities of quartz, synthetic sapphire, and diamond. (Berman, Simon, and Wilks.)

and the value of Λ is often appreciably smaller than d.   The discrepancy in the exponent is thought to represent impurity scattering; the reason for the small values of Λ is not yet known.

Klemens[16] has considered lattice defect scattering in detail, and he suggests that the presence of impurities is the chief factor in determining the conductivity of potassium chloride and potassium bromide

16 P. G. Klemens, Proc. Roy. Soc. (London) **A208**, 108 (1951).

between 10° and 90°K.   In addition to the mechanisms considered by Klemens, it would appear in principle that the distribution of isotopic masses in natural chemical elements will provide a mechanism for scattering.

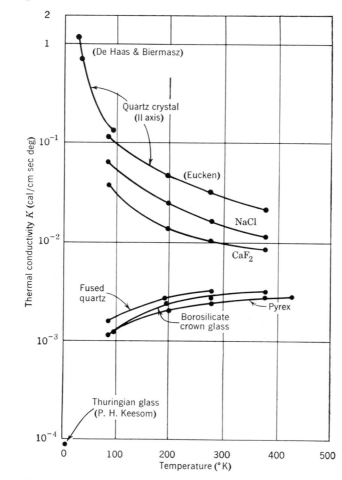

Fig. 6.12.   Temperature dependence of the thermal conductivity of various crystals and glasses.

In glasses the thermal conductivity (Fig. 6.12) decreases as the temperature is lowered; this effect is present even at room temperature.   Furthermore, the values of the thermal conductivity at room temperature run about an order of magnitude lower for glasses than for crystals.   The mean free path in quartz glass at room temperature is 8 A, which is of the order of magnitude of the dimensions of a silicon dioxide tetrahedron (7 A).   The present concept of the nature of the glassy state[17] (Fig. 6.13) pictures a glass such as fused quartz as a random, but continuous, network of silicon-oxygen bonds.   The effective crystallite size is only of the order of a single tetrahedron of the structure.   We expect that (except at low temperatures where the

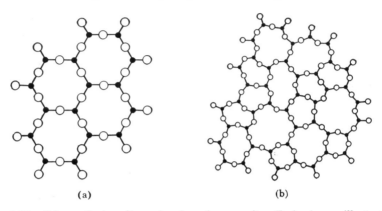

(a)   (b)

Fig. 6.13.   Schematic two-dimensional analogues, after Zachariasen, illustrating the difference between: (a) the regularly repeating structure of a crystal; and (b) the random network of a glass.

phonon wavelengths are long) the phonon mean free path will be constant, limited by the crystallite size, and the decline in the conductivity as the temperature is lowered may be attributed to the decline in the heat capacity.[18]

Synthetic sapphire (Al_2O_3) has one of the highest values of the conductivity[12]: 60 watts/cm-deg at 50°K.   Glasses have values as low as 5×10^{-4} watt/cm-deg at 2°K, and Berman[19] has suggested the conductivity of microcrystalline graphite at 1°K may be 10^{-5} watt/cm-deg.   It may be noted that the maximum of the thermal conductivity in sapphire is greater than the maximum of 50 watts/cm-deg in copper according to the measurements of Berman and MacDonald,[20]

[17] W. H. Zachariasen, J. Am. Chem. Soc. **54**, 3841 (1932); B. E. Warren, J. Appl. Phys. **8**, 645 (1937); **13**, 602 (1942); E. U. Condon, "Physics of the glassy state," Am. J. Phys. **22**, 43, 132, 224, 310 (1954).

[18] C. Kittel, Phys. Rev. **75**, 972 (1949); F. Birch and H. Clark, Am. J. Sci. **238**, 613 (1940); for liquids, see P. W. Bridgman, Proc. Am. Acad. Arts Sci. **59**, 141 (1923).   The low temperature region in glass is treated by P. G. Klemens, Proc. Roy. Soc. (London) **A208**, 108 (1951).   For normal modes, see F. J. Dyson, Phys. Rev. **92**, 1331 (1953).

[19] R. Berman, Phys. Rev. **76**, 315 (1949).

[20] R. Berman and D. K. C. MacDonald, Proc. Roy. Soc. (London) **A211**, 122 (1952).

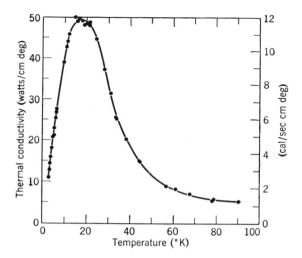

Fig. 6.14.   The thermal conductivity of copper.   (After Berman and MacDonald.)

shown for comparison purposes in Fig. 6.14.   Selected thermal conductivities are given in Table 6.6.   The thermal conductivity of metals is treated in the next section.

TABLE 6.6.   THERMAL CONDUCTIVITY VALUES

| | cal/cm-sec-deg C | |
	−190°C	0°C or 20°C
Al	0.61	0.54
Cd (‖ hex. axis)	0.22	0.20
(⊥ hex. axis)	0.27	0.25
Fe	0.44	0.22
Au	....	0.73
Cu	1.38	0.94
Mg	0.45	0.41
Ni	0.27	0.20
Na	0.37	0.33
Ag	1.02	1.00
KF	0.057	0.017
NaCl	0.064	0.017
KCl	0.050	0.017
CaF$_2$	0.093	0.025
Chrome alum	0.0026	0.0045
Potassium alum	0.0030	0.0047

The transition in properties between crystal quartz and fused quartz or quartz glass is shown in Fig. 6.15, after Berman, Klemens, Simon, and Fry.[21]   The effect of fast neutron irradiation is to produce cas-

[21] R. Berman, P. G. Klemens, F. E. Simon, and T. M. Fry, Nature **166,** 864 (1950).

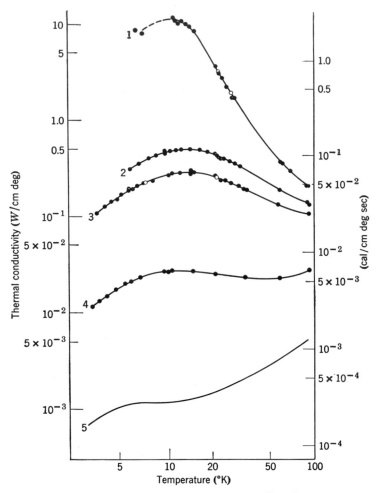

Fig. 6.15.   Thermal conductivity of quartz crystal, irradiated quartz crystal, and quartz glass: (1) quartz crystal perpendicular to axis 5-mm-square cross section; (2) concentration of displaced atoms 1×10^{-4} cm^{-3}; (3) 2×10^{-4}; (4) 2×10^{-3}; (5) quartz glass.

cades of displaced atoms, gradually converting crystalline quartz into a disordered form which may be considered a dilute glass.

THERMAL CONDUCTIVITY OF METALS

The first point to decide in discussing the thermal conductivity of metals is whether the electrons or the phonons carry the greater part of the heat current.   We shall find that in normal pure metals the electrons usually carry almost all the heat current, whereas in very impure metals or in disordered alloys the phonon contribution may be comparable with the electron contribution. Collisions between electrons and phonons are of great importance.

At room temperature the relaxation time of phonon-phonon collisions is of the order of, from Table 6.5,

$$\tau_{pp} = \Lambda_p/u_p \approx 10^{-6}/10^5 \approx 10^{-11} \text{ sec,}$$

while, from Table 10.1, we see the relaxation time of electrons τ_{ep} in electron-phonon collisions is of the order of

$$\tau_{ep} = \Lambda_e/u_e \approx 10^{-5}/10^8 \approx 10^{-13} \text{ sec.}$$

We need further an estimate of the phonon-electron relaxation time τ_{pe}. We make the estimate by considerations of detailed balance. If N_e is the number of electrons available for collision with phonons, and N_p is the number of phonons, then we must have

(6.53) $$N_e/\tau_{ep} = N_p/\tau_{pe},$$

as each side of this relation gives the number of collision processes per unit time. That is, every time an electron collides with a phonon, a phonon collides with an electron. Now in the neighborhood of the Debye temperature N_p is of the order of the total number of atoms N in the metal, while N_e is of the order of NT/T_F, where T_F is the Fermi temperature, defined in Chapter 10 and tabulated in Table 10.3. In this estimate we have taken N as the total number of electrons and T/T_F as the fraction which may participate[22] in collisions; the other electrons are prevented from making collisions by the Pauli exclusion principle. Thus near the Debye temperature, using (6.53), we have

$$\tau_{pe} \approx T_F \tau_{ep}/\Theta \approx 10^2 \tau_{ep} \approx 10^{-11} \text{ sec.}$$

Using (6.45), we see that electron and phonon contributions to the thermal conductivity of a metal will stand approximately in the ratio, for $T \approx 300°\text{K} \approx \Theta$,

(6.54) $$\frac{K_e}{K_p} = \frac{C_e u_e \Lambda_e}{C_p u_p \Lambda_p} \approx \frac{C_e u_e^2 \tau_{ep}}{C_p u_p^2 \tau_{pe}} \approx \frac{10^{-1} R(10^8)^2 10^{-13}}{3R(3 \times 10^5)^2 10^{-11}} \approx 30,$$

so that in pure metals the electronic contribution is dominant; here the subscripts e and p refer to electron and phonon, respectively. It is seen from Table 6.6 that at room temperature metals tend to have values of the thermal conductivity one or two orders of magnitude higher than those of dielectric solids. This is about as expected from

[22] J. H. Van Vleck, Revista univ. nacl. Tucumán **A1**, 81, (1940).

the estimate

$$(6.55) \qquad \frac{K_m}{K_d} \approx \frac{C_e u_e^2 \tau_{ep}}{C_p u_p^2 \tau_{pp}} \approx 30,$$

using the relaxation times given above.

In disordered alloys we might expect to have $\Lambda_e \approx \Lambda_p$, as both phonon and electron mean free paths are limited by the scale of the disorder. Then

$$(6.56) \qquad \frac{K_e}{K_p} \approx \frac{C_e u_e}{C_p u_p} \approx 3,$$

so that the electron and phonon contributions are of the same order of magnitude. Makinson[23] has given a careful treatment of the relative magnitudes of the electron and phonon heat currents for various metals over a wide temperature range, with results generally in agreement with the above estimates. Berman[24] has measured the thermal conductivity of three alloys (German silver, stainless steel, and constantan) between 2° and 90°K and found electron and phonon contributions of equal orders of magnitude.

The total thermal resistivity W of a fairly pure metal at low temperatures ($T < \Theta/10$) may be written in the form

$$(6.57) \qquad W = W_0 + W_i = \frac{1}{K}.$$

Here W_0 is the thermal resistivity due to electron scattering by lattice vibrations and W_i is the thermal resistivity due to electron scattering by impurity atoms. W_i is related to the residual electrical conductivity σ_i of the metal by the Wiedemann-Franz law (Chapter 10), so that

$$(6.58) \qquad W_i = 1/L\sigma_i T,$$

where L is the Lorenz number (10.21) and is a constant. This expression is simply equivalent to setting $\Lambda_i = $ const. in the expression $K_i = 1/W_i = \frac{1}{3} C u \Lambda_i$. The thermal resistivity W_0 can be shown to be proportional to T^2 at $T < \Theta/10$, and so we expect to be able to write the total thermal resistivity in the form

$$(6.59) \qquad W = \alpha T^2 + \beta/T.$$

[23] R. E. B. Makinson, Proc. Cambridge Phil. Soc. **34**, 474 (1938).
[24] R. Berman, Phil. Mag. **42**, 642 (1951).

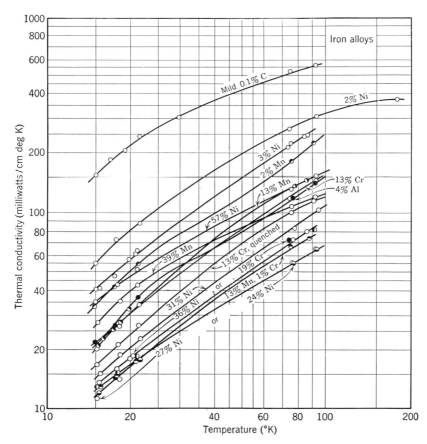

Fig. 6.16.   Thermal conductivity of iron alloys.   [After J. de Nobel, Physica **17**, 551 (1951).]

Values of α and β as deduced from experimental data are tabulated by Rosenberg[25] for a large number of metals.   The curve for copper shown in Fig. 6.14 is fairly typical.   Curves for iron alloys are shown in Fig. 6.16.   The large effect of alloying in reducing thermal conductivity is utilized in the selection of materials for low temperature apparatus.

[25] H. M. Rosenberg, Phil. Trans. Roy. Soc. (London) **A247**, 441–497 (1955); this paper gives experimental curves for many metals at low temperatures.   For a survey of data on metals and alloys, see R. L. Powell and W. A. Blanpied, "Thermal conductivities of metals and alloys at low temperatures," National Bureau of Standards Circular 556; see also R. Berman, E. L. Foster, and H. M. Rosenberg, Brit. J. Appl. Phys. **6**, 181 (1955).

THERMAL EXPANSION

We may understand the origin of thermal expansion by considering the effect of anharmonic terms in the potential energy on the separation of a pair of atoms at a temperature T. We take the potential energy of the atoms at a displacement x from their equilibrium separation at $0°K$ as

$$(6.60) \qquad V(x) = cx^2 - gx^3 - fx^4,$$

where the term in x^3 represents the asymmetry of the mutual repulsion of the atoms and the term in x^4 represents the general "softening" of the vibration at large amplitudes.

We calculate the average displacement by using the Boltzmann distribution function, which weights the possible values of x according to their thermodynamic probability:

$$(6.61) \qquad \bar{x} = \frac{\displaystyle\int_{-\infty}^{\infty} xe^{-V(x)/kT}\,dx}{\displaystyle\int_{-\infty}^{\infty} e^{-V(x)/kT}\,dx}.$$

For small displacement (low anharmonic energy) we expand the integrands:

$$\int xe^{-V/kT}\,dx \cong \int e^{-cx^2/kT}[x + (gx^4/kT) + (fx^5/kT)]\,dx$$
$$= (g/kT)(kT/c)^{5/2}(3\pi^{1/2}/4);$$
$$\int e^{-V/kT}\,dx \cong \int e^{-cx^2/kT}\,dx = (\pi kT/c)^{1/2};$$

and so

$$(6.62) \qquad \bar{x} = 3kTg/4c^2,$$

giving a constant value of the temperature coefficient of thermal expansion. Several values of the linear expansion coefficient are given in Table 6.7

TABLE 6.7. LINEAR COEFFICIENTS OF THERMAL EXPANSION
NEAR ROOM TEMPERATURE

$$l_t = l_0(1 + \beta t)$$

Substance	$10^6 \times \beta$ (per deg C)	Substance	$10^6 \times \beta$ (per deg C)
Au	14	CsCl	50
Li	56	Jena glass (2954—III)	6
Na	71	AlBr$_3$	400
K	83	Zn (parallel to axis)	64
Ni	13	(perpendicular to axis)	14
Pt	9	Te (parallel to axis)	−1.6
KCl	100	(perpendicular to axis)	27

Now kT is classically just the mean energy $\bar{E}$ of the oscillator in the harmonic approximation, so that we may write (6.62) as

$$(6.63) \qquad \bar{x} = 3\bar{E}g/4c^2,$$

which suggests that the approximate quantum-mechanical result would be obtained by substituting for $\bar{E}$ the energy (6.15) of a harmonic oscillator in quantum mechanics. On this argument we should expect the thermal expansion coefficient to decrease rather abruptly as the temperature drops below the characteristic temperature of the oscillator and to go to zero as $T \to 0°K$; this is indeed the observed behavior.[26] The third law of thermodynamics requires that the thermal expansion coefficient vanish as $T \to 0°K$.

EQUATION OF STATE OF SOLIDS

It is possible, by making approximations similar to those made in the Debye theory of specific heats, to derive theoretical expressions[27] for the equation of state, the thermal expansion coefficient, and the temperature variation of the elastic constants, provided that one or two empirical parameters are introduced in the case of cubic crystals. Further constants are required for crystals of lower symmetry.

By a well-known thermodynamic relation

$$(6.64) \qquad U = F - T(\partial F/\partial T)_V = [\partial(F/T)/\partial(1/T)]_V,$$

where U is the internal energy and F is the Helmholtz free energy; the pressure is given by

$$(6.65) \qquad p = -(\partial F/\partial V)_T.$$

Now we may write approximately

$$(6.66) \qquad F = U_0(V) + F_D(T, V),$$

where $U_0(V)$ is the internal energy at $0°K$ and F_D is the contribution (in the Debye approximation) of the lattice vibrations to the free energy. In the spirit of the Debye approximation we may suppose that the dependence of F_D on the volume V is adequately described by specifying the dependence of the Debye temperature Θ on V. Thus,

[26] Low temperature measurements on fused quartz and on a Jena glass are reported by W. H. Keesom and D. W. Doborzynski, Physica **1**, 1085, 1089 (1934).

[27] E. Grüneisen, Handbuch der Physik **10**, 1–59 (1926); P. Debye, in *Vorträge über die kinetische Theorie der Materie und Elektrizität*, by M. Planck *et al.*, Teubner, Leipzig, 1914; J. C. Slater, *Introduction to chemical physics*, McGraw-Hill Book Co., New York, 1939, Chapter XIII. For a discussion of the theory of thermal expansion at low temperatures, see T. H. K. Barron, Phil. Mag. **46**, 720 (1955).

from (6.65) and (6.66),

$$(6.67) \qquad p = -(\partial U_0/\partial V) - (\partial F_D/\partial \Theta)(\partial \Theta/\partial V).$$

In the Debye approximation the internal energy U_D due to lattice vibrations involves T times a function of Θ/T; therefore by (6.64) F_D must be of the same form:

$$(6.68) \qquad F_D = Tf(\Theta/T),$$

so that

$$(6.69) \qquad \partial F_D/\partial \Theta = f' = \Theta^{-1}[(\partial/\partial(1/T))(F_D/T)] = U_D/\Theta.$$

Thus from (6.67) we have the *Debye equation of state,*

$$(6.70) \qquad p = -(\partial U_0/\partial V) + \gamma U_D/V,$$

where

$$(6.71) \qquad \gamma = -d(\log \Theta)/d(\log V) = -(V/\Theta)(d\Theta/dV)$$

is known as the Grüneisen constant. We note that, if ω_k is an eigenfrequency of the solid, $\gamma = -d(\log \omega_k)/d(\log V)$, where we suppose that γ is independent of k. In discussing anharmonic effects in solids, it is always useful to try to express the results in terms of γ.

GRÜNEISEN RELATION

On differentiating (6.70) we have

$$(6.72) \qquad (\partial p/\partial T)_v = \gamma C_v/V.$$

Now the linear expansion coefficient β is one-third of the volume expansion coefficient, so that

$$(6.73) \quad \beta = (1/3V)(\partial V/\partial T)_p = -(1/3V)(\partial p/\partial T)_v/(\partial p/\partial V)_T$$

$$= (K/3)(\partial p/\partial T)_v = K\gamma C_v/3V,$$

where K is now the compressibility. The Grüneisen relation

$$(6.74) \qquad \beta = K\gamma C_v/3V$$

connecting the linear expansion coefficient with the specific heat is satisfied experimentally for cubic crystals, taking γ as independent of temperature.

In Table 6.8 we give a comparison of γ calculated from the Grüneisen relation (6.74) with γ calculated by Slater[28] (with a correction sug-

[28] J. C. Slater, Phys. Rev. **57**, 744 (1940); *Introduction to chemical physics*, McGraw-Hill, New York, 1939, pp. 393, 451; J. S. Dugdale and D. K. C. MacDonald, Phys. Rev. **89**, 832 (1953).

gested by Dugdale and MacDonald) from measurements made by Bridgman and by Slater of the change of compressibility with pressure. The agreement is fairly good.

TABLE 6.8. VALUES OF THE GRÜNEISEN γ

Substance	Grüneisen, Eq. (6.74)	Slater
Na	1.25	1.50
K	1.34	2.32
Al	2.17	0.94
Mn	2.42	5.5
Fe	1.6	1.4
Co	1.87	1.8
Ni	1.88	1.9
Cu	1.96	1.63
Ag	2.40	2.2
Pt	2.54	3.0
NaCl	1.63	1.52
KF	1.45	1.93
KCl	1.60	1.26
KBr	1.68	1.29
KI	1.63	1.21

PROBLEMS

6.1. Show that the expression for the average energy of a classical system may be written as

$$\bar{E} = kT^2 d(\log Z)/dT,$$

where the partition function

$$Z = \iint e^{-E(p,q)/kT} \, dp \, dq.$$

6.2. Show that the heat capacity of a monatomic linear lattice in the Debye approximation is proportional to T/Θ, for low temperatures such that $T \ll \Theta$, where Θ is the effective Debye temperature in one dimension and is defined as $\Theta = \hbar\omega_m/k = \hbar\pi v_0/ka$, k being the Boltzmann constant.

6.3. Using the anharmonic potential $V(x) = cx^2 - gx^3 - fx^4$, show that the approximate heat capacity of the classical anharmonic oscillator is

$$C \cong k\left[1 + \left(\frac{3f}{2c^2} + \frac{15g^2}{8c^3}\right)kT\right].$$

Note: $\log(1 + x) \cong x - \frac{1}{2}x^2$ for $x \ll 1$; the calculation is shorter if the partition function (Problem 6.1) is employed.

6.4. Show by thermodynamics that

$$C_p - C_v = 9\beta^2 T/K,$$

where C_p is the heat capacity per unit volume at constant pressure, C_v at constant volume, β is the temperature coefficient of linear expansion, and K is the compressibility.   Estimate $C_p - C_v$ for copper at 300°K and at 1000°K.

6.5. Derive an expression for the free energy $F = U - TS$ of a collection of quantum harmonic oscillators, and show that the classical limit is

$$F \cong U_0 + kT \sum_k \log (\hbar\omega_k/kT).$$

6.6. By equating the elastic energy per unit cell $\frac{1}{2}ce^2a^3$ with kT, show that the local thermal strain in a crystal at room temperature may be of the order of 0.1; here e is the strain; c is an average elastic constant, and a is the lattice constant.

6.7.* A number of workers, starting with V. V. Tarassov, Compt. rend. acad. sci. U.R.S.S. **46**, (1945), have discussed the theory of the heat capacity of chain and layer crystal lattices. In a chain lattice the interatomic forces are strong along each chain of atoms and weak between chains. In a layer lattice the strong forces connect atoms in each layer, but the layers are only weakly coupled. Give a semiquantitative discussion on the Debye model of the variation of heat capacity with temperature for both lattices; draw rough graphs. For references to experimental and theoretical work in this area, see W. de Sorbo, Acta Metallurgica **2**, 274 (1954) and G. F. Newell, J. Chem. Phys. **23**, 2341 (1955).

6.8. At low temperature the thermal conductivity of metals and alloys is often given by $K = BT$, where B is a constant. Find the steady state temperature distribution on a rod of uniform cross section when one end is kept at T_1 and the other end at T_2.

REFERENCES

R. Berman, "Thermal conductivity in dielectric solids at low temperatures," Advances in Physics **2**, 103–140 (1953).

A Eucken, *Handbuch der Experimentalphysik*, Akademische Verlagsgesellschaft, Leipzig, Vol. 8/1; 1929.

R. H. Fowler and E. A. Guggenheim, *Statistical thermodynamics*, Cambridge University Press, Cambridge, 1939.

J. L. Olsen and H. M. Rosenberg, "Thermal conductivity of metals at low temperatures," Advances in Physics **2**, 28–66 (1953).

J. C. Slater, *Introduction to chemical physics*, McGraw-Hill Book Co., New York, 1939; Chapters XIII–XV.

7

Dielectric Properties

In this chapter we discuss first the relationship between the applied electric field and the local electric field acting on an atom. The interaction of the local field with the atom determines the polarization, yet the local field may itself be a function of the polarization. We then discuss the electric polarization of atoms, molecules, and crystals in static fields and at high frequencies. The polarization is defined as the dipole moment per unit volume, the dipole moment $\wp$ of the specimen as a whole being defined as $\wp = \Sigma \, e_i \mathbf{r}_i$. The sum is extended over all charges in the system; on the supposition that the system is neutral the sum is independent of the origin chosen for the position vector $\mathbf{r}_i$.

LOCAL ELECTRIC FIELD

The calculation of the local field at an atom or ion as affected by the polarization of the specimen as a whole is a problem of central importance in dielectric and magnetic theory. We consider first a solid dielectric with a cubic crystal structure; we suppose that the specimen is in the form of an ellipsoid with one of the axes parallel to the applied electric field (Fig. 7.1).

The field $\mathbf{E}_{loc}$ at any atom may be written as a sum

$$(7.1) \qquad \mathbf{E}_{loc} = \mathbf{E}_0 + \mathbf{E}_1 + \mathbf{E}_2 + \mathbf{E}_3,$$

where $\mathbf{E}_0$ is the electric field applied from external sources; $\mathbf{E}_1$ is the "depolarization field" resulting from polarization charges on the outer surface of the specimen. We imagine as a mathematical fiction a small sphere cut out of the specimen around the reference point; then $\mathbf{E}_2$ is the field of the polarization charges on the inside of the cavity left by the sphere, and $\mathbf{E}_3$ is the field of the atoms within the cavity.

The addition $\mathbf{E}_1 + \mathbf{E}_2 + \mathbf{E}_3$ to the local field is just the total effect at one atom of the dipole moments of all the other atoms in the specimen:

$$(7.2) \qquad \mathbf{E}_1 + \mathbf{E}_2 + \mathbf{E}_3 = \sum_i \frac{3(\mathbf{p}_i \cdot \mathbf{r}_i)\mathbf{r}_i - r_i^2 \mathbf{p}_i}{r_i^5},$$

where $\mathbf{p}_i$ is the dipole moment of atom i. If we are far enough away from the individual dipoles of a uniformly polarized specimen, we may, according to an elementary transformation occurring in electrostatic theory, calculate the field of the specimen as equal to the field of a surface charge distribution of density P_n on the surfaces of the specimen, P_n being the normal component of the polarization $\mathbf{P}$ at the surfaces. The idea in creating the cavity is that we may treat the field $\mathbf{E}_3$ of the dipoles within the cavity on a microscopic basis by such a sum as (7.2),

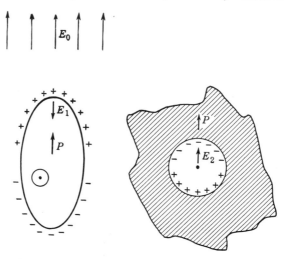

Fig. 7.1. Contributions to the local electric field at the ion at the center of the spherical cavity, showing the applied field E_0, the depolarization field E_1, and the Lorentz field E_2. The local field is the sum of these plus the field of the dipoles within the cavity.

while the rest of the specimen is treated macroscopically by means of integrals over the effective surface charges. One integral is taken over the outer surface, and it gives $\mathbf{E}_1$; the other integral is taken over the surface of the spherical cavity, and it gives $\mathbf{E}_2$. The field $\mathbf{E}_1$ is readily seen from Fig. 7.1 to be opposite in direction to the polarization and hence is called the *depolarization field*.

DEPOLARIZATION FIELD

The calculation of the depolarization field is a well-known problem in classical electricity, and we summarize the results here. It is found that specimens of homogeneous composition will be uniformly polarized when placed in a uniform external field as long as the external shape of the specimen is that of a general ellipsoid or a limiting case of a general ellipsoid. If the ellipsoid is oriented with one of the principal axes parallel to the applied field, the polarization will be parallel to the applied field, as will the depolarization field E_1, which it is found may be calculated from the polarization P by a relation of the form

$$(7.3) \qquad\qquad E_1 = -NP.$$

The constant N is known as the *depolarization factor;* it is precisely the same as the *demagnetization factor*, and its value depends on the axial

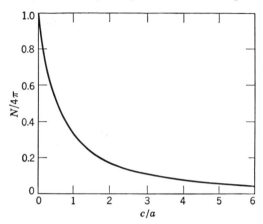

Fig. 7.2. Demagnetization factor N parallel to the figure axis of ellipsoids of revolution, as a function of the axial ratio c/a.

ratio. It is exceptionally important in the field of magnetism. Values of N are plotted in Fig. 7.2 for ellipsoids of revolution, and additional cases have been calculated by Osborn[1] and by Stoner.[2] In the several limiting cases we have the following values:

Shape	Axis	N
Sphere	any	$4\pi/3$
Thin slab	normal	4π
Thin slab	in plane	0
Long circular cylinder	longitudinal	0
Long circular cylinder	transverse	2π

The demagnetization factor has a rigorous meaning only for homogeneous general ellipsoids in uniform applied fields. An important prop-

[1] J. A. Osborn, Phys. Rev. **67**, 351 (1945).

[2] E. C. Stoner, Phil. Mag. **36**, 803 (1945); for approximate values for non-ellipsoidal shapes, see J. Würschmidt, *Theorie des Entmagnetisierungsfaktor*, Vieweg, Braunschweig, 1925; J. L. Snoek, Physica **1**, 649 (1933); R. M. Bozorth and D. M. Chapin, J. Appl. Phys. **13**, 320 (1942).

erty of the demagnetization factor is that $N_a + N_b + N_c = 4\pi$, where N_a, N_b, N_c are the demagnetization factors along the three principal axes of a general ellipsoid.

LORENTZ FIELD

The field $\mathbf{E}_2$ due to the polarization charges on the surface of the fictitious cavity was calculated first by Lorentz. If θ is the polar angle (Fig. 7.3) referred to the polarization direction as axis, the surface charge density on the surface of the cavity is $-P \cos \theta$. The electric field at the center of the spherical cavity of radius a is

$$(7.4) \quad \mathbf{E}_2 = \int_0^\pi (a^{-2})(2\pi a \sin \theta)(a \, d\theta)(\mathbf{P} \cos \theta)(\cos \theta) = 4\pi\mathbf{P}/3.$$

The cavity field is actually uniform, but for our purpose we need only the field at the center, which is what we have just calculated.

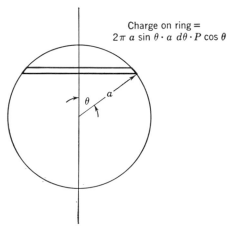

Charge on ring $=$
$2\pi a \sin \theta \cdot a \, d\theta \cdot P \cos \theta$

Fig. 7.3.   Calculation of the field in a spherical cavity in a uniformly polarized medium.

FIELD OF DIPOLES INSIDE CAVITY

The field $\mathbf{E}_3$ caused by the dipoles within the cavity is the only term in the sum which depends on the crystal structure. We shall first consider a cubic structure, for which it is readily shown that $\mathbf{E}_3 = 0$ if all the atoms may be replaced by point dipoles parallel to each other. The axis of the dipoles is taken as the z axis; at the reference point the field caused by the other dipoles p_i is

$$(7.5) \qquad\qquad E_3{}^z = \sum_i \frac{3p_i z_i{}^2 - p_i r_i{}^2}{r_i{}^5}.$$

By the symmetry of the lattice and the cavity, $\Sigma\ (z_i{}^2/r_i{}^5) = \Sigma\ (y_i{}^2/r_i{}^5) = \Sigma\ (x_i{}^2/r_i{}^5)$, so that $\Sigma\ (r_i{}^2/r_i{}^5) = 3\ \Sigma\ (z_i{}^2/r_i{}^5)$, whence $\mathbf{E}_3 = 0$.

The proof we have given for the vanishing of $\mathbf{E}_3$ actually obtains for all cases in which the environment of the reference point is cubic, as long as the dipoles are parallel. Thus $\mathbf{E}_3 = 0$ for induced polarization on simple cubic, body-centered cubic, and face-centered cubic lattices, as well as for an isotropic distribution. Later, in considering the ferroelectric properties of barium titanate (Fig. 8.1), we shall see that here $\mathbf{E}_3 \neq 0$; although the crystallographic symmetry is cubic, the environment of the oxygen ions is not cubic. Values of $\mathbf{E}_3$ for tetragonal and simple hexagonal lattices have been given by Mueller.[3]

FIELD IN DIELECTRIC BETWEEN CONDENSER PLATES

The classical definition of the macroscopic (average) electric field intensity $\mathbf{E}$ inside a dielectric is that $\mathbf{E}$ is the average field inside a long

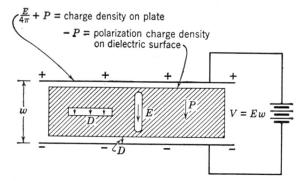

Fig. 7.4.   Definitions of D and E; the voltage V across the condenser plates is E times the separation w, if we neglect the air gaps between the plates and the dielectric.

needle-shaped cavity, parallel to the polarization (Fig. 7.4), while the displacement $\mathbf{D}$ is defined as the average field inside a disk-shaped cavity normal to the polarization. The difference

(7.6) $$\mathbf{D} - \mathbf{E} = 4\pi\mathbf{P}$$

is caused by the field $4\pi\mathbf{P}$ of the polarization charge density $\mathbf{P}$ on the flat surfaces of the disk cavity; the polarization charges on the needle cavity may be neglected. Inside a spherical cavity the field is $\mathbf{E} + (4\pi/3)\mathbf{P}$.

Measurements of the polarization $\mathbf{P}$ or of the dielectric constant $\epsilon = D/E$ are usually made by measuring the capacity $C = Q/V$ of a

[3] H. Mueller, Phys. Rev. **47**, 947 (1935); **50**, 547 (1936); see also L. W. McKeehan Phys. Rev. **43**, 1022, 1025 (1933).

condenser filled with the dielectric. In the absence of the dielectric we suppose that the field between the condenser plates is E', so that the surface charge density on each plate is $\pm E'/4\pi$. When the dielectric is inserted, polarization charge densities $\pm P$ are induced on the surfaces of the dielectric, and these charges are then effectively neutralized by a flow of charge around the condenser circuit. The field E inside the needle-shaped cavity is the sum of a field $-4\pi P$ from the polarization charges and $E' + 4\pi P$ from the original and the neutralization charges on the condenser plates. Thus for the condenser arrangement $E = E'$, and, from (7.1), (7.3), and (7.4), E_{loc} $= E_0 + E_1 + E_2 + E_3 = (E + 4\pi P) + (-4\pi P) + (4\pi P/3) + (0)$ for structures such that $E_3 = 0$. Then

$$(7.7) \qquad\qquad E_{\text{loc}} = E + \frac{4\pi}{3} P.$$

That is, the value of the macroscopic average field E is the same as the field existing between the condenser plates before the dielectric is inserted; the field acting at the center of an atom is E plus a contribution $4\pi P/3$ from the field produced by the polarization of the other atoms in the specimen. It is seen further that the condenser plates, if put in close contact with the dielectric, have the effect of shorting-out the depolarization charge. Evidence for the approximate validity of (7.7) in ionic crystals is given by Tessman, Kahn, and Shockley.[4]

DIELECTRIC CONSTANT AND POLARIZABILITY

The dielectric constant ϵ is defined for an isotropic medium as

$$(7.8) \qquad\qquad \epsilon = D/E = 1 + 4\pi(P/E) = 1 + 4\pi\chi,$$

where χ is the electric susceptibility. The polarizability α is defined as

$$(7.9) \qquad\qquad \alpha_i = p_i/E_{\text{loc}}{}^i,$$

where the index i refers to a particular type of atom; p_i is the dipole moment. The polarization is then

$$P = \sum_i E_{\text{loc}}{}^i N_i \alpha_i,$$

where N_i is the number per unit volume of atoms of type i.

If the local field is connected with the applied field by the Lorentz

[4] J. Tessman, A. Kahn, and W. Shockley, Phys. Rev. **92**, 890 (1953).

relation (7.7), we have

(7.10)
$$\frac{P}{E} = \frac{\Sigma N_i \alpha_i}{1 - \dfrac{4\pi}{3} \Sigma N_i \alpha_i} = \frac{\epsilon - 1}{4\pi},$$

which may be solved for $\Sigma N_i \alpha_i$ to give

(7.11)
$$\frac{\epsilon - 1}{\epsilon + 2} = \frac{4\pi}{3} \sum N_i \alpha_i.$$

This is a common form of the relation between the dielectric constant and the atomic polarizabilities; (7.11) may be rewritten as the Clausius-Mossotti equation (or, with $\epsilon = n^2$, the Lorenz-Lorentz equation),

(7.12)
$$\frac{M}{\rho} \frac{\epsilon - 1}{\epsilon + 2} = \frac{4\pi}{3} L\alpha,$$

where M is the molecular weight, ρ the density, L Avogadro's number, n the refractive index, and α the total polarizability per molecule. The left-hand side of this equation is called the *molar polarizability*.

MEASUREMENT OF DIELECTRIC CONSTANTS

The usual methods of measuring dielectric constants are based on a comparison of the capacity C'' of a condenser filled with the substance

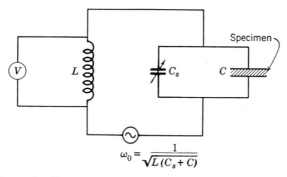

$$\omega_0 = \frac{1}{\sqrt{L(C_s + C)}}$$

Fig. 7.5.   Schematic diagram of apparatus for the measurement of dielectric constants.

and the capacity C' of the empty condenser.   The ratio $C''/C' = \epsilon$, the dielectric constant.   The determination of the value of the capacity may in principle be accomplished by an LC resonant circuit as shown in Fig. 7.5, where C_s is a calibrated variable condenser and C is the condenser in which the specimen may be placed.   By varying the calibrated condenser so as to keep the resonance frequency $\omega_0 =$

$[L(C_s + C)]^{-\frac{1}{2}}$ constant when C is inserted and then filled, we may determine C' and C'', and thus ϵ. The dielectric loss may be obtained from the sharpness of the tuning near resonance.

Descriptions of the actual circuits employed are abundant in the literature. At microwave frequencies the technique of measurement is altered somewhat, and here one often measures essentially the wavelength λ of the microwave radiation in the specimen, obtaining the dielectric constant from the relation $\lambda(\text{vacuum})/\lambda(\text{specimen}) = (\epsilon\mu)^{\frac{1}{2}}$, where μ is the permeability.

ELECTRONIC POLARIZABILITIES

The total polarizability of an atom or ion may usually be separated into three parts:[5] electronic, ionic, and orientational. The electronic contribution arises from the displacement of electrons in an atom relative to the nucleus; that is, from the deformation of the electron shell about a nucleus. The ionic or atomic contribution comes from the displacement and deformation of a charged ion with respect to other ions. The orientational or dipolar polarizability arises when the substance is built up of molecules possessing a permanent electric dipole moment which may be more or less free to change orientation in an applied electric field. It is possible to separate experimentally the different contributions, and one way of doing this is indicated in Fig. 7.6. The usual situation is that both the ionic and the dipolar contributions are seldom large together in the same substance: in ordinary ionic crystals there is no dipolar contribution. In dipolar organic molecules Sugden[6] estimates that the average ionic polarizability is about 10% of the electronic polarizability.

In the optical range of frequency the dielectric constant arises almost entirely from the electronic polarizability, so that in the optical range (7.11) reduces to

$$(7.13) \qquad \frac{n^2 - 1}{n^2 + 2} = \frac{4\pi}{3} \sum N_i \alpha_i \text{ (electronic)};$$

here we have used the relation $n^2 = \epsilon$, where n is the refractive index. By applying this relation to large numbers of crystals we may determine empirical values of the electronic polarizabilities which are

---

[5] In heterogeneous materials there is usually also an *interfacial polarization* arising from the accumulation of charge at structural interfaces. This is of little fundamental interest, but of considerable practical interest as commercial insulating materials are usually heterogeneous.

[6] J. A. Sugden, Trans. Faraday Soc. **30**, 734 (1934).

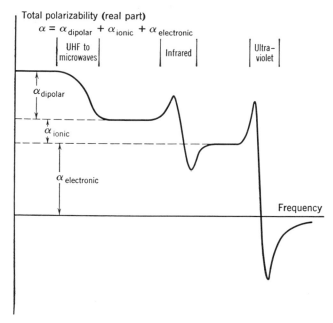

Fig. 7.6.   Frequency dependence of the several contributions to the polarizability (schematic).

reasonably consistent with the observed values of the refractive index. Values obtained in this way are given in Table 7.1.   The scheme is not

TABLE 7.1.   ELECTRONIC POLARIZABILITIES OF IONS

Values from L. Pauling, Proc. Roy. Soc. (London) **A114**, 181 (1927) and from Tessman, Kahn, and Shockley, Phys. Rev. **92**, 890 (1953).   The TKS polarizabilities are for the D lines of sodium.

Units cm³ × 10⁻²⁴

			He	Li⁺	Be²⁺	B³⁺	C⁴⁺
Pauling			0.201	0.029	0.008	0.003	0.0013
TKS				0.03			
	O²⁻	F⁻	Ne	Na⁺	Mg²⁺	Al³⁺	Si⁴⁺
Pauling	3.88	1.04	0.390	0.179	0.094	0.052	0.0165
TKS	(2.4)	0.652		0.41			
	S²⁻	Cl⁻	A	K⁺	Ca²⁺	Sc³⁺	Ti⁴⁺
Pauling	10.2	3.66	1.62	0.83	0.47	0.286	0.185
TKS	(5.5)	2.97		1.33	1.1		(0.19)
	Se²⁻	Br⁻	Kr	Rb⁺	Sr²⁺	Y³⁺	Zr⁴⁺
Pauling	10.5	4.77	2.46	1.40	0.86	0.55	0.37
TKS	(7.)	4.17		1.98	1.6		
	Te²⁻	I⁻	Xe	Cs⁺	Ba²⁺	La³⁺	Ce⁴⁺
Pauling	14.0	7.10	3.99	2.42	1.55	1.04	0.73
TKS	(9.)	6.44		3.34	2.5		

entirely self-consistent, as the electronic polarizability of an ion may depend slightly on the environment in which it is placed.

CLASSICAL THEORY OF ELECTRONIC POLARIZABILITY

According to classical mechanics an electron bound harmonically to an atom will show resonance absorption at a frequency $\omega_0 = (\beta/m)^{\frac{1}{2}}$, where β is the force constant. The average displacement of the electron occasioned by the application of a field E_{loc} will be given by

$$eE_{loc} = \beta \bar{x} = m\omega_0^2 \bar{x},$$

so that the static electronic polarizability is

(7.14) $\qquad \alpha(\text{electronic}) = p/E_{loc} = e\bar{x}/E_{loc} = e^2/m\omega_0^2.$

The electronic polarizability will depend on frequency, and it is shown in Problem 7.3 that the result is, for frequency ω,

(7.15) $\qquad \alpha(\text{electronic}) = \dfrac{e^2/m}{\omega_0^2 - \omega^2},$

but in the visible region the dispersion is not usually very important in most dielectric materials. The corresponding expression in quantum theory is

(7.16) $\qquad \alpha(\text{electronic}) = \dfrac{e^2}{m} \sum_j \dfrac{f_{ij}}{\omega_{ij}^2 - \omega^2},$

where the oscillator strength f_{ij} is given by

(7.17) $\qquad f_{ij} = 2\omega_{ij}m|x_{ij}|^2/\hbar$

in the usual notation. This result is derived in most books on quantum theory, and it is derived in Appendix B for the limiting case $\omega = 0$.

The electronic polarizability is of the order of magnitude, for hydrogen,

$$\alpha \approx \frac{e^2}{m\omega_0^2} \approx \frac{e^2}{m}\left(\frac{\hbar^3}{me^4}\right)^2 = \frac{\hbar^6}{m^3 e^6} = a_H^3 \approx 10^{-25} \text{ cm}^3.$$

IONIC POLARIZABILITIES

In sodium chloride the square of the refractive index is $(1.50)^2 = 2.25$, while the static dielectric constant is 5.62. The difference $\Delta\epsilon$ between the static and optical dielectric constants may be ascribed in ionic crystals to the ionic polarizability; in sodium chloride we see that $\Delta\epsilon = 3.37$. The ionic polarization arises from the displacement of ions of opposite sign when an electric field is applied, and also from the deformation of the electronic shells of the ions as a result of the relative motion of the ions.

We consider the situation in a sodium chloride crystal when a uniform external field E_0 is applied. Each Na^+ ion is displaced in one direction, and each Cl^- ion in the opposite direction. The total relative displacement x is given in terms of the problem discussed in Chapter 5 by setting $\omega = 0$ in (5.28) and (5.29). Then

$$(7.18) \qquad x = \eta - \xi = \frac{eE_0}{\omega_0^2}\left(\frac{1}{m} + \frac{1}{M}\right),$$

where in the present fairly crude treatment we associate E_0 with the applied electric field, neglecting local field effects; ω_0 is the infrared absorption frequency.

The ionic polarization is

$$P = \frac{e(\eta - \xi)}{\Omega},$$

where Ω is the volume per molecule and is equal to $2a^3$ for the sodium chloride structure, a being the nearest neighbor distance. Then

$$(7.19) \qquad P = \frac{e^2 E_0}{2\omega_0^2 a^3}\left(\frac{1}{m} + \frac{1}{M}\right),$$

which gives directly the Born equation for the difference between the static and optical dielectric constants:

$$(7.20) \qquad \Delta\epsilon = \frac{2\pi e^2}{\omega_0^2 a^3}\left(\frac{1}{m} + \frac{1}{M}\right).$$

This exhibits the connection of $\Delta\epsilon$ with the residual ray frequency ω_0. Values of $\Delta\epsilon$ calculated by using this equation are in fairly good agreement with the experimental values. For sodium chloride,

$$\Delta\epsilon = \frac{(6.28)(4.80 \times 10^{-10})^2}{(3.2 \times 10^{13})^2(2.81 \times 10^{-8})^3(1.66 \times 10^{-24})}\left(\frac{1}{23} + \frac{1}{35.5}\right) = 2.7,$$

in fair agreement with the observed $\Delta\epsilon = 3.4$.

There are actually some subtle points neglected in the derivation of the Born equation, points which are connected with differences in the local field effective for optical frequencies and for quasi-static frequencies. Szigeti[7] has shown that the Born equation holds on

[7] B. Szigeti, Trans. Faraday Soc. **45**, 155 (1949); Proc. Roy. Soc. (London) **A204**, 51 (1950).

the assumption of non-deformable and non-overlapping ions. An improved approximate expression is given by Szigeti:

$$(7.21) \qquad \Delta\epsilon = \left(\frac{n^2 + 2}{3}\right)^2 \frac{2\pi(e^*)^2}{\omega_t^2 a^3}\left(\frac{1}{m} + \frac{1}{M}\right),$$

where ω_t is the eigenfrequency of the transverse optical branch, and e^* is the "effective" charge on an ion. Values of e^* are given in Table 7.2. Szigeti has also found a relation involving the compressibility K and the dielectric constant ϵ_0 for static frequencies:

$$(7.22) \qquad \frac{1}{K} = \frac{\epsilon_0 + 2}{6(n^2 + 2)}\,(m\omega_t^2/a).$$

We have written both (7.21) and (7.22) in a somewhat specialized form for sodium chloride structures. A comparison of observed and calculated compressibilities is made in Table 7.2.

TABLE 7.2. DIELECTRIC DATA FOR ALKALI HALIDES HAVING THE SODIUM CHLORIDE STRUCTURE AND TEST OF THE SZIGETI RELATIONS

	ϵ_0	n^2	e^*/e	K_{calc}/K_{obs}
LiF	9.27	1.92	0.87	1.0
NaF	6.0	1.74	0.93	0.83
NaCl	5.62	2.25	0.74	0.99
NaBr	5.99	2.62	0.69	1.13
NaI	6.60	2.91	0.71	1.05
KCl	4.68	2.13	0.80	0.96
KBr	4.78	2.33	0.76	0.95
KI	4.94	2.69	0.69	0.99
RbCl	5	2.19	0.84	0.89
RbBr	5	2.33	0.82	0.83
RbI	5	2.63	0.89	0.66

It is seen from the table that the ratio K_{calc}/K_{obs} is on the whole closer to unity than the ratio e^*/e. Of course it is possible that, owing to an admixture of homopolar bonding, the degree of ionization of the ions in the crystal is somewhat incomplete; however, the generally excellent agreement of the calculated lattice energies with the experimental values, as discussed in Chapter 3, would seem to make it improbable that values of e^*/e differ from unity by more than perhaps 2%. At the present time this disagreement has not been resolved in a satisfactory fashion, although the question is of basic importance in the theory of the dielectric properties of ionic crystals.

ORIENTATIONAL POLARIZABILITIES

The polarizability arising from the orientation in an applied electric field of molecules possessing a permanent electric dipole moment is usually discussed only with reference to gases and liquids, but it is of importance in some solids.   This type of polarization was first discussed by Debye (1912), who showed that by assuming that molecules could have permanent dipole moments one could explain the high dielectric constant of water, alcohol, and similar liquids, and the temperature dependence of their dielectric constants.   The problem of the dielectric constant of water is that the static dielectric constant is

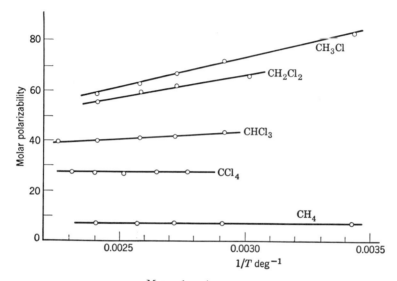

Fig. 7.7.   Plot of the quantity $\dfrac{M}{\rho}\dfrac{\epsilon - 1}{\epsilon + 1} = \dfrac{4\pi}{3} L\alpha$ (known as the molar polarizability) for polar and non-polar substituted methane compounds in gaseous form.   [After R. Sänger, Physik Z. **27**, 556 (1926).]

81 (at room temperature), whereas the dielectric constant at optical frequencies is $(1.33)^2 = 1.77$.   It is now known that the difference is caused chiefly by the orientational polarization which is effective at low frequencies, but is damped out for wavelengths shorter than about 1 cm.   The characteristic temperature dependence of the orientational polarizability is shown in Fig. 7.7: CH_3Cl has a permanent electric dipole moment; CH_4 and CCl_4 do not.

    In the absence of thermal agitation and of interactions among themselves, molecules with permanent dipole moments would all line up completely on application of an arbitrarily small electric field, so that the dielectric constant would be infinite.   Actually, the orienting tendency of the electric field is partly compensated by the thermal agitation, and in solids and some liquids the orientation is hindered by close-range mutual interactions of the molecules.

We consider the effect of the thermal motion on molecules which are free to move. The potential energy of a molecule of permanent moment $\mathbf{p}$ in a field $\mathbf{E}$ is, as shown in Appendix F,

$$(7.23) \qquad V = -\mathbf{p} \cdot \mathbf{E} = -pE \cos \theta,$$

where θ is the angle between the moment and the field direction. The polarization will be

$$P = Np \, \overline{\cos \theta},$$

where N is the number of molecules per unit volume and $\overline{\cos \theta}$ is the average over a distribution in thermal equilibrium.

According to the Boltzmann distribution law the relative probability of finding a molecule in an element of solid angle $d\Omega$ is proportional to $e^{-V/kT}$, and

$$(7.24) \qquad \overline{\cos \theta} = \int e^{-V/kT} \cos \theta \, d\Omega / \int e^{-V/kT} \, d\Omega.$$

The integration is to be carried out over all solid angles, so that

$$\overline{\cos \theta} = \int_0^\pi 2\pi \sin \theta \cos \theta \, e^{pE\cos\theta/kT} \, d\theta \Big/ \int_0^\pi 2\pi \sin \theta \, e^{pE\cos\theta/kT} \, d\theta.$$

We let $x = \cos \theta$ and $a = pE/kT$, so that

$$(7.25) \qquad \overline{\cos \theta} = \int_{-1}^1 e^{ax}x \, dx \Big/ \int_{-1}^1 e^{ax} \, dx = \frac{d}{da} \ln \int_{-1}^1 e^{ax} \, dx$$

$$= \operatorname{ctnh} a - \frac{1}{a} \equiv L(a).$$

This may be viewed as the definition of the Langevin function $L(a)$, which was first introduced in connection with the magnetic susceptibility of paramagnetic substances. The function is plotted in Fig. 7.8, and the saturation property for $pE \gg kT$ is clearly seen.

The most important situation experimentally is when $pE \ll kT$. Dipole moments are of the order of 10^{-18} esu, so that for $E = 3000$ v/cm $= 10$ statv/cm, $pE \approx 10^{-17}$ ergs, and at room temperature $kT \approx 4 \times 10^{-14}$ ergs. Thus $pE/kT \approx 1/4000$, and our condition is satisfied. In this limit of $a \ll 1$,

$$(7.26) \qquad L(a) \cong \frac{a}{3} = \frac{pE}{3kT},$$

and so the polarization is

(7.27) $$P = N\overline{p \cos \theta} = Np^2E/3kT,$$

and the polarizability (per molecule) is

(7.28) $$\alpha(\text{dipolar}) = p^2/3kT.$$

At room temperature this is of the order of $(10^{-18})^2/10^{-13} \approx 10^{-23}$ cm^3, of the same order of magnitude as the electronic polarizability. The total polarizability may then be written, if we let α_0 denote the

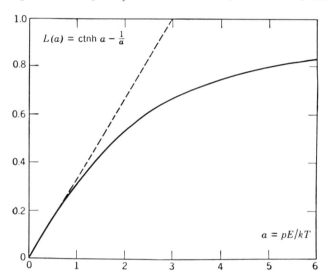

Fig. 7.8.   Plot of Langevin function $L(a)$ as function of $a = pE/kT$; the initial slope is shown by the dashed line.

deformation polarizability (that is, the sum of the electronic and ionic contributions),

(7.29) $$\alpha = \alpha_0 + p^2/3kT,$$

an expression which is known as the Langevin-Debye equation, and which has been of great importance in interpreting molecular structures.   The dipole moment p is determined in practice by plotting either α or the molar polarizability (7.12) as a function of $1/T$ as in Fig. 7.7; the slope is simply related to p.   In this way one obtains, for example, the following dipole moments: $p(\text{HCl}) = 1.03 \times 10^{-18}$ esu; $p(\text{HBr}) = 0.79 \times 10^{-18}$ esu; $p(\text{HI}) = 0.38 \times 10^{-18}$ esu; $p(\text{H}_2\text{O}) = 1.87 \times 10^{-18}$ esu.   The moments are often expressed in Debye units, where a Debye unit is 10^{-18} esu, of the order of the electronic charge times an interatomic distance.

THE POLARIZABILITY CATASTROPHE

In early work the dielectric constant was calculated from the polarizability by use of the Clausius-Mossotti equation (7.12), but although this equation holds fairly accurately for non-polar substances it fails completely in pure polar liquids or solids. To see this failure we neglect the deformation polarizability α_0 and substitute (7.28) in (7.10), obtaining

$$(7.30) \qquad \epsilon = 1 + \frac{4\pi N p^2}{3k(T - T_c)},$$

where we have set

$$(7.31) \qquad T_c = 4\pi N p^2 / 9k.$$

We may not conclude, however, from (7.30) that the dielectric constant would really become infinite at $T = T_c$, but rather that saturation effects should enter and the substance should become spontaneously polarized or "ferroelectric." Actually, ferroelectric behavior is at present unknown in dipolar substances, although it is found in crystals which are more or less ionic in binding. The latter cases are discussed in the following chapter, where it is shown that the mechanism leading to ferroelectricity is usually quite different from that contemplated here. Using the known dipole moment of 1.87 Debye units, we may estimate from (7.31) the critical temperature which would be expected for water. We have

$$T_c = \frac{(12.6)(6.03 \times 10^{23}/18)(1.87 \times 10^{-18})^2}{9(1.38 \times 10^{-16})} \cong 1200°K,$$

in striking contradiction of the fact that neither water nor ice is ferroelectric.

Onsager[8] pointed out that the theoretical basis of the Lorentz field (7.7), from which the catastrophe stems, does not include the case of permanent dipole moments, as here the moments are not in general all parallel, as was assumed in the discussion of the terms E_2 and E_3 in the general expression (7.1) for the local field. Onsager has developed an approximate theory for polar substances. If the induced polariza-

[8] L. Onsager, J. Am. Chem. Soc. **58**, 1486 (1936); for a discussion of various attempts to develop a theory valid for polar liquids and solids, see J. H. Van Vleck, Ann. N.Y. Acad. Sci. **40**, 293 (1940).

tion is neglected, the Onsager model gives

$$(7.32) \quad \epsilon = \tfrac{1}{4}[1 + 3x + 3(1 + \tfrac{2}{3}x + x^2)^{\frac{1}{2}}], \quad x \equiv 4\pi N p^2/3kT.$$

It is easily seen that this expression, which is derived in Appendix C, does not give a critical point. Further discussion of the problem would lead us too far afield. An exact solution has not yet been obtained. Several interesting general theorems relating to the dielectric constant have been discovered by Fröhlich.[9] It may be noted that internal interactions which favor one direction of mutual orientation of adjacent molecules over the opposite direction may also tend to eliminate the critical point displayed by (7.30); the effect is known as "hindered rotation."

DIPOLE ORIENTATION IN SOLIDS

We expect molecules in gases and liquids to be fairly free to rotate, and the permanent dipole moments may be expected to make their full orientational contribution to the polarizability, as calculated above. In molecular solids the ability of a molecule to rotate depends very much on its shape and on the strength of its interactions with the environment. The closer the approach to sphericity and the lower the dipole moment, the more easily the molecule will rotate. Thus solid methane (CH_4), which is a symmetrical non-polar molecule, rotates quite freely in the solid state,[10] and the molecules in solid hydrogen rotate so freely that the Raman lines of gaseous H_2 are found at nearly the same frequencies in the solid phase.[11] In less symmetrical molecules such as HCl and H_2O, at high temperatures there appear to be several stable orientations for each molecule in the solid, and a molecule will change direction from one stable orientation to another in a time which is called the relaxation time.

The dielectric constant of solid H_2S as a function of temperature is shown in Fig. 7.9. The principal feature of the curve is the sharp increase in the dielectric constant as the temperature is lowered and the sudden drop below 105°K which is thought to mark the transition to an ordered state in which the directions of the H_2S molecules are

[9] H. Fröhlich, Trans. Faraday Soc. **44**, 238 (1948).

[10] For an account of the nuclear resonance experiments from which supporting evidence is derived, see N. L. Alpert, Phys. Rev. **75**, 398 (1949).

[11] L. Pauling, Phys. Rev. **36**, 430 (1930). It is not possible to determine the position of hydrogen atoms in a crystal by using x-rays, because of the low scattering power of hydrogen. Neutron diffraction is a possible tool, especially if deuterium is substituted for hydrogen. The transition in ND_4Cl has been investigated by neutron diffraction by H. A. Levy and S. W. Peterson, Phys. Rev. **86**, 766 (1952).

"frozen" in a regular array whose nature has not yet been determined. The behavior of the dielectric constant above the transition temperature is suggestive of free rotation, but we can show that a similar variation with temperature arises even when there are only a discrete number of allowed orientations for each dipole.

Suppose, for example, that a dipole of moment p has two allowed directions, (a) parallel and (b) antiparallel to the applied field E.

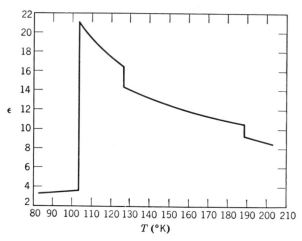

Fig. 7.9. Dielectric constant temperature curve of solid hydrogen sulfide at 5 kc/sec. [After Smyth and Hitchcock, J. Am. Chem. Soc. **56**, 1084 (1934).]

We emphasize that this restriction in orientation is imagined to follow from steric or geometrical hindrances in the solid and not from quantization. Magnetic moments are quantized through their association with angular momenta; electric moments in molecules are not thus associated. The ratio of the occupation numbers of the two sites will be, using the Boltzmann distribution function,

$$N_A/N_B = e^{2Ep/kT},$$

so that the fractional excess oriented parallel to the field is, writing $x = Ep/kT$,

$$(7.33) \qquad \frac{N_A - N_B}{N_A + N_B} = \frac{e^x - e^{-x}}{e^x + e^{-x}} = \tanh x \cong x,$$

provided that $Ep/kT \ll 1$. If there are N molecules per unit volume, the polarization will be, in this approximation,

$$(7.34) \qquad P = Npx = Np^2E/kT,$$

which is, apart from a numerical factor, identical with the result (7.27) derived for freely rotating dipoles.

DIPOLE RELAXATION AND DIELECTRIC LOSSES

The principal part of the difference between the low frequency dielectric constant and the high frequency dielectric constant as measured by the square of the optical refractive index may be attributed to the damping out or relaxation of the orientational contribution to the

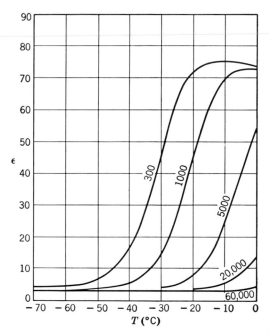

Fig. 7.10.   Variation of the dielectric constant of ice with temperature and frequency, in cycles per second. [After Smyth and Hitchcock, J. Am. Chem. Soc. **54**, 4631 (1932).]

dielectric constant.   We introduce the concept of *relaxation time* as the time interval characterizing the restoration of a disturbed system to its equilibrium configuration; the relaxation frequency is defined as the reciprocal of the relaxation time.   In inhomogeneous dielectrics the Maxwell-Wagner interfacial polarization mechanism discussed in Problem 7.7 leads to another type of relaxation which we shall not go into here.   The orientational relaxation frequencies vary over a wide range and may be strongly dependent on the temperature.   In water at room temperature, relaxation occurs at about 3×10^{10} cps, corresponding to a wavelength for electromagnetic radiation of 1 cm.   In ice at $-20°C$ we see from Fig. 7.10 that the relaxation frequency is of the order of 1 kc.

DEBYE RELAXATION TIME

Debye[12] has given an elegant discussion of dielectric relaxation in polar liquids and in solutions of polar molecules in non-polar solvents; his central result is that the orientational part of the polarizability depends on frequency as

(7.35)
$$\alpha = \frac{\alpha_0}{1 + i\omega\tau},$$

where τ is the relaxation time and α_0 is the static orientational polarizability. Debye has suggested further that in liquids the relaxation time is related to the viscosity η by the approximate relation

(7.36)
$$\tau = 4\pi\eta a^3/kT,$$

where a is the radius of the molecule, which is supposed to be spherical. For water at room temperature we obtain $\tau \approx 10^{-11}$ sec, using $a \approx 10^{-8}$ cm and $\eta = 0.01$ poise, giving a relaxation frequency in approximate agreement with the experimental measurements on water. The form of the expression (7.36) for the relaxation time may be understood by making the plausible supposition that the relaxation frequency $\omega_0 = 1/\tau$ is marked by the approximate equality of the thermal rotational energy kT and the work done against the frictional torque in rotation through 1 radian. According to Stokes the frictional torque is $8\pi\eta a^3\omega$, whence the work done by the frictional torque acting for 1 radian is $8\pi\eta a^3\omega$. Setting this equal to kT for $\omega = \omega_0$, we have

$$\tau \equiv 1/\omega_0 \cong 8\pi\eta a^3/kT,$$

in approximate agreement with (7.36). The idea underlying this discussion is that the thermal energy is insufficient to rotate the molecule against the viscous resistance when ω exceeds ω_0.

RELAXATION IN SOLIDS

Following Debye, we may make a crude model of dielectric relaxation in dipolar solids by supposing that each molecule of the solid carries a permanent electric moment p which can be oriented in two directions, parallel (1) or antiparallel (2) to the field E. These orientations do not arise through quantization, but through the arrangement

[12] P. Debye, *Polar molecules*, Chemical Catalog Co., New York, 1929, Chapter V. For a discussion of the transition from resonance to relaxation-type behavior, see J. H. Van Vleck and V. F. Weisskopf, Revs. Modern Phys. **17**, 227 (1945).

of molecules in the solid. One consequence of the calculation is to demonstrate that α will have a $1/T$ temperature dependence for a two-orientation model just as for the continuous-orientation model considered earlier. We suppose that there are n_1, n_2 molecules in the two groups at a given time and that the probability that a particle in group 1 makes a transition to group 2 in time δt is $w_{12}\,\delta t$, while the probability of the reverse process is $w_{21}\,\delta t$. Then

(7.37)
$$dn_1/dt = -w_{12}n_1 + w_{21}n_2;$$
$$dn_2/dt = w_{12}n_1 - w_{21}n_2.$$

For equilibrium $dn_1/dt = dn_2/dt = 0$; therefore we must have

(7.38)
$$n_1/n_2 = w_{21}/w_{12}.$$

However, in equilibrium n_1 and n_2 must satisfy the Boltzmann distribution, and so

(7.39)
$$n_1 = A e^{pE/kT}; \qquad n_2 = A e^{-pE/kT},$$

where A is a constant. According to (7.38) it is reasonable to take

(7.40)
$$w_{12} = (1/2\tau)e^{-pE/kT}; \qquad w_{21} = (1/2\tau)e^{pE/kT}.$$

Taking $pE \ll kT$, we have from (7.37) and (7.40)

(7.41)
$$2\tau(dn_1/dt) = -(n_1 - n_2) + (pE/kT)(n_1 + n_2);$$
$$2\tau(dn_2/dt) = (n_1 - n_2) - (pE/kT)(n_1 + n_2).$$

If E varies with time as $e^{i\omega t}$, the equations (7.41) are seen to have the solution

(7.42)
$$n_1 - n_2 = \frac{(n_1 + n_2)}{1 + i\omega\tau}\frac{pE}{kT},$$

and so τ as introduced in (7.40) plays the part of a relaxation time. If there are N molecules per unit volume, the polarizability is given by

(7.43)
$$N\alpha = \frac{P}{E} = \frac{p(n_1 - n_2)}{E} = \frac{Np^2}{kT}\cdot\frac{1}{1 + i\omega\tau},$$

of essentially the same form as (7.35).

The relaxation times in solids are usually much longer than in liquids. This behavior is somewhat parallel to the behavior of diffusion rates in liquids and solids. Breckenridge[13] has related the observed dielec-

---

[13] R. G. Breckenridge, in *Imperfections in nearly perfect crystals*, edited by Shockley, Hollomon, Maurer, and Seitz, John Wiley & Sons, New York, 1952.

tric losses in alkali halide crystals to the presence of lattice defects in the crystals, with considerable success.

COMPLEX DIELECTRIC CONSTANTS AND THE LOSS ANGLE

In the presence of relaxation effects the dielectric constant may conveniently be written as complex. For a polarizability

$$\alpha = \frac{\alpha_0}{1 + i\omega\tau}$$

the dielectric constant is, taking the local field as equal to the applied field,

$$\epsilon = \epsilon_1 - i\epsilon_2 = 1 + \frac{4\pi\alpha_0 N}{1 + i\omega\tau}$$

$$= 1 + \frac{4\pi\alpha_0 N}{1 + \omega^2\tau^2} - i\,\frac{4\pi\alpha_0\omega\tau N}{1 + \omega^2\tau^2},$$

so

$$(7.44) \quad \epsilon_1 = \Re(\epsilon) = 1 + \frac{4\pi\alpha_0 N}{1 + \omega^2\tau^2}; \qquad \epsilon_2 = -\mathcal{I}(\epsilon) = \frac{4\pi\alpha_0\omega\tau N}{1 + \omega^2\tau^2};$$

where $\Re$ and $\mathcal{I}$ denote real and imaginary parts, respectively. The variation of ϵ_1 and ϵ_2 with frequency is shown in Fig. 7.11.

The power dissipation per unit volume $\mathcal{P}$ is given by

$$(7.45) \qquad\qquad \mathcal{P} = j_p E,$$

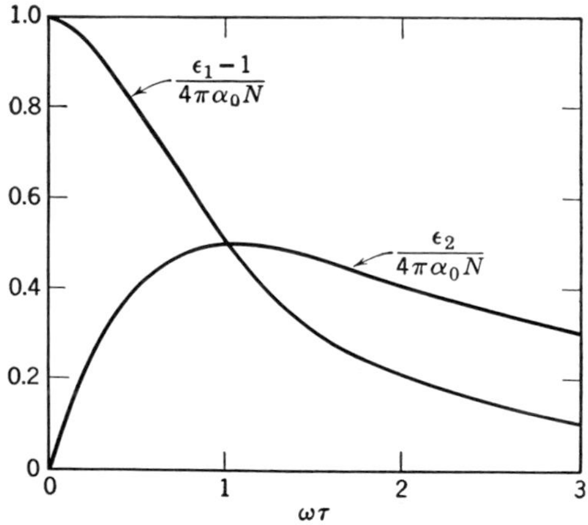

Fig. 7.11. Frequency dependence of real and imaginary parts of the dielectric constant $\epsilon = \epsilon_1 - i\epsilon_2$, for a relaxation mechanism.

where j_p is the component of the current density which is in phase with E. We have

$$(7.46) \qquad j = \sigma E + \frac{1}{4\pi} \frac{\partial D}{\partial t} = \left(\sigma + \frac{i\omega\epsilon}{4\pi} \right) E,$$

which, for $\sigma = 0$ and $\epsilon = \epsilon_1 - i\epsilon_2$, becomes

$$j = \left(\frac{\epsilon_2\omega}{4\pi} + \frac{i\epsilon_1\omega}{4\pi} \right) E,$$

so that the power dissipation is

$$(7.47) \qquad \mathcal{P} = \frac{E^2}{4\pi} \omega\epsilon_2 = \frac{\epsilon_1 E^2}{4\pi} \omega \tan \delta,$$

where the *loss angle* or *power factor* is defined as

$$(7.48) \qquad \tan \delta = \epsilon_2/\epsilon_1.$$

The Q *factor* of a system is defined as

$$(7.49) \qquad Q = \frac{\text{maximum stored energy}}{\text{average energy loss per radian}},$$

which in the dielectric case reduces to

$$(7.50) \qquad Q = \frac{\epsilon_1 E_0{}^2/8\pi}{(\epsilon_1 \overline{E^2}/4\pi) \tan \delta} = \frac{1}{\tan \delta},$$

where we have used the fact that the average value of E^2 over a cycle is $E_0{}^2/2$, the amplitude being E_0.

Values of ϵ and $\tan \delta$ for several insulating materials at a frequency of 25,000 mc are given in Table 7.3. An excellent compilation of dielectric data between 100 cps and 2.5×10^{10} cps has been made by von Hippel.[14]

TABLE 7.3.   DIELECTRIC CONSTANT AND POWER FACTOR VALUES
AT 25,000 MC

Material	ϵ_1	$\tan \delta$
Polystyrene	2.55	0.0012
Lucite	2.57	0.0032
Paraffin wax	2.26	0.0001
Lead glass	6.8	0.009
Ebonite	2.73	0.0038
Teflon		0.0006
Polyethylene		0.0006
Fused quartz		0.00025

[14] A. R. von Hippel, editor, *Dielectric materials and applications*, John Wiley & Sons, New York, 1954.

PROBLEMS

7.1. (a) Show that the expression (7.14) applied to the first Bohr orbit of the hydrogen atom gives $\alpha = a_H{}^3$, where a_H is the Bohr radius. (b) Consider a semi-classical model of the ground state of the hydrogen atom in an electric field normal to the plane of the orbit, and show that for this model $\alpha = a_H{}^3$. *Note:* If the applied field is in the x direction, then the x component of the field of the nucleus at the displaced position of the electron orbit must be equal to the applied field. The correct quantum-mechanical result is larger than this by the factor $\frac{9}{2}$.

7.2. In the local field problem the cavity need not be chosen as spherical, but may be of any shape possessing at least cubic symmetry. We may for example take the cavity as a cube with a face normal parallel to the polarization. In this case the polarization charge density on the upper and lower faces of the cube is uniform and equal to $\pm P$, while the other faces do not carry any charge. Show that, for this cavity, $E_2 = 4\pi P/3$, just as for the spherical cavity.

7.3. For light of frequency ω show that the classical expression for the polariza-bility of a single electron bound to a nucleus is

$$\alpha = \frac{e^2/m}{\omega_0{}^2 - \omega^2},$$

where ω_0 is the resonance frequency of the electron.

7.4. Show that the polarizability of a conducting metallic sphere of radius a is $\alpha = a^3$; this result is most easily obtained by noting that $E = 0$ inside the sphere and then using the depolarization factor. This result gives values of α of the order of magnitude of the observed polarizabilities of atoms. A lattice of N conducting spheres per unit volume has dielectric constant $\epsilon = 1 + 4\pi Na^3$, for $Na^3 \ll 1$; this result has been used in the construction of artificial dielectrics for use in microwave lenses [W. E. Kock, Bell System Tech. J. **27**, 58 (1948)].

7.5. Show that the dielectric constant at frequency ω of a medium containing N free electrons per unit volume is

$$\epsilon = 1 - (4\pi Ne^2/m\omega^2).$$

The presence of the mass in the denominator suggests that we may neglect the contribution of the positive ions present. We suppose, following C. G. Darwin [Proc. Roy. Soc. (London) **A146**, 17 (1934); **A151**, 512 (1935)], that the local field in this case is equal to the applied field E_0. The index of refraction for x-rays is commonly slightly less than unity, e.g., for calcite at 1.54 A, $n - 1 = -8.8 \times 10^{-6}$.

7.6. Using the result of Problem 7.5 discuss the effect of negative values of ϵ on the propagation of electromagnetic waves. We define the cut-off frequency as that for which $\epsilon = 0$; calculate the value of N for a cut-off frequency of 30 mc, and show that the cut-off frequency for metallic sodium would be 1.4×10^{15} cps if there is one free electron present for each sodium atom, in close agreement with the experimental values [R. W. Wood, Phys. Rev. **44**, 353 (1933)].

7.7. Show that a parallel-plate condenser made up of two parallel layers of material, one layer with dielectric constant ϵ, zero conductivity, and thickness d, and the other layer with $\epsilon = 0$ for convenience, finite conductivity σ, and thickness qd, behaves as if the space between the condenser plates were filled with a homogeneous dielectric with dielectric constant

$$\epsilon^* = \frac{\epsilon(1 + q)}{1 + (i\epsilon\omega q/4\pi\sigma)},$$

where ω is the angular frequency [K. W. Wagner, Arch. Elecktrotech. **2,** 371 (1914)]. Values of ϵ as high as 10^4 or 10^5, caused largely by the Maxwell-Wagner mechanism, are sometimes found, but the high values are always accompanied by large losses. An analysis of the dielectric properties of a nickel zinc ferrite is given by C. G. Koops, Phys. Rev. **83,** 121 (1951).

REFERENCES

R. Becker, *Theorie der Elektrizität*, Teubner, Leipzig and Berlin, 6th ed., Vol. II, 1933.

C. J. F. Böttcher, *Theory of electric polarisation*, Elsevier, Amsterdam, 1952.

P. Debye, *Polar molecules*, Chemical Catalog Co., New York, 1929.

Dielectrics conference, Ann. N.Y. Acad. Sci. **40,** 289–481 (1940).

Dielectrics discussion, Trans. Faraday Soc. **42A** (1946).

H. Fröhlich, *Theory of dielectrics: dielectric constant and dielectric loss*, Clarendon Press, Oxford, 1949.

R. J. W. Le Fèvre, *Dipole moments*, Methuen and Co., London, 3rd ed., 1953.

L. Rosenfeld, *Theory of electrons*, Interscience Publishers, New York, 1951.

C. P. Smyth, *Dielectric behavior and structure*, McGraw-Hill, New York, 1955.

J. H. Van Vleck, *Theory of electric and magnetic susceptibilities*, Clarendon Press, Oxford, 1932.

A. R. von Hippel, *Dielectrics and waves*, John Wiley & Sons, New York, 1954.

A. R. von Hippel, editor, *Dielectric materials and applications*, John Wiley & Sons, New York, 1954.

8

Ferroelectric Crystals

A ferroelectric crystal is defined as a crystal which exhibits a spontaneous electric dipole moment; in other words, a crystal for which even in the absence of an applied electric field the center of positive charge does not coincide with the center of negative charge. It can be shown that it is a necessary, but not sufficient, condition for ferroelectricity that the crystal lack a center of symmetry. All ferroelectrics will be piezoelectric, but not all piezoelectrics will be ferroelectric (e.g., quartz). The occurrence of ferroelectricity is generally interpreted to be the result of a polarization catastrophe as treated in the preceding chapter; we discuss this at greater length below.

After a ferroelectric crystal is polarized in a given direction, the action of the polarization outside the crystal is gradually neutralized by the collection on the crystal surface of free charges from the atmosphere and by conduction within the crystal. In a number of substances the polarization appears to have a very high coercive force— the direction of the spontaneous polarization may not be changed by an electric field of the maximum intensity which it is possible to apply without causing electrical breakdown of the crystal. We are often able to observe the spontaneous moment in these substances only when they are heated, as raising the temperature changes the value of the polarization. Thus crystals, such as tourmaline, which develop an observable spontaneous electric moment only on heating are called *pyroelectric*, while crystals with a lower coercive force, such that the direction of the spontaneous moment can be altered by an electric field, are called *ferroelectric* and often have very high dielectric constants.

ELECTRETS

There is another class of substances known as *electrets*, discovered by Eguchi in 1925, which may display "permanent" electric moments. Electrets are produced by the solidification of mixtures of certain organic waxes in a strong electric field. Some of the wax molecules

182

carry permanent dipole moments; they are oriented by the electric field, and frozen in their orientation by the solidification. The moments produced in this way may persist for several years, yet it is generally believed that the polarized state of an electret is only metastable, and that the stable state would be unpolarized. We shall not consider electrets here; for a review of their properties the reader is referred to a paper by Gutmann.[1]

CLASSIFICATION OF FERROELECTRIC CRYSTALS

We list in Table 8.1 some of the crystals which are commonly considered ferroelectric, along with the transition (Curie) temperature T_c at which the crystal changes from the low temperature polarized state to the high temperature unpolarized state. Rochelle salt has both an upper and a lower Curie point, between which the crystal is ferroelectric. The maximum value of the spontaneous polarization P_s is listed where known. It is useful in converting units to recall that $P(\text{esu})$ is obtained by multiplying $P(\mu\text{coul}/\text{cm}^2)$ by 3×10^3 and by multiplying $P(\text{coul}/\text{m}^2)$ by 3×10^5.

The crystals considered in the table may be classified into several quite natural groups. First there is Rochelle salt[2] and the associated isomorphous salts. Rochelle salt is a quite complicated crystal, and little progress has been made toward understanding its behavior on a microscopic basis, although Mueller[3] and others have formulated a phenomenological theory which correlates a number of experimental facts. It seems possible that the ferroelectric behavior of Rochelle salt is connected intimately with the action of the molecules of water of hydration in the crystal. This is suggested by the observation that the substitution of D_2O for H_2O changes the range in which the crystal is ferroelectric from 41.7°C for the ordinary Rochelle salt to 57°C for the deuterated salt,[4] which is quite a large effect. It may be noted, however, that the observed spontaneous polarization 800 esu is considerably less than the polarization which would result from the parallel orientation of all the water molecules; there are 1.52×10^{22} of these per cubic centimeter, and the moment per molecule is 1.85×10^{-18} esu (in the vapor), corresponding to a polarization of 28,000 esu, while the observed spontaneous polarization is only 800 esu.

[1] F. Gutmann, Revs. Modern Phys. **20**, 457 (1948).

[2] Discovered by J. Valasek, Phys. Rev. **17**, 475 (1921); for summary of properties see H. Mueller, Ann. N.Y. Acad. Sci. **40**, 321 (1940).

[3] H. Mueller, Phys. Rev. **57**, 829 (1940); **58**, 565 (1940).

[4] Holden, Kohman, Mason, and Morgan, Phys. Rev. **56**, 378 (1939); J. Hablützel, Helv. Phys. Acta. **12**, 489 (1939).

184 FERROELECTRIC CRYSTALS

The second group of ferroelectric crystals consists of crystals with hydrogen bonds in which the motion of the protons is specifically connected with the ferroelectric properties; the group comprises potassium dihydrogen phosphate[5] (KH_2PO_4) and the isomorphous salts. The behavior of the deuterated crystal strongly suggests the hydrogen atoms are of central importance:

	KH_2PO_4	KD_2PO_4	KH_2AsO_4	KD_2AsO_4
Curie temperature	123°K	213°K	96°K	162°K
Saturation polarization	16,000 esu	27,000 esu		

TABLE 8.1. DATA ON CRYSTALS REPORTED TO BE FERROELECTRIC
(excluding mixed crystals)

(Compiled in part from a tabulation by Walter J. Merz)

Crystal	Structure	T_c(°K)	P_s(esu) at room temp.
$NaK(C_4H_4O_6)\cdot4H_2O$	complex	297 (upper	800
(Rochelle salt)		255 (lower)	
$NaK(C_4H_2D_2O_6)\cdot4D_2O$		308 (upper)	1,100
		251 (lower)	
$LiNH_4(C_4H_4O_6)\cdot H_2O$		106	630
KH_2PO_4	complex	123	16,000
KD_2PO_4		213	27,000
RbH_2PO_4		147	
RbH_2AsO_4		111	
KH_2AsO_4		96.5	
KD_2AsO_4		162	
CsH_2PO_4		160	
CsH_2AsO_4		143	
CsD_2AsO_4		212	
$BaTiO_3$	perovskite	380	78,000
$KTaO_3$	perovskite		
$NaTaO_3$	perovskite		
$KNbO_3$	perovskite	708	80,000
$PbTiO_3$	perovskite	763	
$LiTaO_3$	ilmenite		70,000(425°C)
$LiNbO_3$	ilmenite		
WO_3	modified	(220)(?)	
	perovskite		
$Cd_2Nb_2O_7$	pyrochlorite	185	5,400(100°K)
$C(NH_2)_3Al(SO_4)_2\cdot6H_2O$	complex		1,050
$C(NH_2)_3Cr(SO_4)_2$			1,000
$C(NH_2)_3Ga(SO_4)_2$			1,000
$C(NH_2)_3Al(SeO_4)_2$			1,350
$C(NH_2)_3Cr(SeO_4)_2$			1,400

The substitution of deuterons for protons nearly doubles both T_c and P_s, although the fractional change in the molecular weight of the com-

[5] G. Busch and P. Scherrer, Naturwiss. **23,** 737 (1935).

pound is less than 2%.   This is an extraordinarily large isotope effect, which has been discussed by Pirenne[6] in terms of the motion of the protons and deuterons in a square-well potential between two oxygen ions of different phosphate radicals.

The third group of ferroelectrics consists of ionic crystals with crystal structures closely related to the perovskite and ilmenite structures. The perovskite structure is the simplest crystal structure (Figs. 8.1

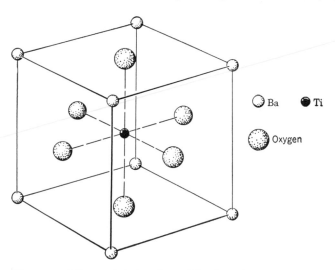

Fig. 8.1.   The perovskite crystal structure of barium titanate.   The structure is cubic, with Ba^{2+} ions at the cube corners, O^{2-} ions at the face centers, and a Ti^{4+} ion at the body center.   Below the Curie temperature the structure is slightly deformed with respect to that described here.   The prototype crystal is calcium titanate (perovskite).

and 8.2) to exhibit ferroelectricity, and we shall devote the rest of this chapter primarily to barium titanate,[7] which has this structure and is the crystal in the third group about which most experimental and theoretical information is available.   The name perovskite applies to the

[6] J. Pirenne, Physica **15**, 1019 (1949).   A detailed theory of the transition of potassium dihydrogen phosphate in terms of hydrogen bonds is given by J. C. Slater, J. Chem. Phys. **9**, 16 (1941); see also S. Yomosa and T. Nagamiya, Prog. Theor. Phys. **4**, 263 (1949); T. Nagamiya, Prog. Theor. Phys. **7**, 275 (1952). Neutron diffraction studies of the crystal structure are reported by B. C. Frazer and R. Pepinsky, Acta Cryst. **6**, 273 (1953); R. S. Pease and G. E. Bacon, Nature **173**, 443 (1954); Proc. Roy. Soc. (London) **A220**, 397 (1953).

[7] Discovered independently in various countries during World War II; for general discussions of the properties see B. Wul, J. Phys. (U.S.S.R.) **10**, 95 (1946), and A. von Hippel, Revs. Modern Phys. **22**, 221 (1950).

mineral $CaTiO_3$. The ilmenite structure, named from the mineral $FeTiO_3$, is quite complicated and we shall not discuss it here.[8]   The last entries in the table are guanadine compounds; little is known of the ferroelectric mechanism in them.

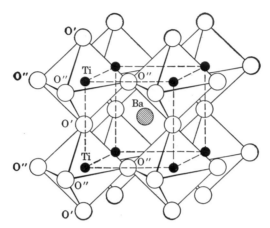

Fig. 8.2.   The $BaTiO_3$ structure, showing the octahedra of oxygen atoms about the titanium atoms.   For later application the oxygen atoms on the lines joining nearest neighbor titanium atoms are labeled O'.

THEORY OF BARIUM TITANATE

We consider first the general order of magnitude of the ferroelectric effects in barium titanate.   It is observed that barium titanate has at room temperature a saturation polarization of 78,000 esu.   As the volume of a unit cube is $(4 \times 10^{-8})^3$ cm^3, the dipole moment per unit cube is 5×10^{-18} esu.   If, for example, all the polarization were caused by a displacement of the central Ti^{4+} ion, we should require a displacement of $5 \times 10^{-18}/4(4.8 \times 10^{-10}) \approx 0.26 \times 10^{-8}$ cm, which seems fairly large.

We suppose that the Curie point is determined approximately by the interaction energy of a dipole with the local internal electric field caused by the polarization itself.   The interaction energy is $-\frac{1}{2}(\mathbf{p} \cdot \mathbf{E})$; as E will be of the order of $-P_s$, the interaction energy is of the order of $\frac{1}{2}(5 \times 10^{-18})(8 \times 10^4) = 2 \times 10^{-13}$ ergs.   We obtain the approximate transition temperature by setting the interaction energy equal to kT_c, giving $T_c \approx (2 \times 10^{-13})/(1.4 \times 10^{-16}) \approx 1400°K$, appreciably higher than the observed 380°K.

---

[8] A theoretical discussion of local electric fields in the ilmenite structure has been given by H. C. Schweinler, Phys. Rev. **87**, 5 (1952).

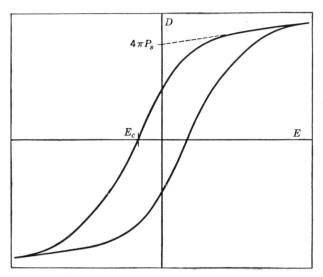

Fig. 8.3. Hysteresis loop in ferroelectric specimen, showing spontaneous polarization P_s and coercive field E_c. In barium titanate the value of $4\pi P_s$ may be of the order of 3×10^8 v/cm, and E_c of the order of 10^3 v/cm.

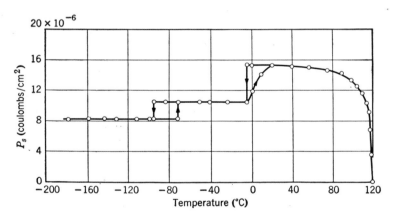

Fig. 8.4. Spontaneous polarization of barium titanate as a function of temperature. The discontinuities near 0°C and −80°C are caused by small changes in the crystal structure. The changes of the polarization measured along a cube edge at these two transition points is consistent with the assumption that the direction of spontaneous polarization, which is parallel to a cube edge above 0°C, becomes parallel to a face diagonal below 0°C and parallel to a body diagonal below −80°C, as the ratios of the P_s at the transition temperatures are approximately $1:1/2^{\frac{1}{2}}:1/3^{\frac{1}{2}}$. [After W. J. Merz, Phys. Rev. **76**, 1221 (1949); for more recent measurements between 20° and 110°C, see W. J. Merz, Phys. Rev. **91**, 513 (1953).]

The most striking indication of ferroelectricity in barium titanate is provided by the hysteresis loops of the form shown in Fig. 8.3 as observed at temperatures below the transition temperature, 107°C; at temperatures above the transition the loop reduces to a straight line.   The spontaneous polarization as a function of temperature is shown in Fig. 8.4.   It is found by x-ray methods that the crystal structure becomes slightly deformed in the direction of the spontaneous

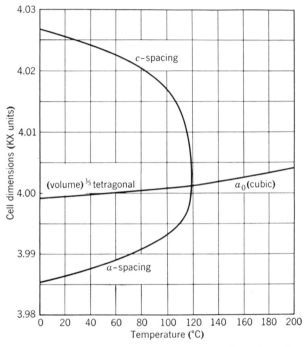

Fig. 8.5.   Cell dimensions of barium titanate as a function of temperature. [After H. D. Megaw, Proc. Roy. Soc. (London) **A189**, 261 (1947).]

polarization, and in the region between 0°C and 107°C the polarization is parallel to a side of the unit cube of the crystal structure, and so the crystal is elongated in this direction, which is called the c axis, and shortened in the directions of the a axes at right angles to the direction of the polarization (Fig. 8.5).   The dielectric constant is usually very much larger when measured perpendicular to the c axis than when measured parallel to it (Fig. 8.6).

THE POLARIZATION CATASTROPHE IN FERROELECTRICS

The occurrence of ferroelectricity in barium titanate is believed to be the result of a polarization catastrophe in which the local electric fields arising from the polarization itself increase faster than the elastic restoring forces on the ions in the crystal, thereby leading ultimately to an asymmetrical shift in ionic positions; the shift is limited to a finite displacement by the onset of anharmonic restoring forces. The occurrence of ferroelectricity in an appreciable number of crystals with the perovskite structure suggests that this structure is in some way favorably disposed to the production of a polarizability catas-

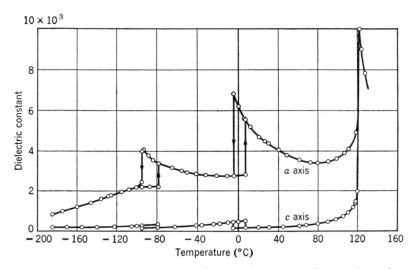

Fig. 8.6. Initial dielectric constants of barium titanate, parallel (c axis) and perpendicular (a axis) to the direction of the spontaneous polarization at room temperature. [After W. J. Merz, Phys. Rev. **76**, 1221 (1949); it is not known why ϵ_c and ϵ_a do not coincide below $-80°C$, as they should by symmetry; it is possible that an anisotropic domain and impurity pattern related to the growth habit of the crystal has frozen in.]

trophe; this suggestion is supported by the fact that the hexagonal modification of barium titanate is not ferroelectric, while the cubic (perovskite) form is ferroelectric. Calculations by Slater[9] and others have made clear the physical reason for the favored position of the perovskite structure. We give first the simple form of the catastrophe theory, supposing that the Lorentz factors are all $4\pi/3$. The theory given now assumes implicitly that the transition is a second order transition, but the physical ideas involved can be carried over in part to a first order transition.

[9] J. C. Slater, Phys. Rev. **78**, 748 (1950).

We may rewrite (7.10) in the form

$$(8.1) \qquad \epsilon = \frac{1 + \dfrac{8\pi}{3} \Sigma\, N_i\alpha_i}{1 - \dfrac{4\pi}{3} \Sigma\, N_i\alpha_i},$$

where α_i is the polarizability of an ion of type i, and N_i the number of ions i per unit volume, noting that the numerical factors multiplying $\Sigma\, N_i\alpha_i$ are the consequence of the use of the Lorentz local field $E + (4\pi/3)P$. It is seen that the dielectric constant becomes infinite, corresponding to a finite polarization for zero applied field, when $\Sigma\, N_i\alpha_i = (4\pi/3)^{-1}$, and for this reason the polarization catastrophe is commonly known as the "$4\pi/3$ catastrophe." Onsager's objection to the Lorentz field, cited in the last chapter, applies only to the fields produced by permanent dipoles and not to the induced moments with which we are now concerned.

We note that the value of ϵ is sensitive to small departures of $\Sigma\, N_i\alpha_i$ from the critical value $3/4\pi$; if we write

$$(8.2) \qquad (4\pi/3)\, \Sigma\, N_i\alpha_i = 1 - s,$$

where $s \ll 1$, we have

$$(8.3) \qquad \epsilon \cong 3/s.$$

If we suppose that near the critical temperature the value of s varies with temperature in a linear fashion,

$$(8.4) \qquad s \cong \beta(T - T_c),$$

where β is a constant, we have above the transition temperature a Curie-Weiss law for the dielectric constant:

$$(8.5) \qquad \epsilon \cong \frac{3/\beta}{T - T_c},$$

which is of the form of the observed temperature variation, as shown in Figs. 8.7 and 8.9:

$$(8.6) \qquad \epsilon \approx \frac{10^5}{T - T_c}.$$

If the ferroelectric state were the result of the dipolar interactions of freely rotating molecules bearing permanent moments, we should have, from (7.30),

$$(8.7) \qquad \epsilon \approx \frac{3T_c}{T - T_c};$$

the numerator $3T_c \approx 1200°K$ is two orders of magnitude smaller than the observed value of 10^5 in expression (8.6); this failure is a fairly strong indication, entirely apart from the x-ray evidence, that we are

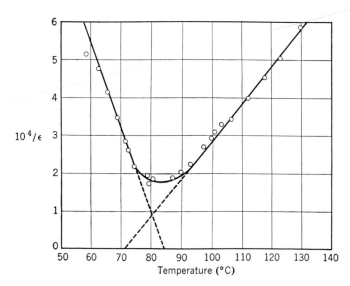

Fig. 8.7. Plot of reciprocal of the dielectric constant of barium titanate vs. temperature. [After B. Wul, J. Phys. (U.S.S.R.) **10**, 95 (1946); it is not known why Wul's Curie point is 40° below that reported by other workers, but one might infer that substantial quantities of impurities were present; the impurities appear to have affected the nature of the phase transition, making it appear to be a second order transition. More recent work, as shown in Fig. 8.8, suggests that the transition is actually first order.]

not concerned in barium titanate with the orientation of molecules bearing permanent dipole moments.

To account for the large value of the numerator observed in (8.6) we note that

$$(8.8) \qquad \beta = ds/dT = (4\pi/3) \Sigma \, [N_i(d\alpha_i/dT) + (dN_i/dT)\alpha_i];$$

now as N_i is the number of ions i per unit volume, the temperature coefficient $N_i^{-1}(dN_i/dT)$ will be of the order of magnitude of the volume expansion coefficient, which is $\approx 10^{-5}$ in barium titanate; the temperature coefficient of polarizability in ionic crystals is known to be of this same order of magnitude, so that β may reasonably be of the order of 10^{-5} as suggested by the observed variation of ϵ. This argument is probably oversimplified.

The refractive index of barium titanate is 2.4; we estimate the electronic contribution to the polarizability from the relation

$$(8.9) \qquad \frac{n^2 - 1}{n^2 + 2} = \frac{4\pi}{3} \sum N_i \alpha_i \text{ (electronic)},$$

according to (7.11). Using Slater's values $\alpha(\text{Ba}) = 1.95 \times 10^{-24}$ cm^3; $\alpha(\text{O}) = 2.4 \times 10^{-24}$ cm^3; $\alpha(\text{Ti}) = 0.19 \times 10^{-24}$ cm^3, we find that $(4\pi/3) \sum N_i \alpha_i(\text{electronic}) = 0.61$, so that a contribution of $1 - 0.61 = 0.39$ would be required from the ionic polarizabilities in order to explain the occurrence of a ferroelectric state. The value of $\alpha(\text{O})$ is selected to fit the observed refractive index. We saw earlier that, even if all the spontaneous polarization arose from the ionic displacement of the titanium ion in the center of each cube, a displacement of 0.26×10^{-8} cm would be required. There is nothing inherently unreasonable about an assumption that 39% of the total polarizability is ionic except that this is something of an *ad hoc* explanation; it does not give us any indication of why the perovskite structure is prone to ferroelectricity, nor does it suggest why crystals such as rutile (TiO$_2$) with an even higher refractive index $[n = 2.8; (4\pi/3) \sum N_i \alpha_i(\text{electronic}) = 0.70]$ are not ferroelectric. We shall see in the following section that the actual local fields in the perovskite structure act to enhance the effect of the polarizability of the titanium ion by a factor of the order of 5 with respect to the situation where $E + 4\pi P/3$ is the local field.

LOCAL FIELD IN THE PEROVSKITE STRUCTURE

The Lorentz local field $E + 4\pi P/3$ holds for a crystal when all atoms have environments with cubic symmetry. In barium titanate the Ba and Ti ions see a cubic environment, but the O ions do not; there are, for example, only two nearest neighbor Ti ions adjacent to each O ion, so that the environment of the O ions cannot be cubic. It is necessary in this circumstance to derive a generalized form of the Lorentz formula; this has been done by several authors,[9,10] and Slater[9] has actually carried out the calculations for barium titanate.

[10] G. J. Skanavi, Doklady Akad. Nauk S.S.S.R. **59**, 231 (1948); J. H. van Santen and W. Opechowski, Physica **14**, 545 (1948).

How we should go about obtaining an expression for the local field in barium titanate is quite obvious. We set up an expression for the local field at each lattice point as the sum of the applied field and the polarization of the several types of ions. We take the applied field parallel to a particular cube side, which we call the z direction; there are then four types of ions to be considered: Ba, Ti, O', O'', where the O' ions are on lines parallel to the z direction and passing through the Ti ions; the remaining oxygen ions are the O'' ions. We have four simultaneous equations for the polarizations:

$$E(\text{Ba}) = P(\text{Ba})/N(\text{Ba})\alpha(\text{Ba})$$
$$= E_0 + q_{11}P(\text{Ba}) + q_{12}P(\text{Ti}) + q_{13}P(\text{O}') + q_{14}P(\text{O}'');$$
$$E(\text{Ti}) = P(\text{Ti})/N(\text{Ti})\alpha(\text{Ti})$$
$$= E_0 + q_{21}P(\text{Ba}) + q_{22}(\text{Ti}) + q_{23}P(\text{O}') + q_{24}P(\text{O}'');$$

(8.10)

$$E(\text{O}') = P(\text{O}')/N(\text{O}')\alpha(\text{O}')$$
$$= E_0 + q_{31}P(\text{Ba}) + q_{32}P(\text{Ti}) + q_{33}P(\text{O}') + q_{34}P(\text{O}'');$$
$$E(\text{O}'') = P(\text{O}'')/N(\text{O}'')\alpha(\text{O}'')$$
$$= E_0 + q_{41}P(\text{Ba}) + q_{42}P(\text{Ti}) + q_{43}P(\text{O}') + q_{44}P(\text{O}'').$$

The coefficient of the P's are lattice sums for dipole arrays and may be calculated by the methods given by Kornfeld and others,[11] which we discuss at the end of Appendix A. The q's have the following values:

$$q_{11} = q_{22} = q_{21} = q_{12} = q_{33} = 4\pi/3;$$
$$q_{13} = q_{31} = (4\pi/3) - 8.668;$$
$$q_{34} = q_{43} = q_{14} = q_{41} = (4\pi/3) + 4.334$$
$$q_{23} = q_{32} = (4\pi/3) + 30.080$$
$$q_{24} = q_{42} = (4\pi/3) - 15.040$$
$$q_{44} = (4\pi/3) - 4.334$$

It should particularly be noted that the interaction between the Ti and O' ions is especially strong, being $(4\pi/3) + 30.080$, which is approximately 8.2 times the ordinary value, $4\pi/3$. It is this factor

[11] H. Kornfeld, Z. Physik **22**, 27 (1924); L. W. McKeehan, Phys. Rev. **43**, 913 (1933); **72**, 78 (1947); J. M. Luttinger and L. Tisza, Phys. Rev. **70**, 954 (1946); **72**, 257 (1947).

which is responsible for the great enhancement of the field at the central ion of the perovskite structure.[12]

The ferroelectric catastrophe occurs when the determinant of the coefficients of the P's in (8.10) vanishes, as this is the condition that the P's have non-trivial solutions for $E = 0$. We substitute the appropriate polarizabilities as used by Slater:

$$\alpha(\text{Ba}) = 1.95 \times 10^{-24} \text{ cm}^3,$$

$$\alpha(\text{O}') = \alpha(\text{O}'') = 2.4 \times 10^{-24} \text{ cm}^3,$$

$$\alpha(\text{Ti}) = 0.19 \times 10^{-24} + \alpha_i(\text{Ti});$$

here we suppose that the polarizabilities are all electronic except for an ionic contribution $\alpha_i(\text{Ti})$ from the titanium ions. We then determine the value of $\alpha_i(\text{Ti})$ which makes the determinant vanish, and find

$$\alpha_i(\text{Ti}) = 0.95 \times 10^{-24} \text{ cm}^3,$$

and
$$(4\pi/3)N(\text{Ti})\alpha_i(\text{Ti}) = 0.062,$$

as compared with 0.39 on the elementary theory, the magnification of about 6 being caused by the nature of the perovskite lattice. In particular the existence of lines of oxygen and titanium ions in the lattice is favorable for the high magnification, as exhibited explicitly in Problem 8.3.

It is not always valid to superpose ionic and electronic polarizabilities in quite the way we have done here, as Cohen[13] has emphasized.

DIELECTRIC CONSTANTS NEAR THE CURIE POINT

If there are non-linear interactions in the crystal (and there must be if the spontaneous polarization is to be contained at a finite value), we may write formally the polarization as a power series in the local field. We may then invert the series, noting that there cannot be terms in even powers of P because the two ends of the crystal are fully equivalent:

(8.11) $$E_{\text{loc}} = g_1 P + g_2 P^3 + g_3 P^5 + \cdots,$$

where the g's may depend on temperature, and where g_1 is simply

[12] The Ba ions play a very minor role; in fact, in WO_3, which near room temperature is ferroelectric, the lattice sites corresponding to the sites occupied by Ba in barium titanate are left vacant. In the hexagonal modification of barium titanate the Ti-O lines are distorted, thereby reducing the interaction significantly. [J. R. Tessman, Phys. Rev. **83,** 677 (1951).]

[13] M. H. Cohen, Phys. Rev. **84,** 368 (1951).

$(\Sigma\, N_i\alpha_i)^{-1}$. The local field may also be written

(8.12) $E_{loc} = E + fP$,

as it must be directly proportional to the polarization. We have, to terms in P^5,

(8.13) $E = (g_1 - f)P + g_2P^3 + g_3P^5$.

Above the Curie point in sufficiently weak applied fields the polarization will be small, and we may neglect the terms in P^3 and P^5, so that the susceptibility is

(8.14) $\chi(+) = \dfrac{dP}{dE} = \dfrac{1}{g_1 - f}$,

where the $+$ sign denotes that the equation applies above the Curie point.

Below the Curie point the spontaneous polarization in zero field (P_s) is given by the stable solution of (8.13) with E set equal to zero:

$$(g_1 - f)P_s + g_2P_s{}^3 + g_3P_s{}^5 = 0.$$

There are two cases of particular interest:

Case A. $(g_1 - f)$ negative; g_2 positive; g_3 may be neglected.
Then

(8.15) $P_s{}^2 = (f - g_1)/g_2$.

In this case there is a spontaneous polarization as long as $f > g_1$. For a small applied field ΔE, the additional polarization ΔP in the ferroelectric state is given by

$$\Delta E = (g_1 - f)\,\Delta P + 3g_2P_s{}^2\,\Delta P$$
$$= 2(f - g_1)\,\Delta P,$$

and so the susceptibility below the Curie point is

(8.16) $\chi(-) = \dfrac{1}{2(f - g_1)}$.

If we make the quite plausible assumption, similar to (8.4), that the variation of $g_1 - f$ is linear about the Curie point:

$$g_1 - f = \beta(T - T_c);$$

then

$$\chi(+) = \dfrac{1}{\beta(T - T_c)};$$

(8.17) $$\chi(-) = -\frac{1}{2\beta(T - T_c)};$$

therefore the ratio of $d(1/\chi)/dT$ above and below the Curie point is $-1/2$, in generally fair agreement with the experimental results of Wul shown in Fig. 8.7, but disagreeing with measurements on purer material, as in Fig. 8.8. In Fig. 8.9 we show the reciprocal dielectric constant corresponding to the results of Fig. 8.8.

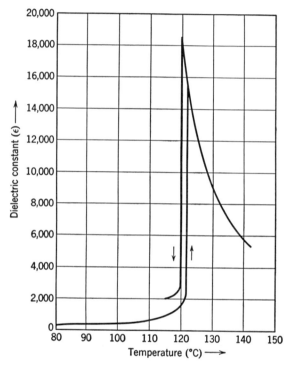

Fig. 8.8.   Dielectric constant of barium titanate vs. temperature. [After M. E. Drougard and D. R. Young, Phys. Rev. **95**, 1152 (1954).]

The reader will find it instructive to study Fig. 8.10 in which the two equations (8.11) and (8.12) are plotted for $E = 0$ to represent the situations above and below the Curie point for case A and also for case B which follows.

Case B. $(g_1 - f)$ positive; g_2 negative; g_3 positive.

The spontaneous polarization is given by a root of

$$(g_1 - f) + g_2 P_s^2 + g_3 P_s^4 = 0,$$

but to obtain the polarization at the transition we must consider the

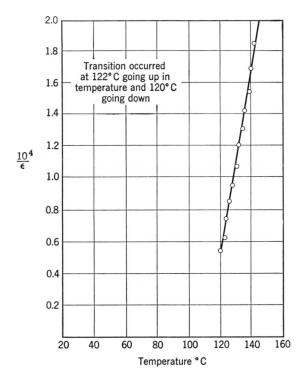

Fig. 8.9.   Reciprocal dielectric constant of barium titanate vs. temperature. (After Drougard and Young.)

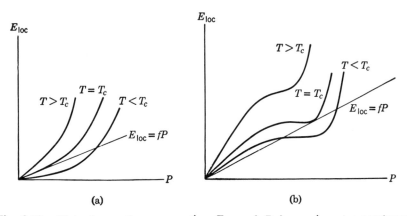

Fig. 8.10.   Plot of equations connecting E_{loc} and P for various temperatures. The intercepts for maximum P determine stable states.   (a) Case A, second order transition; (b) case B, first order transition.

internal potential energy associated with the polarization. As shown in Fig. 8.11, the critical temperature in case B is attained when the depth of the potential energy minima corresponding to a finite polarization is equal to the depth at the center of the well for which the polarization is zero. We should strictly consider the thermodynamic free energy (Appendix R) rather than simply the internal energy in a discussion of this kind, but for elementary textbook purposes the loss in rigor in this particular problem is perhaps more than compensated

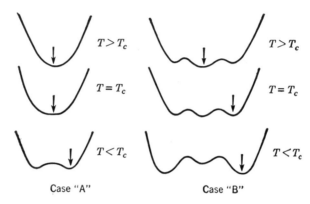

Fig. 8.11. Schematic potential energy wells for the two types of ferroelectric transitions, showing the variation of well shape with temperature.

by the gain in physical insight by speaking in terms of the internal energy. The internal energy associated with the polarization is given according to (F.5) and (8.13) by

$$(8.18) \qquad U_p = \int_0^P E \, dP = \tfrac{1}{2}(g_1 - f)P^2 + \tfrac{1}{4}g_2 P^4 + \tfrac{1}{6}g_3 P^6,$$

so that the Curie point is given by $U_p = 0$, or

$$(g_1 - f) + \tfrac{1}{2}g_2 P_s{}^2(T_c) + \tfrac{1}{3}g_3 P_s{}^4(T_c) = 0;$$

here also, from $E = 0$,

$$(g_1 - f) + g_2 P_s{}^2(T_c) + g_3 P_s{}^4(T_c) = 0,$$

and so

$$P_s{}^2(T_c) = -\frac{3g_2}{4g_3};$$

$$P_s{}^4(T_c) = \frac{3(g_1 - f)}{g_3}.$$

Proceeding in the usual manner, we find for the susceptibility above the Curie point

$$(8.19) \qquad \chi(+) = \frac{1}{g_1 - f},$$

as for case A, with the difference that now $f - g_1$ does not vanish at the Curie point. At the Curie point, but on the low temperature side, we find

$$(8.20) \qquad \chi(-) = \frac{1}{4(g_1 - f)},$$

and so at the Curie point $\chi(+)/\chi(-) = 4$ on this model. The ratio in Fig. 8.8 is higher than 4.

It is plausible to suppose here that we may express the temperature variation of $f - g_1$ approximately in the form

$$g_1 - f = \beta(T - T_0),$$

where T_0 is a parameter to be determined by experiment, but satisfying $T_0 < T_c$. Then

$$(8.21) \qquad \chi(+) = \frac{1}{\beta(T - T_0)} \qquad (T > T_c).$$

The temperature dependences of P_s and $1/\chi$ for the two cases are shown in Fig. 8.12. We note here that it can be shown by standard

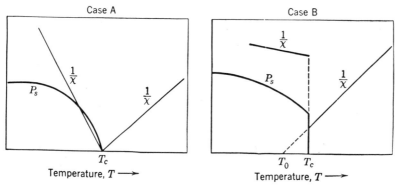

Fig. 8.12. Schematic variation of spontaneous polarization and reciprocal susceptibility for first order (case B) and second order (case A) transitions. The transition in barium titanate is first order, but is close to being second order.

thermodynamic methods that a case A transition does not have a latent heat of transition, but is rather accompanied by a discontinuity in the heat capacity; such a transition is known in thermodynamics as a second order transition; a case B transition is accompanied by a latent heat and is a first order transition. It is likely that ferroelectric transitions in perovskites are first order, but barium titanate probably comes very close to being second order in that T_0 is very close to T_c. The transitions in Rochelle salt and in KH_2PO_4 are probably second order. A good review of the detailed thermodynamic theory of ferroelectrics is given by Devonshire.[14]

FERROELECTRIC DOMAINS

We have seen that a crystal of barium titanate has cubic symmetry above the Curie point and tetragonal symmetry below the Curie point[15]. On cooling a crystal through the Curie point, it is usually found that the entire crystal does not have the same tetragonal axis, but that in one part of the crystal one of the formerly cubic axes has become the tetragonal axis, while in some other region in the crystal another of the cubic axes has become the tetragonal axis. This means that different regions will have different directions of spontaneous polarization. A region within which the spontaneous polarization is in the same direction is called a *domain*. Crystals have been grown which consist entirely of a single domain, and this indeed is expected theoretically to be the stable configuration for a plate-like crystal between condenser plates which are connected. But crystals appear more commonly to grow with inhomogeneous concentrations of impurities leading to mechanical strains in the lattice which may often be reduced by the establishment of a domain structure.

Ferroelectric domains in barium titanate may be observed by optical means, as the crystals are transparent and exhibit different indices of refraction parallel and perpendicular to the tetragonal axis of a domain. In barium titanate the difference of the refractive indices at room temperature is $n_c - n_a = -0.055$. A detailed optical examination of various types of domain structures has been carried out by Forsbergh,[16] and we reproduce Fig. 8.13 from his paper. Schematic domain arrangements are shown in Fig. 8.14.

Merz[17] has studied the kinetics of domain formation and domain wall motions in barium titanate grown as thin flat plates, the normal

[14] A. F. Devonshire, Advances in Physics **3**, 85–130 (1954).

[15] Below 5°C the symmetry changes from tetragonal to orthorhombic, and then near −70°C to trigonal, the crystal remaining ferroelectric.

[16] P. W. Forsbergh, Jr., Phys. Rev. **76**, 1187 (1949); see also W. J. Merz, Phys. Rev. **88**, 421 (1952); E. A. Little, Phys. Rev. **98**, 978 (1955).

[17] W. J. Merz, Phys. Rev. **95**, 690 (1954); this paper contains a discussion of the theory of ferroelectric domains; for application to memory devices, see J. R. Anderson, Am. Inst. Elect. Eng. **71**, 916 (1952).

Fig. 8.13. Wedge-shaped laminar domains in barium titanate single crsytal. (After Forsbergh.)

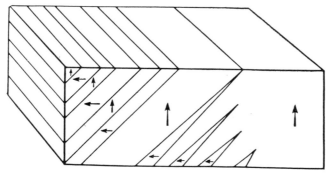

Fig. 8.14. Directions of spontaneous polarization in polydomain barium titanate.

to the plane of the plate being the c or polar direction of the crystal. When the electric field along the c direction is reversed, new domains are formed having opposite polarization. The growth of these domains is rather surprising in view of experience with ferromagnetic materials where domain boundary motion makes a large contribution to the magnetization change, as discussed in Chapter 15. In barium titanate the polarization is changed by the formation of very many new anti-parallel domains which are extremely thin $(10^{-4}$ cm) and appear to grow only in the forward direction. It is likely that the thickness of the wall or transition region is small, of the order of a few lattice constants; the wall energy is of the order of 10 ergs/cm². As there is practically no sidewise motion of the 180° domain walls in an applied electric field, there is no interference or crosstalk between one set of electrodes to another on the same crystal plate even when they are

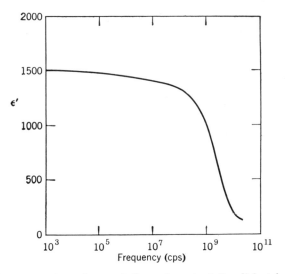

Fig. 8.15. Frequency dependence of the real part of the dielectric constant in barium titanate, from smoothed data of von Hippel and Powles and Jackson.

spaced only 10^{-2} cm apart. This feature is of great importance in the application of crystals of barium titanate in memory devices.

In Fig. 8.15 is shown the frequency dependence of the dielectric constant in polycrystalline barium titanate.[18] The decrease in the dielectric constant at microwave frequencies is not yet understood.

ANTIFERROELECTRIC CRYSTALS

Attention has been directed to the characteristics of antiferroelectric crystals,[19] which are usually defined as ionic crystals having lines of ions spontaneously polarized—but with neighboring lines polarized in antiparallel directions, as shown in Fig. 8.16a. There are also

[18] A. von Hippel, Revs. Modern Phys. **22**, 221 (1950); J. G. Powles and W. Jackson, Proc. Inst. Elec. Eng. (London) **96**, III, 383 (1949).
[19] C. Kittel, Phys. Rev. **82**, 729 (1951).

more general antiferroelectric arrangements, one of them being shown in Fig. 8.16b. It is also likely that ordered antiferroelectric arrangements or clusters of permanent electric dipole moments may occur in crystals such as the hydrogen halides at low temperatures. Several

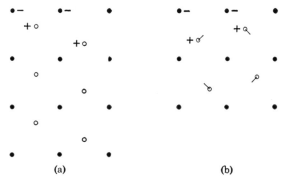

Fig. 8.16. Antiferroelectric arrangements: (a) antiparallel lines; (b) diagonal displacements.

crystals presumed to have an antiferroelectric state are listed in Table 8.2.

TABLE 8.2. ANTIFERROELECTRIC CRYSTALS

(From a compilation by Walter J. Merz)

Crystal	Antiferroelectric Curie Point (°K)
WO_3	1010
$NaNbO_3$	793, 911
$PbZrO_3$	506
$PbHfO_3$	488
$NH_4H_2PO_4$	148
$ND_4D_2PO_4$	242
$NH_4H_2AsO_4$	216
$ND_4D_2AsO_4$	304
$(NH_4)_2H_3IO_6$	254
$Ag_2H_3IO_6$	227

Tungsten trioxide (WO_3) was the first crystal reported to have an antiferroelectric phase. There is x-ray evidence[20] that at temperatures over 1010°K it exists in an antiferroelectric modification, with adjacent lines of tungsten ions displaced in opposite senses. A thorough study of the occurrence of antiferroelectricity in lead zirconate ($PbZrO_3$) has been carried out by several workers.[21] The results

[20] Kehl, Hay, and Wahl, J. Appl. Phys. **23**, 212 (1952).
[21] Sawaguchi, Maniwa, and Hoshino, Phys. Rev. **83**, 1078 (1951); G. Shirane, Phys. Rev. **86**, 219 (1952); Shirane, Sawaguchi, and Takagi, Phys. Rev. **84**, 476 (1951); E. Sawaguchi, J. Phys. Soc. Japan **8**, 615 (1953).

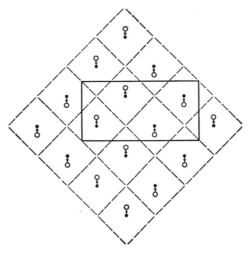

Fig. 8.17.   Antiferroelectric structure of $PbZrO_3$; arrows represent the direction of shifts of Pb ions; the solid line shows an orthorhombic unit cell.   (After Sawaguchi, Maniwa, and Hoshino.)

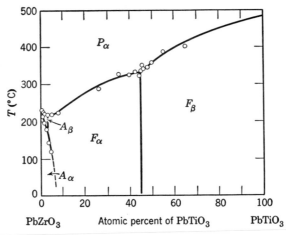

Fig. 8.18.   Phase diagram of $PbZrO_3$-$PbTiO_3$ system; A, F, P denote antiferroelectric, ferroelectric, and paraelectric, respectively. [After F. Sawaguchi, J. Phys. Soc. Japan **8**, 615 (1953).]

confirm the theoretical expectation[22] that in the perovskite structure the energies of ferroelectric and antiferroelectric phases should be quite close, and so almost anything may happen in the perovskite structure.

[22] M. H. Cohen, Phys. Rev. **84**, 369 (1951); see also Y. Takagi, Proceedings of the International Conference of Theoretical Physics, Kyoto and Tokyo, September, 1953, pp. 824–838.

The antiferroelectric structure of lead zirconate at room temperature is shown in Fig. 8.17. A ferroelectric state can be induced by applying a strong electric field or by slightly varying the composition. On heating Pb(Zr97-Ti3)O₃ one passes through four phases: two antiferroelectric, one ferroelectric, and one paraelectric. A paraelectric phase is one neither ferroelectric nor antiferroelectric. The phase diagram of the system PbZrO₃-PbTiO₃ as determined by Sawaguchi is shown in Fig. 8.18. He finds further that near the Curie point 230°C

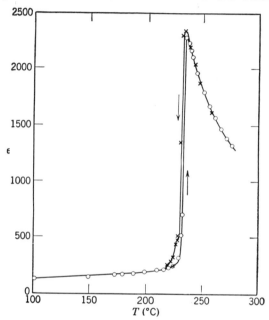

Fig. 8.19. Dielectric constant of lead zirconate at varying temperatures. (After Shirane, Sawaguchi, and Takagi.)

in pure PbZrO₃ the antiferroelectric phase is more stable than the ferroelectric phase by only about 4 cal/mole. The temperature dependence of the dielectric constant of PbZrO₃ is shown in Fig. 8.19.

A thermodynamic treatment of the antiferroelectric transition is given in references 14 and 19.

PROBLEMS

8.1. Consider a system consisting of 2 atoms separated by a fixed distance a, each dipole having a polarizability α. Find the relation between a and α for such a system to be ferroelectric.

8.2. Consider a system consisting of 2 dipoles separated by a fixed distance a along the x axis. Assume that the dipoles are so restrained that they may polarize only along the y axis, and let the polarizability along the y axis be α. Can such a system be ferroelectric? Find the relation between a and α for the system to be antiferroelectric.

8.3. Consider a three-dimensional structure consisting of lines separated by the distance a and parallel to the z direction. Every line contains oxygen and titanium ions alternating in position and separated by $a/2$. Neglect interactions between different lines and consider only interactions between atoms on the same line. Show that, if we have oxygen ions alone separated by a lattice constant a, the local field at an oxygen ion is

$$E_{\text{loc}} = E_0 + (4p/a^3) \sum_{n=1}^{\infty} n^{-3} \cong E_0 + 4.81P,$$

where E_0 is the applied electric field. Now insert the titanium ions on the lines at positions halfway between the oxygens. Taking $\alpha(O) = 2.4 \times 10^{-24}$ cm^3, and $a = 4.0 \times 10^{-8}$ cm, show that at an oxygen ion

$$E_{\text{loc}} = E_0 + 4.81P(O) + 33.7P(Ti),$$

and show that $P(O)/E_0$ contains the denominator $1 - 57\alpha(Ti)/a^3$, which exhibits the great sensitivity of a linear Ti-O structure to the ionic polarizability of the titanium ion.

8.4. Discuss the effect of an air gap between condenser plates and dielectric on the measurement of high dielectric constants. What is the highest apparent dielectric constant possible if the air gap thickness is 10^{-3} of the total thickness?

8.5.* Discuss the operation of the dielectric amplifier [see W. P. Mason and R. F. Wick, Proc. I.R.E. **42**, 1606 (1954)].

8.6.* Discuss in detail the differences in x-ray pattern and dielectric constant expected between ferroelectric and antiferroelectric phases of a crystal.

8.7. In a piezoelectric crystal a strain produces a dielectric polarization. (a) Show that a crystal cannot be piezoelectric if it possesses a center of symmetry (inversion center). (b) What further symmetry condition is required in order that a crystal may be ferroelectric?

REFERENCES

P. W. Anderson, "Theory of the ferroelectric behavior of barium titanate," Ceram. Age (April, 1951).

Baumgartner, Jona, and Känzig, "Seignetteelektrizität," Ergebnisse der exacten Naturwissenschaften **23**, 235 (1950).

M. Born, "On the quantum theory of pyroelectricity," Revs. Modern Phys. **17**, 245 (1945).

W. G. Cady, *Piezoelectricity*, McGraw-Hill Book Co., New York, 1946.

R. M. Cotts and W. D. Knight, "Nuclear resonance of Nb^{93} in KNbO$_3$," Phys. Rev. **96**, 1285 (1954).

A. F. Devonshire, "Theory of barium titanate," Phil. Mag. **40**, 1040 (1949); **42**, 1065 (1951); "Theory of ferroelectrics," Advances in Physics **3**, 85–130 (1954).

E. T. Jaynes, *Ferroelectricity*, Princeton University Press, 1953.

A. von Hippel, "Ferroelectricity, domain structure, and phase transitions of barium titanate," Revs. Modern Phys. **22**, 221–237 (1950).

W. P. Mason, *Piezoelectric crystals*, Van Nostrand, New York, 1950.

G. Shirane, F. Jona, and R. Pepinsky, "Some aspects of ferroelectricity," Proc. I.R.E. **43**, 1738–1793 (1955).

B. Wul, "High dielectric constant materials," J. Phys. (U.S.S.R.) **10**, 95 (1946).

9

Diamagnetism and Paramagnetism

The chapter begins with the classical Langevin theory of the diamagnetic and paramagnetic susceptibilities of gases, followed by a quantum-mechanical treatment. The properties of paramagnetic ions in solids are discussed, and an account is given of the attainment of very low temperatures by the adiabatic demagnetization of paramagnetic salts. Then there is a brief discussion of nuclear and electronic spin resonance absorption at radio and microwave frequencies.

DIAMAGNETISM

Substances with a negative magnetic susceptibility are called *diamagnetic*. Substances with a positive susceptibility are called *paramagnetic*. The magnetic susceptibility per unit volume is defined as

$$\chi = M/H,$$

where M is the magnetic moment per unit volume, or the *magnetization*, and H is the magnetic field intensity. Quite frequently the susceptibility may also be defined referred to unit mass or to a mole of the substance. The molar susceptibility is written χ_M.

Diamagnetism is associated with the tendency of electrical charges partially to shield the interior of a body from an applied magnetic field. In electromagnetism we are familiar with *Lenz's law*, which states that when the flux through an electrical circuit is changed an induced current is set up in such a direction as to oppose the flux change. In a resistanceless circuit, in a superconductor, or in an electron orbit within an atom, the induced current persists as long as the field is present, and the magnetic moment associated with the current is a diamagnetic moment.

DERIVATION OF THE LANGEVIN DIAMAGNETISM EQUATION

The usual derivation employs the Larmor theorem,[1] which states that for an atom in a magnetic field the motion of the electrons is, to

---

[1] For a discussion of the Larmor theorem, see H. Goldstein, *Classical mechanics*, Addison-Wesley, Cambridge, 1953, pp. 176–178.

the first order in H, the same as a possible motion in the absence of H except for the superposition of a common precession of angular frequency

(9.1) $$\omega_L = -eH/2mc,$$

or $f_L = 1.40$ mc/oersted. Furthermore, if the field is applied slowly, the motion in the rotating reference system will be the same as the original motion in the rest system before the application of the field. The precession of the electron distribution is equivalent to diamagnetic current

(9.2) $$I = -(Ze)(eH/2mc)/2\pi c,$$

in electromagnetic units. As the magnetic moment μ of a current loop is given by the product of the current by the area of the loop, we have

(9.3) $$\mu/H = -(Ze^2/4mc^2)\overline{\rho^2},$$

for Z electrons, where $\overline{\rho^2} = \overline{x^2} + \overline{y^2}$ is the average of the square of the perpendicular distance of the electron from the field axis. In terms of the mean square distance $\overline{r^2} = \overline{x^2} + \overline{y^2} + \overline{z^2}$ from the nucleus, we have

(9.4) $$\overline{r^2} = \tfrac{3}{2}\overline{\rho^2}$$

for a distribution of charge which on the average is spherically symmetrical, so that $\overline{x^2} = \overline{y^2} = \overline{z^2}$. Then the diamagnetic susceptibility per unit volume is, if N is the number of atoms per unit volume,

(9.5) $$\chi = -\frac{Ze^2N}{6mc^2}\overline{r^2},$$

which is the Langevin expression as corrected by Pauli. A quantum-theoretical derivation of this result is given in Appendix D.

The problem of calculating the diamagnetic susceptibility is thus reduced to the calculation of $\overline{r^2}$; this means that we must determine the electron charge distribution within the atom. The charge distribution can in principle be calculated by quantum mechanics, but exact solutions are available only for the hydrogen atom and isoelectronic ions. The quality of the approximate solutions which have been worked out deteriorates as the number of electrons increases. By and large, the best we can do is to use the charge distributions calculated by the "self-consistent field" method. An index of wave functions obtained by this method has been prepared by Hartree;[2] Stoner[3] utilized Hartree functions in early susceptibility calculations. Other approximate schemes have been devised by Slater,[4] Brindley,[5] Sommerfeld, and others. A comparison of experimental and theoretical results is shown in Tables 9.1 and 9.2.

TABLE 9.1.   MOLAR DIAMAGNETIC SUSCEPTIBILITIES OF RARE GASES

[For literature references see Landolt-Börnstein, *Tabellen*, 6th ed., Vol. I.1, p. 394; for a careful discussion of the data see W. R. Myers, Revs. Mod. Phys. **24**, 15 (1952).]

	Probable Experimental Values (10^{-6} cm^3/mole)	Theoretical Values (10^{-6} cm^3/mole) Hartree-Stoner	Hartree-Fock
He	-1.9	-1.9	
Ne	-7.2	-8.6	
A	-19.4	-24.8	-20.6
Kr	$-28.$	......	
Xe	$-43.$	......	

TABLE 9.2.   MOLAR DIAMAGNETIC SUSCEPTIBILITIES OF IONS IN CRYSTALS

	Experimental Values[†] (10^{-6} cm^3/mole)	Theoretical Values—Free Ions (10^{-6} cm^3/mole) Hartree[‡]	Slater[§]
F$^-$	-9.4	-17.0	-8.1
Cl$^-$	-24.2	-41.3	-25.2
Br$^-$	-34.5		-39.2
I$^-$	-50.6		-58.5
Li$^+$	-0.7	-0.7	-0.7
Na$^+$	-6.1	-5.6	-4.1
K$^+$	-14.6	-17.4	-14.1
Rb$^+$	-22.0	-29.5	-25.1
Cs$^+$	-35.1	-47.5	-38.7
Mg^{2+}	-4.3	-4.2	-3.1
Ca^{2+}	-10.7	-13.1	-11.1
Sr^{2+}	-18.0		-21.0
Ba^{2+}	-29.0		-32.6

[†] G. W. Brindley and F. E. Hoare, Trans. Faraday Soc. **33**, 268 (1937); Proc. Phys. Soc. (London) **49**, 619 (1937).

[‡] D. R. Hartree, Proc. Cambridge Phil. Soc. **24**, 89 (1928).

[§] As recalculated by W. R. Myers, *loc. cit.*

Derivation of Larmor theorem for a special case.   We consider an electron moving in a circular orbit of radius r about a fixed nucleus.

[2] D. R. Hartree, Repts. Prog. Phys. **11**, 113 (1946–47).

[3] E. C. Stoner, Proc. Leeds Phil. Lit. Soc. Sci. Sect. **1**, 484 (1929).

[4] J. C. Slater, Phys. Rev. **36**, 57 (1930).

[5] G. W. Brindley, Phil. Mag. **11**, 786 (1931).

The balance of forces requires that

$$m\omega_0{}^2 r = e^2/r^2,$$

so that

(9.6) $\omega_0 = (e^2/mr^3)^{1/2}.$

In a magnetic field H normal to the plane of the orbit we have the additional Lorentz force $\mathbf{F} = (e/c)\mathbf{v} \times \mathbf{H}$; therefore

$$m\omega^2 r = (e^2/r^2) - (e/c)r\omega H,$$

and

(9.7) $\omega = \pm[(eH/2mc)^2 + (e^2/mr^3)]^{1/2} - (eH/2mc).$

Now, if $\omega_0 \gg eH/2mc$, we have approximately

(9.8) $\omega = \pm\omega_0 - (eH/2mc),$

in agreement with (9.1). We may note that for a free electron $\omega = eH/mc$; this is known as the magnetron or cyclotron frequency, and it is twice the Larmor frequency for a bound electron.

Diamagnetism of molecules. The derivation of the Larmor equation assumes implicitly that the field direction is an axis of symmetry of the system. In most molecular systems this condition is not satisfied, and the general theory of Van Vleck (Appendix E) must be applied. For a polyatomic molecule with spin quantum number zero we have, according to (E.6), the total molar susceptibility

(9.9) $$\chi_M = -\frac{Le^2}{6mc^2} \sum \overline{r^2} + 2L \sum_n \frac{|(n|\mu_z|0)|^2}{E_n - E_0},$$

where L is the Avogadro number, $(n|\mu_z|0)$ is the matrix element of the z component of the orbital magnetic moment connecting the ground state with the excited state n, and $E_n - E_0$ is the energy separation of the two states. The susceptibility in this case is independent of temperature, but the material is diamagnetic or paramagnetic according to whether the first or second term of (9.9) is greater.

For the normal state of the H_2 molecule Van Vleck and Frank[6] calculate using Wang's wave functions, and measuring r from the center of mass,

$$\chi_M = -4.71 \times 10^{-6} + 0.51 \times 10^{-6} = -4.20 \times 10^{-6},$$

per mole. The experimental values are between -3.9 and -4.0×10^{-6}, per mole.

[6] J. H. Van Vleck and A. Frank, Proc. Natl. Acad. Sci. U.S. **15**, 539 (1929).

Pascal has studied empirically the influence of chemical combination on diamagnetic susceptibility and has formulated a set of rules for estimating susceptibilities, particularly of organic liquids. He expresses the susceptibility of the molecule as a sum of the atomic susceptibilities of the constituents plus a correction factor which depends on the nature of the bonds (such as single or double bonds) between the atoms. In the book listed at the end of the chapter, Stoner discusses the Pascal rules. It has been observed[7] that crystals with layer-like lattices exhibit a marked anisotropy in the diamagnetic susceptibility, the susceptibility being abnormally large when measured in a direction normal to the layers. The effect is particularly marked in antimony, bismuth, graphite, and in aromatic molecules (see Table 9.3). It was pointed out by Ehrenfest and by Raman and Krishnan

TABLE 9.3. DIAMAGNETIC ANISOTROPY OF AROMATIC MOLECULES

(From Krishnan and collaborators, quoted by L. Pauling[8])

Molecule	Molar Molecular Susceptibility $(10^{-6} \text{ cm}^3/\text{mole})$		
	K_1	K_2	$K_\perp$
Benzene:	-37	-37	-91
Naphthalene:	-39	-43	-187
Anthracene:	-46	-53	-273
Terphenyl:	-98	-98	-260

The diamagnetic susceptibilities K_1 and K_2 are the principal susceptibilities in the plane of the molecule; $K_\perp$ is taken normal to the plane.

that the abnormal susceptibilities probably arise from the Larmor precession of electrons in orbits including many nuclei.

METHOD OF MEASUREMENT OF SUSCEPTIBILITIES

The usual methods of measuring diamagnetic and paramagnetic susceptibilities depend in one way or another on the force exerted on a

[7] See, for example, the review by K. S. Krishnan, Strasbourg conference 1939, *Le magnétisme*, vol. III, 247–285; also K. Lonsdale, Repts. Prog. Phys. **4**, 368 (1937).

[8] L. Pauling, J. Chem. Phys. **4**, 673 (1936).

specimen by a non-uniform magnetic field. The force **F** is given by the gradient of the magnetic energy, and so, by (F.6),

$$(9.10) \qquad \mathbf{F} = \tfrac{1}{2} \operatorname{grad} \int \chi H^2 \, dV,$$

where now χ is the volume susceptibility.

If we suppose that the specimen is in the form of a thin rod, as in the Gouy method shown in Fig. 9.1, we may write for the downward pull

$$(9.11) \qquad F_z = \frac{1}{2} \chi A \int \frac{d}{dz} H^2 \, dz = \frac{1}{2} \chi A (H_1{}^2 - H_2{}^2),$$

where A is the sectional area of the specimen. Other methods of measurement are discussed, for example, by Bates.[9] A high sensitivity method has been described by Lewis, Calvin, and Kasha.[10] The application of nuclear resonance absorption to the measurement of electronic susceptibilities has been discussed by Feher and Knight.[11]

PARAMAGNETISM

Electronic paramagnetism (positive contribution to χ) is found in:

(a) All atoms and molecules possessing an odd number of electrons, as here the total spin of the system cannot be zero. Examples: free sodium atoms; gaseous nitric oxide (NO); organic free radicals such as triphenylmethyl, $C(C_6H_5)_3$.

(b) All free atoms and ions with a partly filled inner shell: transition elements; ions isoelectronic with transition elements; rare earth and actinide elements. Examples: Mn^{2+}, Gd^{3+}, U^{4+}. Paramagnetic properties are exhibited by many of these ions when incorporated into solids, and as ions in solution, but not invariably.

(c) A few miscellaneous compounds with an even number of electrons, including molecular oxygen and organic biradicals.

(d) Metals: the paramagnetism of conduction electrons is treated in Chapters 10 and 11.

LANGEVIN THEORY OF PARAMAGNETISM

We treat a medium containing N atoms per unit volume, each bearing a magnetic moment μ. Magnetization results from the orientation of the magnetic moments in an applied magnetic field; thermal dis-

[9] L. F. Bates, *Modern magnetism*, Cambridge University Press, Cambridge, 3rd ed., 1951.
[10] Lewis, Calvin, and Kasha, J. Chem. Phys. **17**, 804 (1949).
[11] G. Feher and W. D. Knight, Rev. Sci. Instr. **26**, 293 (1955).

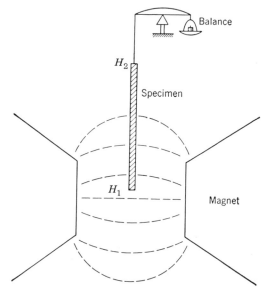

Fig. 9.1.   Gouy method for measuring susceptibilities.

order resists the tendency of the field to orient the moments.   The energy of interaction (F.1) with an applied magnetic field **H** is

$$(9.12) \qquad\qquad V = -\mathbf{\mu} \cdot \mathbf{H}.$$

For thermal equilibrium the magnetization is calculated by following exactly the steps (7.23) to (7.28) in the derivation of the Debye orientational polarizability, with **μ** written for **p** and **H** for **E**.   The magnetization is then given by

$$(9.13) \qquad\qquad M = N\mu L(a),$$

where $a = \mu H/kT$, and the Langevin function $L(a)$ is

$$L(a) = \operatorname{ctnh} a - \frac{1}{a}.$$

For $a \ll 1$, $L(a) = a/3$, and

$$(9.14) \qquad\qquad M \cong N\mu^2 H/3kT.$$

For an electron $\mu \approx 10^{-20}$; at room temperature in a field of 10^4 oersteds we have $\mu H/kT \approx \frac{1}{400}$, so that here we may safely approximate the Langevin function by $\mu H/3kT$.   At low temperatures saturation effects have been observed, as shown in Fig. 9.2.

The magnetic susceptibility in the limit $\mu H/kT \ll 1$ is

(9.15) $$\chi = M/H = N\mu^2/3kT = C/T,$$

where the Curie constant C is equal to $N\mu^2/3k$. The $1/T$ temperature dependence is known as the Curie law, and the whole expression is known as the Langevin equation.

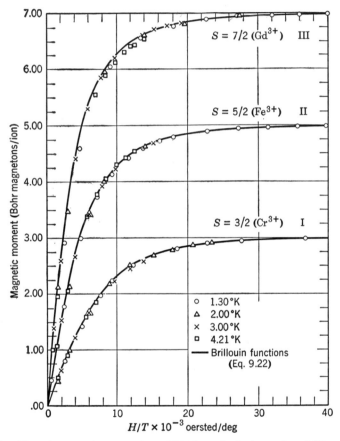

Fig. 9.2.   Plot of magnetic moment vs. H/T for spherical samples of (I) potassium chromium alum, (II) ferric ammonium alum, and (III) gadolinium sulfate octahydrate.   Over 99.5% magnetic saturation is achieved for 1.3°K and about 50,000 gauss.   [After W. E. Henry, Phys. Rev. **88**, 559 (1952).]

Quantum theory of paramagnetism.   We treat first the paramagnetism caused by electron spins with angular momentum $\frac{1}{2}$ as measured in units of $\hbar$.   In a magnetic field H the energy levels are separated according to (9.12), and, as in the elementary theory of the

Zeeman effect, by

$$(9.16) \qquad \Delta W = 2|\mu_z|H = g\frac{e\hbar}{2mc}H = g\mu_B H,$$

where for an electron spin the g factor or *spectroscopic splitting factor* is equal to 2.00; $\mu_B = e\hbar/2mc = -0.927 \times 10^{-20}$ erg/oersted is the Bohr magneton. The splitting for an electron spin is shown in Fig.

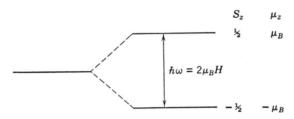

Fig. 9.3. Energy levels splitting scheme for one electron, with only spin angular momentum, in a magnetic field H directed along the positive z axis. Note that the Bohr magneton $\mu_B = e\hbar/2mc$ is a negative number as used here.

9.3. For free atoms where orbital angular momentum may also be present, the g factor is given by the Landé equation

$$(9.17) \qquad g = 1 + \frac{J(J + 1) + S(S + 1) - L(L + 1)}{2J(J + 1)},$$

where J, S, L refer, respectively, to the total, spin, and orbital angular momentum quantum numbers.

Where there are only two levels in the magnetic field the populations in thermal equilibrium are

$$(9.18) \qquad \begin{aligned} \frac{N_1}{N} &= \frac{e^{\mu H/kT}}{e^{\mu H/kT} + e^{-\mu H/kT}}; \\[2mm] \frac{N_2}{N} &= \frac{e^{-\mu H/kT}}{e^{\mu H/kT} + e^{-\mu H/kT}}; \end{aligned}$$

here N_1, N_2 are the populations of the lower and upper levels, and $N = N_1 + N_2$ is the total number of atoms. The projection of the magnetic moment of the upper state along the field direction is $g\mu_B/2$, and of the lower state is $-g\mu_B/2$, so that the resultant magnetization for N atoms per unit volume is

$$(9.19) \qquad M = \frac{Ng\mu_B}{2} \cdot \frac{e^x - e^{-x}}{e^x + e^{-x}} = \frac{Ng\mu_B}{2} \tanh x,$$

where $x = g\mu_B H/2kT$.   For $x \ll 1$, $\tanh x \cong x$, and

$$M \cong \frac{Ng\mu_B}{2} \cdot \frac{g\mu_B H}{2kT}.$$

The susceptibility in this limit is

(9.20) $\chi = N(g^2/4)\mu_B{}^2/kT.$

This equation for an electron spin with $g = 2$ appears to differ from the classical result (9.14) by a factor of 3; however, in quantum mechanics the total spin angular momentum is given by $[S(S+1)]^{1/2} = (\frac{3}{4})^{1/2}$ rather than by $S = \frac{1}{2}$; accordingly the total magnetic moment must be given by $\mu = (3)^{1/2}\mu_B$; therefore (9.20) becomes

$$\chi = N\mu^2/3kT,$$

in accord with the classical result.

An atom with angular momentum quantum number J has $2J + 1$ equally spaced energy levels in a magnetic field.   It is left as a problem (9.6) to show that the magnetization is given by

(9.21) $M = NgJ\mu_B B_J(x),$

where $x = gJ\mu_B H/kT$, and the Brillouin function B_J is given by

(9.22) $B_J = \dfrac{2J+1}{2J} \operatorname{ctnh}\left(\dfrac{(2J+1)x}{2J}\right) - \dfrac{1}{2J}\operatorname{ctnh}\left(\dfrac{x}{2J}\right)$

For $x \ll 1$, the susceptibility is

(9.23) $\chi = NJ(J+1)g^2\mu_B{}^2/3kT = Np^2\mu_B{}^2/3kT,$

where the effective number of Bohr magnetons is defined as

(9.24) $p = g[J(J+1)]^{1/2}.$

The order of magnitude of the volume susceptibility for $N \approx 10^{22}$ atoms/cm^3 as in a solid and $\mu \approx 10^{-20}$ cgs is $\sim 1/(400\ T)$.   For $T = 300°$K, $\chi \sim 10^{-5}$; for $T = 0.3°$K, $\chi \sim 10^{-2}$.

In Fig. 9.4 we show susceptibility measurements on copper potassium sulfate, which obeys the Curie law quite well.

Rare earth ions.   The discussion above applies principally to atoms which in the absence of a magnetic field have a $(2J+1)$-fold degenerate ground state, the degeneracy being lifted upon application of a magnetic field; the influence of all higher energy states of the system is neglected. These conditions appear from Table 9.4 to be satisfied by a number of the rare earth ions. The calculated magneton numbers are obtained by using g values from the Landé formula (9.17) for the ground state level assignment predicted by the Hund theory of spectral terms, which tells us that for equivalent electrons the ground state

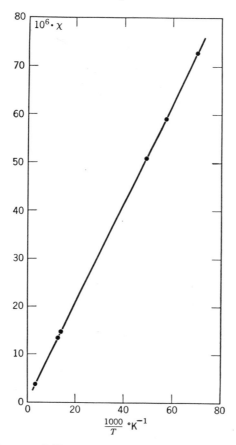

Fig. 9.4. Plot of susceptibility per gm vs. reciprocal temperature for powdered $CuSO_4 \cdot K_2SO_4 \cdot 6H_2O$, showing the Curie law temperature dependence. [Measurements by J. C. Hupse, Physica **9**, 633 (1942).]

has the maximum multiplicity $2S + 1$ allowed by the Pauli principle and the maximum L consistent with this multiplicity; furthermore, the J value is equal to $|L - S|$ when the shell is less than half full and $L + S$ when the shell is more than half full.

The discrepancy between the experimental magneton numbers and those calculated on our present assumptions is quite marked for Eu^{3+}

and Sm^{3+} ions.   In these ions it is necessary to consider the influence of the higher states of the $L-S$ multiplet,[12] as the intervals here are not very large compared to kT.   Van Vleck and Frank have shown that the experimental facts are accounted for in a satisfactory way when the higher levels are considered.

The full theoretical expression for the susceptibility as a function of temperature when higher states are to be considered may be quite complicated.   In Appendix E we consider two limiting cases, when the

TABLE 9.4.   EFFECTIVE MAGNETON NUMBERS FOR TRIVALENT RARE EARTH IONS

(Near room temperature)

Ion	Configuration	Basic Level	$p(\text{calc}) =$ $g[J(J+1)]^{1/2}$	$p(\text{exp})$ approx.
Ce^{3+}	$4f^1 5s^2 p^6$	$^2F_{5/2}$	2.54	2.4
Pr^{3+}	$4f^2 5s^2 p^6$	$^3H_4$	3.58	3.5
Nd^{3+}	$4f^3 5s^2 p^6$	$^4I_{9/2}$	3.62	3.5
Pm^{3+}	$4f^4 5s^2 p^6$	$^5I_4$	2.68	....
Sm^{3+}	$4f^5 5s^2 p^6$	$^6H_{5/2}$	0.84	1.5
Eu^{3+}	$4f^6 5s^2 p^6$	$^7F_0$	0	3.4
Gd^{3+}	$4f^7 5s^2 p^6$	$^8S_{7/2}$	7.94	8.0
Tb^{3+}	$4f^8 5s^2 p^6$	$^7F_6$	9.72	9.5
Dy^{3+}	$4f^9 5s^2 p^6$	$^6H_{15/2}$	10.63	10.6
Ho^{3+}	$4f^{10} 5s^2 p^6$	$^5I_8$	10.60	10.4
Er^{3+}	$4f^{11} 5s^2 p^6$	$^4I_{15/2}$	9.59	9.5
Tm^{3+}	$4f^{12} 5s^2 p^6$	$^3H_6$	7.57	7.3
Yb^{3+}	$4f^{13} 5s^2 p^6$	$^2F_{7/2}$	4.54	4.5

level splitting is $\ll kT$ or $\gg kT$.   Levels $\gg kT$ above the ground state may contribute to the susceptibility a term which is independent of temperature over the appropriate range.   This term is known as Van Vleck paramagnetism; it is in addition to the $1/T$ and diamagnetic terms already discussed.

Iron group ions.   Table 9.5 shows that, for salts of the iron transition group of the periodic table, the experimental magneton numbers are in poor agreement with (9.24), but instead, as noted by Sommerfeld, Bose, and Stoner, agree quite well with magneton numbers

(9.25) $p = 2[S(S+1)]^{1/2}$

calculated as if the orbital moment were not there at all.   One expresses this situation by saying that the orbital moments are "quenched."

[12] A multiplet is the set of levels of different J values arising out of a given L and S.

TABLE 9.5. EFFECTIVE MAGNETON NUMBERS FOR IRON GROUP IONS

Ion	Config-uration	Basic Level	$p(\text{calc}) =$ $g[J(J+1)]^{1/2}$	$p(\text{calc}) =$ $2[S(S+1)]^{1/2}$	$p(\exp)$†	$g(\exp)$‡
Ti^{3+}, V^{4+}	$3d^1$	$^2D_{3/2}$	1.55	1.73	1.8	......
V^{3+}	$3d^2$	$^3F_2$	1.63	2.83	2.8	(1.98)
Cr^{3+}, V^{2+}	$3d^3$	$^4F_{3/2}$	0.77	3.87	3.8	(1.97)
Mn^{3+}, Cr^{2+}	$3d^4$	$^5D_0$	0	4.90	4.9	2.0
Fe^{3+}, Mn^{2+}	$3d^5$	$^6S_{5/2}$	5.92	5.92	5.9	2.0
Fe^{2+}	$3d^6$	$^5D_4$	6.70	4.90	5.4	2.2
Co^{2+}	$3d^7$	$^4F_{9/2}$	6.63	3.87	4.8	2.5
Ni^{2+}	$3d^8$	$^3F_4$	5.59	2.83	3.2	2.3
Cu^{2+}	$3d^9$	$^2D_{5/2}$	3.55	1.73	1.9	2.2

† Representative values.
‡ In this column $g = p(\exp)/[S(S+1)]^{1/2}$.

The basic reason for the difference in behavior of the rare earth and iron group salts is that the $4f$ shell responsible for paramagnetism in the rare earth ions lies deep inside the ions, being partly shielded from the environment by the outer $5s$ and $5p$ shells, whereas in the iron group the $3d$ shell responsible for paramagnetism is the outermost shell in the ionic state. The $3d$ shell is thus exposed to the intense local electric fields produced by neighboring ions and the dipole moments of water of hydration in the crystal. The interaction of the paramagnetic ions with the crystalline electric fields has two major effects: the coupling of **L** and **S** vectors is largely broken up, so that the states are no longer specified by their J values; furthermore, the $2L + 1$ sublevels belonging to a given L which are degenerate in the free ion may now be split up, in some cases with important effects on the contribution of the orbital motion to the magnetic moment.

Quenching of the orbital angular momentum. In an electric field directed toward a fixed center such as a nucleus, the plane of a classical orbit remains fixed in space, and so the orbital angular momentum components L_x, L_y, L_z are constant. In quantum theory only one angular momentum component (usually taken as L_z) and the square of the total orbital angular momentum L^2 are constant in a central field. If an inhomogeneous electric field is superposed on the central field, the plane of the orbit will move about; the angular momentum components are no longer constant and may average to zero. In quantum theory, as shown in detail in Appendix G, L_z will no longer be a constant of the motion, although to a good approximation L^2 may continue to be constant. If L_z averages to zero, it is said to be quenched.

The magnetic moment of a state is given by the average value of the magnetic moment operator $\mu_B(\mathbf{L} + 2\mathbf{S})$ over the state. For a magnetic field in the z direction the orbital contribution to the magnetic moment is proportional to the expectation value of L_z, and so the orbital magnetic moment is quenched if the mechanical moment L_z is quenched.

When the spin-orbit interaction energy is introduced as an additional perturbation on the system, the quenching may be partially lifted as the spin may carry some orbital moment along with it. If the sign of the spin-orbit interaction favors parallel orientation of the spin and orbital magnetic moments, the total magnetic moment will be larger than for the spin alone, and the g value as defined in Table 9.5 will be greater than 2. The experimental results in the table suggest, in good agreement with the known variation of sign[13] of the spin-orbit

TABLE 9.6. NUCLEAR MAGNETIC MOMENTS

(Magnetic moments in units of the nuclear magneton
$\mu_p = e\hbar/2M_p c = 5.05 \times 10^{-24}$ ergs/oersted)

Nucleus	Spin (units $\hbar$)	Magnetic Moment
Neutron	$\frac{1}{2}$	-1.913
H^1	$\frac{1}{2}$	2.793
D^2	1	0.857
Li^7	$\frac{3}{2}$	3.256
Na^{23}	$\frac{3}{2}$	2.217
Mn^{55}	$\frac{5}{2}$	3.468
Co^{59}	$\frac{7}{2}$	4.648
Ta^{181}	$\frac{7}{2}$	2.1

interaction, that $g > 2$ when the $3d$ shell is more than half full, $g = 2$ when the shell is half full, and $g < 2$ when the shell is less than half full. The effect of spin-orbit coupling is worked out in Appendix H for a simple model, with particular reference to the results of electron spin resonance experiments discussed below.

Nuclear paramagnetism. The magnetic moments of nuclei are smaller than the magnetic moment of the electron by a factor $\sim 10^{-3}$; therefore according to (9.4) the susceptibility of a nuclear paramagnetic system for the same number of particles will be smaller by a factor $\sim 10^{-6}$ than that of an electronic paramagnetic system. The susceptibility of solid hydrogen, which is diamagnetic with respect to electrons but paramagnetic with respect to protons, has been measured

[13] See E. U. Condon and G. H. Shortley, *Theory of atomic spectra*, Cambridge University Press, 1935, p. 210; the spin-orbit interaction of a single electron is such that the lowest energy state of a multiplet has S oppositely directed to L; in shells more than half full we think of the motion as that of positive holes in the shell, so that the sign of the interaction is reversed.

at very low temperatures by Lasarew and Schubnikow,[14] who found results consistent with the known magnitude of the proton magnetic moment.

Values of the magnetic moments of several nuclei[15] are given in Table 9.6.

COOLING BY ADIABATIC DEMAGNETIZATION OF A PARAMAGNETIC SALT

The universal method for attaining temperatures below 1°K is that of adiabatic demagnetization.[16] By its use temperatures near 10^{-3}°K have been reached. The method rests on the fact that at a fixed temperature the entropy of a system of magnetic moments is lowered by a magnetic field. The entropy is always a measure of the order of a system; the greater the disorder, the higher is the entropy. In the field the moments will be partly lined up, or partly ordered, so that the entropy is lowered by the field. The entropy is also lowered by lowering the temperature, as more of the moments line up. If the field can be removed without the entropy of the spin system changing, the disorder of the spin system will look as it should at a lower temperature. When the specimen is demagnetized adiabatically, heat can flow into the spin system only from the system of lattice vibrations. At the temperatures of interest the entropy of the lattice system is quite negligible, so that the entropy of the spin system alone is essentially constant during adiabatic demagnetization of the specimen.

We first find an expression for the spin or magnetic entropy of a system of N ions each of spin J at a temperature sufficiently high so that the spin system is entirely disordered. That is, T is supposed to be much higher than some temperature θ_0 which characterizes the energy of interactions tending to orient the spins preferentially. The result for the entropy S is

(9.26) $S = Nk \log (2J + 1).$

We establish this directly from the Boltzmann definition of the entropy of distribution of objects as

(9.27) $S = k \log W,$

[14] B. Lasarew and L. Schubnikow, Physik. Z. Sowjetunion **11**, 445 (1937); see also Evans, Phil. Mag. **1**, 370 (1956); Kurti et al., Nature **178**, 450 (1956).

[15] For a large compilation of nuclear moments, see J. E. Mack, Revs. Modern Phys. **22**, 64 (1950); N. F. Ramsey, *Nuclear moments*, John Wiley & Sons, New York, 1953. Nuclear moments are at present determined principally by nuclear resonance and atomic beam methods.

[16] The method was suggested independently by P. Debye, Ann. Physik **81**, 1154 (1926); and W. F. Giauque, J. Am. Chem. Soc. **49**, 1864 (1927).

where W is the number of independent arrangements of the elements of the system according to the prescribed distribution. At a temperature so high that all sublevels are nearly equally populated, the number of arrangements W is the number of ways of arranging N spins on $2J + 1$ sublevels, as nearly all arrangements will be possible energetically. Thus

$$(9.28) \qquad W = (2J + 1)^N,$$

and

$$(9.29) \qquad S = k \log (2J + 1)^N = Nk \log (2J + 1).$$

It is this entropy which may be reduced by the application of a magnetic field.

We now derive an expression for the field dependence of the entropy. As the entropy is a function of H and T, we have

$$(9.30) \qquad dS = \left(\frac{\partial S}{\partial H}\right)_T dH + \left(\frac{\partial S}{\partial T}\right)_H dT.$$

In an isothermal process the second term may be set equal to zero, and so

$$(9.31) \qquad dS = \left(\frac{\partial S}{\partial H}\right)_T dH.$$

We note that, by a modified Maxwell thermodynamic relation, $(\partial S/\partial H)_T = (\partial M/\partial T)_H$, and so

$$dS = \left(\frac{\partial M}{\partial T}\right)_H dH.$$

Therefore in isothermal magnetization,

$$(9.32) \qquad S(H, T) - S(0, T) = \int_0^H (\partial M/\partial T)_H \, dH.$$

In the Curie law region, using (9.23) and (9.24),

$$(9.33) \qquad S = S_0 - \tfrac{1}{6}Nk(p\mu_B H/kT)^2.$$

The steps carried out in the cooling process are shown in Fig. 9.5. The field is applied at temperature T_1 with the specimen in good thermal contact ($\Delta T = 0$) with the surroundings, giving the isothermal path AB. The specimen is then insulated ($\Delta S = 0$) and the field removed, so that the specimen follows the isoentropic path BC, ending up at temperature T_2.

Ultimate temperature reached. The lowest temperature reached in adiabatic demagnetization is largely limited by the natural splitting of the spin energy levels occurring even in the absence of external magnetic fields. The zero field splitting may be caused by electrostatic

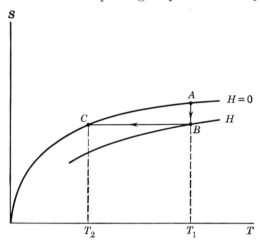

Fig. 9.5.   Entropy-temperature plot for adiabatic demagnetization.

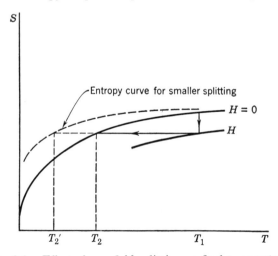

Fig. 9.6.   Effect of zero field splitting on final temperature.

interaction with the other ions in the crystal (Appendix G), by the interaction of the magnetic moments with each other, or by nuclear interactions. The zero field splitting causes the entropy at T_2 in Fig. 9.6 to be less than it would be (T_2') for a smaller splitting, so that the final temperature is not as low as it might otherwise be.

Kurti and Simon[17] have given an approximate formula for estimating the final temperature reached, starting at an initial temperature T_1 and a field H. We take a simple model of the zero field splitting, supposing that the ground level of each ion is split into $2J + 1$ sublevels separated by *equal* energy differences $k\theta_0$. In the field H we suppose that $g\mu_B H$ is the splitting of each of the $2J + 1$ sublevels. At the initial temperature the distribution on the various sublevels, and hence the entropy, is determined by the ratio $g\mu_B H/kT_1$, provided that $T_1 \gg \theta_0$ and $g\mu_B H \gg k\theta_0$. The entropy of the final state at temperature T_2 will be the same function of $k\theta_0/kT_2$ as the initial entropy was of $g\mu_B H/kT_1$, because the entropy depends only on the occupation of the sublevels, and these ratios determine the occupation. As the entropy remains constant during adiabatic demagnetization, we have for this model

$$(9.34) \qquad \frac{T_2}{T_1} = \frac{k\theta_0}{g\mu_B H} = 7.5\,\frac{\theta_0}{H_i},$$

where H_i is in kilo-oersteds, θ_0 in degrees Kelvin, and we have set $g = 2$.

For the salt iron ammonium alum, $FeNH_4(SO_4)_2 \cdot 12H_2O$, we may estimate $\theta_0 = 0.061°K$ from heat capacity data. Starting with $T_1 = 1.2°K$ and $H = 14,000$ oersteds, a final temperature $T_2 = 0.038°K$ was reached. From (9.34) we would have estimated $T_2(\text{est}) = (7.5)(1.2)(0.061)/14 = 0.039°K$.

For a full discussion of the principles and technique of cooling by adiabatic demagnetization, the monograph by Garrett[18] may be consulted.

NUCLEAR AND ELECTRONIC SPIN RESONANCE ABSORPTION

Spin resonance absorption studies have made important contributions to our understanding of interactions in solids and liquids and of the magnetic properties of nuclei. We consider first a free particle of spin S in a magnetic field H. The $2S + 1$ magnetic sublevels labeled by the magnetic quantum number $m_s = S,\ S - 1,\ \cdots,\ -S + 1,\ -S$ are separated in the field by equal energy differences $g\mu_0 H$ between adjacent sublevels. Here μ_0 is usually taken for electrons as the Bohr magneton and for nuclei as the nuclear magneton; g is the appropriate factor which makes the energy come out correctly, and it is called the *g factor* or *spectroscopic splitting factor*. The level scheme for a single electron spin is shown in Fig. 9.3.

[17] N. Kurti and F. Simon, Proc. Roy. Soc. (London) **A149**, 152 (1935).
[18] C. G. B. Garrett, *Magnetic cooling*, Harvard, Cambridge, 1954.

Electromagnetic radiation of frequency such that

(9.35) $\hbar\omega = g\mu_0 H$

will induce transitions between neighboring magnetic levels according to the selection rule $\Delta m_s = \pm 1$ for magnetic dipole transitions. The transition occurs between the Zeeman components of a single spectral level. Energy is absorbed from the radiation field when (9.35) is satisfied. A schematic experimental set-up is shown in Fig. 9.7. The

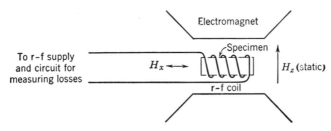

Fig. 9.7. Schematic arrangement for spin resonance absorption experiments.

specimen is placed in the static magnetic field H_z of an electromagnet. An r-f magnetic field H_x of fixed angular frequency ω is applied perpendicular to the static field. The r-f power absorbed in the specimen is determined by electrical measurements, as by measuring the Q of the coil. The resonance effect for electrons was found first by Zavoisky,[19] that for nuclei by Purcell, Torrey, and Pound[20] and by Bloch, Hansen, and Packard.[21]

Experimental results for electron spin resonance in a paramagnetic organic compound are shown in Fig. 9.8, and for proton spin resonance in water (with some dissolved ferric nitrate) in Fig. 9.9. The electron spin resonance relation for $g = 2.00$ is

(9.36) $f(\text{mc}) = 2.80\, H(\text{oersteds})$,

and the proton resonance relation is

(9.37) $f(\text{kc}) = 4.26\, H(\text{oersteds})$.

For $H \sim 5000$ oersteds, the electron resonance frequency falls in the microwave range, and the proton resonance frequency in the short wave communications range. For technical reasons the electron experiments are usually performed at fixed frequency and varying field, while the nuclear experiments are often done at fixed field and

[19] E. Zavoisky, J. Phys. (U.S.S.R.) **9**, 211, 245, 447 (1945).
[20] Purcell, Torrey, and Pound, Phys. Rev. **69**, 37 (1946).
[21] Bloch, Hansen, and Packard, Phys. Rev. **70**, 474 (1946).

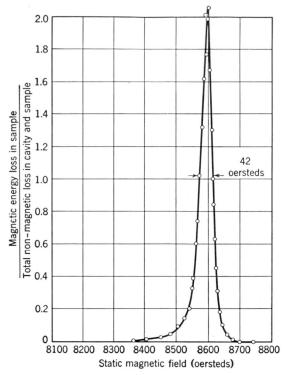

Fig. 9.8.   Electron spin resonance absorption in an organic free radical compound at 24,446 mc/sec.   [After Holden *et al.*, Phys. Rev. **75**, 1614 (1949).]

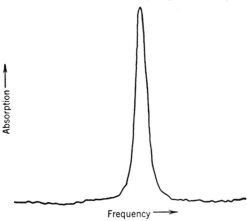

Fig. 9.9.   Proton spin resonance absorption in ferric nitrate solution; fixed magnetic field, varying frequency.   For a frequency of 30 mc/sec the resonance occurs at 7050 oersteds.   [After Bloembergen, Purcell, and Pound, Phys. Rev. **73**, 679 (1948).]

varying frequency. Nuclear resonance is becoming the most important laboratory method for the accurate measurement of magnetic field intensity.

Electron spin resonance[22] has been applied to the study of conduction electrons in metals. A curve obtained for sodium at 4°K by Feher and Kip is shown in Fig. 9.10.

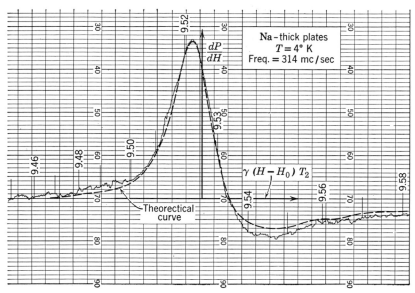

Fig. 9.10. Conduction electron spin resonance in metallic sodium. (After Feher and Kip.) The vertical axis is the derivative of the power absorption with respect to magnetic field intensity; the horizontal axis is proportional to the static magnetic field.

Macroscopic equations. It is sometimes useful to consider the resonance process in terms of the magnetic moment of the entire specimen[23] rather than in terms of the levels of an individual ion. Writing **M** for the magnetization (magnetic moment/volume) and **J** for the angular momentum density, the classical equation of motion

$$dJ/dt = \text{torque/volume}$$

becomes

(9.38) $$d\mathbf{J}/dt = \mathbf{M} \times \mathbf{H}.$$

[22] Griswold, Kip, and Kittel, Phys. Rev. **88**, 951 (1952); for a full treatment, see G. Feher and A. F. Kip, Phys. Rev. **98**, 337 (1955); F. J. Dyson, Phys. Rev. **98**, 349 (1955). Determinations of the conduction electron spin susceptibility by the Illinois group are referred to in the next chapter.

[23] F. Bloch, Phys. Rev. **70**, 460 (1946).

Now, if we may consider the spin system free with respect to lattice interactions, we may write

(9.39) $$\mathbf{M} = \gamma \mathbf{J},$$

where for electrons

(9.40) $$\gamma = ge/2mc.$$

We have then as the equation of motion for the magnetization

(9.41) $$d\mathbf{M}/dt = \gamma \mathbf{M} \times \mathbf{H}.$$

We obtain very simply an approximate solution of this equation. We take the static field as H_z and the r-f field as H_x. The component equations may be written, for time dependence $e^{i\omega t}$,

(9.42)
$$i\omega M_x = \gamma M_y H_z;$$
$$i\omega M_y = \gamma(M_z H_x - M_x H_z);$$
$$M_z = -\gamma M_y H_x \cong 0.$$

The third equation may be neglected as long as $H_x \ll H_z$ and $M_y \ll M_z$. We must bear in mind that there is always a static time-independent term in M_z caused by the static magnetic field H_z. We may then solve for M_x, finding

$$-\omega^2 M_x = \gamma^2(M_z H_z H_x - M_x H_z^2),$$

or, for the r-f susceptibility χ_x,

(9.43) $$\chi_x = M_x/H_x = \frac{\gamma^2 M_z H_z}{(\gamma H_z)^2 - \omega^2}.$$

Setting the resonance frequency $\omega_0 = \gamma H_z$, in agreement with (9.35), and writing $\chi_0 = M_z/H_z$ for the static susceptibility, we have

(9.44) $$\chi_x = \frac{\chi_0}{1 - (\omega/\omega_0)^2}$$

We may picture the magnetization vector as precessing about the static field at an angle which depends on the amplitude of the r-f field, on the proximity to resonance, and on damping factors which we have not introduced here.

Line width. The width of the resonance line is caused usually by the interactions of the spins with each other and by their interaction with the crystal lattice.

If we have N spins per unit volume, of moment μ, oriented more or less at random, the magnetic field any one spin will see is the sum of the external field plus a random field of the order of $\Delta H \approx \mu/a^3 \approx \mu N$, where a is the nearest neighbor distance. We may therefore expect a line width of the order of $\Delta H \approx \mu N$, which for electrons may be $\approx (10^{-20})(10^{23}) = 1000$ oersteds, and for nuclei may be $\approx (10^{-23})(10^{23}) = 1$ oersted. These values are of the order of magnitude of the observed widths in many cases. If, however, the electrons have a strong exchange interaction with each other, the lines may be much sharper.[24] In liquids[25] the nuclear lines are sharpened when the neighboring nuclei are in rapid thermal motion with respect to the reference nucleus. Here the perturbing field caused by neighboring

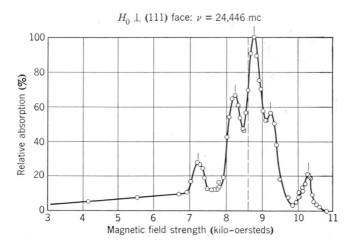

Fig. 9.11.   Absorption in ammonium chrome alum, $NH_4Cr(SO_4)_2 \cdot 12H_2O$ near 1 cm wavelength.   [After Yager et al., Phys. Rev. 75, 1630 (1949).]

nuclei does not look like a random addition to the static field, but rather like a high frequency perturbation, to which the spin does not respond when the frequency of the random field is higher than the frequency corresponding to the unperturbed width of the resonance.

Zero field electronic splitting.   In many solids, as we have previously mentioned, the ground state of the paramagnetic ion is split by the crystalline electric field, and it is possible to observe r-f transitions between the sublevels without necessarily applying a static magnetic field.   This was first done by Bleaney and co-workers.   Usually, however, a static field is applied and the zero field separation of the levels is deduced from a theoretical interpretation of the several absorption

[24] C. J. Gorter and J. H. Van Vleck, Phys. Rev. 72, 1128 (1947); J. H. Van Vleck Phys. Rev. 74, 1168 (1948).
[25] Bloembergen, Purcell, and Pound, Phys. Rev. 73, 679 (1948).

lines observed under these conditions of combined crystalline and Zeeman splittings. Results for ammonium chrome alum at room temperature are shown in Fig. 9.11; the spectrum is interpreted by a zero field splitting of 0.143 cm^{-1} and a g value of 1.99. The theory for this crystal is discussed by Broer[26] and Weiss.[27]

Further remarks. Paramagnetic relaxation effects observed when the r-f field is parallel to the static field, or when there is no static field, are discussed in Gorter's book cited at the end of the chapter. The relaxation frequencies are of the order of 10^6 to 10^9 cps, or higher.

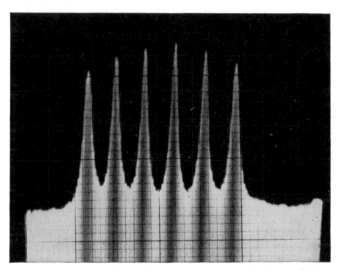

Fig. 9.12. Hyperfine structure of Mn^{2+} ions in water. [After Tinkham, Weinstein, and Kip, Phys. Rev. **84**, 848 (1951).] The nuclear spin is $I = \frac{5}{2}$, and the electronic spin is $S = \frac{5}{2}$.

A review of hyperfine structure effects in electronic resonance has been prepared by Bleaney.[28] In paramagnetic salts which have been diluted with a non-magnetic isomorphous salt it is often possible to resolve a line structure caused by the interaction of electrons with nuclear spins. The hyperfine structure of Mn^{2+} ions in aqueous solution is shown in Fig. 9.12 (from work by Tinkham, Weinstein, and Kip).

Note on units. To convert flux density in gauss to webers/m^2, multiply the value in gauss by 10^{-4}. To convert magnetic field intensity in oersteds to amperes/m, multiply by 79.6.

[26] L. J. F. Broer, Physica **9**, 647 (1942).

[27] P. R. Weiss, Phys. Rev. **73**, 470 (1948).

[28] B. Bleaney, Physica **17**, 175 (1951).

PROBLEMS

9.1. The wave function of the hydrogen atom in its ground state (1s) is

$$\psi = (\pi a_0{}^3)^{-\frac{1}{2}}e^{-r/a_0},$$

where $a_0 = \hbar^2/me^2 = 0.529 \times 10^{-8}$ cm. The charge density is $\rho(x, y, z) = e\,|\psi|^2$, according to the statistical interpretation of the wave function. Show that for this state

$$\overline{r^2} = 3a_0{}^2,$$

and calculate the molar diamagnetic susceptibility of atomic hydrogen (-2.36×10^{-6} cm^3/mole).

9.2. Given a plane slab of a metal containing N resistanceless electrons per unit volume, find an expression for the distance below the surface at which an applied static magnetic field H_0 parallel to the surface is reduced in intensity by e^{-1}.

9.3.* Given an atom with a spherically symmetrical charge distribution in an external field H, show that the field at the nucleus caused by the diamagnetic current is

$$\Delta H = -(eH/3mc^2)v(0),$$

where $v(0)$ is the electrostatic potential produced at the nucleus by the atomic electrons [W. E. Lamb, Jr., Phys. Rev. **60**, 817 (1941).] This diamagnetic correction to the magnetic field at the nucleus is of some importance in connection with the accurate determination of nuclear moments [W. C. Dickinson, Phys. Rev. **81**, 717 (1951).] Estimate very roughly the magnitude of $\Delta H/H$ for an atom with $Z = 50$, and show that the result may be of the order of 10^{-3}.

9.4. Show that on the Langevin theory the first two terms in a series expansion of the differential susceptibility are

$$\chi = dM/dH = (N\mu^2/3kT)\{1 - [(\mu H/kT)^2/5] + \cdots\}.$$

9.5. Bohr (and also van Leeuwen) has shown that, in any dynamical system to which classical statistical mechanics can be applied, the diamagnetic and paramagnetic susceptibilities cancel, so that classically one always has zero susceptibility in thermal equilibrium. Consider a moving charge e constrained to remain at a fixed distance r from an attracting center; show that the magnetic dipole moment is

$$\mu = (e/2mc)mr^2\theta,$$

where θ is the angular velocity. The kinetic energy of the rigid rotator has the average value kT on Boltzmann statistics, as the particle has 2 degrees of freedom. Calculate the mean square dipole moment, and substitute in the Langevin paramagnetic susceptibility equation. Compare the result with the diamagnetic equation (9.5), and show that the total susceptibility vanishes. Quantization completely modifies the picture and makes magnetization possible.

9.6.* There are N atoms per unit volume, each with total angular momentum quantum number J and spectroscopic splitting factor g. Show that the magnetization is given by

$$M = NgJ\mu_B B_J(x)$$

where $x = gJ\mu_B H/kT$ and B_J is the Brillouin function:

$$B_J = \frac{2J + 1}{2J}\,\mathrm{ctnh}\left[\frac{(2J + 1)x}{2J}\right] - \frac{1}{2J}\,\mathrm{ctnh}\left(\frac{x}{2J}\right).$$

Show also that, for $x \ll 1$,

$$B_J \cong (J + 1)x/3J,$$
and
$$M \cong Ng^2\mu_B{}^2J(J + 1)H/3kT.$$

Show that in the limit $J \to \infty$ the Brillouin function goes over into the Langevin function. Note that the classical magnetic moment μ is defined so that

$$\lim_{J\to\infty} (gJ\mu_B) \to \mu.$$

9.7. Some organic molecules have a triplet $(S = 1)$ excited state not far above a singlet $(S = 0)$ ground state. Plot the susceptibility as a function of temperature for a zero field splitting $\Delta/k = 100°$K, where k is the Boltzmann constant. Show that the susceptibility for $kT \gg \Delta$ is approximately independent of Δ.

9.8.* Following the discussion in Appendix H, show that to the first order in λ/Δ the g value measured in the x direction of the system discussed there is equal to 2. The anisotropy in the g value leads to an anisotropy in the susceptibility. Actual paramagnetic salts may exhibit quite large anisotropies in the susceptibility, amounting, for example, to 30% in $Co(NH_4)_2(SO_4)_2\cdot6H_2O$.

9.9. Making *rough* calculations, compare the entropy (for $H = 0$) at 2°K of 1 cm^3 of the salt iron ammonium alum, $FeNH_4(SO_4)_2\cdot12H_2O$, with that of 1 cm^3 of lead at the same temperature. This result shows that one may use the salt to cool other substances. At 2°K, $T/\theta_0 > 10$ for iron ammonium alum, where $k\theta_0$ is the zero field splitting. Neglect nuclear spin effects.

9.10. A paramagnetic salt contains 10^{22} ions/cm^3 with magnetic moment 1 Bohr magneton. (a) Calculate the surplus fraction, i.e., the percentage indicating how many more are parallel rather than antiparallel to a magnetic field of 10,000 oersteds at 300°K. (b) Calculate the magnetization in this field.

9.11* Derive (H.1) in Appendix H, neglecting terms of order $(\lambda/\Delta)^2$.

REFERENCES

E. R. Andrew, *Nuclear magnetic resonance*, Cambridge University Press, 1955.

L. F. Bates, *Modern magnetism*, Cambridge University Press, Cambridge, 3rd ed., 1951.

B. Bleaney and K. W. H. Stevens, "Paramagnetic resonance," Repts. Prog. Phys. **16**, 108 (1953).

K. D. Bowers and J. Owen, "Paramagnetic resonance II," Repts. Prog. Phys. **18**, 304 (1955).

H. B. G. Casimir, *Magnetism and very low temperatures*, Cambridge University Press, Cambridge, 1940.

K. K. Darrow, "Magnetic resonance," Bell System Tech. J. **32**, 74–99, 384–405 (1953).

C. G. B. Garrett, *Magnetic cooling*, Harvard, Cambridge, 1954.

C. J. Gorter, editor, *Progress in low temperature physics*, Interscience, New York, 1955.

C. J. Gorter, *Paramagnetic relaxation*, Elsevier, Amsterdam, 1947.

International Conference on Spectroscopy at Radiofrequencies, Physica **17**, 169 (1951).

C. Kikuchi and R. D. Spence, "Microwave methods in physics: II. Microwave absorption in paramagnetic substances," Am. J. Phys. **18**, 167 (1950).

W. R. Meyers, "Diamagnetism of ions," Revs. Modern Phys. **24,** 15 (1952).

G. E. Pake, "Fundamentals of nuclear magnetic resonance absorption," Am. J. Phys. **18,** 438, 473 (1950).

P. W. Selwood, *Magnetochemistry,* Interscience Publishers, New York, 1943.

E. C. Stoner, *Magnetism and matter,* Methuen and Co., Ltd., London, 1934.

J. H. Van Vleck, "Quelques aspects de la théorie du magnétisme," Ann. inst. Henri Poincaré **10,** 57 (1947).

J. H. Van Vleck, *The theory of electric and magnetic susceptibilities,* Clarendon Press, Oxford, 1932.

10

Free Electron Model of Metals

It is possible to understand a number of important physical properties of some metals, in particular the simple monovalent metals, in terms of the free electron model. According to this model the valence electrons of the constituent atoms of the metal are able to move about freely through the volume of the specimen. The valence electrons are responsible for the conduction of electricity by the metal, and for this reason these electrons are termed conduction electrons, as distinguished from the electrons of the filled shells of the ion cores. The interaction of the conduction electrons with the ion cores of the original atoms is neglected in the free electron approximation, and all calculations proceed as if the conduction electrons were entirely free in the space bounded by the surfaces of the specimen.

Even in the metals for which the free electron model is most useful, such as sodium, copper, and silver, it is wrong to imagine that the charge distribution of the electrons does not reflect the strong attractive electrostatic potential of the ion cores. The usefulness of the free electron model for the discussion of certain properties of metals depends on the circumstance that the energy of a conduction electron may depend on the square of the velocity, just as for an electron in free space, without the implication that the charge distribution should be that of a free electron. This point will be developed further in the next chapter, which is concerned with the effects of the interaction of the lattice with the conduction electrons.

The concept that metallic properties may be described in terms of free electrons was developed long before the invention of wave mechanics. The early theory had several conspicuous successes and several remarkable failures. Among the successes were the derivation of the functional form of Ohm's law connecting the electric current with the electric field and, in particular, the validity of the Wiedemann-Franz relation between the electrical conductivity and the thermal conductivity. The outstanding failures relate to discrepancies between observed and calculated values of the electronic heat capacity and also of the paramagnetic susceptibility of the conduction electrons. There is a further difficulty: it is not possible to understand on the classical model the occurrence of long electronic mean free paths, which at low temperatures may be as much as 10^3 or more longer than the values expected on a classical hard sphere model of the scattering of electrons by the ion cores.   In fact, it will be seen later that on the quantum theory the ion cores do not scatter the conduction electrons at all, as long as the ion cores are arranged in a perfectly regular array; this is truly a remarkable result.   We discuss these points in detail in the sections which follow.

ELECTRICAL CONDUCTIVITY AND OHM'S LAW

We shall first consider the effect of an electric field $\mathbf{E}$ on a classical gas of free electrons.   We suppose that there are N electrons per unit volume.   We imagine that the electrons are moving around in a random way, with a velocity distribution appropriate to a condition of thermal equilibrium at temperature T.   In the absence of an applied electric field the average or drift velocity,

$$(10.1) \qquad \mathbf{v}_D = \frac{1}{N} \sum_{i=1}^{N} \mathbf{v}_i,$$

will be zero, as in equilibrium there are just as many electrons moving in one direction as in the opposite direction.

We introduce now the concept of the *relaxation time*, denoted by τ. The relaxation time is closely related to the mean time of flight between collisions and also to the mean free path of the conduction electrons, which is the average distance of undisturbed motion between collisions.   All the details of the collision processes occurring in the electron gas are summarized for the present purpose when the relaxation time is given.   The collisions are caused by thermal or structural imperfections in the lattice.   The relaxation time is introduced as the characteristic time governing the establishment of equilibrium (through collisions) from an initial disturbed situation in which $\mathbf{v}_D \neq 0$.   If we write as the equation of motion for the drift velocity

$$(10.2) \qquad m\left(\frac{d\mathbf{v}_D}{dt} + \frac{1}{\tau}\mathbf{v}_D\right) = \mathbf{F},$$

where $\mathbf{F}$ is the average external force acting on an electron, we see that in the absence of external forces the free motion satisfies

$$(10.3) \qquad \frac{d\mathbf{v}_D}{dt} + \frac{1}{\tau}\mathbf{v}_D = 0,$$

or, if $\mathbf{v}_D(0)$ is the initial drift velocity in the non-equilibrium distribution, the approach to equilibrium is described by the appropriate solution of (10.3):

(10.4) $$\mathbf{v}_D(t) = \mathbf{v}_D(0)e^{-t/\tau}.$$

We have thus arranged things so that a disturbance from equilibrium dies out exponentially, with the characteristic time τ. We note further that the term $m\mathbf{v}_D/\tau$ introduced in (10.2) has the familiar form of a frictional or damping force, with m/τ playing the part of a coefficient of friction.

If there were no friction in the electron system—that is, if the relaxation time were infinitely long—the conduction electrons would accelerate without limit in a constant applied electric field. The equation of motion

(10.5) $$m\dot{\mathbf{v}}_D = e\mathbf{E}$$

has the solution

(10.6) $$\mathbf{v}_D(t) = \mathbf{v}_D(0) + e\mathbf{E}t/m,$$

which does not give a steady state of the type described by Ohm's law.

With a finite relaxation time the equation of motion in a constant electric field is

(10.7) $$m\left(\frac{d\mathbf{v}_D}{dt} + \frac{1}{\tau}\mathbf{v}_D\right) = e\mathbf{E},$$

which has the particular solution

(10.8) $$\mathbf{v}_D = e\tau\mathbf{E}/m.$$

This solution represents a situation in which the drift velocity does not change with time and is obtained from (10.7) by setting the term $d\mathbf{v}_D/dt = 0$. The latter term describes inertial effects and should be included in problems where $\mathbf{E}$ is not constant, but is time-dependent.

The electric current density $\mathbf{j}$ is defined as the electric charge transported through unit area in unit time. The net number of electrons passing through a unit area in unit time is $N\mathbf{v}_D$, where N is the number of electrons per unit volume. The electric current density is therefore given by

(10.9) $$\mathbf{j} = Ne\mathbf{v}_D.$$

Using (10.8), we have in the steady state

(10.10) $$\mathbf{j} = (Ne^2\tau/m)\mathbf{E},$$

showing that the current is directly proportional to the electric field. We have thus established Ohm's law.

The electrical conductivity σ is defined by the relation

$$(10.11) \qquad \mathbf{j} = \sigma \mathbf{E},$$

and so, using (10.10), we have the important result

$$(10.12) \qquad \sigma = Ne^2\tau/m.$$

As the resistivity ρ is defined as the reciprocal of the conductivity, we have

$$(10.13) \qquad \rho = 1/\sigma = m/Ne^2\tau.$$

It is easy to understand the result (10.12) for the conductivity. We expect the charge transported to be proportional to the charge density Ne; the factor e/m enters because the acceleration in a given electric field is proportional to e and inversely proportional to the mass m; the time τ describes the free time during which the field acts on the carrier, the next collision removing all memory of the drift velocity. Quantum theory does not alter the result (10.12) in any essential way; rather, it tells us how to make a theoretical calculation of the relaxation time starting from first principles.

It is instructive to estimate from the observed conductivity the order of magnitude of the relaxation time τ, using (10.12). We consider copper at room temperature. The handbook value of the resistivity is 1.7 microhm-cm, and so $\sigma = 6 \times 10^5$ (ohm-cm)$^{-1}$. This value is in practical units. To convert to esu we must multiply by $(10)^{-1}(3 \times 10^{10})(300) = 9 \times 10^{11}$. The factor $(10)^{-1}$ converts the current to absolute amperes and the factor 3×10^{10} converts to statamperes; the factor 300 is involved reciprocally in the conversion of volts/cm to statvolts/cm. That is, we are given

$$\mathbf{j} \text{ (practical)} = \sigma \text{ (practical) } \mathbf{E} \text{ (practical)}$$

and wish to find σ (esu) defined by

$$\mathbf{j} \text{ (esu)} = \sigma \text{ (esu)} \mathbf{E} \text{ (esu)}.$$

Thus on division

$$(10.14) \qquad \frac{\sigma \text{ (esu)}}{\sigma \text{ (practical)}} = \frac{\mathbf{j} \text{ (esu)}}{\mathbf{j} \text{ (practical)}} \frac{\mathbf{E} \text{ (practical)}}{\mathbf{E} \text{ (esu)}}$$

$$= (3 \times 10^9)(300) = 9 \times 10^{11}.$$

In these conversions we have taken the value of the velocity of light to be 3×10^{10} cm/sec. For our problem we have then that σ (esu) $\cong$ 5×10^{17} sec^{-1}, recalling that in esu the conductivity has the dimensions of a frequency.

It is reasonable to suppose that each atom of copper in the metal contributes one valence electron to the conduction band.[1] The concentration N of conduction electrons on this assumption will be equal to the number of copper atoms per unit volume, which may be found from the Avogadro number divided by the molar volume. The molar volume is the molecular weight divided by the density, or

$$\text{Molar volume} = 63.5/8.94 = 7.1 \text{ cm}^3.$$

Hence

$$N = 6.025 \times 10^{23}/7.1 = 8.5 \times 10^{22} \text{ cm}^{-3}.$$

We have

$$\tau = \sigma m/Ne^2 \cong (5 \times 10^{17})(9 \times 10^{-28})/(9 \times 10^{22})(5 \times 10^{-10})^2$$

$$\cong 2 \times 10^{-14} \text{ sec.}$$

We have not yet built up enough background material or carried the theory far enough along to enable the reader at this point to judge for himself if this estimated value of the relaxation time is reasonable on the basis of other evidence. One piece of evidence may be cited to suggest that the relevant relaxation time should be shorter than 10^{-11} sec, in agreement with the above estimate: the microwave attenuation of copper wave guide at a frequency of 2.4×10^{10} cps and at room temperature is known to be in quite good agreement with that calculated according to the ordinary theory of the r-f skin effect, provided the surfaces of the guide are suitably polished. The result of the theory is expressed in terms of the static electrical conductivity. If the inertial term $m d\mathbf{v}_D/dt$ in the equation of motion (10.7)

$$m \left(\frac{d\mathbf{v}_D}{dt} + \frac{1}{\tau} \mathbf{v}_D \right) = e\mathbf{E}$$

were more important than the relaxation term $m\mathbf{v}_D/\tau$, we would not expect to find agreement with the wave guide losses as calculated using the d-c conductivity. Using complex notation, if the electric field varies with time as $e^{i\omega t}$, the equation of motion may be written

(10.15) $$m \left(i\omega + \frac{1}{\tau} \right) \mathbf{v}_D = e\mathbf{E},$$

[1] The configuration of the ground state of the free copper atom is $1s^2 2s^2 2p^6 3s^2$-$3p^6 3d^{10} 4s$; the valence electron of copper is the $4s$ electron, the other electrons in closed shells forming the ion core.

and so the relaxation term is dominant as long as $1/\tau \gg \omega$, or

(10.16) $\tau \ll (1/\omega) = (1/2\pi f) \cong 7 \times 10^{-12}$ sec.

It is satisfying that our time of 2×10^{-14} sec as estimated from the conductivity does indeed satisfy this inequality.

We may introduce the mean free path Λ by the relation

(10.17) $\Lambda = \tau u,$

where u is an appropriate average electron velocity. We shall see later in this chapter that the appropriate value of u for copper is

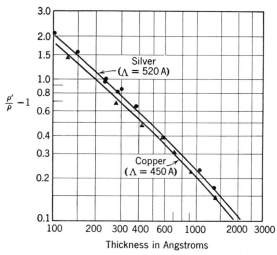

Fig. 10.1. Experimental points involving resistivity measurements of Cu and Ag films at room temperature, shown with curves calculated from theory to obtain approximate values of mean free paths. Here ρ' is the resistivity in the film; ρ is the bulk resistivity. (Reynolds and Stilwell.)

about 1.6×10^8 cm/sec; with $\tau \cong 2 \times 10^{-14}$ sec at room temperature we have $\Lambda \cong 3 \times 10^{-6}$ cm, or about 100 times the lattice constant of copper. There is some experimental evidence that this value is reasonable: for example, Reynolds and Stilwell[2] have measured the resistivity of good films of copper and silver as a function of the thickness of the film. The resistivity will have two contributions, one from collisions in the bulk of the material of the type that we are discussing and another contribution from diffuse scattering of the electrons at the surface of the film. In thick specimens the bulk scattering is dom-

[2] F. W. Reynolds and G. R. Stilwell, Phys. Rev. **88**, 418 (1952); a review of theoretical and experimental work on the mean free path of electrons in metals is given by E. H. Sondheimer, Advances in Physics **1**, 1 (1952).

inant; in thin films the surface scattering is dominant. The theory of the combined scattering has been worked out by K. Fuchs[3] and, as shown in Fig. 10.1, is in good agreement with the observations, provided the bulk mean free path is taken to be 4.5×10^{-6} cm in copper, in satisfactory agreement with our rough estimate. The results of more careful calculations are given in Table 10.1.

TABLE 10.1. CONDUCTIVITY DATA FOR METALS AT 0°C

One free electron per atom is assumed: Λ is calculated by using Eq. (10.17); values after Mott and Jones, with an error of a factor of 2 in their Λ's corrected; u_F is calculated by setting $\frac{1}{2}mu_F{}^2 = E_F$, where the Fermi energy E_F is given by (10.43).

Metal	Free Electrons per cm³, $N \times 10^{-22}$	Observed Conductivity at 0°C, $\sigma \times 10^{-17}$ (esu)	Calculated $u_F \times 10^{-8}$ (cm/sec)	Calculated Mean Free Path $\Lambda \times 10^8$ (cm)
Li	4.6	1.06	1.31	110
Na	2.5	2.09	1.07	350
K	1.3	1.47	0.85	370
Rb	1.1	0.78	0.80	220
Cs	0.85	0.49	0.75	160
Cu	8.5	5.76	1.58	420
Ag	5.8	6.12	1.40	570
Au	5.9	4.37	1.40	410

We note, according to Table 3.6, that the ionic radius R of the Cu^+ ion core is 0.96×10^{-8} cm. Now, according to simple dimensional reasoning or elementary kinetic theory, the mean free path should be given by $\Lambda \approx 1/(N\pi R^2) \approx 4 \times 10^{-8}$ cm if the interaction of a conduction electron with a copper ion core may be treated classically. However, we have seen that the actual mean free path is of the order of 5×10^{-6} cm at room temperature, and it may be as long as 10^{-3} cm or more at low temperatures. We conclude the interaction cannot be treated classically.

The mobility μ is defined as the drift velocity per unit electric field:

$$(10.18) \qquad \mu = \mathbf{v}_D/\mathbf{E} = e\tau/m,$$

according to (10.8). To get an idea of the order of magnitude of the mobility, we consider copper at room temperature:

$$\mu \cong (5 \times 10^{-10})(2 \times 10^{-14})/(9 \times 10^{-28}) \cong 10^4 \text{ cm}^2/\text{statvolt-sec}$$

$$\cong 30 \text{ cm}^2/\text{volt-sec}.$$

[3] K. Fuchs, Proc. Cambridge Phil. Soc. **34**, 100 (1938).

The mobility is a particularly useful quantity in dealing with semi-conductors, Chapter 13.

We have quoted (but not yet derived) the value 1.6×10^8 cm/sec for the intrinsic velocity of the conduction electrons in copper. The drift velocity acquired in an external electric field will be small in comparison with this as long as the electric field intensity does not exceed 10^6 volts/cm. For fields of this magnitude or higher we expect non-linear effects to modify the form of Ohm's law. Because of the high fields required such effects are of only little importance in normal metals;[4] they are important however in semiconductors,[5] where high electric field intensities may exist at p-n junctions. The theory of p-n junctions is discussed in Chapter 14.

We must emphasize that the expression $\sigma = Ne^2\tau/m$ has been discussed here on a purely classical model, with no use of quantum mechanics or quantum statistics. It will be shown later in this chapter that the result is preserved in the quantum treatment.

WIEDEMANN-FRANZ RATIO

In Chapter 6 we discussed expressions for the thermal conductivity of conduction electrons. Using the free electron model and Fermi-Dirac statistics, we have (6.47) for the thermal conductivity:

(10.19) $$K = \frac{\pi^2}{3} k^2 T N \tau/m.$$

The electrical conductivity is given by $\sigma = Ne^2\tau/m$, according to (10.12). Thus

(10.20) $$\frac{K}{\sigma} = \frac{\pi^2}{3} \left(\frac{k}{e}\right)^2 T.$$

A relationship of this type was first observed by Wiedemann and Franz, and the ratio is named after them. The Lorenz number L is defined by

(10.21) $$L = K/\sigma T,$$

and according to (10.20) should be given on the free electron model by

(10.22) $$L = \frac{\pi^2}{3}\left(\frac{k}{e}\right)^2 = 2.72 \times 10^{-13} \text{ esu/deg}^2$$

$$= 2.45 \times 10^{-8} \text{ watt-ohm/deg}^2,$$

for electronic conduction only. This is a remarkable result, as it

[4] See, for example, E. Guth and J. Mayerhöfer, Phys. Rev. **57**, 908 (1940).
[5] W. Shockley, Bell System Tech. J. **30**, 990 (1951).

involves neither N, m, or τ. A more detailed study of the quantum theory of transport processes in metals shows that the Lorenz number is expected to be independent of temperature only above the Debye temperature,[6] as the differences between the types of collision averages involved in electrical and thermal conductivity become important when at low temperatures small angle electron-phonon collisions are dominant. At room temperature the values observed are in quite good agreement with the theoretical value given in (10.22), as shown in Table 10.2. The Lorenz number of pure copper at liquid hydrogen temperature ($\sim$15°K) is an order of magnitude smaller than at room temperature.

TABLE 10.2. EXPERIMENTAL LORENZ NUMBERS

$L \times 10^8$ watt-ohms/deg^2			$L \times 10^8$ watt-ohms/deg^2		
Metal	0°C	100°C	Metal	0°C	100°C
Ag	2.31	2.37	Pb	2.47	2.56
Au	2.35	2.40	Pt	2.51	2.60
Cd	2.42	2.43	Sn	2.52	2.49
Cu	2.23	2.33	W	3.04	3.20
Ir	2.49	2.49	Zn	2.31	2.33
Mo	2.61	2.79			

HEAT CAPACITY OF CONDUCTION ELECTRONS

According to the classical theory discussed in Chapter 6, the conduction electrons of a metal should make a contribution

$$C \text{ (electronic)} = \tfrac{3}{2}Rz$$

to the molar heat capacity of the metal; here R is the gas constant and z is the number of valence electrons per atom. As discussed earlier, there is no experimental evidence for an electronic contribution of anything like this magnitude. The value of the heat capacity of metals at room temperature and above is usually quite close to the value 6 cal/mole-deg, just as for dielectric solids, and this value may be attributed to lattice vibrations, to a fair approximation. The discrepancy represents an outstanding failure of the classical free electron gas model. It is a particularly puzzling failure in the light of the partial successes of the model in explaining electrical and thermal conductivity in metals: it is difficult to see classically how the electrons can participate in transport processes as if they were free and yet give only a very small contribution to the heat capacity.

[6] Experimental studies of the temperature dependence of L at low temperatures in sodium and copper have been carried out by R. Berman and D. K. C. MacDonald, Proc. Roy. Soc. (London) **A209**, 368 (1951;) **A211**, 122 (1952).

PARAMAGNETIC SUSCEPTIBILITY OF CONDUCTION ELECTRONS

The classical free electron theory also gives an unsatisfactory account of the paramagnetic susceptibility of the conduction electrons. We know from elementary atomic physics that an electron has associated with it a magnetic moment of value equal to a Bohr magneton:

$$(10.23) \qquad \mu_B = \frac{e\hbar}{2mc} = -0.927 \times 10^{-20} \text{ erg/oersted.}$$

One would expect that the conduction electrons, according to the results of the preceding chapter, would make a paramagnetic contribution, [Eq. (9.20)],

$$\chi = N\mu_B{}^2/kT,$$

to the susceptibility of the metal. Instead it is observed that the susceptibility of normal non-ferromagnetic metals is independent of temperature and of magnitude at room temperature perhaps only $\frac{1}{100}$ of that expected.

QUANTUM THEORY OF FREE PARTICLES IN A BOX

The difficulties encountered by the classical free electron theory in attempting to explain the observations of the heat capacity and magnetic susceptibility of simple metals are corrected in a simple and satisfying way on taking account of the requirements of the Pauli exclusion principle. We are familar with the central and crucial part played by the Pauli principle in accounting for the composition and even the existence of the periodic table of elements.[7] The most elementary statement of the Pauli principle as applied to isolated atoms is that no two electrons of the same atom may have all their individual quantum numbers equal. The individual quantum numbers in an atom may be taken as n, the principal quantum number; l, the orbital quantum number; m_l, the azimuthal quantum number representing the projection of l on a given direction; m_s, the spin quantum number, which may be either $\pm\frac{1}{2}$.

We remind the reader of an elementary application of the exclusion principle. If we take the quantum numbers for the ground state of hydrogen to be $n = 1$, $l = 0$, $m_l = 0$, $m_s = \frac{1}{2}$, then the next electron added in forming the ground state of helium, which has two electrons, must occupy the set of quantum numbers $n = 1$, $l = 0$, $m_l = 0$,

---

[7] For introductory discussions of the Pauli principle the reader may refer to the following references, among others: J. C. Slater, *Introduction to chemical physics*, McGraw-Hill, New York, 1939, Chapter XXI; M. Born, *Atomic physics*, Hafner, New York, 5th ed., 1951, Chapter VI.

$m_s = -\frac{1}{2}$. In helium all the sets of quantum numbers associated with $n = 1$ are occupied, so that when we go on to the lithium atom the third electron in the ground state must start with $n = 2$, and we can complete the set by taking $l = 0$, $m_l = 0$, $m_s = +\frac{1}{2}$. Proceeding in this way we can construct the entire periodic table, with the results shown in Table 3.2.

It is evident when we try to determine the consequences of the Pauli principle for the conduction electrons of a metal that we must first set up a proper system of quantum numbers for the problem, a system which will specify the state of the conduction electrons in the same way as the set of quantum numbers n, l, m_l, m_s specify the state of the electrons in the problem of the free atom.

For the present purpose the most important fact about the free electron is that there is a wave associated with it, of wavelength

$$(10.24) \qquad\qquad \lambda = h/p,$$

where h is Planck's constant and p is the momentum mv of the electron, considered to be in free space. This is the celebrated de Broglie relation. The wave nature of the electron has been demonstrated by many experiments, in the first instance the electron diffraction experiments of Davisson and Germer and of G. P. Thomson. In these experiments one detects a beam of electrons diffracted on reflection from the surface of a crystal or diffracted in passing through a polycrystalline foil; the angles at which diffracted electron beams are found are just the angles satisfying the Bragg condition $2d \sin \theta = n\lambda$, where the wavelength in the Bragg equation (Chapter 2) is to be calculated from the de Broglie relation above. The electron momentum p is related to the accelerating voltage applied to the electron beam by

$$p = (2mE)^{\frac{1}{2}},$$

where E is the energy of the electrons. A convenient practical relation for electrons is

$$\lambda \text{ (A)} \cong (150/V)^{\frac{1}{2}},$$

where λ is given in Angstrom units (10^{-8} cm) and V is the accelerating voltage in volts. We see that the wavelength of a 150-volt electron is 1 A; of a 1.5 volt electron, 10 A.

The Schrödinger wave equation

$$(10.25) \qquad\qquad \left[-\frac{\hbar^2}{2m} \nabla^2 + V(\mathbf{r}) \right] \psi = E\psi$$

is in effect a generalization of the de Broglie relation to situations in which the potential energy $V(\mathbf{r})$ of the electron is a function of the position $\mathbf{r}$. In this equation

$$\nabla^2 \equiv \frac{\partial^2}{\partial x^2} + \frac{\partial^2}{\partial y^2} + \frac{\partial^2}{\partial z^2};$$

$\hbar = h/2\pi$; and E is the total energy, which is constant. The function ψ is the wave function or eigenfunction, and has the significance that, when properly normalized, $\psi^*\psi\, dxdydz$ is the probability of finding the electron in the volume element $dxdydz$. Here ψ^* denotes the complex conjugate function to ψ.

We can see a connection of the Schrödinger equation with the de Broglie relation by considering an electron in free space, with $V(\mathbf{r}) = 0$. The wave equation becomes

(10.26)
$$-\frac{\hbar^2}{2m}\nabla^2\psi = E\psi.$$

We may obtain a solution of this equation with E constant on taking $\psi \sim e^{i\mathbf{k}\cdot\mathbf{r}}$. We see that

$$\nabla^2\psi = -k^2\psi,$$

and so ψ is a solution when $\mathbf{k}$ and E are related by

(10.27)
$$E = \frac{\hbar^2}{2m}k^2.$$

Now $\mathbf{k}$, called the wave vector, has the significance for free electrons that

(10.28)
$$k = |\mathbf{k}| = 2\pi/\lambda,$$

where λ is the wavelength. On substitution back in (10.27), we have

(10.29)
$$E = \frac{\hbar^2}{2m}\left(\frac{2\pi}{\lambda}\right)^2 = \frac{1}{2m}\left(\frac{h}{\lambda}\right)^2.$$

If the momentum and wavelength are connected by the de Broglie relation $\lambda = h/p$, we have on substitution

$$E = \frac{1}{2m}p^2 = \frac{1}{2}mv^2,$$

which is exactly the classical energy for a free particle of mass m. We see that for a free particle that the wave equation leads to the same connection between energy and wavelength as does the de Broglie relation.

In the approximation that the conduction electrons are entirely free we may take their wave functions to have the form

(10.30) $$\psi \sim e^{i\mathbf{k}\cdot\mathbf{r}}.$$

We must do two things to this function before it can be an acceptable solution to the problem. We must normalize it so that the integral of the probability density $\psi^*\psi$ over the allowed region of space is unity:

(10.31) $$\int \psi^*\psi \, dV = 1.$$

We accomplish this by setting

(10.32) $$\psi = (1/V)^{1\!/\!2}e^{i\mathbf{k}\cdot\mathbf{r}};$$

here V is the volume of the solid within which the electron is confined. We also want the wave function to satisfy reasonable boundary conditions on the surface of the solid. For example, we can require the wave function to go to zero on the surface.

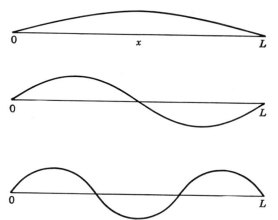

Fig. 10.2. First three wave functions for electron constrained to move on a line of length L.

The boundary conditions introduce a type of quantization into the problem. Consider an electron confined to a line of length L, as in Fig. 10.2. If we require that $\psi(0) = 0$ and $\psi(L) = 0$, then the solutions of the wave equation in one dimension must be of the form

(10.33) $$\psi_n = (2/L)^{1\!/\!2} \sin (n\pi x/L).$$

We obtain the energy by substituting ψ_n in Eq. (10.26), finding

(10.34) $$E_n = \frac{\hbar^2}{2m}\left(\frac{\pi}{L}\right)^2 n^2, \quad (n = 1, 2, 3, \cdots).$$

The allowed energy levels are quantized in this way, other values of the energy being excluded as the corresponding ψ's do not satisfy the boundary conditions.

It is often convenient, particularly in three dimensions, to introduce the boundary conditions in a different way. The method of periodic boundary conditions was introduced in Chapter 5 in connection with lattice vibrations. We quantize the electrons in a cube of side L and require the wave functions to be periodic in x, y, z with period L. We require, for example, that

$$(10.35) \qquad \psi(x + L, y, z) = \psi(x, y, z),$$

with similar relations for the y and z coordinates. Free particle wave functions satisfying the periodicity requirement will be of the form

$$(10.36) \qquad \psi_\mathbf{n} = (1/L)^{3/2} e^{i\frac{2\pi}{L}(n_x x + n_y y + n_z z)}$$

where

$$n_x = 0, \pm 1, \pm 2, \cdots ;$$

$$n_y = 0, \pm 1, \pm 2, \cdots ;$$

$$n_z = 0, \pm 1, \pm 2, \cdots .$$

It is easy to see that this function is satisfactory, for

$$\psi_\mathbf{n}(x + L, y, z) = (1/L)^{3/2} e^{i\frac{2\pi}{L}[n_x(x+L) + n_y y + n_z z]},$$

$$= (1/L)^{3/2} e^{i\frac{2\pi}{L}(n_x x + n_y y + n_z z)}$$

$$= \psi_\mathbf{n}(x, y, z),$$

as required. Here $\mathbf{n}$ denotes the triplet of integers (n_x, n_y, n_z). The energy corresponding to the solution (10.36) is easily seen to be

$$(10.37) \qquad E_\mathbf{n} = \frac{\hbar^2}{2m} \left(\frac{2\pi}{L}\right)^2 (n_x{}^2 + n_y{}^2 + n_z{}^2) = \frac{h^2 n^2}{2m V^{2/3}};$$

here the volume $V = L^3$ and $n^2 = n_x{}^2 + n_y{}^2 + n_z{}^2$. We note that the allowed values of the wave vector are given by

$$(10.38) \qquad \mathbf{k} = (2\pi/L)\mathbf{n}.$$

We see that the two types of boundary conditions are associated with two different types of wave functions. The solutions (10.33) for the condition $\psi = 0$ at the boundaries are of the form of standing waves and have the property that the probability density

$$(10.39) \qquad \psi^*\psi = (2/L) \sin^2 (n\pi x/L)$$

is a periodic function of x. However, the solutions (10.36) for periodic boundary conditions are of the form of traveling waves and give a uniform probability density, as

$$(10.40) \qquad\qquad \psi^*\psi = 1/V.$$

These differences are not significant in the free electron problem, but it turns out that when the interaction with the crystal lattice is taken into account the traveling wave solutions have more direct physical importance than the standing wave solutions. We shall work with traveling waves.

It will be evident that we may take, as the quantum numbers appropriate to the free electron problem, the three components of either **k** or **n**, as connected by (10.38), together with the spin quantum number $m_s = \pm\frac{1}{2}$ according to whether the electron spin is pointing up or down. That is, the state of an electron is specified when we are given the values of n_x, n_y, n_z, m_s, or, alternatively, k_x, k_y, k_z, m_s. We must now consider the effects of the Pauli exclusion principle on the energy distribution of the conduction electrons.

We see from (10.37) that the energy of an electron depends on $n^2 \equiv n_x{}^2 + n_y{}^2 + n_z{}^2$, where the n_x, n_y, n_z are positive or negative integers. The ground energy level of the system may be taken as $n_x = n_y = n_z = 0$. We may put two electrons into this level, one for each of the two possible spin orientations, $m_s = \pm\frac{1}{2}$. The next electron added to the system will have to go into a higher energy level, as the exclusion principle prevents it from going into either of the two ground states already occupied. The next energy level above the ground level will have $n^2 = 1$ and may be attained in twelve ways:

n_x	n_y	n_z	m_s
1	0	0	$\frac{1}{2}$
1	0	0	$-\frac{1}{2}$
-1	0	0	$\frac{1}{2}$
-1	0	0	$-\frac{1}{2}$
0	1	0	$\frac{1}{2}$
0	1	0	$-\frac{1}{2}$
0	-1	0	$\frac{1}{2}$
0	-1	0	$-\frac{1}{2}$
0	0	1	$\frac{1}{2}$
0	0	1	$-\frac{1}{2}$
0	0	-1	$\frac{1}{2}$
0	0	-1	$-\frac{1}{2}$

The first excited energy level of the system represents twelve independent states, and it will accommodate twelve electrons, according to the Pauli principle.

The ground level and the first excited level can hold a maximum of $2 + 12 = 14$ electrons, and at absolute zero the 14 states will be occupied by 14 electrons. The fifteenth electron to be added to the system then will have to go into another level: the level of lowest energy available to it will have $n^2 = 2$. The reader may confirm for himself that the level $n^2 = 2$ can hold a maximum of 24 electrons. Proceeding in this way we gradually move up the energy levels of the system until all the available electrons are accommodated. At absolute zero all the levels below a certain level will be filled with electrons, and all levels above it will be empty of electrons. The level which divides the filled and vacant levels is known as the Fermi level at absolute zero and is denoted by $E_F(0)$.

There is considerable interest in knowing the value of the Fermi level as a function of the electron concentration N. The number of states having n less than a certain value n_F is simply $2 \times (4\pi/3)n_F{}^3$, as there are two independent states (of different spin orientation) per unit volume in $\mathbf{n}$ space, each integral triplet n_x, n_y, n_z giving two states. To hold NL^3 electrons at absolute zero, all $\mathbf{n}$ values must then be filled up to

$$(10.41) \qquad (8\pi/3)n_F{}^3 = NL^3,$$

and so

$$(10.42) \qquad (n_F/L)^2 = (3N/8\pi)^{\frac{2}{3}}.$$

The energy corresponding to n_F is

$$(10.43) \qquad E_F(0) = \frac{\hbar^2}{2m}\left(\frac{2\pi}{L}\right)^2 n_F{}^2 = \frac{\hbar^2}{2m}(3\pi^2 N)^{\frac{2}{3}},$$

on combining (10.37) and (10.42).

The order of magnitude of $E_F(0)$ is about 5 ev; that is, at absolute zero the conduction electrons in a metal are not all condensed into a state of zero energy as on classical mechanics, but rather they fill all allowed energy levels over a range of some 5 ev above the ground state. Values of the Fermi energy on the free electron model are given in Table 10.3, together with values of the effective Fermi temperature T_F defined by

$$(10.44) \qquad T_F = E_F(0)/k.$$

The electron velocity u_F at the Fermi level is defined by

$$(10.45) \qquad \tfrac{1}{2}mu_F{}^2 = E_F(0).$$

TABLE 10.3. CALCULATED FERMI LEVEL VALUES
ON THE FREE ELECTRON MODEL

	Li	Na	K	Rb
E_F (ev)	4.72	3.12	2.14	1.82
T_F (deg)	55,000	37,000	24,000	21,000
u_F (cm/sec)	1.31×10^8	1.07×10^8	0.85×10^8	0.80×10^8
	Cs	Cu	Ag	Au
E_F (ev)	1.53	7.04	5.51	5.51
T_F (deg)	18,000	82,000	64,000	64,000
u_F (cm/sec)	0.75×10^8	1.58×10^8	1.40×10^8	1.40×10^8.

It is interesting to find the number of states per unit energy range per unit volume as a function of the energy. Denoting the density of states by $g(E)$, we know that

$$(10.46) \qquad \int g(E) \, dE = N = \frac{1}{3\pi^2} (2mE/\hbar^2)^{3/2},$$

using (10.43). Thus

$$(10.47) \qquad g(E) = \frac{1}{2\pi^2} (2m/\hbar^2)^{3/2} E^{1/2}.$$

A plot is given in Fig. 10.3.

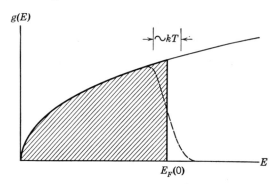

Fig. 10.3. Plot of density of states $g(E)$ as a function of energy. At absolute zero the states up to $E_F(0)$ are filled. The dotted curve indicates the density of filled states at a temperature $T \ll E_F/k$.

Let us now consider the effect of warming up the electrons from absolute zero to temperature T. In classical mechanics the general effect is to increase the energy of each particle by an amount of the order of kT, which at room temperature is of the order of 0.02 ev. We have seen that the energy distribution in the conduction electron problem extends over several electron volts even at absolute zero. It is very unlikely that an electron in this distribution will be excited at room temperature if it lies more than 0.1 ev below the Fermi level, as the states within an energy range of kT of such an electron are almost entirely filled, and it is generally not very probable that the electron will gain the $5kT \approx 0.1$ ev necessary to excite it into an otherwise unoccupied state above the Fermi level.

We can say then that the Pauli exclusion principle has a considerable effect on the thermal behavior of the conduction electrons. On heating from absolute zero every electron does not gain an energy $\sim kT$ as happens classically, but only those electrons already within an energy range of the order of kT of the Fermi level can be excited thermally; these electrons gain an energy which is itself of the order of kT, as sketched in Fig. 10.3.

This drastic modification of the thermal properties of the conduction electrons as compared with classical behavior gives an immediate qualitative solution to the problem of the heat capacity of the conduction electron gas. If N is the total number of electrons, only a fraction of the order of T/T_F can be excited thermally at temperature T, because only these lie within an energy range of the order of kT of the top of the energy distribution. These NT/T_F electrons have each gained a thermal energy of the order of kT, and so the total electronic thermal energy U is of the order of

$$(NT/T_F)kT = RT^2/T_F \text{ per mole.}$$

The electronic heat capacity is given by

$$C_v = \partial U/\partial T \approx RT/T_F,$$

which is proportional to T, in concord with the experimental data discussed in Chapter 6; at room temperature C_v is smaller than $\frac{3}{2}R$, the classical value, by a factor of the order of 0.01 or less. We recall $T_F \sim 5 \times 10^4$ deg.

We now go on to discuss quantitatively the effect of the exclusion principle on the thermal equilibrium distribution of the conduction electrons.

FERMI-DIRAC DISTRIBUTION LAW[8]

From the elementary kinetic theory of gases we are familiar with the Maxwell-Boltzmann distribution law. This law is a result of classical theory and is valid under the ordinary conditions of molecules in a gas. Electrons are much lighter than molecules; also, in a metal

[8] For an elementary exposition of quantum statistics, see M. Born, *Atomic physics*, Hafner, New York, 5th ed., 1951, Chapter VIII.

the concentration of valence electrons is 10^4 higher than the concentration of molecules in a gas at S.T.P.   Under these conditions classical statistics is no longer a valid approximation to the correct quantum statistics.   The classical distribution is a good approximation to the true state of affairs only when the average spacing between particles is large in comparison with the de Broglie wavelength (10.24) calculated using the thermal velocity of the particles.

As applied to electrons, quantum statistics requires that we treat all electrons as *indistinguishable* and that each state of the system may be occupied by at most one electron.   A one-particle state of the free particle system is determined by a specification of the values of the quantum numbers n_x, n_y, n_z, and the spin quantum number $m_z = \pm\frac{1}{2}$ of the electron.   If we can have only one electron in a state, it follows, when we are dealing with large numbers of electrons, that even in the lowest state of the total system many high quantum number states of the individual electrons will be occupied.   This is very different from the Maxwell-Boltzmann case where any number of particles can have the identical energy and momentum.   In the lowest state of a classical system all particles can have zero energy and momentum.

We define a cell by the set of numbers n_x, n_y, n_z, m_z.   The occupation number of a cell is either 0 or 1.   We consider now a set of g_s cells having approximately the same energy E as given by (10.37), and we let the number of electrons in the set be n_s, so that of the g_s cells n_s are (singly) occupied (1) and $g_s - n_s$ are empty (0).   The distribution is characterized uniquely by assigning to each cell its occupation number:

Cell	z_1	z_2	z_3	z_4	z_5	z_6	$z_7 \cdot \cdot \cdot$
Occupation number	0	1	0	0	1	1	$1 \cdot \cdot \cdot$

We may also give a complete characterization by specifying the cells which are vacant and those occupied by one particle, as in the following sequence:

$$1 \qquad\qquad\qquad 0$$
$$z_1\, z_3\, z_4 \cdot \cdot \cdot \qquad z_2\, z_5\, z_6\, z_7 \cdot \cdot \cdot$$

We now enumerate the *distinguishable distributions*.   There are $g_s!$ sequences in which we can write down the names (the z_i) of the g_s cells on a line, as the first spot may be chosen in g_s ways, the second in $g_s - 1$ ways, etc.   But many of these sequences are indistinguishable if the electrons are indistinguishable; for example, interchanging the order $z_2\, z_5$ to $z_5\, z_2$ is not a distinguishable change.

We must not count as distinguishable distributions those which differ from one another only by permutation of the n_s occupied cells or the

$g_s - n_s$ vacant cells.   The number of distinguishable sequences w_s is given by

(10.48) $$w_s(g_s - n_s)!n_s! = g_s!,$$

because the total number of sequences must be given by the number of distinguishable sequences times the number of indistinguishable sequences contained within each distinguishable sequence.   We have then

(10.49) $$w_s = \frac{g_s!}{(g_s - n_s)!n_s!}.$$

If now we cover the whole energy range by considering also the other sets g_i, we have for the total number of distinguishable arrangements in the entire system

(10.50) $$w = \prod_p w_p = \prod_p \frac{g_p!}{(g_p - n_p)!n_p!}.$$

It is a fundamental result of statistical mechanics that the observable average properties of a thermodynamic system in equilibrium are quite accurately given by the properties of the most probable distribution. To obtain the most probable distribution we make w a maximum as a function of the n_p, subject to the conditions that the total number of particles should be constant:

(10.51) $$\Sigma\, n_p = N,$$

and that the total energy should be constant:

(10.52) $$\Sigma\, n_p E_p = E,$$

where E_p is the energy of a particle in the set g_p, and E is the total energy of the system.

The calculation proceeds most conveniently by working with $\log w$:

(10.53) $$\log w = \sum_p [\log g_p! - \log(g_p - n_p)! - \log n_p!].$$

We expand the logarithms, using Stirling's approximation, valid for large numbers:

(10.54) $$\log n! \cong n \log n - n.$$

Thus

(10.55) $$\log w = \sum_p [g_p \log g_p - (g_p - n_p) \log (g_p - n_p) - n_p \log n_p].$$

We apply the method of Lagrangian multipliers to find the maximum of $\log w$, subject to the conditions (10.51) and (10.52):

(10.56) $\quad \dfrac{\partial}{\partial n_i} [\log w + \alpha(N - \Sigma n_p) + \beta(E - \Sigma n_p E_p)]$

$$= \log (g_i - n_i) - \log n_i - \alpha - \beta E_i = 0.$$

This gives

$$\frac{g_i - n_i}{n_i} = e^{\alpha + \beta E_i},$$

or

(10.57) $$n_i = \frac{g_i}{e^{\alpha + \beta E_i} + 1}.$$

The Lagrangian multiplier α is determined by the condition $\Sigma n_i = N$. We may determine the constant β by the observation that at very high temperatures n_i/g_i must be $\ll 1$, as very many states are then energetically accessible, and we therefore have in the high temperature limit

(10.58) $$n_i \approx g_i e^{-\beta E_i}.$$

By comparison with the Boltzmann distribution law valid in this limit we see that

(10.59) $$\beta = 1/kT.$$

It is convenient to work with the distribution function

(10.60) $$f = \frac{n}{g} = \frac{1}{e^{\alpha} e^{E/kT} + 1},$$

which gives the probability that a given state is occupied. This is called the Fermi-Dirac distribution function, and is plotted in Fig. 10.4. To study the behavior of the function, we define an energy E_F such that

(10.61) $$\alpha = -E_F/kT,$$

giving

(10.62) $$f = \frac{1}{e^{(E - E_F)/kT} + 1};$$

E_F is called the *Fermi energy*. At $T = 0°K$, $f = 1$ for $E < E_F$, and $f = 0$ for $E > E_F$. Thus at absolute zero E_F has the significance of a cut-off energy; all states with energy less than E_F are completely filled and all states with energy greater than E_F are vacant. As T

increases, the distribution rounds off as shown in the figure, states within about kT below E_F being partly depopulated and states within about kT above E_F being partly populated. The value of E_F is determined by (10.51) and depends on the temperature, but for $kT/E_F \ll 1$ it can be shown that $E_F(T)$ is closely equal to its value at 0°K. At any temperature f has the value $\frac{1}{2}$ for $E = E_F$. The distribution is called *degenerate* when $kT \ll E_F$, and *non-degenerate* when $kT \gg E_F$ (classical limit).

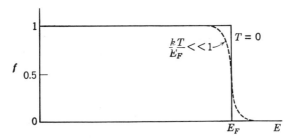

Fig. 10.4. Sketch of the Fermi-Dirac distribution function, for absolute zero and for a low temperature. The region over which the distribution is affected by temperature is of the order of kT in width.

In thermal equilibrium the number of electrons dn with energy between E and $E + dE$ is given by [using (10.47) and the Fermi-Dirac distribution function (10.62)]

$$(10.63) \qquad dn = fg(E)\,dE = \frac{1}{2\pi^2}\left(\frac{2m}{\hbar^2}\right)^{3/2}\frac{E^{1/2}\,dE}{e^{(E-E_F)/kT} + 1},$$

per unit volume. It is often handy to introduce

$$(10.64) \qquad C = \frac{1}{2\pi^2}\left(\frac{2m}{\hbar^2}\right)^{3/2},$$

and so

$$(10.65) \qquad dn = \frac{C E^{1/2}\,dE}{e^{(E-E_F)/kT} + 1},$$

and E_F is determined by setting the integral of dn equal to the number of particles per unit volume, N.

We now consider several limiting cases.

ABSOLUTE ZERO

Here f is unity for E less than $E_F(0)$, the value of E_F at 0°K, and is zero for greater values. Thus all states are filled up to E_F, and the value of E_F is determined in terms of the number of electrons per unit volume, N, by

(10.66) $$N = C \int_0^{E_F(0)} E^{1/2} \, dE = \tfrac{2}{3} C [E_F(0)]^{3/2},$$

so that

(10.67) $$E_F(0) = \frac{\hbar^2}{2m} (3\pi^2 N)^{2/3},$$

in agreement with the earlier result (10.43). Calculated energy values are given in Table 10.3.

It is left to Problem 10.4 to show that the kinetic energy of the Fermi gas at 0°K is

(10.68) $$U_0 = \tfrac{3}{5} N E_F(0).$$

LOW TEMPERATURES $(kT \ll E_F)$

In the following three sections we discuss quantitatively the problems which were discussed qualitatively earlier in the chapter. At low temperatures the change in the distribution function from its form at 0°K takes place chiefly when close to $E_F(0)$. We make use of this fact to obtain an important and useful series expansion for E_F. First consider the integral

(10.69) $$I = \int_0^\infty f(E) \frac{d}{dE} F(E) \, dE,$$

where $f(E)$ is the Fermi-Dirac distribution function, and $F(E)$ is any function which vanishes for $E = 0$. Integrating by parts,

(10.70) $$I = [f(E)F(E)]_0^\infty - \int_0^\infty F(E)f'(E) \, dE;$$

the first term on the right vanishes at the upper limit because of the form of $f(E)$ and vanishes at the lower limit because we supposed that $F(0)$ was zero.

We now expand $F(E)$ by Taylor's theorem about E_F:

(10.71) $$F(E) = F(E_F) + (E - E_F)F'(E_F) \\ + \tfrac{1}{2}(E - E_F)^2 F''(E_F) + \cdots.$$

On substituting in (10.70) we have

(10.72) $$I = L_0 F(E_F) + L_1 F'(E_F) + L_2 F''(E_F) + \cdots,$$

where

(10.73) $$L_0 = - \int_0^\infty f'(E) \, dE; \qquad L_1 = - \int_0^\infty (E - E_F)f'(E) \, dE;$$
$$L_2 = - \tfrac{1}{2} \int_0^\infty (E - E_F)^2 f'(E) \, dE.$$

At low temperatures we may replace the lower limits on the integrals by $-\infty$. We see then that $L_0 = 1$, and, as it is readily shown that $f'(E)$ is an even power of $E - E_F$, we have $L_1 = 0$. For L_2, we have, writing $x = (E - E_F)/kT$,

$$(10.74) \qquad L_2 = \frac{1}{2} (kT)^2 \int_{-\infty}^{\infty} \frac{x^2 e^x \, dx}{(1 + e^x)^2} = \frac{\pi^2}{6} (kT)^2,$$

where the definite integral is given in standard tables. Finally,

$$(10.75) \quad I = \int_0^{\infty} f(E)F'(E) \, dE = F(E_F) + \frac{\pi^2}{6} (kT)^2 F''(E_F) + \cdots .$$

The number of electrons is given by setting [using (10.47)]

$$(10.76) \qquad F(E) = \int_0^E g(E) \, dE,$$

so that

$$(10.77) \quad N = \int_0^{\infty} f(E)g(E) \, dE = \int_0^{E_F} g(E) \, dE + \frac{\pi^2}{6} (kT)^2 g'(E_F).$$

If we subtract from this the relation

$$(10.78) \qquad N = \int_0^{E_F(0)} g(E) \, dE,$$

we obtain

$$(10.79) \qquad \int_{E_F(0)}^{E_F} g(E) \, dE + \frac{\pi^2}{6} (kT)^2 g'(E_F) = 0,$$

or, approximately,

$$(10.80) \qquad [E_F - E_F(0)]g(E_F) + \frac{\pi^2}{6} (kT)^2 g'(E_F) = 0.$$

Inserting (10.47), we obtain

$$(10.81) \qquad E_F \cong E_F(0) \left[1 - \frac{\pi^2}{12} \left(\frac{kT}{E_F(0)} \right)^2 \right].$$

The second term in the brackets being small, it is of no consequence whether we write $E_F(0)$ or E_F in the denominator.

QUANTUM THEORY OF THE HEAT CAPACITY OF THE ELECTRON GAS

We have given earlier a qualitative discussion of the electronic heat capacity; we now discuss the problem quantitatively. The total energy per unit volume is given by

(10.82) $$U = \int_0^\infty Ef(E)g(E)\ dE.$$

Setting

(10.83) $$F(E) = \int_0^E Eg(E)\ dE,$$

we have from (10.75), at low temperatures,

(10.84) $$U = \int_0^{E_F} Eg(E)\ dE + \frac{\pi^2}{6}(kT)^2 \left[\frac{d}{dE}(Eg)\right]_{E_F(0)}$$

$$\cong U_0 + [E_F - E_F(0)]E_F(0)g[E_F(0)] + \frac{3}{2}\frac{\pi^2}{6}(kT)^2 g[E_F(0)],$$

using (10.68) and (10.47).   Now, using (10.81), we have

(10.85) $$U = U_0 + \frac{\pi^2}{6}(kT)^2 g[E_F(0)].$$

The heat capacity is, per unit volume,

(10.86) $$C_v = \frac{\pi^2}{3}g[E_F(0)]k^2 T.$$

Now, from (10.47) and (10.66),

(10.87) $$g[E_F(0)] = [3N/2E_F(0)] = 3N/2kT_F,$$

so that

(10.88) $$C_v = \tfrac{1}{2}\pi^2 NkT/T_F,$$

per unit volume; or, per mole,

(10.89) $$C_v = \tfrac{1}{2}\pi^2 zRT/T_F = \gamma T,$$

where

(10.90) $$\gamma = \tfrac{1}{2}\pi^2 zR/T_F;$$

here z is the number of valence or conduction electrons per atom. This equation is of the form predicted by our earlier qualitative argument.

For metals for which the free electron model might be applicable we may expect the molar electronic heat capacity to be of the order of $10^{-4}T$ cal/mole-deg. The observed values given in Table 10.4 are often larger than this. In the next chapter we shall discuss the anomalous values of γ.

TABLE 10.4. COEFFICIENT γ OF THE LINEAR TERM γT
IN THE MOLAR HEAT CAPACITY OF METALS

(For superconducting metals, γ refers to the normal state.   The significance
of the column m^*/m will be discussed in the next chapter.   To convert a
value in 10^{-4} cal/mole-deg^2 to millijoule/mole-deg^2, multiply by 0.418.)
Reference: J. G. Daunt, *Progress in low temperature physics*, C. J. Gorter,
editor, North-Holland, Amsterdam, 1955, Chapter XI.

Metal	$\gamma \times 10^4$ cal/mole-deg^2	Valence	Apparent m^*/m
Na	4.3	1	0.6
Cu	1.73–1.80	1	1.5
Ag	1.54–1.6	1	0.95–1.0
Au	1.8		
Be	0.54	2	0.46
Mg	3.25	2	1.33
Zn	1.25–1.42	2	0.8–0.9
Cd	1.7	2	0.75
Hg	4.5–5.3	2	1.8–2.2
Al	3.48	3	1.6
In	4.0–4.33	3	1.3–1.4
Tl	3.65	3	1.15
La	16	3	4.3
Sn (white)	4.0	4	1.2
Pb	7.5	4	2.1
Bi	0.11		
Ti	8		
V	15–22		
Cr	3.80		
α-Mn	33		
α-Fe	12	2.1	12
Co	12	1.6	14
Ni	17.4	0.6	28
Zr	3.9–6.9		
Nb	21		
Mo	5.1		
Pd	26–31	0.5	27
Ta	13–19		
W	3.5		
Pt	16.0–16.5	0.6	13

QUANTUM THEORY OF SPIN PARAMAGNETISM

In most metals the conduction electrons have a small temperature-
independent paramagnetic volume susceptibility, of the order of 10^{-6},
in striking disagreement with the Langevin formula which predicts a
susceptibility of the order of 10^{-4} at room temperature and varying as
$1/T$.   Pauli[9] showed that the application of Fermi-Dirac statistics
would correct the theory as required.

[9] W. Pauli, Z. Physik **41**, 81 (1927).

The Langevin equation (9.15) tells us that the probability that an atom will be lined up parallel to the field H exceeds the probability of the antiparallel orientation by a factor $\sim \mu H/kT$. For N atoms, this gives a net magnetic moment $\sim N H \mu^2/kT$, which is the classical result. For electrons in a metal, however, most of them have zero probability of turning over when a field is applied, because the states with parallel spin are already occupied, at least if they are within the energy $2\mu H$ of the given antiparallel state. As only the electrons within $\sim kT$ of the top of the Fermi distribution have a chance to turn over in the

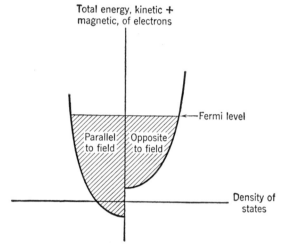

Fig. 10.5. Pauli paramagnetism at 0°K; the levels in the shaded regions are occupied. At higher temperatures the electrons near the Fermi level will spread out.

field, only the fraction $\sim T/T_F$ of the total number of electrons should be counted as contributing to the susceptibility. Hence $\chi \sim (N\mu^2/kT) \times (T/T_F) = N\mu^2/kT_F$, which is independent of temperature and of the correct order of magnitude, as T_F is of the order of 10^4 to 10^5°K. This argument supposes that $\mu H \ll kT$, which is true at room temperature as the strongest field yet obtained, 10^6 oersteds, corresponds to a temperature of only ~ 100°K.

We now calculate the expression for the paramagnetic susceptibility of a free electron gas. Following the notation of (10.47) and the method of calculation suggested by Fig. 10.5, we have for the net magnetization

(10.91) $M = \mu_B \int [\tfrac{1}{2}g(E + \mu_B H) - \tfrac{1}{2}g(E - \mu_B H)]f(E)\, dE,$

where E is the total energy, kinetic plus magnetic, of an electron.   For small H, by series expansion,

(10.92) $$M \cong \mu_B{}^2 H \int g'(E)f(E) \, dE.$$

We set

(10.93) $$F(E) = \int_0^E g'(E) \, dE,$$

so, by (10.75),

(10.94) $$M \cong \mu_B{}^2 H g(E_F),$$

and at low temperatures we have

(10.95) $$\chi = M/H = \mu_B{}^2 g[E_F(0)].$$

Using (10.87),

(10.96) $$\chi = 3N\mu_B{}^2/2kT_F,$$

the Pauli result. This is of the form suggested by our qualitative argument.

In deriving the paramagnetic susceptibilty we have supposed that the spatial motion of the electrons is not affected on applying the magnetic field. Actually the running wave functions (10.36) are

TABLE 10.5. SUSCEPTIBILITY OF THE ALKALI METALS

$\chi \times 10^6$, per gram

	Li	Na	K	Rb	Cs
I. Calculated spin susceptibility, from (10.96)	1.5	0.66	0.60	0.31	0.24
II. As corrected for exchange, correlation, and effective mass [D. Pines, Phys. Rev. **95**, 1090 (1954)]	3.5	0.88	0.71	0.35	0.24
III. Experimental spin susceptibility by electron resonance. [Schumacher and Slichter, Phys. Rev. **101**, 58 (1956)]	3.9	0.98			
IV. Calculated diamagnetic susceptibility of ion cores, after Slater	−0.01	−0.18	−0.37	−0.30	−0.30
V. Estimated diamagnetic susceptibility of conduction electrons, $-\frac{1}{3}$ of I	−0.5	−0.22	−0.20	−0.10	−0.08
VI. Calculated bulk susceptibility, II + IV + V	2.9	0.5	0.1	−0.05	−0.15
VII. Observed bulk susceptibility	3.54	0.70	0.54	0.22	0.20

modified by the magnetic field, and Landau[10] has shown that there is from this cause a diamagnetic moment which for free electrons is equal to $-\frac{1}{3}$ of the paramagnetic moment (10.96), and so the total susceptibility of a free electron gas is

$$(10.97) \qquad \chi_T = N\mu_B{}^2/kT_F.$$

In comparing this with the observed bulk susceptibility, a correction must be applied for the diamagnetism of the ionic cores. A comparison of theoretical (free electron) and experimental values of the susceptibility of the alkali metals is given in Table 10.5.

EFFECT OF FERMI-DIRAC DISTRIBUTION ON THE ELECTRICAL CONDUCTIVITY

It is a somewhat surprising fact that the introduction of the Fermi-Dirac distribution in place of the classical Maxwell-Boltzmann distribution usually has little influence on the electrical conductivity, often only changing the kind of average involved in the specification of the relaxation time. One might have expected at first sight to find a more drastic change because with the Fermi-Dirac distribution only those electrons near the Fermi surface can participate in collision processes. This results as all collisions either conserve electron energy or change it by no more than $\sim kT$, the thermal energy of a lattice wave.

Using the classical distribution we found earlier in this chapter the expression (10.12) for the conductivity:

$$\sigma = Ne^2\tau/m,$$

where N is the electron concentration and τ the relaxation time. It is instructive to give a qualitative classical derivation of this equation from a new point of view, using Fig. 10.6. The figure is drawn for a one-dimensional gas, in the interest of simplicity. In (a) we show the classical distribution of velocities in thermal equilibrium; in (b) the distribution is shifted to the right by $eE\tau/m$ as a result of the application of an electric field E for a time τ. If τ is the relaxation time, the shifted distribution will represent the steady-state distribution in the presence of the electric field. The difference between the steady-state and equilibrium distributions is indicated in (c); by Taylor's theorem the difference is given, to first order in the electric field, by $-(eE\tau/m) \times (dP/dv_x)_{t=0}$. We assume the distribution function P is normalized to unity: $\int P \, dv_x = 1$. The average velocity taken over

[10] L. Landau, Z. Physik **64**, 629 (1930).

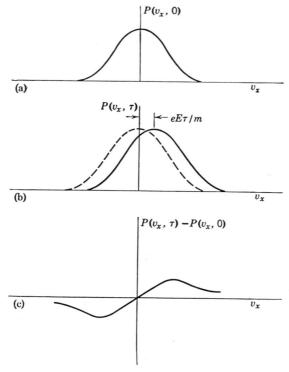

Fig. 10.6.   Maxwellian velocity distribution in one dimension. $P(v_x)\,dv_x$ is the fraction of the total number of particles having velocity in dv_x at v_x.   (a) Equilibrium velocity distribution.   (b) Distribution shifted by electric field applied for time τ.   (c) Difference between steady-state distribution and equilibrium distribution.

the steady-state distribution,

$$(10.98) \qquad P(v_x, \tau) \cong P(v_x, 0) - (eE\tau/m)(dP/dv_x)_{t=0},$$

is given by

$$(10.99) \qquad \bar{v}_x = -(eE\tau/m) \int v_x(dP/dv_x)_0 \, dv_x;$$

the term in $P(v_x, 0)$ is symmetrical in v_x and does not contribute to $\bar{v}_x$. That is, the drift velocity is zero in thermal equilibrium. On integrating by parts,

$$\int v_x(dP/dv_x)_0 \, dv_x = - \int P_0 \, dv_x = -1,$$

as

$$[v_x P_0]_{-\infty}^{\infty} = 0,$$

where P_0 denotes $P(v_x, 0)$.   From (10.99),

(10.100) $v_D = \bar{v}_x = eE\tau/m,$

and so

(10.101) $j = Nev_D = Ne^2E\tau/m,$

or

(10.102) $\sigma = Ne^2\tau/m,$

in agreement with the earlier result.

The corresponding situation with the Fermi-Dirac distribution is shown in Fig. 10.7.   The exclusion principle has no effect on the

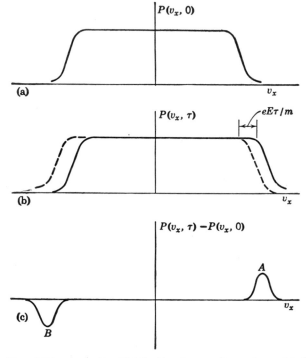

Fig. 10.7.   Fermi-Dirac velocity distribution in one dimension.   (a) Equilibrium velocity distribution.   (b) Distribution shifted by electric field applied for time τ. (c) Difference between steady-state distribution and equilibrium distribution.

response of the distribution to the electric field, because each electron in the distribution suffers the same velocity change $eE\tau/m$.   There is always a vacant state ready to receive an electron which is changing its state under the action of the electric field, the vacancy being created by the simultaneous change of the state of another electron. The relaxation effects are a little deceptive, as it would seem that many possible collision processes are forbidden by the exclusion principle because the final states are already occupied. But relaxation requires only that the excess electrons, those in A in part (c) of the figure, should be able to get back by collisions to B, where there is an electron deficiency. The states in B are vacant, and so the required collisions may take place. That is, the exclusion principle does prevent many collisions, but it does allow those collisions needed to restore equilibrium. We can then carry over without change the derivation leading to the result (10.102) above: $\sigma = Ne^2\tau/m$.

TRANSPARENCY OF ALKALI METALS IN THE ULTRAVIOLET

We mention here one interesting feature of the optical properties of the alkali metals, their transparency in the ultraviolet; the effect was discovered by Wood[11] and explained by Zener.[12] The reflection of light in the infrared is the basis of Problem 10.9.

For good conductors the relaxation time τ is long in comparison with the period $1/\omega$ of light in the visible part of the spectrum, and so to a fair approximation we may omit the resistance term in the equation of motion and write simply

$$(10.103) \qquad m\ddot{x} = eE,$$

which reduces for a periodic field to

$$(10.104) \qquad x = -eE/m\omega^2.$$

As the polarization is $P = Nex$, the complex refractive index n is given by

$$(10.105) \qquad \epsilon = n^2 = 1 + 4\pi(P/E) = 1 - \frac{4\pi Ne^2}{m\omega^2}.$$

If $4\pi Ne^2/m\omega^2$ is less than unity (short wavelengths), the refractive index is real and the metal is transparent to light at normal incidence. If $4\pi Ne^2/m\omega^2$ is greater than unity, n is imaginary, and total reflection may be shown to occur.

The critical wavelength is then, setting $\epsilon = 0$,

$$(10.106) \qquad \lambda_0 = 2\pi(mc^2/4\pi Ne^2)^{1/2}.$$

[11] R. W. Wood, Phys. Rev. **44**, 353 (1933); R. W. Wood and C. Lukens, Phys. Rev. **54**, 332 (1938); H. E. Ives and H. B. Briggs, J. Opt. Soc. Am. **26**, 238 (1936); **27**, 181 (1937).
[12] C. Zener, Nature **132**, 968 (1933).

The agreement with observation is quite good, as shown in Table 10.6, although the experimental determinations of λ_0 are not too definite because of the width of the cut-off region. Calculated values are also given in the table, using effective masses m^*. The concept of an effective mass is discussed in the next chapter.

TABLE 10.6. ULTRAVIOLET TRANSMISSION OF ALKALIS

	Li	Na	K	Rb	Cs
λ_0 (calculated, free electrons, mass m) (A)	1550	2090	2870	3220	3620
Effective mass ratio m^*/m, according to Brooks (see Chapter 11)		1.40	0.98	0.94	0.87	0.83
λ_0 (calculated for m^*) (A)		1840	2070	2750	3000	3300
λ_0 observed (A)		1550	2100	3150	3400

THERMIONIC EMISSION EQUATION

We now calculate the Richardson-Dushman equation for the saturation electron current density evaporated from a metal, using the free electron model. We suppose, following Fig. 10.8, that E_0 is the work

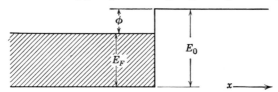

Fig. 10.8.   Model for calculation of thermionic emission.

necessary to remove to infinity an electron from the lowest free electron state in the metal. If the electron is taken from the Fermi level, the work is

$$(10.107) \qquad \phi = E_0 - E_F;$$

this is the definition of the *work function* ϕ.

The rate at which electrons in the momentum range between $\mathbf{p}$ and $\mathbf{p} + d\mathbf{p}$ strike unit area of the surface is

$$(10.108) \qquad v_x n(\mathbf{p}) \, d\mathbf{p} = \frac{\partial E}{\partial p_x} \, n(\mathbf{p}) \, d\mathbf{p} = n(\mathbf{p}) \, dE \, dp_y \, dp_z,$$

as E is the kinetic energy; here $n(\mathbf{p})$ is the number of electrons per unit volume of phase space and is given by

$$(10.109) \qquad n(\mathbf{p}) = (2/h^3)f,$$

in terms of the Fermi-Dirac distribution function f. The electronic charge e times the rate at which electrons having

$$p_x^2/2m > \phi + E_F$$

strike unit area of the surface will be the emission current density j, apart from a factor representing quantum reflection effects which we neglect. Then

(10.110) $$j = \frac{2e}{h^3} \int_{-\infty}^{\infty} \int_{-\infty}^{\infty} \int_{\phi+E_F}^{\infty} \frac{dp_y \, dp_z \, dE}{e^{(E-E_F)/kT} + 1}$$

$$= \frac{2kTe}{h^3} \int_{-\infty}^{\infty} \int_{-\infty}^{\infty} \log \left[1 + e^{-\theta}\right] dp_y \, dp_z,$$

where

$$\theta = \frac{1}{kT} \left[\phi + (p_y^2 + p_z^2)/2m\right].$$

For ordinary conditions $\theta \gg 1$, so that we may expand the logarithm and retain only the first term:

(10.111) $$j = \frac{2kTe}{h^3} e^{-\phi/kT} \iint e^{-(p_y^2 + p_z^2)/2mkT} \, dp_y \, dp_z$$

$$= 4\pi me(kT)^2 h^{-3} e^{-\phi/kT}.$$

This is the Richardson-Dushman equation. We may write the result as

(10.112) $$j = AT^2 e^{-\phi/kT},$$

where

(10.113) $$A = 4\pi mek^2 h^{-3} = 120 \text{ amp/cm}^2\text{-deg}^2.$$

Experimental values of A and ϕ are given in Table 10.7. The values

TABLE 10.7. REPRESENTATIVE THERMIONIC EMISSION DATA

Metal	A (amp/cm^2-deg^2)	ϕ (ev)
W	~75	4.5
Ta	55	4.2
Ni	30	4.6
Ag	. . . . . .	4.8
Cs	160	1.8
Pt	32	5.3
Ba on W	1.5	1.56
Cs on W	3.2	1.36
Cr	48	4.60

are sensitive to surface conditions, particularly to surface films and non-uniform surfaces.[13] Work functions from photoelectric data are

[13] For a careful discussion of the data, see C. Herring and M. H. Nichols, Revs. Modern Phys. **21**, 185 (1949).

given in Table 10.8, obtained from the minimum photon energy which will eject a photoelectron.

TABLE 10.8. WORK FUNCTIONS FROM PHOTOELECTRIC DATA

Metal	ϕ (ev)
Na	2.3
K	2.26
Cr	4.37
Zn	4.24
W	4.49
Pt	6.2

PROBLEMS

10.1. (a) Using the boundary condition $\psi = 0$ on the surfaces of a cube of side L, find **all** the wave functions for the first four distinct energy levels. (b) Give the energy of each level. (c) What is the degeneracy of each level? That is, what is the number of independent wave functions having the same energy?

10.2. Repeat the work of Problem 10.1, but use periodic boundary conditions.

10.3. We may obtain time-dependent wave functions by multiplying a solution of the wave equation of energy E by the factor $e^{-iEt/\hbar}$. The factor $E/\hbar$ has the dimensions of a frequency. (a) Show that

$$\psi(x, t) \sim e^{-i[(E/\hbar)t - kx]}$$

represents a wave traveling in the positive x direction with phase velocity $E/\hbar k$. (b) What is the group velocity? According to the de Broglie relation, what momentum is associated with the wave?

10.4. Show that the kinetic energy of a free electron gas at $0°K$ is

$$U_0 = \tfrac{3}{5} N E_F(0).$$

10.5. Using conventional valencies, show that for sodium, potassium, and aluminum the values of $E_F(0)$ are 3.1, 2.1, and 11.7 ev, respectively.

10.6. By qualitative reasoning, show that on the free electron model the electronic paramagnetic susceptibility of a metal at low temperatures under the conditions

$$kT \ll \mu H \ll kT_F$$

is

$$\chi \sim N\mu^2/kT_F,$$

of the same form as under the usual conditions $\mu H \ll kT \ll kT_F$.

10.7. An infinite plane metal surface with the normal in the z direction has a work function ϕ and temperature T. The electrons inside the metal obey Fermi-Dirac statistics with Fermi energy E_F.

(a) Write down the integral expression for the number of electrons per unit volume with an x component of velocity between v_x and $v_x + dv_x$ inside the metal.

(b) Write down the integral expression for the flux of electrons escaping with an x component of velocity between v_x and $v_x + dv_x$ *after* escape.

(c) Similarly for those with a z component of velocity between v_z and $v_z + dv_z$ *after* escape.

(d) Neglecting the one in the denominator of the distribution function with respect to the exponential function, calculate the average square of the velocity in the x direction and the average square of the velocity in the z direction of the escaping electrons *after* escape.

10.8. Derive an equation connecting the pressure and volume of a Fermi electron gas at 0°K.

10.9. Show that the complex refractive index of a metal at long wavelengths is given by

$$(n + ik)^2 = 1 + 4\pi i\sigma_0/\omega,$$

where σ_0 is the conductivity for static fields. Using the relation

$$R = \frac{(n-1)^2 + k^2}{(n+1)^2 + k^2}$$

for the reflection coefficient at normal incidence, show that

$$R \cong 1 - (2\omega/\pi\sigma_0)^{1/2}.$$

This is the Hagen-Rubens relation. Show that the condition for the validity of the derivation of the results is that $\omega \ll 1/\tau$, where τ is the relaxation time of the electrons. Estimate τ for sodium at room temperature, using the observed conductivity.

10.10.* Apply the Boltzmann transport equation to the free electron theory of thermoelectric effects, following the treatment in the book by Seitz listed in the references.

REFERENCES

R. Becker, *Theorie der Elektrizität*, B. Teubner, Leipzig, 1933, Vol. II.

F. Bloch, *Elektronentheorie der Metalle*, Handbuch der Radiologie, **6.1**, 226–278 (1933).

G. Borelius, *Physikalische Eigenschaften der Metalle*, Handbuch der Metallphysik, Akademische Verlagsgesellschaft, Leipzig, **1**, 181–485 (1935).

L. Brillouin, *Die Quantenstatistik*, Springer, Berlin, 1931.

H. Fröhlich, *Elektronentheorie der Metalle*, Springer, Berlin, 1936.

W. Hume-Rothery, *Electrons, atoms, metals and alloys*, Iliffe, London, 1955.

N. F. Mott and H. Jones, *Theory of the properties of metals and alloys*, Clarendon Press, Oxford, 1936.

R. Peierls, *Quantum theory of solids*, Clarendon Press, Oxford, 1955.

Proceedings of the Tenth Solvay Congress, Brussels, 1954.

F. O. Rice and E. Teller, *Structure of matter*, John Wiley & Sons, New York, 1949.

F. Seitz, *Modern theory of solids*, McGraw-Hill Book Co., New York, 1940.

F. Seitz and D. Turnbull, editors, *Solid state physics: advances in research and applications*, Academic Press, New York, 1955, vol. I.

J. C. Slater, "Electronic structure of metals," Revs. Modern Phys. **6**, 209 (1934).

J. C. Slater, *Quantum theory of matter*, McGraw-Hill Book Co., New York, 1951.

A. Sommerfeld and H. Bethe, *Elektronentheorie der Metalle*, Handbuch der Physik, Springer, Berlin, **24/2**, 333–622 (1933).

A. H. Wilson, *Theory of metals*, Cambridge University Press, Cambridge, 1953, 2nd ed.

11

Band Theory of Solids; Brillouin Zones

The free electron model of metals developed in the preceding chapter gives us a good deal of insight into several of the physical properties of metals, yet there are other properties for which the free electron model is quite uninstructive. The model cannot help us understand why some chemical elements crystallize to form good conductors of electricity and others to form insulators; still others are semiconductors, with electrical properties varying markedly with temperature. Yet the distinction between the resistivity values of conductors, superconductivity apart, and insulators is striking: the resistivity of a pure metal at low temperatures may be of the order of 10^{-8} ohm-cm, and the resistivity of a good insulator may be as high as 10^{22} ohm-cm, provided precautions are taken to dry the surface of the specimen. It has been remarked[1] that this observed range of 10^{30} in resistivity may be the widest range of any common physical property of matter.

We can gain some insight into the nature of the difference between insulators and conductors only by extending the free electron model to take account of the interaction of electrons with the periodic lattice of the solid. We shall encounter some quite remarkable properties possessed by electrons in crystals: we shall see that they may respond to applied electric or magnetic fields as if the electrons are endowed with an effective mass m^*, which may be larger or smaller than the free electron mass, or may even be negative. Further, there are situations in which it is convenient to attribute to the charge carriers in crystals a positive charge $+|e|$; we denote such carriers as *holes*, in contrast to electrons which behave with their normal negative charge $-|e|$. Students with no familiarity with the ideas of quantum theory will have some difficulty with the present chapter. The necessary background is developed in Born's *Atomic physics*.

On the free electron model the allowed energy values are distributed quasi-continuously from zero to infinity. We saw in the preceding chapter that

[1] E. M. McMillan, private communication.

$$E = (\hbar^2/2m)(k_x{}^2 + k_y{}^2 + k_z{}^2),$$

where, for a cube of side L,

$$k_x, k_y, k_z = (2\pi/L)(0, \pm 1, \pm 2, \pm 3, \cdots).$$

The free electron wave functions are of the form

$$\psi \sim e^{i\mathbf{k}\cdot\mathbf{r}}$$

and represent running waves carrying momentum $\mathbf{p} = \hbar\mathbf{k}$, according to the de Broglie relation.

We have seen in the earlier discussions of x-ray and elastic wave propagation in crystals that Bragg reflection is an important and characteristic feature of wave propagation in periodic structures. Bragg reflection occurs also for electron waves in crystals. The observations of Davisson and Germer on the wave nature of the electron were observations of the Bragg reflection of an electron beam from the crystal surface. The most important consequence of Bragg reflection for our present discussion is that it leads to the existence of an energy gap in the distribution in energy of the states of the conduction electrons. That is, there may arise a substantial region of energy in which solutions of the wave equation do not exist. Such energy gaps or forbidden energy bands, as they are also called, are of decisive significance in determining whether a solid is to be an insulator or a conductor. We shall find that the solid will be an insulator if all the energy levels below a forbidden band are filled with electrons and all levels above the forbidden band are vacant.

Let us try to understand physically the reasons for the existence of a forbidden band, considering first the simple problem of a monatomic one-dimensional lattice. The low energy portions of the band structure are shown qualitatively in Fig. 11.1, in (a) for entirely free electrons and (b) for electrons which are nearly free, but which have an energy discontinuity at $k = \pm\pi/a$, giving rise to a forbidden energy band. In one dimension the Bragg equation $2d \sin \theta = n\lambda$ becomes

(11.1) $$k = n\pi/a.$$

The first reflections occur at $k = \pm\pi/a$, and the first energy gap also occurs at these points. Other energy gaps occur for the other positive and negative integral values of n. The reflection at $k = \pm\pi/a$ arises because the wave reflected from the $(p \pm 1)$st atom interferes constructively with the original wave at the pth atom, the difference in phase being just $\pm 2\pi$ for these particular values of k. The region in k-space between $-\pi/a$ and π/a is referred to in this instance as the first

Brillouin zone. The energy is quasi-continuous within a Brillouin zone and may be discontinuous on the boundaries of a zone. The energy is quasi-continuous rather than continuous within a zone because of the imposition of boundary conditions on the problem.

At $k = \pm \pi/a$ the stationary state wave functions are not traveling waves as for the free electron model, but the solutions at these particular k values are made up equally of waves traveling to the right and

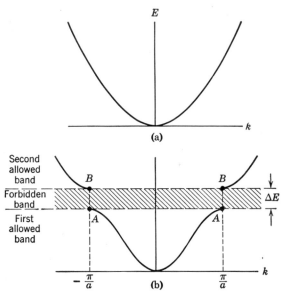

Fig. 11.1.   (a) Plot of energy vs. wave vector for a free electron.   (b) Plot of energy vs. wave vector for a monatomic linear lattice of lattice constant a.   The energy gap shown is associated with the first Bragg reflection at $k = \pm \pi/a$.

to the left: they are standing waves.   It is really obvious that the solutions when the Bragg condition is satisfied cannot be in the form of traveling waves, for a wave traveling in one sense is soon Bragg-reflected and then travels in the opposite sense.   The next Bragg reflection reverses the direction of travel again.   The only stationary situation is that represented by standing waves.   In the lowest approximation we have at $k = \pm \pi/a$ the two independent standing wave solutions

(11.2)
$$\psi_1 \sim \sin \pi x/a \sim (e^{i\pi x/a} - e^{-i\pi x/a});$$
$$\psi_2 \sim \cos \pi x/a \sim (e^{i\pi x/a} + e^{-i\pi x/a}).$$

Both these solutions hold equally at $k = +\pi/a$ and also at $k = -\pi/a$. The solutions are both made up, as can be seen from the right-hand forms, of equal parts of waves traveling to the right ($e^{i\pi x/a}$) and to the left ($e^{-i\pi x/a}$). [See Problem 10.3].

We now must show that the two solutions ψ_1, ψ_2 correspond to different values of the energy, even though the functions have the same values of the wave vector. In Fig. 11.2(a) we have indicated the general nature of the variation of the electrostatic potential energy of a conduction electron in the field of the positive ion cores of a monatomic linear lattice. We expect the ion cores to bear a positive charge, as

V, potential energy

(a)

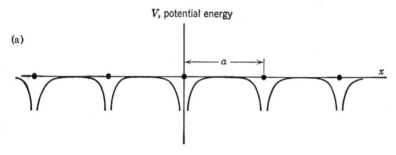

(b)

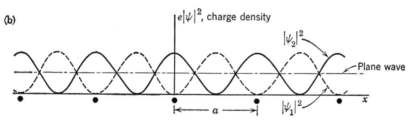

Fig. 11.2. (a) Variation of potential energy of a conduction electron in the field of the positive ion cores of a monatomic linear lattice. (b) Distribution of probability density in the lattice for $|\psi_1|^2 \sim \sin^2 \pi x/a$; $|\psi_2|^2 \sim \cos^2 \pi x/a$; and for a plane traveling wave.

each has lost one or more valence electrons in forming the metal. In (b) we sketched the distribution of charge density corresponding to the standing waves ψ_1, ψ_2 and to a plane traveling wave. We note the traveling wave $\sim e^{ikx}$ distributes electronic charge uniformly over the line with the origin as shown, the standing wave $\psi_1 \sim \sin \pi x/a$ distributes charge preferentially midway between ion cores; and the standing wave $\psi_2 \sim \cos \pi x/a$ distributes charge preferentially on the ion cores, where the potential energy is a minimum. On calculating average values of the potential energy over the three charge distributions, we expect to find the potential energy ψ_2 less than that of a plane wave, while the potential energy of ψ_1 is greater than that of a plane wave. If the potential energies of ψ_1 and ψ_2 differ by an amount ΔE we have, referring to Fig. 11.1(b), an energy gap of width ΔE. The wave function at points A will be ψ_2, and the wave function above the energy gap at points B will be ψ_1.

Let us review briefly how the forbidden band came about. If the wave functions at values of k far removed from the Brillouin zone boundaries $\pm\pi/a$ may be represented by plane waves e^{ikx}, then in forming a solution of the wave equation as the boundaries are approached and Bragg reflection becomes imminent the wave e^{ikx} gradually is supplemented by an increasing admixture of the wave $e^{i[k-(2\pi/a)]x}$, until at the zone boundary $k = \pm\pi/a$ the solution is $e^{i\pi x/a} \pm e^{i\pi x/a}$. The evolution of the standing wave solution is traced through in detail in Appendix I. What is important at present is that the solutions for $k = \pm\pi/a$ combine to give standing waves of different energies, the energies being different not through the kinetic term, but through the potential energy of interaction with the ion cores. The two wave functions distribute the electronic charge in distinctly different ways with respect to the positive ion core field. The difference in potential energy leads to a splitting of the energy bands at $k = \pm\pi/a$.

It is useful also to look at the formation of allowed and forbidden bands in another way, starting from the energy levels of the neutral separated atoms and watching the changes in the levels as the charge distributions of adjacent atoms overlap when the atoms are brought together to form the metal. We can understand the origin of the splitting of free atom energy levels into bands as the atoms are brought together by considering two hydrogen atoms,[2] each with its electron in the $1s$ (ground) state. In Fig. 11.3 the wave functions ψ_A, ψ_B on the separated atoms are shown in (a). As the atoms are brought closer together and their wave functions overlap, we are led to consider the two combinations $\psi_A \pm \psi_B$. Each combination preserves the equality of electron distribution between the two protons, but an electron in the state $\psi_A + \psi_B$ will have a somewhat lower energy than in the state $\psi_A - \psi_B$. In the former state shown in (b) the electron spends part of the time in the region midway between the two protons, and in this region it is under the influence of the attractive potential of both protons at once, thereby increasing the binding energy. In the state $\psi_A - \psi_B$ shown in (c) the probability density vanishes midway between the nuclei, and the extra contribution to the binding does not appear. Thus as two atoms are brought together two sep-

[2] For a detailed treatment of the binding of the hydrogen molecule-ion, see L. Pauling and E. B. Wilson, *Introduction to quantum mechanics*, McGraw-Hill, New York, 1935, Chapter XII.

arated energy levels are formed for each level of the isolated atom. For N atoms, N levels are formed for each level of the isolated atom, and these N levels will be associated with one or more bands.

The results for six hydrogen atoms in a line are sketched in Fig. 11.4. As the free atoms are brought together the Coulomb interaction between the atom cores and the overlapping parts of the electron distribution splits the energy levels of the combined system, spreading

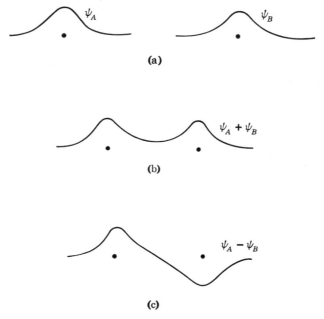

(a)

(b)

(c)

Fig. 11.3. (a) Wave functions of electrons on two hydrogen atoms at large separation. (b) Ground state combination at closer separation. (c) Excited state combination.

the levels out into bands. Each level ns of the free atom is spread out in the metal into a band of energies. Here n denotes the principal quantum number, and s indicates zero orbital angular momentum. The width of the band is proportional to the strength of the interaction or overlap between neighboring atoms, each in the state ns. There will be bands formed as well from p, d, $\cdots$ states ($l = 1, 2, \cdots$) of the free atoms. Each of the $(2l + 1)$ levels degenerate in the free atom will form a band, and one of these bands will not have in general the same energy as any other band over any substantial proportion of the range of the wave vector. Two or more bands may coincide in energy at certain special positions in the Brillouin zone. Bands formed from a p level are indicated in Fig. 11.5.

The approximation which starts out from the wave functions of the free atoms is known as the tight binding approximation; a simple example of its use is given in Appendix J.   The tight binding approximation is thought generally to be quite good for the inner electrons of atoms, but it is probably not often a good description of the conduction electrons themselves.   It is often used to describe approximately the d bands of transition metals.   The tight binding approximation does

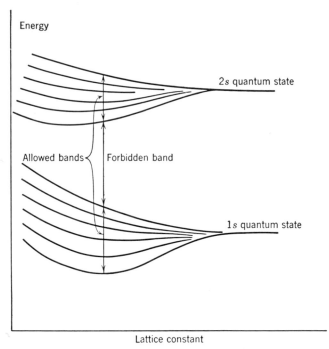

Fig. 11.4.   Dependence of energy levels upon lattice constant, for a line of 6 hydrogen atoms, showing the incipient formation of allowed and forbidden energy bands.   As the atoms are moved closer together the coupling between atoms increases, splitting the energy levels as shown here.   The problem is similar to that of a line of coupled electrical or mechanical oscillators.

show clearly the connection between number of atoms and number of states in the band.

It will turn out that the special **k** values for which energy discontinuities occur do not depend on the particular approximation used to calculate the wave functions or the energies, but are a general property of the space group of the crystal structure.   Returning for the moment to our monatomic linear lattice, we recall that the first allowed energy band extends from $-(\pi/a) \leq k \leq (\pi/a)$.   In this range k has the

values $(2\pi/L)[0, \pm1, \pm2, \cdots \pm (L/2a)]$, Now L/a is just equal to
the number of atoms, as a is the lattice constant and L the length of
the region over which the periodic boundary conditions are applied.
Recalling that the state at $k = +\pi/a$ is not independent of the state
at $k = -\pi/a$, but is identical with it, we see that there are a total of
L/a independent values of k. Further, for each value of k there are
two values of m_s, the spin quantum number.

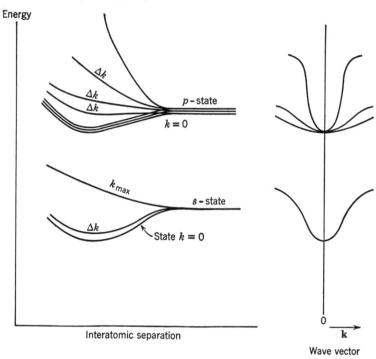

Fig. 11.5.   Effect of orbital degeneracy on band structure.

We have then the important result that a band formed from L/a
atoms contains $2L/a$ states. If each atom contributes one valence
electron to the band, the band will be half full and the solid will possess
the characteristic properties of a metal.   If each atom contributes two
valence electrons the band will be exactly full provided that no other
bands overlap it in energy.   If there are no overlapping bands, the
band of interest will not contribute to electrical conductivity.   All
states in the band being full, an applied electric field cannot cause the
electrons in the band to change their state, and therefore they cannot
be accelerated.   Thus the bands formed from the filled inner electronic
shells of an atom do not normally lead to conductivity.   These bands

are narrow because the inner wave functions of the separate atoms do not overlap very much in the metal. The narrow low-lying bands do not overlap in energy the outer vacant or partly filled bands. As a closed shell always contains an even number of electrons, the corresponding energy bands will be filled.

For a solid to be an insulator it is necessary for it to contain an even number of electrons per atom or per primitive cell, and further it is necessary for the uppermost band containing electrons to be separated from other bands above by an energy gap $\gg kT$ at the temperature of interest. The alkaline earth metals are not insulators even though

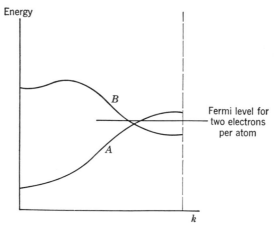

Fig. 11.6. Sketch showing how overlapping bands, A and B, make it possible for a crystal of a divalent element to show metallic conductivity. The bands are filled up to the Fermi level as shown, so that A is nearly filled and B is slightly filled. The overlap need not be in the same direction in k space for both bands.

they are divalent, because bands overlap, as indicated in Fig. 11.6. In this way a band which might be exactly filled in the absence of overlap is not entirely filled, and a band which might be vacant in the absence of overlap is partly filled. The alkali metals and the noble metals are good conductors because they are monovalent and the conduction band is only half filled. Diamond is an insulator because it has four valence electrons and the relevant bands are separated by some 5 ev. Silicon and germanium have the same valence and crystal structure as diamond, but are semiconductors: the band separation here is of the order of 1 ev. Sodium chloride is an insulator; the group NaCl associated with each lattice point has twenty-eight electrons, an even number. The essential differences between insulators and metallic conductors may be attributed in this way to differences in valency and sometimes also to differences in the energy relationships of the various bands.

WAVE FUNCTIONS IN A PERIODIC LATTICE

Bloch[3] has proved the important theorem that the solutions of the Schrödinger equation with a periodic potential are of the form

(11.3) $$\psi_{\mathbf{k}} = u_{\mathbf{k}}(\mathbf{r})e^{i\mathbf{k}\cdot\mathbf{r}},$$

where $u_{\mathbf{k}}(\mathbf{r})$ is a function, depending in general on the wave vector $\mathbf{k}$, which is periodic in x, y, z with the periodicity of the potential; that is, with the period of the lattice. We see that the plane wave $e^{i\mathbf{k}\cdot\mathbf{r}}$ is modulated with the period of the lattice. The solutions (11.3) are known as Bloch functions.

A standard proof of the Bloch result is given in the book by Mott and Jones, pp. 57–59. Bloch[3] gives a rather more satisfying proof based on elementary group theory. We give here an abbreviated and somewhat incomplete indication of the argument. We consider N lattice points on a ring of length Na, and suppose that the potential is periodic in a, so that

(11.4) $$V(x) = V(x + ga),$$

where g is an integer. Because of the symmetry of the ring we look for eigenfunctions ψ such that

(11.5) $$\psi(x + a) = C\psi(x),$$

where C is a constant. Then

(11.6) $$\psi(x + ga) = C^g\psi(x);$$

and, if the eigenfunction is to be single-valued,

(11.7) $$\psi(x + Na) = \psi(x) = C^N\psi(x),$$

so that C is one of the N roots of unity, or

(11.8) $$C = e^{i2\pi g/N}; \quad g = 0, 1, 2, \cdots, N - 1.$$

We have then

(11.9) $$\psi(x) = e^{i2\pi x g/Na}u_g(x)$$

as a satisfactory solution, where $u_g(x)$ has periodicity a. Letting

(11.10) $$k = 2\pi g/Na,$$

[3] F. Bloch, Z. Physik **52**, 555 (1928); the result was known earlier to mathematicians as Floquet's theorem.

we have

(11.11) $$\psi_{\mathbf{k}} = e^{ikx}u_k(x),$$

which is the Bloch result.

KRONIG-PENNEY MODEL

We demonstrate some of the characteristic features of electron propagation in crystals by considering the periodic square-well structure[4] in one dimension (Fig. 11.7).   This is a highly artificial model,

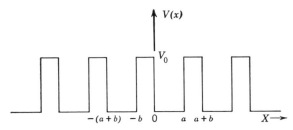

Fig. 11.7.   Kronig and Penney one-dimensional periodic potential.

but it is a model which can be treated explicitly, using only elementary functions.   The wave equation of the problem is

(11.12) $$\frac{d^2\psi}{dx^2} + \frac{2m}{\hbar^2}(E - V)\psi = 0.$$

The running wave solutions will be of the form of a plane wave modulated with the periodicity of the lattice.   Using (11.11), we obtain solutions of the form

(11.13) $$\psi = u_k(x)e^{ikx},$$

where $u(x)$ is a periodic function in x with the period $(a + b)$ and is determined by substituting (11.13) into (11.12):

(11.14) $$\frac{d^2u}{dx^2} + 2ik\frac{du}{dx} + \frac{2m}{\hbar^2}(E - E_k - V)u = 0,$$

where $E_k = \hbar^2 k^2/2m$.

In the region $0 < x < a$ the equation has the solution

(11.15) $$u = Ae^{i(\alpha-k)x} + Be^{-i(\alpha+k)x},$$

[4] R. de L. Kronig and W. G. Penney, Proc. Roy. Soc., (London) A130, 499 (1931); see also D. S. Saxon and R. A. Hutner, Philips Research Repts. 4, 81 (1949); J. M. Luttinger, Philips Research Repts. 6, 303 (1951).

provided that

(11.16) $$\alpha = (2mE/\hbar^2)^{1/2}.$$

In the region $a < x < a + b$ the solution is

(11.17) $$u = Ce^{(\beta-ik)x} + De^{-(\beta+ik)x},$$

provided that

(11.18) $$\beta = [2m(V_0 - E)/\hbar^2]^{1/2}.$$

The constants A, B, C, D are to be chosen so that u and du/dx are continuous at $x = 0$ and $x = a$, and by the periodicity required of $u(x)$ the values at $x = a$ must equal those at $x = -b$. Thus we have the four linear homogeneous equations:

$$A + B = C + D;$$

$$i(\alpha - k)A - i(\alpha + k)B = (\beta - ik)C - (\beta + ik)D;$$

$$Ae^{i(\alpha-k)a} + Be^{-i(\alpha+k)a} = Ce^{-(\beta-ik)b} + De^{(\beta+ik)b}$$

$$i(\alpha - k)Ae^{i(\alpha-k)a} - i(\alpha + k)Be^{-i(\alpha+k)a} = (\beta - ik)Ce^{-(\beta-ik)b}$$
$$- (\beta + ik)De^{(\beta+ik)b}.$$

These have a solution only if the determinant of the coefficients vanishes, or[5]

(11.19) $$\frac{\beta^2 - \alpha^2}{2\alpha\beta} \sinh \beta b \sin \alpha a + \cosh \beta b \cos \alpha a = \cos k(a + b).$$

In order to obtain a handier equation we represent the potential by a periodic delta function, passing to the limit where $b = 0$ and $V_0 = \infty$ in such a way that $\beta^2 b$ stays finite. We set

(11.20) $$\lim_{\substack{b \to 0 \\ \beta \to \infty}} \frac{\beta^2 ab}{2} = P,$$

so that the condition (11.19) becomes

(11.21) $$P\frac{\sin \alpha a}{\alpha a} + \cos \alpha a = \cos ka.$$

This transcendental equation must have a solution for α in order for wave functions of the form (11.13) to exist.

[5] Before verifying this for himself the reader should refer to the alternative derivation in the following section.

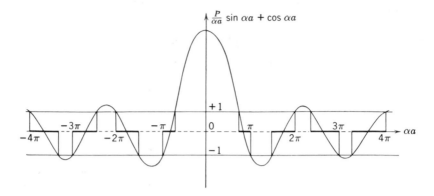

Fig. 11.8.   Plot of the function $P \dfrac{\sin \alpha a}{\alpha a} + \cos \alpha a$, for $P = 3\pi/2$.   The allowed values of the energy E are given by those ranges of $\alpha = [2mE/\hbar^2]^{1/2}$ for which the function lies between $+1$ and -1.   (After Kronig and Penney.)

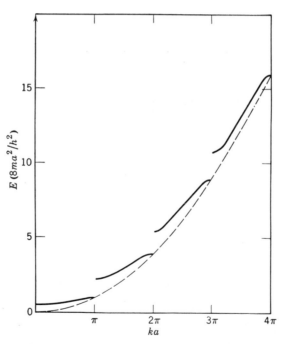

Fig. 11.9.   Plot of energy vs. wave number for the Kronig-Penney potential, with $P = 3\pi/2$.   (After Sommerfeld and Bethe.)

In Fig. 11.8 we have plotted the left side of (11.21) as a function of αa, for the arbitrary value $P = 3\pi/2$. As the cosine term on the right side can have values only between $+1$ and -1, only those values of αa are allowed for which the left side falls in this range. The allowed ranges of αa are drawn heavily in the figure, and through the relation $\alpha = [2mE/\hbar^2]^{\frac{1}{2}}$ they correspond to allowed ranges of the energy E. The boundaries of the allowed ranges of αa correspond to the values $n\pi/a$ for k. In Fig. 11.9 E vs. k is plotted.

If P is small, the forbidden ranges disappear. If $P \rightarrow \infty$, the allowed ranges of αa reduce to the points $n\pi$ $(n = \pm 1, \pm 2, \cdots)$. The energy spectrum becomes discrete, and the eigenvalues

$$E = n^2 h^2/8ma^2$$

are those of an electron in a box of length a.

ALTERNATIVE DERIVATION OF THE KRONIG-PENNEY RESULT

We derive here by a direct method the result (11.21) for the delta-function potential array, avoiding the very considerable labor incident to (11.19). We note first that in the region under the delta-function $\beta \gg k$, so that d^2u/dx^2 is much larger than du/dx in this region. Our boundary conditions are then that in the limit of a delta-function potential the value of u is continuous through the potential, or, using the periodicity condition,

(11.22) $A + B \cong Ae^{i(\alpha-k)a} + Be^{-i(\alpha+k)a};$

furthermore, the derivatives are related by

(11.23) $(du/dx)_a \cong (du/dx)_0 - (d^2/dx^2)_0 b \cong (du/dx)_0 - b\beta^2 u(0)$

$$= (du/dx)_0 - (2P/a)u(0),$$

where P is defined by (11.20). Therefore

(11.24) $[i(\alpha - k) - (2P/a)]A - [i(\alpha + k) + (2P/a)]B$
$$= i(\alpha - k)Ae^{i(\alpha-k)a} - i(\alpha + k)e^{-i(\alpha+k)a}B.$$

The determinantal equation for the existence of a solution of (11.22) and (11.24) is

$$\begin{vmatrix} 1-e^{i(\alpha-k)a} & 1-e^{-i(\alpha+k)a} \\ i(\alpha-k)(1-e^{i(\alpha-k)a})-(2P/a) & -i(\alpha+k)(1-e^{-i(\alpha+k)a})-(2P/a) \end{vmatrix} = 0.$$

This is readily multiplied out to give (11.21).

WAVE FUNCTIONS FOR ZERO WAVE VECTOR

It may appear to the reader that there is a certain inconsistency between the discussion of the preceding chapter, in which we emphasized the usefulness of the free electron model as applied to the monovalent metals, and the discussion of the present chapter emphasizing the importance of the states of the isolated atom and also the interaction between the conduction electron and the ion cores. It happily turns out that in the monovalent metals the inconsistency is sometimes only apparent. It is possible for the energy in a band to depend on the wave vector in approximately the same way as for a free electron while at the same time the wave function may be quite unlike a plane wave, but may pile up charge on the positive ion cores much as in the isolated atom.

In the last chapter the important result of the free electron model was the relation

$$(11.25) \qquad E_{\mathbf{k}} = (\hbar^2/2m)k^2.$$

We can broaden the scope of the treatment by observing that the really important part of the result is the quadratic dependence of the energy on the wave vector. We can carry over all the results even if the constant of proportionality is changed, with

$$(11.26) \qquad E_{\mathbf{k}} = (\hbar^2/2m^*)k^2,$$

where m^* is called the effective mass. We may simply substitute m^* for m in the expressions for the Fermi energy, heat capacity, susceptibility, and conductivity, among others.

Let us first see how it can happen that we have $E_{\mathbf{k}} \cong (\hbar^2/2m)k^2$ while the wave functions are not like plane waves. Suppose that we have solved the wave equation in the periodic potential for $\mathbf{k} = 0$, obtaining the solution $\psi = u_0(\mathbf{r})$, where $u_0(\mathbf{r})$ will have the periodicity of the lattice and will naturally reflect in its shape the variation of the potential energy near the ion cores. We construct next the function

$$(11.27) \qquad \psi = u_0(\mathbf{r})e^{i\mathbf{k}\cdot\mathbf{r}}.$$

This function is of the Bloch form (11.3), but will not be in general an exact solution of the wave equation because we have suppressed the dependence of u on $\mathbf{k}$. However, it is obvious that the function is likely to be a much better approximation than a plane wave to the correct wave function. The energy of the approximate solution still depends on $\mathbf{k}$ as $(\hbar^2/2m)k^2$, exactly as for the plane wave, even though the modulation represented by $u_0(\mathbf{r})$ may be very strong. We calculate the average value of the energy as follows: we have from the prescription for taking averages in quantum mechanics

$$(11.28) \quad \bar{E} = \int u_0{}^*(\mathbf{r}) e^{-i\mathbf{k}\cdot\mathbf{r}} \left[-\frac{\hbar^2}{2m} \nabla^2 + V(\mathbf{r}) \right] e^{i\mathbf{k}\cdot\mathbf{r}} u_0(\mathbf{r}) \, d\tau.$$

Now

$$\nabla e^{i\mathbf{k}\cdot\mathbf{r}} u_0(\mathbf{r}) = i\mathbf{k} e^{i\mathbf{k}\cdot\mathbf{r}} u_0(\mathbf{r}) + e^{i\mathbf{k}\cdot\mathbf{r}} \nabla u_0(\mathbf{r});$$

$$\nabla^2 e^{i\mathbf{k}\cdot\mathbf{r}} u_0(\mathbf{r}) = -k^2 e^{i\mathbf{k}\cdot\mathbf{r}} u_0(\mathbf{r}) + 2i\mathbf{k} e^{i\mathbf{k}\cdot\mathbf{r}} \nabla u_0(\mathbf{r}) + e^{i\mathbf{k}\cdot\mathbf{r}} \nabla^2 u_0(\mathbf{r});$$

and so

$$(11.29) \quad \bar{E} = \frac{\hbar^2}{2m} k^2 + \int u_0{}^*(\mathbf{r}) \left[-\frac{\hbar^2}{2m} \nabla^2 + V(\mathbf{r}) \right] u_0(\mathbf{r}) \, d\tau$$

$$= \frac{\hbar^2}{2m} k^2 + E_0.$$

The term in $\int u_0{}^*(\mathbf{r}) \nabla u_0(\mathbf{r}) \, d\tau$ is zero by symmetry: it can be shown that for the $\mathbf{k} = 0$ state u_0 must be either an even or an odd function of $\mathbf{r}$. We therefore have the desired result in (11.29).

There is then considerable interest in obtaining reliable calculations of $u_0(\mathbf{r})$, as this function often will give us a good picture of the distribution of charge within a unit cell. Wigner and Seitz have developed a simple and fairly accurate method of calculating $u_0(\mathbf{r})$ if the field of the free ion is known. We discuss their method below. There have been many developments in the calculation of wave functions in solids since their work, but this is not the place to discuss them.

WIGNER-SEITZ METHOD

The Wigner-Seitz[6] method is applied most simply to body-centered cubic and face-centered cubic structures. In these structures it is possible to fill up the whole space with polyhedra by drawing planes bisecting the lines joining each atom to its nearest neighbors and (for bcc) next nearest neighbors. The atomic polyhedra obtained in this way are shown in Fig. 11.10.

An ion core is located at the center of each polyhedron. We direct attention to the fact that the ionic radius of the Na^+ ion is about 0.95 A, while the half-distance between nearest neighbors is 1.85 A. Thus throughout most of the volume of an atomic polyhedron in sodium the potential energy of a conduction electron is small, and inside the ion core where the potential is large it is also approximately

[6] E. P. Wigner and F. Seitz, Phys. Rev. **43**, 804 (1933); **46**, 509 (1934).

spherically symmetric. We may take the potential to be spherical throughout each polyhedron, to a fair approximation.

The wave function for $\mathbf{k} = 0$ is periodic with the period of the lattice and is also symmetrical about any lattice point. To satisfy these two conditions the normal derivative $\partial u_0 / \partial n$ must vanish on the boundary planes of each polyhedron. The polyhedra actually approximate not too badly to spheres; Wigner and Seitz replace them by spheres, which are referred to as s spheres. The radius r_0 of the

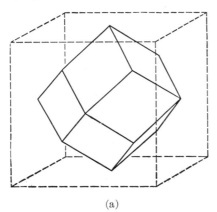
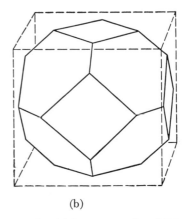

(a)   (b)

Fig. 11.10. Atomic polyhedra surrounding an atom, for (a) face-centered and (b) body-centered cubic structures. The cubes show the unit cells in either case.

sphere is determined by the condition that the volume of the s sphere be equal to the atomic volume, and so for a bcc structure

$$\frac{4\pi}{3} r_0{}^3 = \frac{1}{2} a^3,$$

where a is the lattice constant. We have

(11.30) $$r_0 = (3/8\pi)^{1/3} a \cong 0.49a.$$

The boundary condition $\partial u_0 / \partial n = 0$ on the polyhedron is replaced by the simpler condition

(11.31) $$(\partial u_0 / \partial r)_{r_0} = 0$$

on the surface of the s sphere.

The problem has been reduced by these approximations to finding the solution of the wave equation

(11.32) $$\left[-\frac{\hbar^2}{2mr^2} \frac{d}{dr} \left(r^2 \frac{d\psi}{dr} \right) + V(r) \right] \psi = E\psi,$$

subject to the boundary condition 11.31; here $V(r)$ may be taken as the potential of the ion core as obtained by self-consistent field calculations or by an empirical fit of the energy levels of the free atom as determined spectroscopically. The wave function of lowest state in the conduction ($3s$) band of metallic sodium determined by solving (11.32) is shown in Fig. 11.11. It may be noted that the function is practically constant over 90 percent of the atomic volume. To the extent that the solutions for higher $\mathbf{k}$ may be approximated by $e^{i\mathbf{k}\cdot\mathbf{r}}u_0(\mathbf{r})$, as in (11.27), it will be true that the wave functions in the

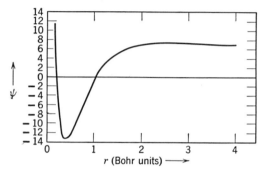

Fig. 11.11.   The lowest wave function of metallic sodium.   A Bohr unit of length is 0.529×10^{-8} cm.

conduction band are similar to plane waves over most of the atomic volume, but oscillate and increase markedly in the region of the ion core.

Wigner and Seitz went on to calculate the cohesive energy of metallic sodium, with quite good results. For other alkali metals it is of some importance to take some account of the $\mathbf{k}$ dependence of the part $u_{\mathbf{k}}(\mathbf{r})$ of the Bloch function, rather than to approximate it by $u_0(\mathbf{r})$. By applying the Hamiltonian operator

$$-\frac{\hbar^2}{2m}\nabla^2 + V(\mathbf{r})$$

to the Bloch function $e^{i\mathbf{k}\cdot\mathbf{r}}u_{\mathbf{k}}(\mathbf{r})$ it is a simple matter for the reader to verify that $u_{\mathbf{k}}(\mathbf{r})$ must satisfy the differential equation

$$(11.33) \quad \left[-\frac{\hbar^2}{2m}\nabla^2 - \frac{i\hbar^2}{m}\mathbf{k}\cdot\nabla + V(\mathbf{r})\right]u_{\mathbf{k}}(\mathbf{r}) = \left(E_{\mathbf{k}} - \frac{\hbar^2 k^2}{2m}\right)u_{\mathbf{k}}(\mathbf{r}).$$

The term in $\mathbf{k}\cdot\nabla$ is often treated as a perturbation. To the second order in k^2, the energy turns out to be, for a cubic crystal and a band which is not degenerate at $\mathbf{k} = 0$,

$$(11.34) \qquad E_{\mathbf{k}} = E_0 + \frac{\hbar^2 k^2}{2m}\left[1 + \frac{2}{m}\sum_{\alpha}\frac{\langle 0|p_x|\alpha\rangle\langle\alpha|p_x|0\rangle}{E_0 - E_\alpha}\right],$$

where $\langle 0|p_x|\alpha\rangle$ is the matrix element of the x component of the momentum operator between the states $\mathbf{k} = 0$ in the band 0 under consideration and another band α. This is a result of standard perturbation theory.

From the form of (11.34) we are led to suspect that a conduction electron may behave in some respects as if it had an effective mass

$$(11.35) \qquad \frac{1}{m^*} = \frac{1}{m}\left[1 + \frac{2}{m}\sum_{\alpha}\frac{\langle 0|p_x|\alpha\rangle\langle\alpha|p_x|0\rangle}{E_0 - E_\alpha}\right].$$

We shall examine the effective mass concept in the sections below.

Values of m^*/m of alkali metals are given below, as calculated by Brooks [7]

	Li	Na	K	Rb	Cs
(m^*/m)	1.40	0.98	0.94	0.87	0.83

EFFECTIVE MASS OF ELECTRONS IN CRYSTALS

We shall consider the concept of an effective mass from several points of view. We first look at the motion of a wave packet in an applied electric field $\mathcal{E}$. We suppose that the wave packet is made up of states near a particular k value in a single band.

The general expression for the group velocity v_g is

$$(11.36) \qquad v_g = d\omega/dk.$$

This is a familiar result in physical optics. Now the frequency associated with a wave function of energy E is given by $\omega = E/\hbar$, and so

$$(11.37) \qquad v_g = \hbar^{-1}\, dE/dk.$$

The work δE done on the electron by the electric field $\mathcal{E}$ in the time interval δt is

$$(11.38) \qquad \delta E = e\mathcal{E}v_g\,\delta t.$$

We observe however

$$(11.39) \qquad \delta E = (dE/dk)\,\delta k = \hbar v_g\,\delta k,$$

[7] H. Brooks, private communication; see also values quoted by D. Pines, Phys. Rev. **95**, 1090 (1954).

using (11.37). Thus, on comparing (11.38) with (11.39), we have

(11.40) $$\delta k = (e\mathcal{E}/\hbar)\,\delta t,$$

or

(11.41) $$\hbar\,dk/dt = e\mathcal{E}.$$

This is an important relation, showing that in a crystal $\hbar\,dk/dt$ is equal to the external force on the electron, whereas in free space it is, of course, $m\,dv/dt$ that is equal to the force. We are not overthrowing Newton's second law of motion; the point is that the electron in the crystal is subject to forces from the crystal lattice as well as from external sources. If we choose to express the motion in terms of the external force alone, it is not surprising that the resulting equation of motion is not simply $F = ma$. It is surprising that any good at all comes out of an approach in terms of external forces alone, but we shall see that the effective mass is a most useful quantity.

From (11.37) we have

(11.42) $$dv_g/dt = \hbar^{-1}\,d^2E/dk\,dt = \hbar^{-1}(d^2E/dk^2)(dk/dt).$$

Using (11.41) for dk/dt, we have

(11.43) $$\frac{dv_g}{dt} = \frac{d^2E}{dk^2}\frac{e\mathcal{E}}{\hbar^2}.$$

It appears on comparison with the classical equation $dv/dt = e\mathcal{E}/m$ that $\hbar^2/(d^2E/dk^2)$ plays the role of a mass, and we call this quantity the *effective mass* m^*:

(11.44) $$m^* = \frac{\hbar^2}{(d^2E/dk^2)}.$$

We note that, if the energy is given by $E = (\hbar^2/2m^*)k^2$, then m^* here is consistent with (11.44).

It is easy to generalize (11.44) to take account of an anisotropic energy surface. We find for the components of the effective mass tensor

(11.45) $$\left(\frac{m}{m^*}\right)_{ij} = \frac{m}{\hbar^2}\frac{d^2E_{\mathbf{k}}}{dk_i\,dk_j},$$

where i, j are Cartesian coordinates.

PHYSICAL BASIS OF EFFECTIVE MASSES

We now attempt to shed some light on how it is that an electron of mass m when put into a crystal may respond to applied fields as if the mass were m^*. The interaction with the lattice is responsible for the difference between m and m^*. It is helpful in this connection to think of the process of Bragg reflection of electron waves in a lattice.

We consider the Bloch eigenfunction ψ_k belonging to the energy eigenvalue E_k and wave vector $\mathbf{k}$. We may analyze ψ_k in a Fourier series, thereby obtaining the expansion of ψ_k in the plane wave or momentum representation:

$$(11.46) \qquad \psi_k = \sum_G a_G(\mathbf{k}) \exp [i(\mathbf{G} + \mathbf{k}) \cdot \mathbf{r}].$$

Here $\mathbf{G}$ is 2π times a vector in the reciprocal lattice (Chapter 2). The expectation value of the momentum of an electron in the state $\mathbf{k}$ is

$$(11.47) \qquad \mathbf{p}_{el} = (\mathbf{k}|-i\hbar\nabla|\mathbf{k}) = \sum_G \hbar(\mathbf{G} + \mathbf{k})|a_G(\mathbf{k})|^2$$

$$= \hbar \left(\mathbf{k} + \sum_G \mathbf{G}|a_G(\mathbf{k})|^2 \right),$$

taking ψ normalized in unit volume. We now examine the transfer of momentum between the electron and the lattice when the state $\mathbf{k}$ of the electron is changed to $\mathbf{k} + \Delta\mathbf{k}$ by the application of an external force.

We imagine an insulating crystal electrostatically neutral except for a single electron in the state $\mathbf{k}$ of the otherwise empty conduction band of the crystal. We suppose that a weak external electric field is applied for a long time interval, such that the total impulse given to the entire crystal system is

$$(11.48) \qquad \mathit{g} = \int e\mathbf{E} \, dt.$$

The interval is taken as long in order to make possible in principle the approximate definition of the final state of the system.

If the conduction electron were free ($m^* = m$), the total momentum imparted to the crystal system by the impulse would appear in the change of momentum of the conduction electron:

$$(11.49) \qquad \mathit{g} = \Delta\mathbf{p}_{tot} = \Delta\mathbf{p}_{el} = \hbar\Delta\mathbf{k}.$$

The neutral crystal suffers no net interaction with the electric field, either directly or indirectly through the conduction electron.

If the conduction electron interacts with the periodic potential of the crystal lattice, we must have

$$(11.50) \qquad \mathit{g} = \Delta\mathbf{p}_{tot} = \Delta\mathbf{p}_{lat} + \Delta\mathbf{p}_{el}.$$

From Eq. (11.47) we have

(11.51) $\qquad \Delta \mathbf{p}_{el} = \hbar\,\Delta \mathbf{k} + \sum_G \hbar \mathbf{G}[(\nabla_\mathbf{k}|a_G(\mathbf{k})|^2)\cdot\Delta \mathbf{k}].$

The change $\Delta \mathbf{p}_{lat}$ in the lattice momentum resulting from the change of state of the electron may be derived by an elementary physical consideration. We are familiar with the circumstance that an x-ray photon suffering Bragg reflection from a crystal lattice transfers momentum to the lattice. Similarly, an electron reflected by the lattice transfers momentum to the lattice. If an incident electron with plane wave component of momentum $\hbar\mathbf{k}$ is reflected with momentum $\hbar(\mathbf{k} + \mathbf{G})$, the lattice acquires the momentum $-\hbar\mathbf{G}$ as required by momentum conservation. The momentum transfer when the state $\psi_\mathbf{k}$ goes over to $\psi_{\mathbf{k}+\Delta\mathbf{k}}$ is now seen to be

(11.52) $\qquad \Delta \mathbf{p}_{lat} = -\hbar \sum_G \mathbf{G}[(\nabla_\mathbf{k}|a_G(\mathbf{k})|^2\cdot\Delta \mathbf{k}],$

as only the portion

$$\nabla_\mathbf{k}|a_G(\mathbf{k})|^2\cdot\Delta \mathbf{k}$$

of each individual component of the initial state is effectively reflected during the state change $\Delta\mathbf{k}$.

The total momentum change is therefore

(11.53) $\qquad \Delta \mathbf{p}_{el} + \Delta \mathbf{p}_{lat} = \boldsymbol{\mathcal{I}} = \hbar\,\Delta\mathbf{k},$

exactly as for free electrons, Eq. (11.49). Thus from Eq. (11.53) and the definition of $\boldsymbol{\mathcal{I}}$, Eq. (11.48), we have

(11.54) $\qquad d\mathbf{k}/dt = e\mathbf{E}/\hbar.$

This is a well-known relation and was derived earlier in this chapter by a different method.

A natural definition of the effective mass is that m^* is the mass a free electron would need in order for the velocity increment under the applied impulse to be equal to the actual velocity increment of the conduction electron under the same impulse

(11.55) $\qquad \Delta\mathbf{p}_{el}/m = \hbar\,\Delta\mathbf{k}/m^*.$

The reciprocal effective mass tensor is defined by this equation and is equal to, using Eq. (11.51),

(11.56) $\qquad \left(\dfrac{m}{m^*}\right)_{ij} = \delta_{ij} + \sum_G G_i\,\dfrac{\partial}{\partial k_j}\,|a_G(\mathbf{k})|^2.$

The present derivation has been motivated by physical considerations in which the momentum exchange with the lattice enters directly. The tensor is actually symmetric, as shown below.

By comparing the expressions (11.37) and (11.47) for the velocity associated with the state $\psi_{\mathbf{k}}$, we have

$$(11.57) \qquad \hbar \mathbf{v} = \nabla_{\mathbf{k}} E = \frac{\hbar^2}{m} \left[\mathbf{k} + \sum_{\mathbf{G}} \mathbf{G} |a_{\mathbf{G}}(\mathbf{k})|^2 \right].$$

On further differentiation we find

$$(11.58) \qquad \frac{\partial^2 E_{\mathbf{k}}}{\partial k_i \, \partial k_j} = \frac{\hbar^2}{m} \left[\delta_{ij} + \sum_{\mathbf{G}} G_i \frac{\partial}{\partial k_j} |a_{\mathbf{G}}(\mathbf{k})|^2 \right].$$

Now from the usual definition of the effective mass tensor (11.45) we have

$$(11.59) \qquad \left(\frac{m}{m^*} \right)_{ij} = \frac{m}{\hbar^2} \frac{\partial^2 E_{\mathbf{k}}}{\partial k_i \, \partial k_j} = \delta_{ij} + \sum_{\mathbf{G}} G_i \frac{\partial}{\partial k_j} |a_{\mathbf{G}}(\mathbf{k})|^2,$$

in agreement with (11.56). This proves the equivalence of the two definitions.

Consider the physical implications of (11.56) with reference to the familiar weak binding approximation in one dimension with a perturbation $V = 2V_0 \cos Gx$, representing the interaction of the electron with the lattice. The band structure is shown in Fig. 11.12. At a point A near the bottom of the lower band the state is represented quite adequately by a plane wave e^{ikx}; the reflected component is small and increases only slowly as k is increased, and so in this region $m^* \cong m$. At B the reflected component $e^{i(k-G)x}$ is quite large; it is larger still at C and becomes equal in amplitude to e^{ikx} at D, at which point (as at E also) the eigenfunctions are standing waves, rather than running waves.

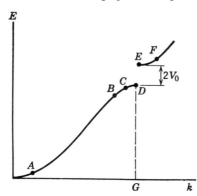

Fig. 11.12. Band structure arising from the perturbation $2V_0 \cos Gx$. The eigenfunctions ψ_k may be written approximately as linear combinations of e^{ikx} and $e^{i(k-G)x}$, with relative amplitudes depending on k.

It is thus not surprising to find in the region B to D negative values for m^*. A negative m^* means only that on going from state k to state $k + \Delta k$ the momentum transfer to the lattice is opposite to and larger than the momentum transfer to the electron.   Although k is increased by Δk by the applied electric field, the consequent Bragg reflections result in an overall decrease in the momentum of the electron, so that the effective mass may be described as being negative.   As we proceed from E towards F, the amplitude of $e^{i(k-G)x}$ decreases and m^* assumes a small positive value; that is, the increase in electron velocity resulting from a given impulse is larger than that which a free electron would experience.   The lattice makes up the difference through the recoil that it experiences when the amplitude of $e^{i(k-G)x}$ is diminished.

The most direct experimental determination of the effective mass is by means of cyclotron resonance experiments, as will be discussed in the chapter on the physics of semiconductors.   The theoretical justification for the use of the effective mass in various circumstances has been considered by a number of workers.[8]

CONSEQUENCES OF THE EFFECTIVE MASS

We suppose for simplicity that in the portion of a band of interest all the states may be described by the same value of the effective mass m^*.   One has from (10.67)

$$E_F(0) = \frac{\hbar^2}{2m^*}\,(3\pi^2 N)^{\frac{2}{3}},$$

and so the Fermi energy E_F and the Fermi temperature T_F of a degenerate electron gas are inversely proportional to m^*; we may then introduce m^* consistently in the theory in place of m.   In this fashion we may transcribe various results of the free electron theory.

We find for the electronic heat capacity that (10.89) gives us

(11.60) $C_v \propto m^*.$

Values of m^* deduced from heat capacity data are given in Table 10.4. For the Pauli spin susceptibility (10.96) gives

(11.61) $\chi_s \propto m^*.$

The proportionality of the heat capacity and spin susceptibility to m^* reflects directly the proportionality of the density of states at the top

    [8] Representative treatments include those by G. H. Wannier, Phys. Rev. **52**, 191 (1937); J. C. Slater, Phys. Rev. **76**, 1592 (1949); R. Karplus and J. M. Luttinger, Phys. Rev. **95**, 1154 (1954); S. Pekar, J. Phys. U.S.S.R. **10**, 431 (1946); E. N. Adams and P. N. Argyres, Phys. Rev. **102**, 605 (1956); J. M. Luttinger and W. Kohn, Phys. Rev. **97**, 869 (1955).   The last paper gives the best treatment for magnetic fields.

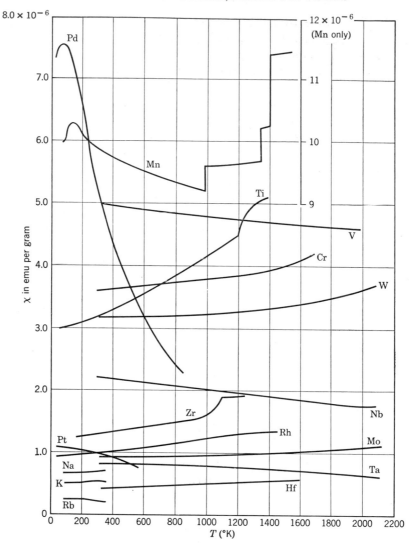

Fig. 11.13.   Temperature dependence of the magnetic susceptibility of metals.
(Courtesy of C. J. Kriessman.)

of the Fermi distribution to the effective mass.   The extension[9] of
the Landau diamagnetism theory to the effective mass case involves
other factors, such as the modification of the Larmor frequency equation, and it turns out for the Landau diamagnetic susceptibility that

$$(11.62) \qquad\qquad \chi_d \propto 1/m^*.$$

[9] R. Peierls, Z. Physik, **80**, 763 (1933).

We note further from Chapter 10 that the electrical conductivity and mobility are proportional to $1/m^*$, so that

(11.63) $$\sigma = Ne^2\tau/m^*,$$

and the mobility

(11.64) $$\mu = e\tau/m^*.$$

We may draw several qualitative conclusions from this discussion. The metals of the transition groups of the periodic table are known to have unfilled inner shells, and the corresponding bands may be unfilled. As the overlap of inner shells on adjacent atoms is likely to be relatively small, the bands will be quite narrow in energy, and the density of states will be high. We therefore expect the transition metals to have values of $m^*/m \gg 1$, and to have high electronic heat capacities and high paramagnetic susceptibilities. High diamagnetic susceptibilities will occur when $m^*/m \ll 1$.

The observations are in agreement with this idea. Reference to Table 10.4 shows that many of the transition metals, including cobalt, iron, manganese, niobium, nickel, palladium, and platinum, have unusually large electronic heat capacities, suggesting the effective mass ratio m^*/m is of the order of 10 or more. The magnetic susceptibilities are shown in Fig. 11.13; it is seen that some of the transition metals have abnormally high susceptibilities. A compilation of values of the magnetic susceptibility of transition elements is given in Table 11.1; values for the alkali metals were given in Table 10.5.

TABLE 11.1. COMPILATION OF VALUES OF THE MAGNETIC SUSCEPTIBILITY OF TRANSITION ELEMENTS AT ROOM TEMPERATURE

[Selected by C. J. Kriessman and H. B. Callen, Phys. Rev. **94**, 837 (1954)]

Element	χ (emu/gram) $\times 10^6$	Element	χ (emu/gram) $\times 10^6$
Ti	3.2	Mn	9.7
Zr	1.3	Re	0.37
Hf	0.42	Ru	0.43
V	5.0	Os	0.05
Nb	2.24	Rh	0.99
Ta	0.84	Ir	0.18
Cr	3.3	Pd	5.23
Mo	0.94	Pt	0.97
W	0.30		

According to (11.35) we may expect values of the effective mass ratio $m^*/m \ll 1$ for states near a small energy discontinuity, and H. Jones[10] has explained on this basis the strong diamagnetism of

[10] H. Jones, Proc. Roy. Soc. (London) **A144**, 225 (1934); **A147**, 396 (1934); for references to later work on bismuth see M. Tinkham, Phys. Rev. **101**, 902 (1956).

bismuth and gamma-brass, which have diamagnetic susceptibilities ~5 to 10 times larger than normal. In certain directions in the bismuth crystal values of m^*/m of the order of 10^{-2} are required to explain the susceptibility and its anisotropy.

HALL EFFECT

The most striking experimental evidence leading us to introduce the concept of positive current carriers or holes in crystals is furnished by the Hall effect. When a conductor is placed in a magnetic field perpendicular to the direction of current flow, a voltage is developed across the specimen in the direction perpendicular to both the current

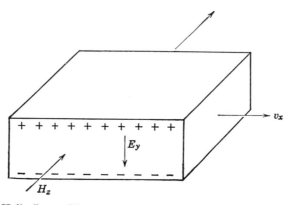

Fig. 11.14. Hall effect. Electrons flowing in the x direction in the presence of the magnetic field H_z are deflected toward the lower face of the specimen, which then charges up until the resulting electric field cancels the effect of the magnetic field.

and the magnetic field, as shown in Fig. 11.14. The voltage is called the Hall voltage. It is developed because the moving charges making up the current are forced to one side by the magnetic field. The charges accumulate on a face of the specimen until the electric field associated with the accumulated charge is large enough to cancel the force exerted by the magnetic field. The Hall effect is an important tool especially in semiconductor research, as in simple situations the effect provides a direct estimate of the concentration of charge carriers.

It is usually assumed in calculating the Hall voltage that the specimen is in the form of a thin plane slab and the voltage is developed across the narrow dimension, as in Fig. 11.14. The Lorentz force on a charge carrier is

$$(11.65) \qquad \mathbf{F} = e \left[\mathbf{E} + \frac{1}{c} \mathbf{v} \times \mathbf{H} \right].$$

The Hall electric field in the y direction is given by the condition

(11.66) $$F_y = 0 = e\left(E_y - \frac{1}{c}v_xH_z\right),$$

for the geometry in Fig. 11.14. Thus

(11.67) $$E_y = v_xH_z/c = j_xH_z/Nec,$$

where j_x is the current density and N is the carrier concentration. The ratio

(11.68) $$R_H = E_y/j_xH_z = 1/Nec$$

is called the Hall constant and is negative for free electrons. The value of the Hall coefficient in electrostatic units statvolt-cm/statamp-oersted is of the magnitude 10^{-24} for normal metals; it will be much larger in semiconductors, as N is much smaller. The value of the Hall coefficient in practical units volt-cm/amp-oersted is 9×10^{11} times the value in electrostatic units.

It is often convenient to consider the Hall angle

(11.69) $$\phi = E_y/E_x = \sigma H_z/Nec$$

$$= e\tau H/m^*c = \mu H/c,$$

using (11.63) and (11.64). We note from Problem 11.2 that eH/m^*c is just the cyclotron angular frequency ω_c for a free particle of mass m^* in a magnetic field H; thus

$$\phi = \omega_c\tau,$$

where τ is the relaxation time. The Hall angle is equal to the average number of radians (usually fractional) traversed by a particle between collisions. All results quoted assume implicitly the energy band is of the simple form $E_k = \hbar^2k^2/2m^*$.

The simple result $R_H = 1/Nec$ can be shown by more rigorous methods to apply to a Fermi-Dirac distribution of identical carriers. The numerical factor is altered slightly for a Maxwellian distribution. The expression becomes somewhat more complicated if both electrons and holes contribute to the conductivity; the solution is considered in a problem at the end of Chapter 12.

Observed values of the Hall constant for several metals are compared in Table 11.2 with values calculated directly from the concentration of valence electrons. For the monovalent metals the agreement between observed and calculated values is quite satisfactory. However, the sign of the effect in beryllium, zinc, and cadmium is opposite to that predicted for electrons. This situation represented a famous unsolved problem until clarified by band theory. A positive Hall constant implies that the current is carried by positive charges. We shall see that on band theory vacant states near the top of an otherwise filled energy band behave as if endowed with a positive charge. States of this character give rise to the positive Hall constants. The anomalous large value of the constant for bismuth is interpreted on band theory as caused by a low concentration of electrons outside nearly filled bands.

Ferromagnetic metals and alloys display several quite remarkable features in their Hall effects. An account of the experimental position is given by Pugh and Rostoker;[11] a theoretical explanation has been proposed by Karplus and Luttinger,[12] and by Smit.

TABLE 11.2.   COMPARISON OF OBSERVED HALL CONSTANTS WITH THOSE CALCULATED ON FREE ELECTRON THEORY

	$R_H \times 10^{13}$ (v-cm/amp-oersted) at room temperature	
Metal	Observed	Calculated
Li	−17.0	−13.1
Na	−25.0	−24.4
K	−42	−47
Cs	−78	−73
Cu	− 5.5	− 7.4
Ag	− 8.4	−10.4
Au	− 7.2	−10.5
Be	+24.4	− 2.5
Zn	+ 3.3	− 4.6
Cd	+ 6.0	− 6.5
Al	− 4	. . . . . .
Bi	∼−1000	− 4.1

MOTION OF HOLES

The circumstance that vacant states near the top of an otherwise filled band behave in every way as particles of positive charge $+|e|$ is one of the most interesting features of the band theory of solids. It is also a feature of considerable practical importance, as the operation of transistors depends directly on the coexistence of holes and electrons within semiconducting crystals. The first experimental evidence for holes came from the occurrence of positive values of the Hall coefficient,

[11] E. M. Pugh and N. Rostoker, Revs. Modern Phys. **25**, 151 (1953); data on rare earth metals are given by Kevane, Legvold, and Spedding, Phys. Rev. **91**, 1372 (1953).

[12] R. Karplus and J. M. Luttinger, Phys. Rev. **95**, 1154 (1954); J. Smit, Physica **21**, 877 (1955).

as discussed above. There is other evidence in connection with transistor physics. It has been established by means of cyclotron resonance experiments[13] with circularly polarized radiation that holes and electrons rotate in opposite senses in a magnetic field, just as one would expect for charges of opposite sign.

It is not difficult to understand[14] the reason for the behavior of holes. We now consider in detail the motion of a hole in an applied electric field. We treat the one-dimensional example illustrated by Fig. 11.15. Initially the band is filled except for the single vacant state F at the top of the band. An electric field $\mathcal{E}_x$ is now applied in the $+x$ direction. The resulting motion of the electrons in the band is governed by the equation

$$(11.70) \quad \hbar \dot{k}_x = F = -|e|\mathcal{E}_x,$$

and each electron changes its k_x value at the same rate. The equation of motion tells us that Δk_x is negative for the situation illustrated. The vacant state initially at F is displaced first to E and at a later

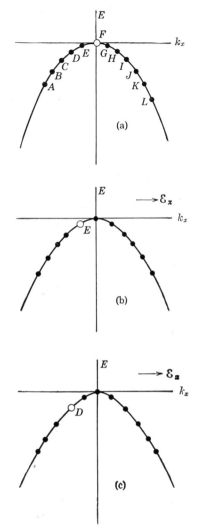

(a)

(b)

(c)

Fig. 11.15. (a) At $t = 0$ all states are filled except F at the top of the band. (b) An electric field $\mathcal{E}_x$ is applied in the $+x$ direction. The force on the electrons is in the $-k_x$ direction and all electrons make transitions together in the $-k_x$ direction, moving the hole to E. (c) After a further interval the electrons move farther along and the hole is now at D. In this way the hole has moved to decreasing k_x values, corresponding to higher positive velocities.

[13] Dresselhaus, Kip, and Kittel, Phys. Rev. **98**, 368 (1955).

[14] A proof along lines first given by Heisenberg may be found in W. Shockley, *Holes and electrons in semiconductors*, Van Nostrand, New York, 1950.

time moves to D. That is, the hole moves along with the electrons in the direction of decreasing k_x. (One should note that the "parking lot" analogy to the motion of holes does not really give the picture correctly.)

For the portion of the energy surface to the left of F the slope $\partial E/\partial k_x$ is positive; from (11.37) the group velocity is

$$(11.71) \qquad v_g = \hbar^{-1}\,\partial E/\partial k_x,$$

so that we have a positive velocity. We see then that the velocity of the hole increases in the direction of the electric field. This fact alone would be compatible with the assignment to the hole of either a positive charge and positive mass or negative charge and negative mass. The following consideration shows that only the positive possibility is correct.

If the band were entirely filled the total velocity summed over every electron in the band would be zero: a filled band cannot carry current. The contribution of a single electron in the state E to the velocity sum is positive. Now, if the band is filled except for the state E, the rest of the electrons in the band must have a negative net velocity $\hbar \bar{v}_x = -(\partial E/\partial k_x)$, in order for the total velocity to be zero for the band when completely filled. As the hole is accelerated the electrons are accelerated in the opposite direction, in effect transporting negative charge to the left as drawn; but the hole is accelerated to the right and thus the motion of the hole in effect transports positive charge to the right. We must therefore assign the hole a positive charge. But to be consistent with the rate of change of velocity we must then assign the hole a positive effective mass

$$(11.72) \qquad m^*\,(\text{hole}) = -\hbar^2/(\partial^2 E/\partial k_x{}^2).$$

It is useful to summarize the equations which govern the motion of a hole in an otherwise filled band:

$$(11.73) \qquad \hbar \mathbf{k}_h = -\,|e|\left[\boldsymbol{\varepsilon} + \frac{1}{c}\mathbf{v}_h \times \mathbf{H}\right] \qquad$$

$$(11.74) \qquad \hbar \bar{\mathbf{v}}_h = \nabla_{\mathbf{k}} E \qquad\qquad\qquad\quad \text{holes}$$

$$(11.75) \qquad \left(\frac{1}{m_h{}^*}\right)_{ij} = -\frac{1}{\hbar^2}\frac{\partial^2 E}{\partial k_i\,\partial k_j}$$

For electrons the right-hand side of the relation (11.75) must be multiplied by -1. We should emphasize that all problems can be solved by considering the notion of electrons alone, but if the band is nearly filled it is more convenient to deal with the vacant states or holes.   It is now evident that the Hall constant $R_H = 1/Nec$ will be negative for electrons and positive for holes.   We note that, if $E = E_0 - (\hbar^2/2m^*)k^2$, then $\bar{v}_h = -\hbar k/m^*$ and $m^* \dot{v}_h = +|e| \left[\varepsilon + \frac{1}{c} v_h \times H \right]$.

CALCULATION OF THE CONDUCTIVITY OF METALS

The calculation of the electrical conductivity of a metal is usually carried out separately for two different temperature regions, $T \gg \Theta$ and $T \ll \Theta$, where Θ is the Debye temperature of the lattice.   The

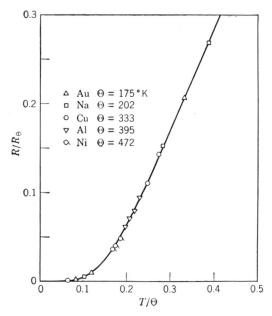

Fig. 11.16.   Theoretical (Grüneisen) temperature variation of electrical resistance, and experimental values for various metals.   (After Bardeen.)

first quantum calculations were made by Bloch.   In the high temperature region the calculated conductivity is proportional to T^{-1}, and in the low temperature region it is proportional to T^{-5}.   The agreement of the calculated temperature dependence with experiment is quite good, as shown in Fig. 11.16, although T^{-5} is seldom actually obtained.

The calculation of the resistivity is simpler at high temperatures than at low temperatures.   The high temperature theory developed here follows the elementary approximate presentation by Weisskopf;[15] the low temperature theory is discussed in Appendix K.

If the lattice of a metal is perfect and there are no lattice vibrations, the electron waves pass through the lattice unscattered, without resistance, just as light passes through a perfect crystal without scattering or attenuation. The electric resistance of an actual metal arises from deviations from a perfect lattice caused by thermal motion of the atoms and by structural irregularities such as impurity atoms and lattice defects. In disordered (random) alloys the structural irregularities may dominate the resistance even at room temperature, but in very pure metals the thermal motion is dominant above liquid hydrogen temperatures.

We consider first the effective cross section Q of an ion for the scattering of an electron. The cross section is related to the relaxation time τ by the gas-kinetic relation

$$(11.76) \qquad \tau = 1/NvQ,$$

where v is the velocity of the electron and N is the number of ions per unit volume.

We approximate the wave function of an electron incident upon an ion by

$$(11.77) \qquad \psi_i = e^{i\mathbf{k}\cdot\mathbf{r}},$$

neglecting the modulation of the plane wave by the lattice. The wave scattered by an ion at $\mathbf{r}_0$ is written

$$(11.78) \qquad \psi_s = Be^{i\mathbf{k}'\cdot(\mathbf{r}-\mathbf{r}_0)},$$

where B is the amplitude;[16] we suppose that $\mathbf{r}$ is sufficiently far from $\mathbf{r}_0$ so that in the vicinity of $\mathbf{r}$ the scattered wave may be treated as a plane wave in the direction $\mathbf{k}$. The amplitude B will be proportional to the strength of the incident wave at $\mathbf{r}_0$, so that

$$(11.79) \qquad B = B_0\psi_i(\mathbf{r}_0)$$

and

$$(11.80) \qquad \psi_s(\mathbf{r}_0;\mathbf{r}) = B_0 e^{i(\mathbf{k}-\mathbf{k}')\cdot\mathbf{r}_0}e^{i\mathbf{k}'\cdot\mathbf{r}}.$$

[15] V. Weisskopf, Am. J. Phys. **11**, 1 (1943). Complete derivations are given in all the standard texts on the electron theory of metals. The derivation for $T \ll \Theta$ given by Weisskopf is oversimplified.

[16] The scattered wave actually also contains the factor $|\mathbf{r} - \mathbf{r}_0|^{-1}$, but we may for the present discussion neglect this variation without doing serious damage to the result.

Now in the perfect crystal the totality of scattered waves gives rise to an unscattered but refracted beam. Only if one or more of the ions is displaced from its regular position do we get scattering. We must therefore calculate the effective scattered wave ψ_d as the difference between the wave scattered from the regular position of the ion at $\mathbf{r}_0$ and from the displaced position $\mathbf{r}_0 + \mathbf{d}$:

(11.81) $$\psi_d = \psi_s(\mathbf{r}_0 + \mathbf{d}; \mathbf{r}) - \psi_s(\mathbf{r}_0; \mathbf{r}).$$

If we suppose $d \ll \lambda$, we may expand ψ_d as

(11.82) $$\psi_d = \mathbf{d} \cdot \text{grad } \psi_s,$$

where the gradient is taken with respect to $\mathbf{r}_0$. Then, from (11.80),

(11.83) $$\psi_d(\mathbf{r}_0; \mathbf{r}) = i(\mathbf{k} - \mathbf{k}') \cdot \mathbf{d}\psi_s(\mathbf{r}_0; \mathbf{r}).$$

The amplitude of the effective scattered wave from a displaced ion in a periodic lattice is then different from the scattering from an isolated ion by the factor $i(\mathbf{k} - \mathbf{k}') \cdot \mathbf{d}$.

The cross sections being proportional to the squares of the amplitudes, we have

(11.84) $$Q_d = [(\mathbf{k} - \mathbf{k}') \cdot \mathbf{d}]^2 Q_s,$$

where Q_d is the effective cross section for scattering of an electron by a displaced ion in an otherwise perfect lattice, and Q_s is the free space scattering cross section for an isolated ion. We write the average of Q_d over all the directions of the displacement $\mathbf{d}$ and over all values of the angle between $\mathbf{k}$ and $\mathbf{k}'$ as

(11.85) $$\overline{Q_d} = Ck^2 \, \overline{d^2 Q_s},$$

where C is a constant of the order of unity; it may be shown[15] that its value is $\frac{2}{3}$.

The conductivity is then, using (11.76) and (11.63),

(11.86) $$\sigma = (\tfrac{3}{2})(e^2\hbar^2/mvp^2 \, \overline{d^2 Q_s}),$$

where $p = \hbar k$ is the electronic momentum, and we have assumed one conduction electron per atom. We now calculate the mean square value of the ionic displacement d caused by thermal motion. At high temperatures $(T \gg \Theta)$ we may use the Einstein model of independent harmonic oscillators of angular frequency,

(11.87) $$\omega = k\Theta/\hbar.$$

The mean square displacement of a harmonic oscillator of mass M is given by $\overline{d^2} = E/M\omega^2$, where the energy E is equal to $3kT$. Thus

(11.88) $$\overline{d^2} = 3T\hbar^2/Mk\Theta^2.$$

The electrical conductivity is then

(11.89) $$\sigma = \frac{e^2 Mk\Theta^2}{2p^3 \overline{Q_s} T}; \qquad (T \gg \Theta).$$

The elastic properties of the metal enter through the Debye temperature Θ. It must be pointed out that in this expression the momentum p is to be evaluated at the top of the Fermi distribution; because $\Theta \ll T_F$ in metals, only the electrons near the top are able to be scattered by the lattice vibrations into vacant states. We may estimate the magnitude of $\overline{Q_s}$ as of the order of a^2, where a is the nearest neighbor distance in the lattice. The values of the conductivity for $T \gg \Theta$ calculated in this way from (11.89) are of the correct order of magnitude for monovalent metals and have the correct temperature dependence. The extension of the theory to the region $T \ll \Theta$ is indicated in Appendix K.

It has been found by Grüneisen[17] that the observed temperature dependence of the resistivity is described quite well at all temperatures by the semi-empirical formula

(11.90) $$\rho \propto TG(\Theta/T),$$

where

(11.91) $$G(x) = x^{-4} \int_0^x \frac{s^2\, ds}{(e^s - 1)(1 - e^{-s})}.$$

The formula gives proportionality to T for $T \gg \Theta$ and to T^5 for $T \ll \Theta$, as required by theory. The optimum value of Θ to be used here may differ[18] somewhat from the value deduced from heat capacities for several reasons, including the fact that longitudinal and transverse phonons may contribute differently to the electrical resistivity and to the heat capacity. Figure 11.16 shows that the Grüneisen relation works quite well for the metals indicated there; at quite low temperatures, however, departures from the T^5 law are usually observed.

Reference to detailed theoretical calculations of the conductivity of metals are given in the review by Bardeen.[19] A comparison of

---

[17] E. Grüneisen, Ann. Physik **16**, 530 (1933).

[18] M. Blackman, Proc. Phys. Soc. (London) **A64**, 681 (1951); P. G. Klemens, Proc. Phys. Soc. (London) **A65**, 71 (1952).

[19] J. Bardeen, J. Appl. Phys. **11**, 88 (1940).

observed and calculated values of the conductivity of a number of monovalent metals is reproduced from this paper in Table 11.3.   The

TABLE 11.3. COMPARISON OF OBSERVED AND CALCULATED VALUES OF THE ELECTRICAL CONDUCTIVITY AT 0°C, IN 10^4 OHM^{-1} CM^{-1}

Metal	Observed	Calculated
Li	11.8	28.
Na	23.4	23.
K	16.4	20.
Rb	8.6	33.
Cs	5.3	22.
Cu	64.	174.
Ag	66.	143.
Au	49.	142.

agreement is best for sodium and potassium, the two metals for which the assumptions made in the calculations were expected to be valid.

RESIDUAL RESISTANCE

The resistivity of a metal containing impurity atoms may usually be written in the form

(11.92) $$\rho = \rho_i + \rho_L,$$

where ρ_L is the resistivity caused by thermal motion of the lattice, and ρ_i is the resistivity caused by scattering of the electron waves by impurity atoms which disturb the periodicity of the lattice.   If the concentration of impurity atoms is small, ρ_i is independent of temperature; this statement is known as *Matthiessen's rule*.

The residual resistance is the extrapolated resistivity at 0°K and is equivalent to ρ_i, as ρ_L vanishes as $T \to 0$.   Measurements on sodium in Fig. 11.17 show that the residual resistance may vary from specimen to specimen, while the resistivity caused by thermal motion is independent of the specimen.

A clear minimum in the electrical resistivities of several metals[20,21] has been observed around 5°K.   The effect has so far received no entirely satisfactory explanation,[22] although it appears to be associated with impurities.

[20] de Haas, de Boer, and v. d. Berg, Physica **1**, 1115 (1933).

[21] D. K. C. MacDonald and K. Mendelssohn, Proc. Roy. Soc. (London) **A202**, 523 (1950).

[22] D. K. C. MacDonald and I. M. Templeton, Phil. Mag. **42**, 432 (1951); D. K. C. MacDonald, Phys. Rev. **88**, 148 (1952); J. Korringa and A. N. Gerritsen, Physica **19**, 457 (1953).

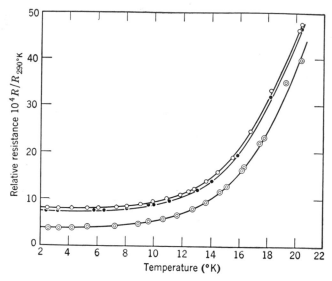

Fig. 11.17.   Resistance of sodium below 20°K, as measured on three specimens by MacDonald and Mendelssohn [Proc. Roy. Soc. (London) **A202**, 103 (1950)].

BRILLOUIN ZONES

We have seen, from (11.1) and the Kronig-Penney problem, that the energy discontinuities in the monatomic one-dimensional lattice occur when the wave number satisfies

$$(11.93) \qquad k = n\pi/a,$$

where n is any positive or negative integer.   Thus it is the value of the wave number which is important for the energy discontinuities. In three dimensions the wave vector $\mathbf{k}$ plays the same role, as we see from the Bragg equation (2.1) or (2.12).   The equation determining the position of the energy discontinuities which actually occur will depend on the type of the crystal lattice.

In the one-dimensional monatomic lattice a line representing the value of k is divided up by the energy discontinuities into segments of length π/a, as shown in Fig. 11.18.   The line segments are known as *Brillouin zones*; the segment $-\pi/a < k < \pi/a$ is the first Brillouin zone; the two segments $-2\pi/a < k < -\pi/a$ and $\pi/a < k < 2\pi/a$ form the second Brillouin zone, etc.   The zone description was introduced by Brillouin, who pointed out that many important and characteristic features of electron propagation in periodic structures could be described by considering the positions in $\mathbf{k}$-space of the boundaries of the zones; these positions are independent of the details of the electron-lattice interaction, being determined instead by the geometry of the crystal structure. Energy discontinuities occur on the zone boundaries.

The Brillouin zones may be found most directly from the Bragg equation in the form (2.12):

$$(11.94) \qquad 2\mathbf{k} \cdot \mathbf{G} + G^2 = 0,$$

where $\mathbf{G}$ is 2π times a reciprocal lattice vector. As an example of the connection of the Bragg equation with Brillouin zones, we consider

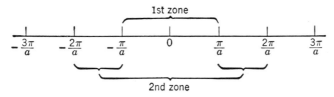

Fig. 11.18. Brillouin zones of a linear monatomic lattice with lattice constant a.

the simple square lattice in two dimensions. The reciprocal lattice vectors are of the form $(n_1/a)\mathbf{i} + (n_2/a)\mathbf{j}$, for lattice constant a; here n_1, n_2 are integers. We have then

$$\mathbf{G} = (2\pi/a)(n_1\mathbf{i} + n_2\mathbf{j}).$$

The Bragg equation (11.94) for reflection of a wave by a periodic lattice becomes

$$(11.95) \qquad k_x n_1 + k_y n_2 = \pi(n_1{}^2 + n_2{}^2)/a.$$

We find the boundaries of the first zone by first setting $n_1 = \pm 1$, $n_2 = 0$, obtaining

$$(11.96) \qquad k_x = \pm \pi/a,$$

and then setting $n_1 = 0$, $n_2 = \pm 1$, obtaining

$$(11.97) \qquad k_y = \pm \pi/a.$$

The four lines (11.96) determine the boundary of the first zone, forming a square, as shown in Fig. 11.19.

The outer boundary of the second zone is determined by setting $n_1 = \pm 1$, $n_2 = \pm 1$, obtaining the equations of the four lines

$$(11.98) \qquad \pm k_x \pm k_y = 2\pi/a,$$

where the signs are independent.

The extension to the sc, bcc, and fcc lattices follows directly. The first Brillouin zone of the simple cubic lattice is a cube of edge $2\pi/a$.

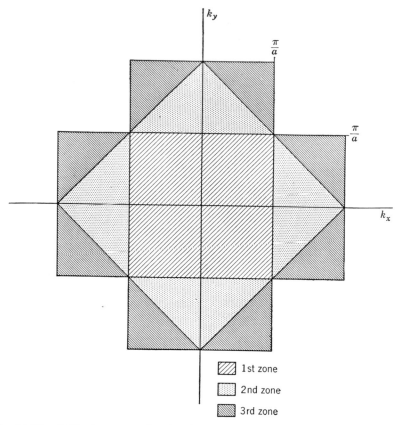

Fig. 11.19. Brillouin zones of a simple square lattice in two dimensions. The first three zones are marked.

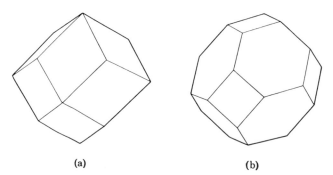

Fig. 11.20. The first Brillouin zone in (a) the bcc lattice and (b) the fcc lattice.

The first zones of the bcc and fcc lattices are shown in Fig. 11.20. They are discussed in detail in the following chapter. It turns out to be possible to restrict consideration to the first Brillouin zone in all problems, as the wave vector $\mathbf{k}$ can always be reduced by subtracting 2π times an appropriate reciprocal lattice vector to give a $\mathbf{k}'$ lying in the first zone, while still preserving the Bloch form of the wave function:

$$(11.99) \qquad \psi_{\mathbf{k}} = e^{i\mathbf{k}\cdot\mathbf{r}}u_{\mathbf{k}}(\mathbf{r}) = e^{i(\mathbf{k}-\mathbf{G})\cdot\mathbf{r}}u_{\mathbf{k}}(\mathbf{r})e^{i\mathbf{G}\cdot\mathbf{r}}$$
$$= e^{i\mathbf{k}'\cdot\mathbf{r}}u_{\mathbf{k}'}'(\mathbf{r}) = \psi_{\mathbf{k}'},$$

as $e^{i\mathbf{G}\cdot\mathbf{r}}$ is periodic in the lattice. The scheme in which all $\mathbf{k}$'s are considered to lie in the first zone is known as the reduced zone scheme.

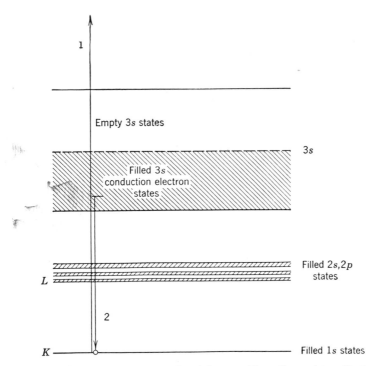

Fig. 11.21. Origin of K emission band in metallic sodium: (1) a K electron is ejected from the metal by electron impact; (2) an electron from the conduction band drops down to fill the vacant K level, emitting an x-ray quantum. The width of the emission line is equal to the width of the filled region of the conduction band, as all conduction electrons may have a chance to emit. The L band originates in a similar process.

SOFT X-RAY EMISSION SPECTRA

The radiation emitted[23] when conduction electrons make transitions into the relatively sharp $K(1s)$ or $L(2s, 2p)$ levels which have been ionized by electron impact is a direct source of information about the band structure of metals. The situation is exhibited in Fig. 11.21 drawn for the K emission band of sodium. The experimental K emission band of lithium is shown in Fig. 11.22. It is important to observe that the width of emission band should be a good measure of the width of the filled portion of the conduction band, although the actual shape of the band will depend on the final state and on the details of the conduction band states. The observed band widths for lithium and sodium are 4.2 ± 0.3 ev and 3.0 ± 0.2 ev, respectively, while the corresponding Fermi energies calculated for free electrons are 4.8 ev and 3.2 ev. The method may also be applied to non-metals: the observed width of the filled valence band in diamond is 33 ± 3 ev, as compared to 29.5 ev calculated for four free valence electrons per atom.

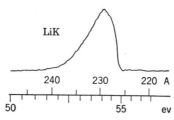

Fig. 11.22. K emission band of lithium. [After H. W. B. Skinner, Trans. Roy. Soc. **A239**, 95 (1940).]

PROBLEMS

11.1. Compare observed electrical conductivity values for two monovalent metals at room temperature with values estimated from (11.89).

11.2. Show that $\omega_c = eH/m^*c$ is the angular frequency of the motion in a magnetic field H of an electron having energy $E_\mathbf{k} = \hbar^2 k^2/2m^*$.

11.3. In an anisotropic crystal the energy may be given in terms of the components of the wave vector by

$$E = \alpha_x k_x{}^2 + \alpha_y k_y{}^2 + \alpha_z k_z{}^2.$$

Find the equations of motion which replace $\mathbf{F} = md^2\mathbf{r}/dt^2$.

11.4. Discuss the information on energy bands in metals which may be deduced from the soft x-ray emission spectra; for references to the literature see footnote 23 below.

11.5. Derive the form of the first Brillouin zone for a sc lattice.

11.6. Make a plot of the first two Brillouin zones of a primitive rectangular two-dimensional lattice with axes a, $b = 3a$.

[23] Early work on several light metals in the 50-500 A region is reported by H. M. O'Bryan and H. W. B. Skinner, Phys. Rev. **45**, 370 (1934); for references to the literature see H. W. B. Skinner, Repts. Prog. Phys. **5**, 257 (1939); Trans. Roy. Soc. (London) **A239**, 95 (1940); see also E. M. Gyorgy and G. G. Harvey, Phys. Rev. **93**, 365 (1954).

11.7. (a) Show for a simple square lattice (two dimensions) that the kinetic energy of a free electron at a corner of the first zone is higher than that of an electron at the midpoint of a side face of the zone by a factor of 2.

(b) What is the corresponding factor for a simple cubic lattice (three dimensions)?

(c) What bearing might similar considerations have on the conductivity of divalent metals?

11.8.* The cohesion of the alkali metals may be thought of in a *rough* approximation as arising from the Coulomb energy of point positive changes arranged on a bcc lattice and imbedded in a uniform sea of conduction electrons. To a close approximation the Coulomb energy of this model is obtained by calculating the energy of a point charge $+ |e|$ interacting electrostatically with a negative charge $- |e|$ distributed uniformly throughout the volume of the s-sphere, of radius given by (11.30). The repulsive part of the energy is given by the electrostatic interaction energy of the electron distribution with itself and also by the kinetic energy of the electron gas.

(a) Show that the electrostatic energy is $E_c = -\dfrac{9}{10}\dfrac{e^2}{r_0}$ of which $-\dfrac{3}{2}\dfrac{e^2}{r_0}$ arises from the interaction of the point charge with the electron distribution and $\dfrac{3}{5}\dfrac{e^2}{r_0}$ arises from the interaction of the electron distribution with itself.

(b) Show that the average kinetic energy of an electron at 0°K is

$$\bar{E}_0 = \frac{3}{10}\frac{\hbar^2}{m^*}\left(\frac{9\pi}{4}\right)^{2/3}\frac{1}{r_0^2}.$$

(c) The total energy of the system $E = \bar{E}_0 + E_c$ is a function of r_0; minimize E as a function of r_0. Evaluate E and r_0 at equilibrium, taking $m = m^*$, and compare with the observed cohesive energy (Table 4.3) and lattice parameter of sodium. In making the comparison, add the ionization energy of atomic sodium to the cohesive energy.

(d) Calculate the compressibility.

REFERENCES

All the references cited at the end of Chapter 10 are relevant to the present chapter; the following references apply to electrical conductivity:

J. Bardeen, "Electrical conductivity of metals," J. Appl. Phys. **11,** 88 (1940).

E. Justi, *Leitfähigkeit und Leitungsmechanismus fester Stoffe*, Vandenhoek, Göttingen, 1948.

D. K. C. MacDonald, "Properties of metals at low temperatures," Progress in Metal Physics, **3,** 42–57 (1952).

D. K. C. MacDonald and K. Sarginson, "Galvanomagnetic effects in conductors," Repts. Prog. Phys. **15,** 249–274 (1952).

R. E. Peierls, *Quantum theory of solids*, Clarendon Press, Oxford, 1955.

W. Shockley, *Electrons and holes in semiconductors*, Van Nostrand, New York, 1950.

V. F. Weisskopf, "On the theory of the electric resistance of metals," Am. J. Phys. **11,** 1 (1943).

12

Application of Brillouin Zone Theory to Metals and Alloys

In this chapter we shall apply band theory in a descriptive and qualitative way to account for a number of physical properties of metals and alloys. We shall be concerned in the main with the relationship between the Fermi surface and the boundary of the Brillouin zone. As the number of conduction electrons is varied by alloying constituents of valency different from that of the solute matrix, the relative positions of the Fermi surface and zone boundary are altered. In certain circumstances this alteration may induce a crystallographic transformation in the alloy, or there may be marked changes in other properties, such as lattice parameters, elastic constants, magnetic susceptibility, and number of effective conduction electrons. The magnetic properties of transition metals are particularly sensitive indicators of the effects of alloying. The electrical properties of semiconductors are often entirely dependent on the presence of trace amounts of impurity atoms, as discussed in detail in Chapter 13.

We shall first discuss in detail the first Brillouin zones of the body-centered cubic, face-centered cubic, and hexagonal close-packed crystal structures. The properties of the metals will be discussed in terms of the band structure as an introduction to the discussion of alloys.

BODY-CENTERED CUBIC LATTICE

The zone boundaries are determined as we have seen by the Bragg equation (2.12):

$$(12.1) \qquad 2\mathbf{k} \cdot \mathbf{G} + G^2 = 0,$$

where $\mathbf{G}$ is 2π times a reciprocal lattice vector. It is seen that each zone boundary is normal to a $\mathbf{G}$ at its midpoint. We must first find the form of $\mathbf{G}$, using the definitions (2.9) and (2.10) of a reciprocal lattice vector.

The primitive translation vectors of the bcc lattice as shown in Fig. 1.13 may be taken as

$$\mathbf{a} = (a/2)(\mathbf{i} + \mathbf{j} + \mathbf{k});$$

(12.2)
$$\mathbf{b} = (a/2)(-\mathbf{i} + \mathbf{j} + \mathbf{k});$$

$$\mathbf{c} = (a/2)(-\mathbf{i} - \mathbf{j} + \mathbf{k});$$

where a is the side of the conventional unit cube and $\mathbf{i}$, $\mathbf{j}$, $\mathbf{k}$ are orthogonal unit vectors parallel to the cube edges. The volume of the primitive cell is

(12.3)
$$V = \mathbf{a} \cdot \mathbf{b} \times \mathbf{c} = \tfrac{1}{2}a^3;$$

we see that this is correct because the unit cube of volume a^3 contains two lattice points. The primitive translations $\mathbf{a}^*$, $\mathbf{b}^*$, $\mathbf{c}^*$ of the reciprocal lattice are given, according to (2.10), by relations of the form

(12.4)
$$\mathbf{a}^* = \frac{\mathbf{b} \times \mathbf{c}}{\mathbf{a} \cdot \mathbf{b} \times \mathbf{c}}.$$

Thus, using (12.2), we have

$$\mathbf{a}^* = (1/a)(\mathbf{i} + \mathbf{k});$$

(12.5)
$$\mathbf{b}^* = (1/a)(-\mathbf{i} + \mathbf{j});$$

$$\mathbf{c}^* = (1/a)(-\mathbf{j} + \mathbf{k}).$$

These are the primitive vectors of a fcc lattice. If h, k, l are integers,

(12.6)
$$\mathbf{G} = 2\pi(h\mathbf{a}^* + k\mathbf{b}^* + l\mathbf{c}^*)$$

$$= (2\pi/a)[(h - k)\mathbf{i} + (k - l)\mathbf{j} + (h + l)\mathbf{k}].$$

The shortest non-zero $\mathbf{G}$'s are the twelve vectors:

(12.7) $(2\pi/a)(\pm\mathbf{i} \pm \mathbf{j});\ (2\pi/a)(\pm\mathbf{j} \pm \mathbf{k});\ (2\pi/a)(\pm\mathbf{i} \pm \mathbf{k}).$

The zone boundaries determined by (12.1) are planes normal to each $\mathbf{G}$ at the midpoint. The first Brillouin zone will be formed from the shortest $\mathbf{G}$'s, of which there are twelve given by (12.7). The zone is therefore the rhombic dodecahedron shown previously in Fig. 11.20a. Now the rhombic dodecahedron constructed in this fashion is a possible choice for the primitive cell of the fcc lattice, as the figures fill all space and each figure contains one lattice point. We have then for the volume of the zone in $\mathbf{k}$-space $\tfrac{1}{4}(4\pi/a)^3 = 2(2\pi/a)^3$. The number of states per unit volume of $\mathbf{k}$-space is $2/(2\pi)^3$ per unit volume of the crystal, so that there are $4/a^3$ states in the zone per unit volume of crystal. A bcc crystal contains $2/a^3$ atoms per unit volume;

thus there are two states in the zone per atom, one state for each spin orientation. This result agrees with our earlier statement that an energy band contains two states for every atom in the crystal.

There are several further points of interest about the first zone of the bcc lattice. The radius k_i of a sphere inscribed in the zone is $k_i = \sqrt{2}\,\pi/a$, so that the volume of the sphere is $(4\pi/3)2^{3/2}\pi^3/a^3$, which is $\pi/3(2)^{1/2} = 0.74$ of the volume of the zone. If the Fermi surface is spherical it will just contact the zone boundary for a conduction electron concentration of $2 \times 0.74 = 1.48$ per atom. The importance of this fact will be developed below with reference to the Hume-Rothery rules of alloy structure.

FACE-CENTERED CUBIC LATTICE

The primitive translation vectors of the fcc lattice as shown in Fig. 1.14a may be taken as

$$\mathbf{a} = (a/2)(\mathbf{i} + \mathbf{j});$$

(12.8)
$$\mathbf{b} = (a/2)(\mathbf{i} + \mathbf{k});$$

$$\mathbf{c} = (a/2)(\mathbf{j} + \mathbf{k}).$$

The volume of the primitive cell is $\mathbf{a} \cdot \mathbf{b} \times \mathbf{c} = \frac{1}{4}a^3$. Using (12.4) the primitive translations of the reciprocal lattice are found to be

$$\mathbf{a}^* = (1/a)(-\mathbf{i} - \mathbf{j} + \mathbf{k});$$

(12.9)
$$\mathbf{b}^* = (1/a)(-\mathbf{i} + \mathbf{j} - \mathbf{k});$$

$$\mathbf{c}^* = (1/a)(\mathbf{i} - \mathbf{j} - \mathbf{k}).$$

These are the primitive translations of a bcc lattice. We have now

$$(12.10) \quad \mathbf{G} = (2\pi/a)[(-h - k + l)\mathbf{i} + (-h + k - l)\mathbf{j} + (h - k - l)\mathbf{k}].$$

The shortest non-zero G's are the eight vectors

$$(12.11) \qquad (2\pi/a)(\pm\mathbf{i} \pm \mathbf{j} \pm \mathbf{k}).$$

The zone boundaries are determined for the most part by the eight planes normal to these vectors at their midpoints, but it may be seen that the corners of the octahedron thus formed are truncated by the planes which are the perpendicular bisectors of the six vectors

$$(12.12) \qquad (2\pi/a)(\pm 2\mathbf{i}); \; (2\pi/a)(\pm 2\mathbf{j}); \; (2\pi/a)(\pm 2\mathbf{k}).$$

The first zone is then the truncated octahedron shown in Fig. 11.20b.

The zone is a possible choice of the primitive cell of a bcc lattice, and so the volume is $\frac{1}{2}(4\pi/a)^3 = 4(2\pi/a)^3$. There are then $8/a^3$ states in the zone per unit volume of crystal. A fcc crystal contains $4/a^3$ atoms per unit volume, and so we have again two states per atom.

The radius of the inscribed sphere is $k_i = \sqrt{3}\,\pi/a$; the volume of the sphere is $(4\pi/3)3^{3/2}\pi^3/a^3$, which is $3^{1/2}\pi/8 = 0.68$ of the volume of the zone. If the Fermi surface is spherical it will contact the zone boundary when the electron concentration is $2 \times 0.68 = 1.36$ electrons per atom.

HEXAGONAL CLOSE-PACKED STRUCTURE

The primitive translation vectors of the hexagonal space lattice as shown in Fig. 1.15 may be taken as

$$\mathbf{a} = (a/2)\mathbf{i} + (3^{1/2}a/2)\mathbf{j};$$

(12.13) $$\mathbf{b} = (-a/2)\mathbf{i} + (3^{1/2}a/2)\mathbf{j};$$

$$\mathbf{c} = c\mathbf{k}.$$

The volume of the primitive cell is $(3^{1/2}a/2)a^2c$. The basis of the hcp structure contains two atoms. Note that hcp is a structure and not a space lattice; the space lattice is the hexagonal space lattice. The primitive translations of the reciprocal lattice are:

$$\mathbf{a}^* = (1/a)\mathbf{i} + (1/3^{1/2}a)\mathbf{j};$$

(12.14) $$\mathbf{b}^* = -(1/a)\mathbf{i} + (1/3^{1/2}a)\mathbf{j};$$

$$\mathbf{c}^* = (1/c)\mathbf{k};$$

thus the lattice is its own reciprocal. This may be verified by computing $\mathbf{a} \cdot \mathbf{a}^*$, etc. We have

$$(12.15) \quad \mathbf{G} = 2\pi[(1/a)(h - k)\mathbf{i} + (1/3^{1/2}a)(h + k)\mathbf{j} + (1/c)l\mathbf{k}].$$

The shortest non-zero $\mathbf{G}$'s are the eight vectors

$$(2\pi/a)[\pm\mathbf{i} \pm (1/3^{1/2})\mathbf{j}];$$

(12.16) $$(2\pi/a)[\pm (2/3^{1/2})\mathbf{j}];$$

$$(2\pi/c)(\pm\mathbf{k}).$$

The first zone shown in Fig. 12.1a is formed by the planes normal to these vectors at their midpoints. It can be shown for the basis of the hcp structure there is no energy discontinuity across the horizontal faces of the first zone.   This is essentially because the reflections from the plane of atoms midway between the planes bounding the primitive cell will just cancel in phase the reflections from the basal plane.   We are therefore led to consider the second Brillouin zone.   The second

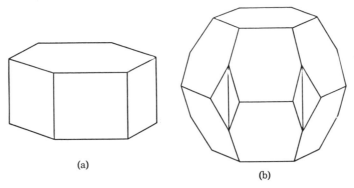

(a)

(b)

Fig. 12.1.   First and second Brillouin zones for the hexagonal close-packed structure.   There is no discontinuity in energy across the top and bottom faces of the first zone if the structure is hexagonal close-packed; so one often encounters a composite zone called the first Jones zone made up of the side faces of (a) with all parts of the second zone (b) above and below the lines of interception with (a).

zone is shown in Fig. 12.1b and may be found directly by the methods employed above.

The first zone contains two states per primitive cell or one state per atom; the combined first and second zones contain four states per primitive cell or two states per atom.   The composite zone (Fig. 12.2) contains

$$(12.17) \quad n = 2 - \frac{3}{4}\left(\frac{a}{c}\right)^2\left[1 - \frac{1}{4}\left(\frac{a}{c}\right)^2\right]$$

states per atom.   This zone is the smallest region bounded by planes of energy discontinuity.   Such a zone is sometimes called a Jones zone, after H. Jones who introduced it.

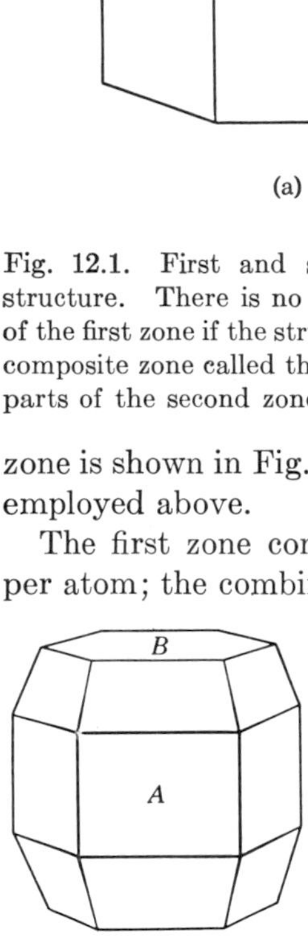

In Fig. 12.2, we note the **k**-value at A is $2\pi/3^{1/2}a$ and at B the **k**-value is $2\pi/c$.   For the ideal close-packed arrangement $c/a = (\frac{8}{3})^{1/2} = 1.63$, and so $k_A/k_B = (\frac{8}{9})^{1/2}$ and the ratio of the free electron energies at the two points is $E_A/E_B = \frac{8}{9}$.   We therefore expect contact of the Fermi surface with the zone boundary to be established first at point A.   The axial ratios of zinc and cadmium depart considerably

Fig. 12.2.   The composite zone for the hexagonal close-packed structure.   [After H. Jones, Proc. Roy. Soc. (London) **A147**, 396 (1934).]

from the ideal ratio; for zinc $c/a = 1.86$, and so $k_A/k_B = 1.07$; $E_A/E_B = 1.15$; and contact with the zone boundary may be established first at point B.

BAND STRUCTURE OF METALS

ALKALI METALS

The alkali atoms have one s valence electron on each atom: $2s$ in lithium, $3s$ in sodium, $4s$ in potassium, $5s$ in rubidium, and $6s$ in cesium. In the alkali metals, the s levels are spread out into a wide band and in some respects the conduction electrons act as if they were free. The crystal structures are all body-centered cubic at room temperature. The s band is half-filled, and so if the Fermi surface is spherical it should lie comfortably within the first Brillouin zone. We have seen above that the sphere inscribed in the first zone holds 1.48 electrons per atom. For lithium there is some theoretical evidence that the Fermi surface does not depart much from a sphere: Kohn and Rostoker[1] have calculated the energies on the Fermi surface in the [100] and [111] directions, finding that the energies differ by only 3 percent.

The effective masses of the conduction electrons in the alkali metals have been calculated by Brooks:[2]

	Li	Na	K	Rb	Cs
m^*/m	1.40	0.98	0.94	0.87	0.83

It will be noticed that the electrons in sodium have nearly the free electron mass, so that sodium in some respects may be expected to behave like an ideal free electron gas. Lithium is different from the other alkalis in having an effective mass heavier than the free electron mass. This feature of lithium may be attributed to the circumstance that in it alone among the alkali metals there is not a p state below the valence s state. As matrix elements between s states vanish, all the perturbations in lithium which determine the effective mass according to (11.35) arise from states above the conduction band, giving a negative energy denominator and hence $m^* > m$. In the other alkali metals there are p states above and below the conduction band. In sodium it appears that the perturbations from above and below tend to cancel, and so $m^* \cong m$. In the series K, Rb, and Cs, perturbations from below have increasing importance and the effective mass becomes lighter along the series.

---

[1] W. Kohn and N. Rostoker, Phys. Rev. **94**, 1111 (1954).

[2] H. Brooks, private communication.

NOBLE METALS

Copper, silver, and gold are monovalent metals, but they differ from the alkali metals by having a d shell in the free atoms filled just at these points in the periodic system. The crystal structures are all face-centered cubic. While the alkali metals have a small ion embedded in a large atomic volume, the noble metals have their filled d shells nearly in contact and acting as rigid spheres. The nearest neighbor distance in sodium is 3.71 A, and the ionic diameter of Na^+ is 1.9 A, giving a clearance of 1.8 A. In copper, the nearest neighbor distance is 2.55 A and the ionic diameter of Cu^+ is I.92 A, giving a clearance of 0.63 A. The clearance in silver is 0.36 A, and in gold

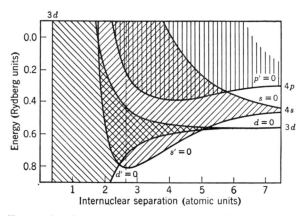

Fig. 12.3.   Energy bands in copper as a function of internuclear separation. [After H. M. Krutter, Phys. Rev. **48**, 664 (1935).]

0.14 A. The compressibility of the alkali metals are 50 to 100 times higher than those of the corresponding noble metals; the cohesive energies are 4 to 5 times lower in the alkalies. The low compressibility of the noble metals is an effect of the exclusion principle: the high electron density in the d shells resists interpenetration. The cohesive energies are thought to be high because of interactions between the d shells.

The d band is believed to overlap the s band, as shown in Fig. 12.3. Calculations by Howarth[3] for copper suggest that the $3d$ band is 3.46 ev in width and the Fermi surface lying in the $4s$ band is 3.7 ev above the top of the $3d$ band. The Fermi surface is estimated on a free electron model to be 7.1 ev above the bottom of the $4s$ band. The reddish color of copper arises from a strong absorption band (Fig. 12.4) cover-

---

[3] D. J. Howarth, Proc. Roy. Soc. (London) **A220**, 513 (1953).

ing the blue-green spectral region.   The onset of the band is at 5750 A
or 2.1 ev, approximately.   It was suggested by Mott and Jones that
the absorption arises from transitions between the 3d band and the
unfilled portions of the 4s band.   One might then expect the figure of
2.1 ev to give the height of the Fermi surface above the top of the 3d
band, but Friedel[4] has suggested that the simple interpretation must
be corrected for the Coulomb energy of the 3d hole created by the
absorption of a photon.   The corresponding band onsets for silver
and gold are 4.0 and 2.5 ev, respectively.

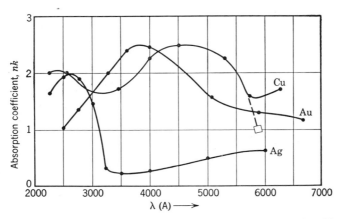

Fig. 12.4. Optical absorption coefficients for copper, silver, and gold. (After
Minor and Meier.)   The point for copper denoted by a hollow square is from work
by Lowery, Bor, and Wilkinson, using a lightly polished surface.

It is believed that the effective masses of the conduction electrons
in the noble metals are close to the free electron mass.   Calculations
by Kambe[5] give the values as tabulated.   The electronic heat capacity

	Cu	Ag	Au
m^*/m	1.012	0.992	0.994

of silver is in close agreement with the calculated value, assuming
$m^* = m$; for copper the heat capacity suggests $m^* \cong 1.4m$.   There
are, however, various effects (such as correlation and exchange) which
may change the effective density of states at the Fermi surface and
thus may change the electronic heat capacity.   We do not know how
to calculate these changes with confidence, and so it would be cautious
not to push too hard the interpretation of the experimental data.

[4] J. Friedel, Proc. Phys. Soc. (London) **65B**, 769 (1952).
[5] K. Kambe, Phys. Rev. **99**, 419 (1955).

DIVALENT METALS

The metals Be, Mg, Ca, Zn, Sr, Cd, Ba, and Hg are characterized by an outer s^2 configuration; that is, there are two valence electrons in the s state of the free atom. The crystal structures are: hcp (Be, Mg, Ca, Zn, Cd); fcc (Ca, Sr); bcc (Ba); complex (Hg). The divalent metals have an even number of valence electrons and would be insulators were it not for the presumed overlap of higher bands with the s band. Be, Zn, and Cd are known to have positive Hall constants, suggesting that the major contribution to the conductivity arises from holes at the top of the s band, the holes being left by the electron overspill into the next band. It is likely that the overlap of the Fermi surface is particularly small for beryllium, which may be not far from an insulator. The large Hall constant (Table 11.2) suggests that perhaps only $\sim$10 percent of the total number of valence electrons are effective in conductivity. Theoretical calculations of the electronic structure of metallic beryllium have been given by Herring and Hill.[6]

The axial ratio c/a is close to the ideal 1.63 for Be (1.585), Mg (1.625), and the high temperature modification of Ca (1.615). The ratio is 1.861 for Zn and 1.890 for Cd. In consequence of the anomalous values for Zn and Cd the interatomic distances between each atom and its nearest neighbors in the basal plane are appreciably smaller than with its nearest neighbors in the planes above and below. The relevant interatomic distances are 2.66 and 2.91 A for zinc and 2.97 and 3.29 A for cadmium. We must conclude that the bonds in the hexagonal layers of these metals are stronger than those between layers. This conclusion is supported by the observed elastic constants.

TRIVALENT METALS

The trivalent metals are B, Al, Ga, In, and Tl; the electronic configuration is s^2p. Of these, only aluminum can be considered to be a typical metal. Boron is a semiconductor and has a complicated crystal structure. Aluminum has a higher ratio of electrical conductivity to density than does copper; the crystal structure of aluminum is fcc. Gallium melts at 30°C; the crystal structure is orthorhombic. Indium has a face-centered tetragonal structure: it may be thought of as a face-centered cubic lattice distorted by an 8 percent elongation parallel to a cube edge. Thallium occurs in hcp and bcc modifications.

Although boron has an odd number of valence electrons, it does not necessarily follow that it must show metallic conductivity. Consider solid molecular hydrogen: hydrogen has only one valence electron, but

    [6] C. Herring and A. G. Hill, Phys. Rev. **58**, 132 (1940); for magnesium, see S. Raimes, Phil. Mag. **41**, 568 (1950).

if the basis associated with each lattice point contains two atoms we have to deal with an even number of valence electrons per lattice point. In this situation it is possible to have an insulator as long as the second atom does not have a special relationship to the primitive cell so as to give zero energy gap across a zone boundary. In the hcp structure the second atom has such a special relationship as we have seen, but with

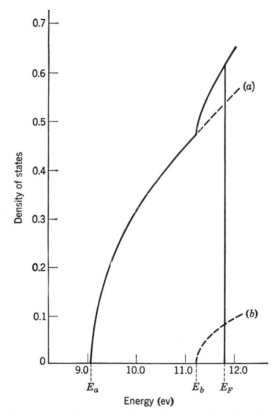

Fig. 12.5. Estimated contribution for aluminum to the density of states per electron volt per atom from overlapping electrons over (a) hexagonal faces and (b) square faces of the Brillouin zone. [After R. S. Leigh, Phil. Mag. **42**, 139 (1951).]

a molecular unit such as H_2 we may expect the energy gap to be preserved. We would expect a similar argument to apply to boron.

In aluminum it is thought that the first Brillouin zone (Fig. 11.20b) is filled, or very nearly filled, and that the third valence electron is contained in the second zone principally in that portion of the Fermi surface which overlaps the hexagonal faces of the zone boundary. The result of a consideration of elastic data is shown in Fig. 12.5.

The only other metals we are in a position to treat in any detail are the transition metals, and it is convenient to defer the discussion of these until after we have discussed the electronic structure of simple substitutional binary alloys of the uni-, di-, and trivalent metals.

BINARY ALLOYS

We are now concerned primarily with substitutional solid solutions of one metal in another. We are going to examine some aspects of the changes in physical properties consequent to the addition of atoms A to a metal B. We suppose that the A atoms enter the metal in a random fashion in lattice positions equivalent to those occupied by the B atoms. The distinct effects which occur when the A atoms enter the structure in a regular, rather than random, fashion are considered briefly at the end of this chapter under the heading of the order-disorder transformation.

Hume-Rothery[7] has discussed the general requirements for solid solutions to occur. He suggests that the solid solution range is very restricted if the atomic diameters of solvent and solute differ by more than 15 percent. The atomic diameter for this purpose is usually taken as the closest distance of approach in the crystal structure of the element (Table 1.8). Thus the size factor is favorable in the Cu (2.55 A) − Zn (2.66 A) system, and zinc dissolves in copper as a fcc solid solution up to 38 atomic percent zinc. The size factor is somewhat unfavorable in the Cu (2.55 A) − Cd (2.97 A) system and only 1.7 atomic percent cadmium is soluble in copper. The size factors expressed as percentages referred to copper are 4 percent for Zn in Cu and 16.5 percent for Cd in Cu. Further examples are the subject of Problem 12.1.

Although the size factor may be favorable, solid solutions will not form if there is a strong tendency to form stable intermediate compounds. Thus if the solvent is strongly electronegative and the solute element strongly electropositive (or *vice versa*) it is likely that intermediate compounds will precipitate out of solution. Although the size factor is favorable (2 percent) for As in Cu, only 6 percent As is soluble. The size factor is also favorable (9 percent) for Sb in Mg, yet the solubility of Sb in Mg is very small. Other valency criteria are discussed by Hume-Rothery.

In the following sections we discuss various aspects of the electronic structure of alloys. The discussions are phrased in terms of the average number of conduction electrons per atom: for example, the electron concentration n in the alloy 50 Cu-50 Zn is 1.50; in 50 Cu-50 Al,

[7] See the books by Hume-Rothery cited at the end of the chapter.

$n = 2.00$. We shall usually shut our eyes to any change caused by alloying in the energy gap at the zone boundary and in the nature of the wave functions and energy eigenvalues. We assume in fact that the lattice still possesses translational symmetry, which it does not, and that the principal effect of alloying elements of different valency is simply to change the electron concentration. The consequences of these assumptions are often in remarkable agreement with experiment, to the astonishment of the theoretical physicist. Friedel[8] has given a plausible explanation of some aspects of the situation.

It has been suggested[9] that a small overlap of electrons across the boundary planes of a Brillouin zone causes an internal stress tending to expand the lattice. We suggest that the principal contribution may arise from the dependence of the energy gap on the lattice constant. The effect could then have either sign, but it is a fact that in many semiconducting crystals the gap is known to increase with the application of external pressure and to decrease with increasing temperature. In crystals where the gap decreases as the lattice expands we would expect to find that overlapping electrons expand the lattice in order to reduce the gap energy. This is in addition to the usual tendency of a free electron Fermi gas to expand in order to reduce the Fermi energy E_F.

Measurements of the lattice parameter of Li-Mg alloys are shown in Fig. 12.6. In the range shown the structure is bcc. The lattice contracts[10] during the initial stages of the addition of Mg to Li. When the lithium content drops below 50 atomic percent, corresponding to an average electron concentration increasing above 1.5 per atom, the lattice starts to expand. We have seen above for a spherical Fermi surface that contact with the zone boundary is established at $n = 1.48$ electrons per atom, for a bcc lattice. It therefore appears that the expansion of the lattice arises from the onset of overlap across the zone boundary.

Hume-Rothery and Raynor have measured the changes in the c and a lattice parameters of magnesium as a function of solute content. We have seen (Fig. 12.2) that the electron overlap for the ideal c/a ratio occurs first across the side faces, equivalent to A, of the zone. Overlap across the hexagonal end face B at this c/a occurs first for an elec-

[8] J. Friedel, Advances in Physics, **3**, 446 (1954).

[9] H. Jones, Proc. Roy. Soc. (London) **A144**, 225 (1934); the standard argument is not very convincing as the value of the energy gap does not enter and it is difficult to see the role of the zone boundary in the discussion.

[10] The contraction may probably be understood in terms of the solution to Problem 11.8; the increase in average Coulomb energy in adding Mg dominates the increase in Fermi energy, thus tending to contract the lattice.

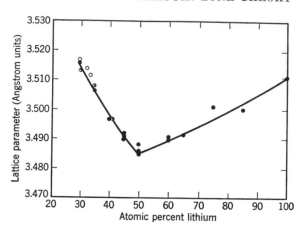

Fig. 12.6.   Lattice parameter of body-centered cubic magnesium-lithium alloys.
[After D. W. Levinson, Acta Met. **3**, 294 (1955).]

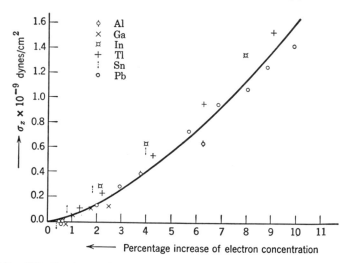

Fig. 12.7.   Effective internal stress in Mg parallel to the c axis as a function of the
increase of electron concentration on alloying.   [After H. Jones, Physica **15**, 13
(1949).]

tron concentration of 2.0075, assuming a spherical Fermi surface.   As
Mg has two valence electrons per atom, one would expect a sharp
change in the rate of variation of the parameter c and the ratio c/a for
very small amounts of solutes of higher valency.   This effect has been
detected with the solutes In, Tl, Sn, and Pb.   After overlap has
occurred across the hexagonal face one might expect an expansion of
the crystal in this direction.   In Fig. 12.7 there are shown values of

the effective stress in magnesium parallel to the c axis as a function of the increase of electron concentration caused by alloying; the stress is deduced from the observed lattice parameters and elastic moduli.

HUME-ROTHERY RULES FOR ALLOY PHASES

Hume-Rothery first drew attention to the importance of the average valence electron/atom ratio as a kind of universal parameter in the

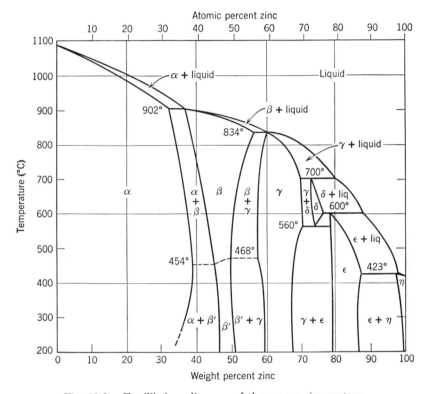

Fig. 12.8.   Equilibrium diagram of the copper-zinc system.

description of the properties of alloys.   He was concerned with the occurrence of certain alloy structures at a definite electron/atom ratio. The phase diagram of the copper-zinc system is shown in Fig. 12.8. The phases of interest are: α (fcc), β (bcc), γ (complex cubic cell of 52 atoms), and ϵ (hcp).

The α phase of pure copper ($n = 1$) persists until an electron concentration of about 1.38.   The β phase has a minimum electron concentration of about 1.48.   The γ phase exists for the approximate range of n between 1.58 and 1.66, and the ϵ phase occurs near 1.75.

The term electron compound denotes in an alloy system an intermediate phase where crystal structure is determined by the establishment of a certain electron/atom ratio. The empirical values usually quoted as the Hume-Rothery rules are $\frac{3}{2}(= 1.50)$ for the β phase, $\frac{21}{13}(= 1.62)$ for the γ phase, and $\frac{7}{4}(= 1.75)$ for the ϵ phase. Representative experimental data are collected in Table 12.1, based on the usual chemical valency assignments.

TABLE 12.1. ELECTRON/ATOM RATIOS OF ELECTRON COMPOUNDS

Alloy	α-phase Boundary	Minimum β-phase Boundary	γ-phase Boundaries	ϵ-phase Boundaries
Cu-Zn	1.38	1.48	1.58–1.66	1.78–1.87
Cu-Al	1.41	1.48	1.63–1.77	
Cu-Ga	1.41			
Cu-Si	1.42	1.49		
Cu-Ge	1.36			
Cu-Sn	1.27	1.49	1.60–1.63	1.73–1.75
Ag-Zn	1.38		1.58–1.63	1.67–1.90
Ag-Cd	1.42	1.50	1.59–1.63	1.65–1.82
Ag-Al	1.41			1.55–1.80

The Hume-Rothery rules find a simple explanation on band theory in the approximation of nearly free electrons. Jones pointed out that the observed limit of the α phase (fcc) occurs very close to the electron concentration of 1.36 for which the inscribed Fermi sphere makes contact with the Brillouin zone surface for the fcc lattice. The observed electron concentration of the β phase (bcc) is close to the concentration 1.48 for which the inscribed Fermi sphere makes contact with the Brillouin zone surface for the bcc lattice. Contact of the Fermi sphere with the zone boundary for the γ sphere is at the concentration 1.54, according to Jones. Contact for the ϵ phase (hcp) is at the concentration 1.69 for the ideal c/a ratio.

It is apparent that there is an intimate connection between the electron concentration at which a new phase appears and the electron concentration at which the Fermi surface makes contact with the Brillouin zone boundary. The general explanation of the association is that it is expensive energetically to add further electrons once the filled states contact the zone boundary. Additional electrons can be accommodated only in states above the energy gap characterizing the boundary or in the states near the corners of the first zone. The number of states near the corners falls off markedly as a function of energy. In this circumstance it is often energetically favorable for the crystal structure to change, the final structure being one which contains a larger Fermi surface. In this way the sequence α (1.36), β (1.48), γ (1.54), ε (1.69) is made plausible, where the numbers in parentheses refer to the electron concentrations at which contact occurs.

The transformation from fcc to bcc is illustrated by Fig. 12.9 showing the number of states per unit energy range as a function of energy, for the fcc and bcc structures. It is seen that as the number of electrons is increased a point is reached above which it is easier to accommodate additional electrons in the bcc lattice.

There are numerous other applications to other structures of reasoning similar to the above in the more recent metallurgical literature.

VARIATION OF HALL CONSTANT

The dependence of the Hall coefficient on alloy composition should

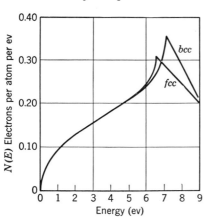

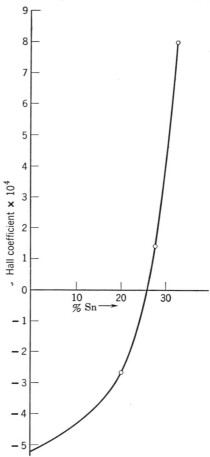

Fig. 12.9. $N(E)$, number of states per unit energy range for fcc and bcc lattices, as a function of energy.

Fig. 12.10. Dependence of Hall constant on tin content in the Cu-Sn system, in emu. (After Stephens.)

be a useful tool in the investigation of electron overlap effects, but little Hall effect work has been done on non-ferromagnetic alloy systems. Representative systems studied[11] are Cd-Cu and Cu-Sn. Results on the copper-rich side of the Cu-Sn system are shown in Fig. 12.10.

[11] Cd-Cu: W. Richards and E. J. Evans, Phil. Mag. 13, 201 (1932). Cu-Sn: E. Stephens, Phil. Mag. 8, 273 (1929).

There is a gradual transition between conditions where the conductivity is dominated by electrons as for pure Cu and where holes are dominant, as appears to occur in the β phase.

For conductivity when both electrons and holes contribute, the Hall constant R may be written

$$(12.18) \qquad R = -\left|\frac{1}{ec}\right|\left[\frac{N_e\mu_e{}^2 - N_h\mu_h{}^2}{(N_e\mu_e + N_h\mu_h)^2}\right],$$

where N_e, N_h are the electron and hole concentrations, and μ_e, μ_h are the electron and hole mobilities. The derivation of this relation is left to the reader as Problem 12.3. It is assumed there is present only one type of electron and one type of hole.

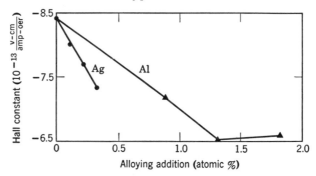

Fig. 12.11.   Hall constant of magnesium containing small amounts of silver and aluminum.   (After Schindler and Salkovitz.)

Schindler and Salkovitz[12] have studied the Hall effect in magnesium alloyed with silver and aluminum, with the results shown in Fig. 12.11. The break at 1.3 percent aluminum is thought to be associated with overlap across the hexagonal face (B) of the Brillouin zone (Fig. 12.2). It is apparent that the effective number of carriers in magnesium is highly sensitive to alloying additions: 0.1 atomic percent of silver changes the Hall constant by 5 percent, a magnification of 50.

VARIATION OF MAGNETIC SUSCEPTIBILITY

We often find the states near zone boundaries have light effective masses, and, accordingly, crystals with the Fermi surface near zone boundaries may have high diamagnetic susceptibilities from the conduction electrons and holes. The effect is strikingly illustrated by Fig. 12.12 from the work of Klee and Witte[13] on the ternary system

[12] A. I. Schindler and E. I. Salkovitz, Phys. Rev. **91**, 1320 (1953).

[13] H. Klee and H. Witte, Z. physik. Chem. **202**, 352 (1953–1954); this paper contains a full discussion of the results in terms of band theory.

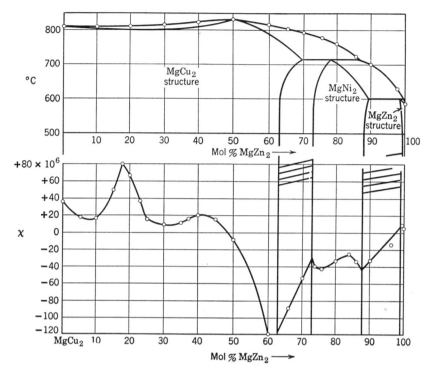

Fig. 12.12. Phase diagram and molar magnetic susceptibility of the MgCu₂-MgZn₂ alloy system. (After Klee and Witte.)

MgCu₂-MgZn₂. Similar results are obtained for the MgCu₂-MgAl₂ and MgCu₂-MgSi₂ systems: there is in all three systems a large diamagnetic contribution to the susceptibility as the electron/atom ratio approaches 1.75. Susceptibility measurements[14] on the Cu-Zn system show a large diamagnetic effect near 30Cu-70Zn. The very large diamagnetic susceptibility of bismuth is sensitive[15] to alloying additions, as one would expect from the small number of effective carriers indicated by the large value of the Hall constant.

TRANSITION ELEMENTS

We list for convenience the elements of the three groups of transition metals.

Sc	Ti	V	Cr	Mn	Fe	Co	Ni
Y	Zr	Nb	Mo	Tc	Ru	Rh	Pd
La	Hf	Ta	W	Re	Os	Ir	Pt

[14] H. Endo, Science Repts. Tôhoku Univ. **14**, 479 (1925); this paper reports measurements on a number of binary systems.

[15] A. Goetz and A. B. Focke, Phys. Rev. **45**, 170 (1934).

It is thought that the transition metals have partly filled d shells in the metallic state. The shells concerned are $3d$, $4d$, and $5d$, for the

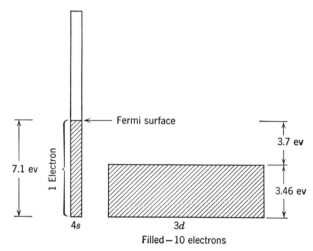

Fig. 12.13. Schematic relationship of $4s$ and $3d$ bands in metallic copper. The $3d$ band holds ten electrons per atom and is filled in copper. The $4s$ band can hold two electrons per atom; it is shown half-filled, as copper has one valence electron outside the filled $3d$ shell. The energies shown are from calculations by Howarth; it is coincidental that the bottoms of both bands fall nearly at the same energy.

respective groups. Despite intensive effort and speculation, little is actually known about the electronic structure of the metals. More is known perhaps about Fe, Co, Ni, Pd, and Pt than about the other transition metals because the five mentioned have been studied magnetically in some detail. Readers with little or no previous knowledge of ferromagnetism may find it convenient to read Chapter 15 before the present section.

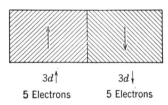

Fig. 12.14. The filled $3d$ band of copper shown as two separate sub-bands of opposite electron spin orientation, each band holding five electrons. With both sub-bands filled as shown, the net spin (and hence the net magnetization) of the d band is zero.

Several of the characteristic properties of the transition metals are believed to arise from the overlap of the s conduction band with the d band immediately below in energy. In the transition metals the d band is not normally filled entirely, but let us first consider the relationship of the bands in copper which has a filled d band. Figure 12.13 is drawn following the discussion of copper earlier in the present chapter.   There is a considerable energy gap between the top of the d band and the Fermi surface lying in the s band.   It is useful for later applications to show the bands divided in two halves, one half for each orientation of the electron spin.   In Fig. 12.14 we show the d band of copper divided into two sub-bands, one for electrons having spin up, the other for spin down.   Each sub-band holds five electrons.

Let us now consider nickel, having one less electron than copper. Nickel is ferromagnetic and has at absolute zero a saturation magnetic

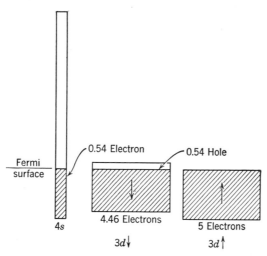

Fig. 12.15.   Schematic relationship of bands in nickel at absolute zero.   The energies of the $3d \uparrow$ and $3d \downarrow$ sub-bands are separated by an exchange interaction. The $3d \uparrow$ band is filled; the $3d \downarrow$ band contains 4.46 electrons and 0.54 hole.   The $4s$ band is usually thought to contain approximately equal numbers of electrons in both spin directions, and so we have not troubled to divide it into sub-bands. The net magnetic moment of 0.54 μ_B per atom arises from the excess population of the $3d \uparrow$ band over the $3d \downarrow$ band.   It is often convenient to speak of the magnetization as arising from the 0.54 hole in the $3d \downarrow$ band.

moment of 0.60 Bohr magnetons per atom.   After an appropriate correction[16] for a small contribution from orbital electronic motion, one has in nickel at saturation an excess of 0.54 electron per atom having spin preferentially oriented in one direction.   Stoner showed how one can interpret non-integral values of the saturation magneton

[16] P. Argyres and C. Kittel, Acta Met. **1**, 241 (1953).   The saturation magneton number n_s is defined by the relation $n_s \mu_B N = M_s(0)$, where $M_s(0)$ is the saturation magnetization at absolute zero, N is the number of atoms per unit volume, and μ_B is the Bohr magneton.   The number of effective electrons is just n_s corrected for the orbital contribution or $n_s(2/g)$, where g is the spectroscopic splitting factor defined in Chapter 9.

number in terms of the energy band model.   For nickel we have to accommodate 10 electrons outside the filled inner shells.   If we distribute the 10 electrons as shown in Fig. 12.15, we can account for the observed saturation moment in a natural way.   We take one $3d$ sub-band as filled, the other as filled except for 0.54 hole.   This assumption takes care of the magnetic moment and leaves 0.54 electron for the $4s$ band.   The separation in energy between the $3d$ sub-bands is a result of the exchange interaction discussed in Chapter 15.   When the metal is heated above the Curie temperature the holes distribute themselves

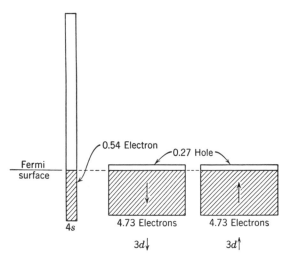

Fig. 12.16.   Band relationships in nickel over the Curie temperature.   The net magnetic moment is zero, as there are equal numbers of holes in both $3d \downarrow$ and $3d \uparrow$ bands.

equally in the two sub-bands, the exchange interaction is dominated by thermal effects, and the saturation moment disappears.   The situation in nickel above the Curie temperature is shown in Fig. 12.16.

There is a certain arbitrariness in the distribution of Fig. 12.15, as we can transfer electrons from both d sub-bands to the s band provided we take 0.54 more from one sub-band than from the other.   Evidence that our particular choice may correspond to reality is provided by Fig. 12.17 giving the effect on the magneton number of alloying copper in nickel.   As we add copper we are adding one extra electron per copper atom.   The density of states in the d band is believed to be over ten times greater than in the s band, so that the extra electron goes at least 90 percent into the d band and less than 10 percent into the s band.   The magneton number is observed to go to zero at about

60 atomic percent copper, according to Fig. 12.17. Let us try to understand the effect of adding copper. At this concentration we have

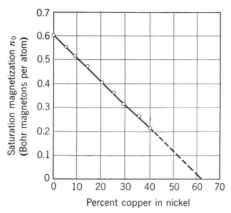

Fig. 12.17.   Bohr magneton numbers of nickel-copper alloys.

added about 0.54 electron to the d band and about 0.06 electron to the s band.   But 0.54 electron added to the d band in Fig. 12.15 will just fill both d sub-bands and will bring the magnetization to zero, in excellent agreement with observation. The distribution of electrons for 60Cu40Ni is shown in Fig. 12.18; the decrease in magneton number should be a linear function of the concentration of copper at lower concentrations, in agreement with Fig. 12.17.

For simplicity the block drawings above represent the density of states as uniform in energy. The actual density may be quite far from uniform: Fig. 12.19 gives the results of a calculation by Koster for nickel. The width of the band is about 2.8 ev. We see the d band is characterized by a high density of states: there

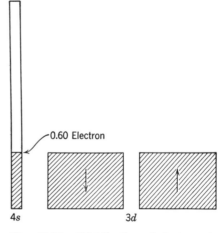

Fig. 12.18.   Distribution of electrons in the alloy 60Cu40Ni.   The extra 0.6 electron provided by the copper has filled the d band entirely and increased slightly the number of electrons in the s band with respect to Fig. 12.15.

are 10 electrons in about 3 ev, whereas in the s band there is 1 electron in about 7 ev.   The average density of states is of the order of

20 times greater in the d band than in the s band.   This value of the density of states ratio provides a rough indication of the expected enhancement of the electronic heat capacity and the paramagnetic susceptibility in nonferromagnetic transition metals as compared with monovalent metals.

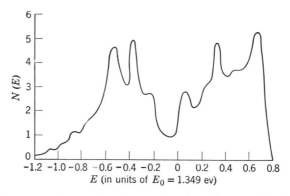

Fig. 12.19.   Density of states $N(E)$ as a function of energy for the d bands in nickel.   [According to calculations by G. F. Koster, Phys. Rev. **98**, 901 (1955).]

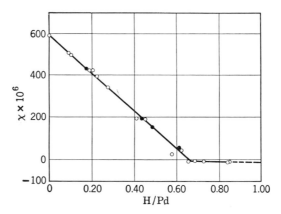

Fig. 12.20.   Effect of dissolved hydrogen on the susceptibility of palladium: molar susceptibility vs. H/Pd ratio.

It is believed that palladium may have a distribution of electrons similar to that of nickel.   At room temperature the picture for palladium is like Fig. 12.16 for nickel over the Curie point, except that now we have to deal with a $5s$ band instead of $4s$ and $4d$ instead of $3d$. The addition of hydrogen in solution in metallic palladium reduces the susceptibility as shown in Fig. 12.20.   When hydrogen goes into solution it is thought to ionize: the electrons join the bands of the palladium just as the valence electron of copper joins the bands of nickel. The bare protons diffuse around in the metal. Proton resonance experiments by Norberg[17] support this model. When 0.6 extra electrons per atom have been added, the $4d$ bands are filled and further addition of hydrogen has no marked effect. The paramagnetic susceptibility can be high only as long as the d bands are not entirely filled.[18]

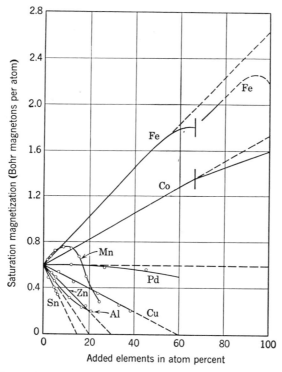

Fig. 12.21. Saturation magnetization of nickel alloys in Bohr magnetons per atom as a function of the atomic percent of solute element.

Let us now consider the effects of small amounts of other alloying additions to nickel. On the model proposed above an alloying metal with $10 + z$ valence electrons outside a filled p shell (rare gas configuration) is expected to decrease the magnetization of nickel by approximately z Bohr magnetons per solute atom. Referring to Fig. 12.21,

[17] R. E. Norberg, Phys. Rev. 86, 745 (1952).

[18] The magnetic properties of palladium at low temperatures are of considerable interest: see F. E. Hoare, J. C. Matthews and J. C. Walling, Proc. Roy. Soc. (London) A216, 502 (1953); A. B. Lidiard, Proc. Roy. Soc. (London) A224, 161 (1954).

we see this simple relationship is obeyed extraordinarily well for small amount of

	Sn	Al	Zn	Cu	Pd	Co	Fe	Mn
$z =$	4	3	2	1	0	-1	-2	-3

We should emphasize that the description of the magnetization of transition metal alloys in terms of the band model is not the only description possible.[19]

The average atomic moments of binary alloys of the elements in the iron group are plotted in Fig. 12.22 as a function of electron concentration. What we may call the main sequence of alloys on the

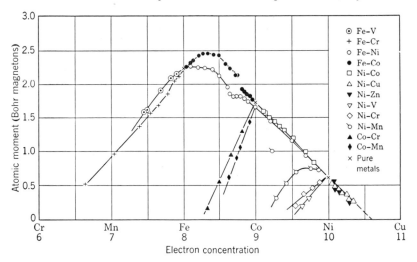

Fig. 12.22.   Average atomic moments of binary alloys of the elements in the iron group.   (After Bozorth.)

right-hand branch follows the simple rule given above, but as the electron concentration is decreased a point is reached below which neither of the $3d$ sub-bands is completely filled. We shall see in Chapter 15 that pure Cr and Mn are believed to be weakly antiferromagnetic.

Let us turn briefly to the question of the electrical conductivity of the transition metals. It might be thought that the availability of the d band as a path for conduction in parallel with the s band would increase the conductivity, but this is not the case. We compare below the electrical resistivities in microhm-cm at 18°C of Ni, Pd, and Pt

[19] The reader interested in pursuing these questions further may consult the series of papers by Zener and Heikes, Slater, Wohlfarth, and Van Vleck in the Revs. Modern Phys. **25**, No. 1, January, 1953; see also L. Pauling, J. Am. Chem. Soc. **69**, 542 (1947); Proc. Roy. Soc. (London) **A196**, 343 (1949).

with the noble metals immediately following them in the periodic table:

Ni	Pd	Pt
7.4	10.8	10.5
Cu	Ag	Au
1.7	1.6	2.2

It is apparent that the resistivities of the transition metals cited are higher than those of the noble metals by a factor of the order of 5. It is believed the high resistivities of the transition metals are caused by collisions in which an s electron is scattered into the d band, this being an extra scattering mechanism not present when the d band is filled.

The low compressibilities (Table 4.2) of the transition metals are believed to arise from the overlapping d shells, but satisfactory quantitative calculations have not been carried out.

ORDER-DISORDER TRANSFORMATION[20]

Although the topic does not lend itself simply to interpretation in terms of band theory, we are at a convenient point to discuss the ordering of alloys. The dashed horizontal lines in the phase diagram

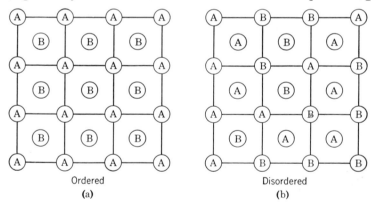

Ordered
(a)

Disordered
(b)

Fig. 12.23. Ordered (a) and disordered (b) arrangements of AB ions in the alloy AB.

of the Cu-Zn system (Fig. 12.8) represent the Curie temperature for order in the alloy. Let us consider a binary alloy AB composed of equal numbers of two types of metal atoms, A and B. The alloy is said to be *ordered* if the A and B atoms stand in a regular periodic arrangement with respect to one another, as in Fig. 12.23a. The alloy

[20] For reviews see F. C. Nix and W. Shockley, Revs. Modern Phys. **10**, 1 (1938); H. Lipson, Progress in Metal Physics **2**, 1–52 (1950); T. Muto and Y. Takagi, Solid State Phys. **1**, 194 (1955).

is *disordered* if the A and B atoms are randomly arranged, as in Fig. 12.23b. Many of the properties of an alloy are sensitive to the degree of order. A common ordered arrangement is one in which all the nearest neighbor atoms of a B atom are A atoms, and *vice versa;* this results when the dominant interaction among the atoms is a strong attraction between AB pairs. If dissimilar atoms avoid each other, a two-phase system is formed.

The system is considered completely ordered at absolute zero; it becomes less ordered as the temperature is increased, until a transition temperature is reached above which the disorder is complete. To be more precise, the transition temperature marks the disappearance of *long range order* over many interatomic distances, but some *short range*

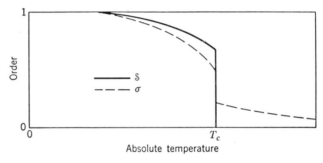

Fig. 12.24. Long range ($\underset{\sim}{S}$) and short range (σ) order vs. temperature, for an AB_3 alloy. (After Nix and Shockley.)

order or correlation among near neighbors may persist above the transition. A qualitative plot of the equilibrium order is given in Fig. 12.24; long and short range order are defined below. If an alloy is cooled rapidly (quenched) from high temperatures to below the transition temperature, a metastable state may be produced in which a non-equilibrium disorder is "frozen" in the structure. An ordered specimen may be disordered at constant temperature by heavy irradiation with nuclear particles.

The degree of order may be investigated experimentally by several methods, the most powerful being x-ray diffraction. The disordered structure in Fig. 12.23b will have diffraction lines at the same positions as if the lattice points were all occupied by only one type of atom, because the effective scattering power of each plane is equal to the average of the A and B scattering powers. The ordered structure in Fig. 12.23a has extra diffraction lines not possessed by the disordered structure. The extra lines are called *superstructure lines*, and they characterize the diffraction by the A or B lattices separately. Thus in the ordered CuZn alloy the structure is the cesium chloride structure with atoms on a body-centered cubic lattice. This may be thought of as arising from the superposition of two interpenetrating simple cubic lattices, one of copper atoms alone and the other of zinc atoms alone. For example, a bcc lattice of one atom type alone does not have a (100) diffraction line, as the reflection from the atoms at the body centers is 180° out of phase and cancels the reflection from the cube

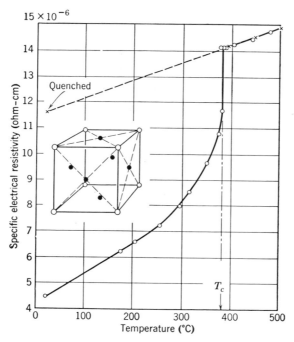

Fig. 12.25. Electrical resistivity vs. temperature for Cu_3Au. The alloy was in equilibrium at temperatures above 350°C. (After Nix and Shockley.)

face. This tells us that the form factor $S\{100\} = 0$, as discussed in Chapter 2. The same result holds in a disordered bcc structure, but in the ordered bcc structure the amplitude of the reflection from the body center will in general differ from the amplitude of the reflection from the cube face; the cancellation will now not be complete, so that we have a (100) superstructure reflection.

The electrical resistivity (Fig. 12.25) is lower in the ordered state than in the disordered state, as expected on the theory of lattice scattering developed in Chapter 11. The heat capacity has an anomaly in the neighborhood of the transition temperature, as shown in Fig. 12.26. The anomaly is associated with the extra internal energy required to

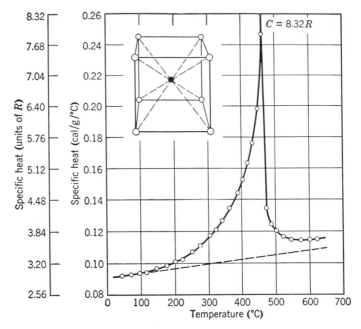

Fig. 12.26.   Specific heat vs. temperature of CuZn (β-brass) alloy.   (After Nix and Shockley.)

disorder the structure.   The ferromagnetic properties of alloys may be sensitive to the degree of order; in some cases, as in Ni_3Mn, the disordered alloy is weakly ferromagnetic and the ordered alloy is strongly ferromagnetic.[21]

ELEMENTARY THEORY OF ORDER

We give now a simple statistical treatment of the dependence of order on temperature for the case of an AB alloy with a bcc structure. We may mention that the case A_3B differs from AB, the former having a first order transition marked by a latent heat and the latter having a second order transition[22] marked by a discontinuity in the heat capacity.   We first introduce the long range order parameter S.   We call one simple cubic lattice a and the other b: the bcc structure is composed of the two interpenetrating sc lattices, and the nearest neighbors of an

[21] For a discussion of the influence of order on magnetic properties, see R. Smoluchowski, J. phys. radium **12**, 389 (1951); J. E. Goldman J. Appl. Phys. **20**, 1131 (1949).

[22] For an excellent treatment of second order phase changes, see Chapter 18 of J. C. Slater, *Introduction to chemical physics*, McGraw-Hill Book Co., New York, 1939.

atom on one lattice lie on the other lattice. If there are N atoms A and N atoms B in the alloy, the *long range order parameter* S is defined so that the number of A's on lattice a is equal to

$$\tfrac{1}{2}(1 + S)N.$$

When $S = \pm 1$, the order is perfect and each lattice contains only one type of atom. When $S = 0$, each lattice contains equal numbers of A and B atoms and there is no long range order.

We consider now that part of the internal energy associated with AA, AB, and BB nearest neighbor bond energies, with the ultimate object of discussing equilibrium conditions. The concept of individual bond energies is undoubtedly an oversimplification in metals, but we are unable at present to give a proper treatment using band theory and elastic theory. The energy is

$$(12.19) \qquad U = N_{AA} V_{AA} + N_{BB} V_{BB} + N_{AB} V_{AB},$$

where N_{ij} is the number of nearest neighbor ij bonds, and V_{ij} is the energy of an ij bond. We have approximately that the number of AA bonds is equal to the number of A's on lattice a times $8/N$ times the number of A's on lattice b. This approximation is similar to the molecular field assumption in the Weiss theory of ferromagnetism. Thus, by the definition of S,

$$N_{AA} = [\tfrac{1}{2}(1 + S)N][\tfrac{1}{2}(1 - S)N](8/N) = 2(1 - S^2)N;$$

$$(12.20) \quad N_{BB} = [\tfrac{1}{2}(1 + S)N][\tfrac{1}{2}(1 - S)N](8/N) = 2(1 - S^2)N;$$

$$N_{AB} = [\tfrac{1}{2}(1 + S)N]^2(8/N) + [\tfrac{1}{2}(1 - S)N]^2(8/N)$$
$$= 4(1 + S^2)N.$$

The energy (12.19) becomes

$$(12.21) \qquad\qquad U = U_0 + 2NS^2 V,$$

where

$$(12.22) \qquad\qquad U_0 = 2N(V_{AA} + V_{BB} + 2V_{AB});$$

$$V = 2V_{AB} - V_{AA} - V_{BB}.$$

We now calculate the entropy S. There are $\tfrac{1}{2}(1 + S)N$ atoms A and $\tfrac{1}{2}(1 - S)N$ atoms B on lattice a; there are $\tfrac{1}{2}(1 - S)N$ atoms A and $\tfrac{1}{2}(1 + S)N$ atoms B on lattice b. The number of arrangements of these numbers of atoms is

$$(12.23) \qquad w = \left[\frac{N!}{[\tfrac{1}{2}(1 + S)N]![\tfrac{1}{2}(1 - S)N]!} \right]^2.$$

Recalling the Boltzmann definition of the entropy,

$$(12.24) \qquad\qquad S = k \log w,$$

we have, using Stirling's approximation $\log x! \cong x(\log x - 1)$,

$$(12.25) \quad S = 2Nk \log 2 - Nk[(1 + \mathsf{S}) \log (1 + \mathsf{S}) \\ + (1 - \mathsf{S}) \log (1 - \mathsf{S})].$$

We see that the entropy has the proper limiting behavior: for $\mathsf{S} = \pm 1$, $S = 0$; for $\mathsf{S} = 0$, $S = 2Nk \log 2$.   This result may be illuminated by the discussion of (9.26).

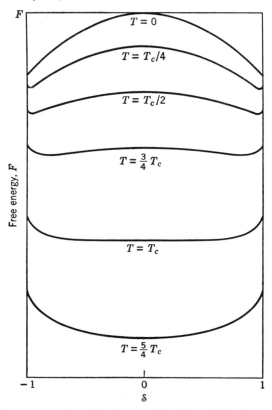

Fig. 12.27.   Free energy of an AB alloy as a function of the degree of order S, for various temperatures.   (By permission from *Introduction to chemical physics*, by J. C. Slater.   Copyright, 1939.   McGraw-Hill Book Co.)

The order is determined as a function of temperature by the requirement that the free energy $F = U - TS$ be a minimum with respect to the order parameter S, where U and S are given as functions of S by (12.21) and (12.25).   In Fig. 12.27 we have plotted F as a function of temperature. At low temperatures the position of the minimum, giving the stable condition, comes at values of S different from zero, approaching ± 1 as the temperature approaches zero. Above the transition temperature T_c the minimum occurs at $\mathsf{S} = 0$, and so the equilibrium state for $T > T_c$ is disordered. On differentiating F with respect to S, we have as the condition for the minimum

$$(12.26) \qquad 4N\mathsf{S}V + NkT \log \frac{1 + \mathsf{S}}{1 - \mathsf{S}} = 0.$$

This transcendental equation for S may be solved graphically, and it

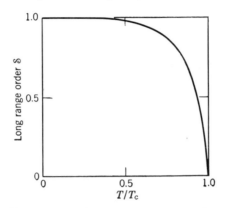

Fig. 12.28. Long range order S vs. temperature for an AB alloy.

gives the smoothly decreasing curve shown in Fig. 12.28. Near the transition we may expand (12.26), finding

$$4N\mathsf{S}V + 2NkT\mathsf{S} = 0,$$

and so the transition temperature is

$$(12.27) \qquad T_c = -2V/k.$$

LONG AND SHORT RANGE ORDER

We have defined the long range order parameter S so that the number of A's on lattice a is equal to $\frac{1}{2}(1 + \mathsf{S})N$. If we call a right or r atom an A on a, and a wrong or w atom a B on a, then

$$(12.28) \qquad \mathsf{S} = \frac{r - w}{r + w};$$

this may be considered an alternative but equivalent definition of S.

The *short range order parameter* σ is defined as

$$\text{(12.29)} \qquad \sigma = \frac{q - q(\text{rand.})}{q(\text{max}) - q(\text{rand.})},$$

where q is the fraction of the total number of nearest neighbor bonds in the solid which are between unlike atoms; σ has the limits zero and unity. For the AB structure, $q(\text{rand.}) = \frac{1}{2}$ and $q(\text{max}) = 1$; so

$$\text{(12.30)} \qquad \sigma = 2(q - \tfrac{1}{2}).$$

We may estimate the short range order in an AB alloy at a temperature $T > T_c$, so that there is no long range order. Consider a particular A atom: the probability[23] that a particular nearest neighbor is a B atom is q, while the probability that it is an A atom is $(1 - q)$. The ratio of the probabilities is equal to the Boltzmann factor $e^{(V_{AA}-V_{AB})/kT}$; thus

$$\text{(12.31)} \qquad \frac{1 - q}{q} = \frac{1 - \sigma}{1 + \sigma} = e^{(V_{AA}-V_{AB})/kT} = x,$$

and so

$$\text{(12.32)} \qquad \sigma = \frac{1 - x}{1 + x}.$$

There is no sign of a transition temperature here, and even at high temperatures there are more than the random number of AB pairs;

Fig. 12.29. X-ray powder photographs of Cu_3Au alloy. (a) Disordered by quenching from $T > T_c$; (b) ordered by annealing at $T < T_c$. (Courtesy of C. S. Barrett.)

although they are unable to link up together into regions of long distance order, they are able to form very small domains within which there is order. At T_c the domains begin to join together and cohere into long range order, and as the temperature is lowered the long range

---

[23] This estimate assumes that the probability is independent of the other neighbors of the central ion. For a careful discussion of long and short range order, see H. A. Bethe, Proc. Roy. Soc. (London) **A150**, 552 (1935).

order approaches perfection.   Many of the details of the theory have been confirmed by x-ray work.[24]

In Fig. 12.29 we show x-ray powder photographs of the alloy Cu_3Au in the disordered and ordered conditions.   The superstructure lines appear in the ordered state.   We should call attention to the fact that the order-disorder transition in AB_3-type alloys is a first order transition[25], with a discontinuity in the order parameter at the transition temperature.

PROBLEMS

12.1. Using reference books, give the size factors and limit of solid solution in metal of lower valency for the following alloy systems: Ag-Mg, Ag-Zn, Ag-Al, Cu-Mg, Cu-Al, Cu-Si, Cu-Pb, Cu-Bi.

12.2. Calculate for the composite zone of the ideal hcp structure the electron concentration at which a spherical Fermi surface touches (a) the hexagonal end face; (b) the side face of the first zone at position A in Fig. 12.2.

12.3. Show that, when concentrations N_e of electrons and N_h of holes are present, the Hall coefficient is equal to

$$(1/ec)[(N_e b^2 - N_h)/(N_e b + N_h)^2],$$

where $b = \mu_e/\mu_h$ is the mobility ratio.

12.4. (a) Using Fig. 12.19, estimate the value of the electronic heat capacity of nickel.   Compare the result with the observed value.

(b) What value of the average effective mass would describe the estimated value if each atom were supposed for purposes of calculation to contribute 0.6 electron to the band?

12.5. Discuss a plausible distribution of electrons in metallic iron among the $4s$ and $3d$ sub-bands; indicate recent revisions of this model.

12.6.* Discuss the theoretical difficulties presented by the results of neutron diffraction experiments in connection with the simple band theory of ferromagnetic alloys.   (See the publications of Shull and collaborators, including the review by Shull in the Proceedings of the Tenth Solvay Congress.)

12.7. Cu_3Au alloy (75% Cu, 25% Au) has an ordered state below 400°C, in which the gold atoms occupy the 000 positions and the copper atoms the $\frac{1}{2} \frac{1}{2} 0$, $\frac{1}{2} 0 \frac{1}{2}$, and $0 \frac{1}{2} \frac{1}{2}$ positions in a face-centered cubic lattice.   Give the indices of the new x-ray reflections which appear when the alloy goes from the disordered to the ordered state.   List all new reflections with indices $\leqq 3$.   Can you give a general rule for the indices of the additional reflections?

12.8. Derive an expression for the anomalous or configurational heat capacity of an AB alloy (50% A, 50% B), sketching the form of the heat capacity vs. T, using Fig. 12.28.

REFERENCES

J. Friedel, "Electronic structure of primary solid solutions in metals," Advances in Physics **3**, 446 (1954).

W. Hume-Rothery, *Electrons, atoms, metals and alloys*, Iliffe, London, 1955.

[24] Lipson, reference 20; J. M. Cowley, J. Appl. Phys. **21**, 24 (1950).

[25] F. C. Nix and W. Shockley, Revs. Modern Phys. **10**, 1 (1938).

W. Hume-Rothery, *Structure of metals and alloys*, Institute of Metals, London, 1947.

W. Hume-Rothery and B. R. Coles, "Transition metals and their alloys," Advances in Physics **3**, 149–243 (1954).

M. A. Jaswon, *Theory of cohesion*, Pergamon Press, London, 1954.

N. F. Mott, "Recent advances in the electron theory of metals," Progress in Metal Physics **3**, 76–114 (1952).

L. Pauling, *Nature of the chemical bond*, Cornell Univ. Press, Ithaca, 1945, Chapter XI.

G. V. Raynor, *Introduction to the electron theory of metals*, Institute of Metals, London, 1949.

G. V. Raynor, "Progress in the theory of alloys," Progress in Metal Physics **1**, 1–76 (1949).

G. V. Raynor, "The band structure of metals," Repts. Prog. Phys. **15**, 173–248 (1952).

E. C. Stoner, "Magnetic susceptibility and electronic specific heat of transition metals in relation to their electronic structure," Acta Met. **2**, 259 (1954).

E. P. Wigner and F. Seitz, "Qualitative analysis of the cohesion in metals," Solid State Physics **1**, 97 (1955).

13

Semiconductor Crystals

Semiconductors are electronic conductors with values of the electrical resistivity at room temperature generally in the range $\sim 10^{-2}$ to $\sim 10^9$ ohm-cm, intermediate between good conductors ($\sim 10^{-6}$ ohm-cm) and insulators ($\sim 10^{14}$ to $\sim 10^{22}$ ohm-cm). At absolute zero a pure and perfect crystal of most semiconductors would behave as an insulator; the characteristic semiconducting properties are usually brought about by thermal agitation, impurities, or lattice defects. A number of devices of wide industrial application are based on the properties of semiconductors: they include rectifiers, modulators, detectors, thermistors, photocells, and crystal triodes or transistors. We discuss in this chapter the central physical features of semiconductor crystals. The general model of semiconductors is due largely to A. H. Wilson. In Chapter 14 we shall discuss the physical principles of rectification and transistor action. We shall be concerned primarily with the properties of silicon and germanium, as their properties are perhaps generally the best understood at present. Other important semiconducting substances include cuprous oxide, Cu_2O; selenium; lead telluride, PbTe; lead sulfide, PbS; and silicon carbide, SiC.

INTRINSIC CONDUCTIVITY

Except at low temperatures a highly purified semiconductor often exhibits *intrinsic conductivity*, as distinguished from the *impurity conductivity* of less pure specimens. We shall speak of the *intrinsic temperature range* as the temperature range in which the electrical properties of a semiconductor are not essentially modified by impurities in the crystal. The character of the electronic band scheme leading to intrinsic conductivity is exhibited in Fig. 13.1. At absolute zero we postulate a vacant conduction band, separated by an energy gap E_g from a filled valence band. As the temperature is increased, electrons are thermally excited from the valence band to the conduction band. Both the electrons in the conduction band and the vacant states or holes left behind in the valence band will contribute to the

electrical conductivity, as shown in Fig. 13.2.   At temperatures below
the intrinsic range the electrical properties are controlled by impurities,
and here we speak of *impurity conductivity* or *extrinsic conductivity*.

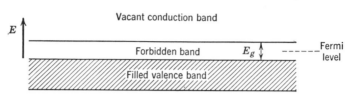

Fig. 13.1.   Band scheme for intrinsic conductivity.   At 0°K the conductivity is
zero, all states in the valence band being filled and all states in the conduction
band being vacant.   As the temperature is increased, the conductiviy increases
because electrons are thermally excited up to the conduction band, where they
become mobile.

To calculate the intrinsic conductivity at temperature T we must
find the equilibrium concentration n_e of electrons in the conduction
band, which under intrinsic conditions is equal to the equilibrium
concentration n_h of holes in the valence band.   We also must know the

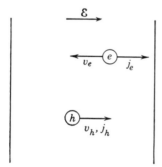

mobilities (drift velocity/electric field) μ_e
for electrons and μ_h for holes.   The conductivity is then given, according to the earlier
definitions, by

$$(13.1)\qquad \sigma = |e|(n_e\mu_e + n_h\mu_h).$$

By convention the mobilities of both electrons and holes are taken to be positive; we
must remember that the drift velocities are
actually opposite, as in Fig. 13.2.

We may anticipate a temperature dependence of the form $e^{-E/kT}$ for the concentration of electrons in the conduction
band, and, as it is unlikely that the mobility
will depend on temperature in as strong a
fashion, we may expect that the intrinsic
conductivity may vary as $e^{-E/kT}$, or the

Fig. 13.2.   Motion of electrons (e) and holes (h) in an
electric field ε; the directions of the velocity (v) and
current (j) flows are shown.
The concept of holes is discussed in detail in Chapter 11.

resistivity ρ as $e^{E/kT}$.   It will turn out that E should be taken as $E_g/2$,
where E_g is the energy gap between bands.   If

$$(13.2)\qquad\qquad \rho = Ae^{E_g/2kT},$$

then

$$(13.3)\qquad\qquad \log \rho = \log A + (E_g/2kT),$$

so that in the intrinsic range log ρ should be approximately a linear function of $1/T$. This is observed experimentally, as shown in Fig. 13.3.

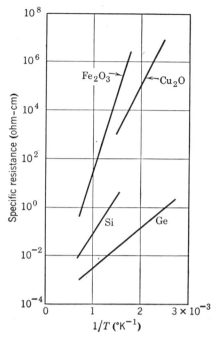

Fig. 13.3. Plot of log ρ vs. $1/T$ for several semiconductors in the intrinsic range. (After J. A. Becker.)

We now calculate in terms of the Fermi energy E_F the number of electrons excited to the conduction band at temperature T. We measure the energy E from the top of the valence band, as in Fig. 13.1. At low temperatures we may suppose $E - E_F \gg kT$, so that the Fermi-Dirac distribution function reduces to

$$(13.4) \quad f \cong e^{(E_F-E)/kT}.$$

This is the probability that a conduction electron state is occupied. If we suppose that the electrons in the conduction band behave as if they are free, we may take the density of states in the conduction band as equal to that for free electrons, with the energy referred to the bottom of the band. Thus, from (10.47), the number of states with energy between E and $E + dE$ is

$$(13.5) \quad g_e(E)\,dE = \frac{1}{2\pi^2}\left(\frac{2m_e}{\hbar^2}\right)^{3/2}(E-E_g)^{1/2}\,dE$$

per unit volume, where m_e is the effective mass of an electron in the conduction band. Here all energies are measured relative to the top of the valence band. Combining (13.4) and (13.5), we have for the number of electrons per unit volume in the conduction band

$$(13.6) \quad N_e = \int_{E_g}^{\infty} g_e(E)f_e(E)\,dE$$

$$= \frac{1}{2\pi^2}\left(\frac{2m_e}{\hbar^2}\right)^{3/2} e^{E_F/kT}\int_{E_g}^{\infty}(E-E_g)^{1/2}e^{-E/kT}\,dE$$

which integrates to

$$(13.7) \quad N_e = 2(2\pi m_e kT/h^2)^{3/2}e^{(E_F-E_g)/kT}.$$

In problems of this character the determination of the Fermi level E_F may sometimes be difficult. In the present instance it is useful to calculate the equilibrium concentration of holes, N_h. The distribution function f_h for holes is related to the electron distribution function f_e by

$$(13.8) \qquad\qquad f_h = 1 - f_e,$$

because a hole is the absence of an electron. We have

$$(13.9) \quad f_h = 1 - \frac{1}{e^{(E-E_F)/kT} + 1} = \frac{1}{e^{(E_F-E)/kT} + 1} \cong e^{(E-E_F)/kT},$$

if $(E_F - E) \gg kT$. If we suppose that the holes near the top of the valence band behave as free particles with effective mass m_h, the density of hole states is given by

$$(13.10) \qquad\qquad g_h(E)\, dE = \frac{1}{2\pi^2} \left(\frac{2m_h}{\hbar^2}\right)^{3/2} (-E)^{1/2}\, dE,$$

recalling that the energy is measured positive upwards from the top of the valence band. Proceeding as before, we find

$$(13.11) \quad N_h = \int_{-\infty}^{0} g_h(E) f_h(E)\, dE = 2(2\pi m_h kT/h^2)^{3/2} e^{-E_F/kT}$$

for the concentration of holes in the valence band.

On multiplying together the expressions for N_e and N_h we have the useful equilibrium relation

$$(13.12) \qquad N_e N_h = np = 4(2\pi kT/h^2)^3 (m_e m_h)^{3/2} e^{-E_g/kT}.$$

Here we have introduced the notation $n \equiv N_e$; $p \equiv N_h$, in conformity with current practice in the field. We note the important fact from (13.12) that the product of the electron and hole concentrations is a constant for a given material at a given temperature: introducing an impurity to increase n, say, will decrease p, as the product must remain constant. The only assumption made is that the distance of the Fermi level E_F from the edge of both bands should be large in comparison with kT.

For an intrinsic semiconductor $n = p$, as the thermal excitation of an electron from the valence band leaves behind a hole. Thus from (13.12) we have, letting the subscript i denote intrinsic,

$$(13.13) \qquad n_i = p_i = 2(2\pi kT/h^2)^{3/2} (m_e m_h)^{3/4} e^{-E_g/2kT},$$

showing that the excitation depends exponentially on $E_g/2kT$, where

E_g is the width of the forbidden gap. On setting (13.7) and (13.11) equal we have

$$(13.14) \qquad e^{2E_F/kT} = (m_h/m_e)^{3/2} e^{E_g/kT},$$

or

$$(13.15) \qquad E_F = \tfrac{1}{2}E_g + \tfrac{3}{4}kT \log (m_h/m_e).$$

If $m_h = m_e$, $E_F = \tfrac{1}{2}E_g$; that is, the Fermi level is in the middle of the forbidden gap.

From (13.1) and (13.13) the electrical conductivity in the intrinsic region will be

$$(13.16) \qquad \sigma_i = 2|e|(2\pi kT/h^2)^{3/2}(m_e m_h)^{3/4} e^{-E_g/2kT}(\mu_e + \mu_h).$$

As the mobilities are likely to depend on temperature only as a simple power law over an appropriate region, the temperature dependence of the conductivity will be dominated by the exponential dependence of the carrier concentration. Values of the energy gap determined for a number of substances are given in Table 13.1. Many of the values were determined from the slope of plots of log σ vs. $1/T$; some of the other values were determined from the long wavelength limit of the optical absorption arising from the promotion of an electron from the valence band to the conduction band, accompanied by the absorption of a photon. If for the photon $h\nu \geq E_g$, strong optical absorption may occur; if the photon energy is less then the gap energy the absorption is usually much weaker.

TABLE 13.1. VALUES OF THE ENERGY GAP BETWEEN THE VALENCE AND
CONDUCTION BANDS IN SEMICONDUCTORS, AT ROOM TEMPERATURE

Crystal	E_g(ev)	Crystal	E_g(ev)
Diamond	6	ZnSb	0.56
Si	1.10	GaSb	0.78
Ge	0.68–0.72	PbS	0.34–0.37
Sn (gray)	0.08	PbSe	0.27
InSb	0.18	PbTe	0.30
InAs	0.33	CdS	2.42
InP	1.25	CdSe	1.74
GaAs	1.4	CdTe	1.45
AlSb	1.6–1.7	ZnSe	2.60
InSe	(1)	AgI	2.8
GaP	2.25	Ag$_2$Te	0.17
α-Mg$_3$Sb$_2$	0.82	Cu$_2$O	2.1
Ca$_2$Si	0.9	Mg$_2$Si	0.7
Ca$_2$Sn	0.9	Mg$_2$Ge	0.7
Ca$_2$Pb	0.46	Mg$_2$Sn	0.3

MOBILITY IN THE INTRINSIC REGION

The mobility μ is defined as the drift velocity per unit electric field. In an ideal intrinsic semiconductor the mobility is determined by lattice scattering; that is, by collisions between lattice waves and electron waves. In actual intrinsic specimens there are always some impurity atoms which may dominate the scattering of electrons at low temperatures when the lattice waves are quiescent, but at higher temperatures the lattice scattering is dominant.

The mobility associated with lattice scattering in a non-polar (covalent) crystal such as diamond, silicon, or germanium has been calculated by Seitz and others. Seitz[1] finds

$$(13.17) \qquad \mu = \frac{2^{1/2}6^{1/3}}{4\pi^{5/6}} \cdot \frac{N^{1/3}e\hbar^2 k^2 \Theta^2 M}{m^{*5/2}C^2(kT)^{3/2}},$$

where Θ is the Debye temperature; k is the Boltzmann constant; N is the density of unit cells; m^* is the effective mass; M is the atomic mass; and C is defined using the Bloch function $u(\mathbf{r})e^{i\mathbf{k}\cdot\mathbf{r}}$ by (see Appendix L)

$$(13.18) \qquad C = \frac{\hbar^2}{2m} \int |\text{grad } u|^2 \, d\tau,$$

and is treated as an unknown parameter of value of the order of 1 to 10 ev.

TABLE 13.2. CARRIER DRIFT MOBILITIES AT ROOM TEMPERATURE

(Most of the values are probably determined by lattice scattering)

Mobility (cm²/v-sec)

Crystal	Electrons	Holes
Diamond	1,800	1200
Si	1,600	400
Ge	3,800	1800
InSb	77,000	1250
InAs	23,000	~100
InP	3,400	650
GaSb	2,500–4,000	650
PbS	600	200
PbSe	900	700
PbTe	17,000	. . . . .
AgCl	50	. . . . .

Experimental values of the mobility at room temperature are given in Table 13.2. In most substances quoted the values are probably representative of lattice scattering. We notice a tendency for crystals

[1] F. Seitz, Phys. Rev. **73**, 549 (1948); for the detailed calculation of mobility in non-polar crystals, see J. Bardeen and W. Shockley, Phys. Rev. **80**, 72 (1950).

with small energy gaps (Table 13.1) to have high values of the electron mobility. This is because small gaps imply small effective masses, according to (11.35), and (13.17) shows that small masses favor high mobilities. The low mobilities generally characteristic of holes in diatomic crystals are believed to be connected with the complex degenerate forms of the energy surfaces in such crystals at the top of the valence band.[2] By comparison the mobility of metallic copper is 35 cm^2/v-sec at room temperature.

IMPURITY OR EXTRINSIC CONDUCTIVITY

Certain types of impurities and imperfections may affect drastically the electrical properties of a semiconductor. For example, the addi-

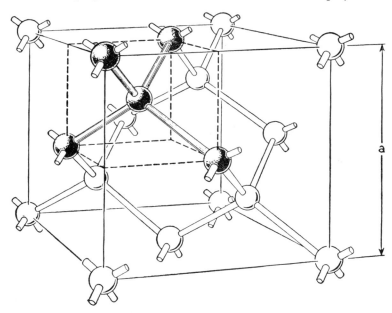

Fig. 13.4. Crystal structure of diamond, showing the tetrahedral bond arrangement. Germanium, silicon, and gray tin have the same structure. Many diatomic semiconductors have the zinc blende (ZnS) structure which may be derived from the diamond structure by decomposing the latter into two fcc lattices, the cations (Zn) populating one fcc lattice and the anions (S) populating the other. (After W. Shockley, *Electrons and holes in semiconductors.* Copyright 1950. Van Nostrand.)

tion of boron to silicon in the proportion of 1 boron atom to 10^5 silicon atoms increases the conductivity of pure silicon by a factor of 10^3 at

[2] G. Dresselhaus, Phys. Rev. **100**, 580 (1955); R. H. Parmenter, Phys. Rev. **100**, 573 (1955).

room temperature. In a compound semiconductor a stoichiometric deficiency of one constituent will act as an impurity; thus semiconductors such as Cu_2O or ZnO are known as *deficit* semiconductors.

We consider in particular the effect of impurities in silicon and germanium. These elements crystallize in the diamond structure as shown

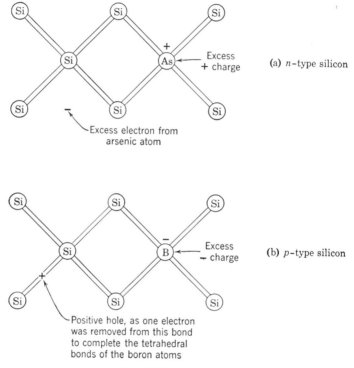

(a) *n*–type silicon

(b) *p*–type silicon

Fig. 13.5. Charges associated with impurity atom in silicon; (a) with arsenic impurity an electron is available for conduction; (b) with boron impurity a positive hole is available. The type designation is *n* for negative carriers and *p* for positive carriers or holes. The arsenic atom is called a *donor* atom because on becoming ionized it gives up an electron to the conduction band. The boron atom is called an *acceptor* atom because on becoming ionized it takes up an electron from the valence band; that is, the ionization of the hole associated with the acceptor corresponds to the addition of an electron to the acceptor, the hole moving to the former state of the valence electron.

in Fig. 13.4, with each atom forming four covalent bonds, one with each of its four nearest neighbors, corresponding to the chemical valence four. The bonds make tetrahedral angles, similar to the arrangement of C-H bonds in methane, CH_4. If now an impurity atom of valence five, such as phosphorus, arsenic, or antimony, is substituted in the lattice in place of a normal atom, there will be one valence electron from the impurity atom left over after the four covalent bonds are established with the nearest neighbors, that is, after the impurity atom has been accommodated in the structure with as little disturbance as possible. The situation as shown in Fig. 13.5 is that we have in the structure an excess positive charge from the impurity atom which has lost one electron, and we have also the excess electron. It is verified by lattice constant studies and by determining the density of carriers that the pentavalent impurities enter the lattice by substitution for normal atoms, rather than by going into interstitial positions. Impurity atoms which may be ionized to give up an electron are called *donors*.

The excess electron moves in the Coulomb potential $e/\epsilon r$ of the impurity ion, where ϵ is the dielectric constant of the medium. The factor $1/\epsilon$ takes account of the reduction in the Coulomb force between charges caused by the electronic polarization of the medium. This treatment is valid for orbits large in comparison with the distance between atoms, and for slow motions of the electron such that the time required to pass an atom is long in comparison with the period of the motion of the inner bound electrons of the atom, conditions satisfied by the extra electron of P, As, Sb, in Ge or Si.

We wish now to calculate the binding energy of the donor impurity. The Bohr theory of the hydrogen atom may readily be modified to take into account both the dielectric constant of the medium and the effective mass of an electron in the periodic potential of the crystal. Formally, we need only replace e^2 by e^2/ϵ and m by m^* in the standard results.

IMPURITY STATES

Let us consider the Bohr model of the hydrogen atom, using the old quantum theory. The quantization condition is

$$(13.19) \qquad \oint p \, dq = nh,$$

where n is the principal quantum number; we have thus

$$(13.20) \qquad (m^* r^2 \omega)(2\pi) = nh.$$

The total energy is the sum of the potential and kinetic energies:

$$(13.21) \qquad E = -\frac{e^2}{\epsilon r} + \frac{1}{2} m^* r^2 \omega^2.$$

The force equation is

$$(13.22) \qquad m^* \omega^2 r = e^2/\epsilon r^2,$$

and so the substitution of ω^2 from (13.20) gives

$$(13.23) \qquad r = \epsilon n^2 \hbar^2 / e^2 m^*$$

for the orbital radius.

Substitution of (13.22) in (13.21) gives

$$(13.24) \qquad E = -\frac{e^2}{2\epsilon r}.$$

Eliminating r with the help of (13.23), we have for the energy

$$(13.25) \qquad E = -\frac{e^4 m^*}{2\epsilon^2 \hbar^2 n^2}.$$

These results for E and r are in accord with the prescription stated above.

The application of these formulae to germanium and silicon is complicated by the anisotropic effective mass of the conduction electrons in these crystals, as discussed below in this chapter under the subject of cyclotron resonance. However, the dielectric constant enters the energy (13.25) as the square, whereas the effective mass enters only as the first power. We may obtain a general impression of the impurity levels by using an average value of the anisotropic effective masses: we shall use $m^* \approx 0.12m$ for electrons in germanium and $m^* \approx 0.25m$ for electrons in silicon. The dielectric constant has the value 15.8 for germanium and 11.7 for silicon; the values apply with fair accuracy from low frequencies up to the frequencies corresponding to the energy gap, so that the values should be applicable to the present problem where the orbital frequencies involved are very much less than the frequency corresponding to the gap.

The ionization potential of the free hydrogen atom is 13.6 ev, corresponding to the use of (13.25) with $\epsilon = 1$; $m^* = m$; $n = 1$. For germanium the ionization potential on the present model should be reduced with respect to hydrogen by the factor $m^*/m\epsilon^2 = (0.12)/250 = 4.8 \times 10^{-4}$, giving $(13.6)(4.8 \times 10^{-4}) = 0.0065$ ev, while the corresponding result for silicon is 0.025 ev. Calculations[3] using the correct anisotropic mass tensor give 0.00905 ev for germanium and 0.0298 ev for silicon. Further corrections for silicon have been considered by Luttinger and Kohn.[3] Observed values of the donor ionization energies for pentavalent impurities in germanium and silicon are given in Table 13.3. The values are obtained largely by thermal considerations to be

[3] J. M. Luttinger and W. Kohn, Phys. Rev. **98**, 915 (1955); M. Lampert, Phys. Rev. **97**, 352 (1955); C. Kittel and A. H. Mitchell, Phys. Rev. **96**, 1488 (1954).

described; some of the values have also been obtained by direct optical absorption.[4]

TABLE 13.3. DONOR IONIZATION ENERGIES OF PENTAVALENT IMPURITIES IN GERMANIUM AND SILICON, IN EV

	P	As	Sb
Si	0.045	0.049–0.056	0.039
Ge	0.0120	0.0127	0.0096

We note that the radius of the first Bohr orbit is increased by the factor $\epsilon m/m^*$ over the value 0.53 A for the free hydrogen atom. The corresponding radius is $(132)(0.53) = 70$ A in germanium and $(47)(0.53) = 25$ A in silicon.

Just as an electron may be bound to a pentavalent impurity, a hole may be bound to a trivalent impurity in germanium or silicon. The two situations are compared in Fig. 13.5. Typical trivalent impurities are B, Al, Ga, and In; such impurities are called *acceptors*, because they can take up electrons from the valence band, leaving holes in the band. The acceptor problem is similar in principle to that for electrons, although the initial strain of visualization on the reader is greater. Experimental values of the ionization energies of acceptors in germanium and silicon are given in Table 13.4. It is seen that the ionization energies for acceptors are not unlike those for donors. The equivalent Bohr model carries over in principle for holes just as for electrons, except that in germanium and silicon there is, as we shall see, an orbital degeneracy at the top of the valence band which complicates the theoretical problem enormously.[5]

TABLE 13.4. ACCEPTOR IONIZATION ENERGIES OF TRIVALENT IMPURITIES IN GERMANIUM AND SILICON, IN EV

	B	Al	Ga	In
Si	0.045	0.057–0.067	0.065–0.071	0.16
Ge	0.0104	0.0102	0.0108	0.0112

A glance at Tables 13.3 and 13.4 shows that the donor and acceptor ionization energies are comparable with kT at room temperature (0.026 ev). We expect then to find the thermal ionization of donor and acceptor impurity atoms to be important in the electrical conductivity of germanium and silicon at room temperature. If donor atoms are present in considerably greater numbers than acceptors the thermal ionization of donors will cause electrons to be freed in the conduc-

[4] For a review of the optical properties of germanium and silicon, see E. Burstein, *Photoconductivity Conference Held in Atlantic City, November 4-6, 1954*, pages 353–413, John Wiley & Sons, New York, 1956.

[5] W. Kohn and D. Schecter, Phys. Rev. **99**, 1903 (1955).

tion band. The conductivity of the specimen will be controlled by electrons (negative charges) and the material is said to be n type. If acceptors are dominant, holes will be freed in the valence band and the conductivity of the specimen will be controlled by holes (positive charges): the material is then said to be p type. We recall that in the absence of impurities the numbers of holes and electrons are equal and the material is described as intrinsic. The intrinsic electron concentration n_i at 300°K is 2.5×10^{13} cm^{-3} in germanium and 1.4×10^{10} cm^{-3} in silicon; the electrical resistivity of intrinsic material is 43 ohm-cm for germanium and 2.6×10^5 ohm-cm for silicon. As the lowest impurity concentrations attained at present are of the order of 10^{12} impurity atoms per cm^3, it is evident we may expect to be able to work with germanium intrinsic at room temperature, but not with silicon intrinsic at room temperature. Impurities with no effect on the carrier concentration are probably present in higher proportions.

THERMAL IONIZATION OF IMPURITIES

We now consider the problem of determining the concentration of ionized donors and acceptors in thermal equilibrium at a temperature T. The energy level diagram is shown in Fig. 13.6, the energies being

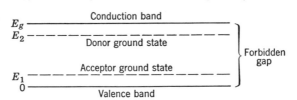

Fig. 13.6. Conventional energy level diagram showing the un-ionized ground states of donors and acceptors. It is convenient to think of electrons as tending to sink and holes as tending to float. The donor ionization energy is $E_g - E_2$; the acceptor ionization energy is E_1.

measured upward from the top of the valence band. We let N_d, N_a denote the concentrations of donor and acceptor atoms, respectively; $N_d{}^0$, $N_a{}^0$ the concentration of neutral (un-ionized) donors and acceptors; $N_d{}^+$, $N_a{}^-$ the concentration of ionized donors and acceptors. Recalling that the Fermi distribution function tells us the fractional occupation by an *electron* of a state at a given energy, we have

$$(13.26) \qquad N_d{}^0 = \frac{N_d}{1 + e^{(E_2 - E_F)/kT}};$$

$$(13.27) \qquad N_d{}^+ = N_d - N_d{}^0 = \frac{N_d}{1 + e^{-(E_2 - E_F)/kT}};$$

$$(13.28) \qquad N_a^- = \frac{N_a}{1 + e^{(E_1 - E_F)/kT}}.$$

We introduce the notation

$$(13.29) \quad n_-^0 = 2(2\pi m_e kT/h^2)^{3/2}; \qquad n_+^0 = 2(2\pi m_h kT/h^2)^{3/2}.$$

In writing (13.26) we have omitted in the interest of simplicity a factor $\frac{1}{2}$ which often is seen in front of the exponential. The factor arises when one takes into account the fact that the energy of a spin-degenerate donor level occupied by two electrons, one of each spin orientation, is probably quite high because of the electrostatic interaction of the two electrons, so that the level is usually occupied by at most one electron. The consequences of our simplification are not serious.

We require electrical neutrality of the system as a whole. The statement that the number of positive charges must equal the number of negative charges is expressed by the equation

$$(13.30) \qquad p + N_d^+ = n + N_a^-,$$

where, as before, n and p are the concentrations of electrons in the conduction band and holes in the valence band, respectively. Using (13.7) and (13.11),

$$(13.31) \quad n_+^0 e^{-E_F/kT} + \frac{N_d}{1 + e^{-(E_2 - E_F)/kT}}$$

$$= n_-^0 e^{(E_F - E_g)/kT} + \frac{N_a}{1 + e^{(E_1 - E_F)/kT}}.$$

We now treat the special case of $N_a = 0$; that is, no acceptors are present. It is convenient to assume further that there are a sufficient number of donors present to give enough conduction electrons to suppress p, the hole concentration, to a value much below the intrinsic value (13.13). The suppression occurs because (13.12), which is essentially an expression of the law of mass action, requires the product np to be constant; thus, if n is increased by a certain factor, p is decreased by the reciprocal factor. Neglecting p is equivalent to saying that

$$(13.32) \qquad e^{(E_F - E_g)/kT} \gg e^{-E_F/kT}.$$

Then (13.31) reduces to

$$(13.33) \qquad \frac{N_d}{1 + e^{-(E_2 - E_F)/kT}} = n_-^0 e^{(E_F - E_g)/kT}.$$

This may be written as

$$e^{2E_F/kT}[n_-^0 e^{-(E_2+E_g)/kT}] + e^{E_F/kT}[n_-^0 e^{-E_g/kT}] - N_d = 0,$$

and so the Fermi energy is determined by

$$(13.34) \qquad e^{E_F/kT} = \frac{\{-1 + [1 + 4(N_d/n_-^0)e^{(E_g-E_2)/kT}]^{1/2}\}}{2e^{-E_2/kT}}.$$

We evaluate E_F in two limiting situations. First, we suppose

$$(13.35) \qquad 4(N_d/n_-^0)e^{(E_g-E_2)/kT} \ll 1,$$

corresponding to small N_d or high T. Then

$$e^{E_F/kT} \cong (N_d/n_-^0)e^{E_g/kT},$$

and

$$(13.36) \qquad E_F \cong E_g + kT \ln (N_d/n_-^0),$$

and so

$$(13.37) \qquad n = n_-^0 e^{(E_F-E_g)/kT} \cong N_d,$$

which means that the number of conduction electrons is equal to the number of donors, under the above conditions.

In a second limit we suppose

$$(13.38) \qquad 4(N_d/n_-^0)e^{(E_g-E_2)/kT} \gg 1,$$

corresponding to large N_d or low T. Now

$$(13.39) \qquad e^{E_F/kT} \cong (N_d/n_-^0)^{1/2}e^{(E_g+E_2)/2kT},$$

giving

$$(13.40) \qquad n = (2N_d)^{1/2}(2\pi kTm_e/h^2)^{3/4}e^{-E_d/2kT},$$

defining $E_d = E_g - E_2$ as the donor ionization energy. In this limit the electron concentration varies as the square root of the donor concentration. However, we cannot usually determine the donor ionization energy by measuring the conductivity or, better, the Hall coefficient in the limit in which (13.40) applies. At low temperatures there are usually fewer conduction electrons than there are acceptor atoms present as an unavoidable impurity. A number of donor atoms are ionized in filling up the acceptors, and this process tends to pin down the Fermi level at E_2, rather than as given by (13.39). In this situation n varies as $\exp(-E_d/kT)$ and not as $\exp(-E_d/2kT)$. Identical results hold for acceptors, appropriate changes being made, under the assumption $N_d = 0$. If the donor and acceptor concentrations are of comparable orders of magnitude, affairs are quite complicated, and one usually has to solve (13.31) by graphical methods.

MOBILITY IN THE PRESENCE OF IMPURITY ATOMS

When relatively few impurity atoms are present, or at high temperatures, lattice scattering will determine the mobility. At higher impurity concentrations, electron scattering by impurity atoms may be important. The scattering will depend on whether the impurity is neutral or ionized. The neutral atom problem is equivalent to the scattering of an electron by a hydrogen atom, but with the dielectric

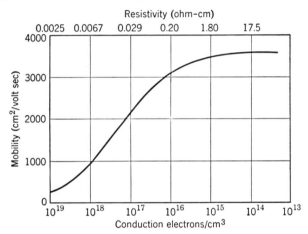

Fig. 13.7. Calculated curves of mobility vs. carrier density and resistivity for n-type germanium at 300°K. It is assumed that all the donor atoms are ionized and that there are no acceptors. (After Conwell.)

constant correction. We note that the area of the first Bohr orbit is increased by $(\epsilon m/m^*)^2$, or $(47)^2$ in silicon. An exact solution for the scattering cross section is quite difficult in the energy range of interest in semiconductors.

The scattering by ionized donors or acceptors has been solved by Conwell and Weisskopf,[6] who utilized the Rutherford scattering formula.[7] We give a brief derivation of the expression for the mobility in Appendix M. Conwell and Weisskopf find

$$(13.41) \qquad \mu = [2^{7/2}\epsilon^2(kT)^{3/2}]/N_e\pi^{3/2}e^3m^{*1/2}\log(1+x^2)$$

[6] E. Conwell and V. F. Weisskopf, Phys. Rev. **77**, 388 (1950); see also S. Chapman, Monthly Notices Roy. Astron. Soc. **82**, 294 (1922); for scattering by neutral impurities see C. Erginsoy, Phys. Rev. **79**, 1013 (1950).

[7] See, for example, M. Born, *Atomic physics*, Hafner, New York, 5th ed., 1951, App. IX, p. 325.

where

$$x = 6\epsilon \, dkT/e^2.$$

In these equations N_e is the concentration of ionized donors (or acceptors), and $2d$ is the average distance between ionized donor neighbors. The effect of impurity scattering in reducing the mobility is shown in Fig. 13.7.

ANALYSIS OF EXPERIMENTAL RESULTS

A good general picture of the physical behavior of a semiconductor can be obtained by measuring the electrical conductivity and Hall coefficient as functions of temperature and impurity doping over wide ranges. A great deal of work has been done in this way, particularly by the Purdue and Murray Hill groups and many others. We discuss here results obtained by Conwell and Debye[8] on n-type germanium. These results will convey an impression of the kind of information which can be obtained from a systematic analysis of conductivity and Hall data.

We have seen (Chapter 11) that in a simple metal the Hall coefficient is given by

$$(13.42) \qquad R_H = -\frac{1}{N|e|c},$$

where N is the electron concentration. In semiconductors we often deal with a Maxwellian distribution of velocities, and the connection between R_H and N may vary slightly from (13.42) by a factor close to unity according to the form of the dependence of the mean free path on velocity. Results deduced from measurements of the Hall voltage for the carrier density vs. temperature for a set of germanium crystals doped with arsenic donors are shown in Fig. 13.8. It is seen that for temperatures between liquid air and room temperature the donors are essentially all ionized. Thus crystal 55 has 8×10^{12} excess donors per cm^3, while crystal 54 has 7×10^{15} excess donors per cm.^{3} A little above room temperature crystal 55 becomes intrinsic, and the carrier concentration rises sharply. Below $20°K–50°K$ the carrier concentration decreases as the donors become un-ionized. From the slope of the plot we estimate the ionization energy to be ~ 0.01 ev. In crystal 58 the donor concentration ($\sim 10^{18}$ cm^{-3}) is sufficiently high so that neighboring donor states overlap appreciably and the donor

[8] E. M. Conwell, Proc. I.R.E. **40**, 1327 (1952); P. P. Debye and E. M. Conwell, Phys. Rev. **93**, 693 (1954).

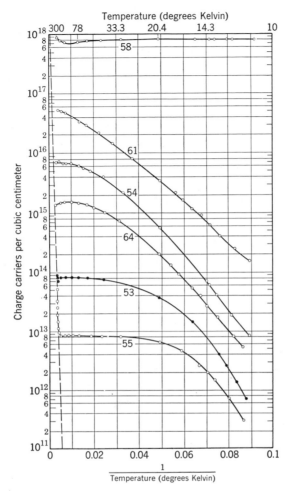

Fig. 13.8. Density of charge carriers vs. the reciprocal of absolute temperature for a set of arsenic-doped germanium crystals. The data were taken by Debye. The numbers identify particular samples. The dashed line represents the density of intrinsic carriers. (After Conwell.)

ionization energy has apparently vanished: the carrier concentration is independent of temperature.

The temperature dependence of the electrical conductivity of the same set of crystals is shown in Fig. 13.9. The decrease at low temperatures is caused by the decrease in the concentration of conduction electrons. The decrease on going from 78°K to 300°K is caused by increased lattice scattering. The sudden increase above 300°K for crystal 55 is caused by the onset of intrinsic conductivity. The slope of the intrinsic region leads to the value 0.7 ev for the energy gap of germanium.

If the current carriers are predominantly of one type only, we may obtain the mobility simply from the product of the conductivity and

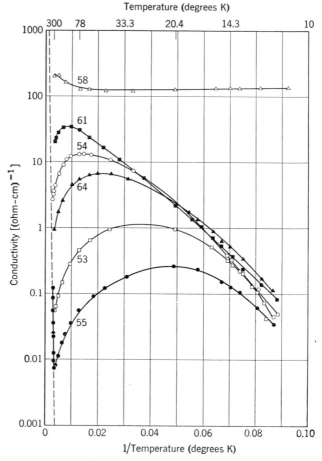

Fig. 13.9. Conductivity vs. absolute temperature for the same set of arsenic-doped germanium crystals. The data were taken by Debye. The dashed line represents intrinsic conductivity. (After Conwell.)

the Hall coefficient:

$$(13.43) \qquad cR_H\sigma = c\left(\frac{1}{N|e|c}\right)\left(\frac{Ne^2\tau}{m^*}\right) = \frac{e\tau}{m^*} = \mu,$$

apart from factors of the order of unity. The temperature dependence of the mobility as obtained in this way for the set of As-doped germanium crystals is shown in Fig. 13.10. The temperature dependence of the mobility in the purest crystal (55) follows approximately the $T^{-3/2}$ law predicted by the simple theory. For crystal 61 one sees a decrease in mobility at low temperatures thought to be characteristic of scattering by ionized impurity atoms.

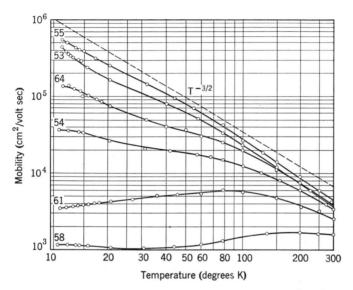

Fig. 13.10. Mobility vs. temperature for the same set of arsenic-doped germanium crystals. The data were taken by Debye. The dashed line represents a $-\frac{3}{2}$ slope characteristic of lattice scattering. (After Conwell.)

We note here a small selection from analyses of semiconductor materials carried out by similar methods:

Germanium	H. Fritzsche, Phys. Rev. **99**, 406 (1955); P. P. Debye and E. M. Conwell, Phys. Rev. **93**, 693 (1954).
Silicon	G. L. Pearson and J. Bardeen, Phys. Rev. **75**, 865 (1949); **77**, 303 (1950); F. J. Morin and J. P. Maita, Phys. Rev. **96**, 28 (1954).
InSb	H. Fritzsche and K. Lark-Horovitz, Phys. Rev. **99**, 400 (1955).
Lead salts	R. A. Smith, Physica **20**, 910 (1954); W. W. Scanlon, Phys. Rev. **92**, 1573 (1953).
Cu_2O	V. W. Vogt, Ann. Physik **7**, 183 (1930); S. J. Angello, Phys. Rev. **62**, 371 (1942); W. H. Brattain, Revs. Modern Phys. **23**, 203 (1951).
Graphite	G. H. Kinchin, Proc. Roy. Soc. (London) **A217**, 9 (1953).

CdS   F. A. Kröger, H. J. Vink, and J. Volger, Physica **20**, 1095 (1954).

Naphthalene   H. Pick and W. Wissman, Z. Physik **138**, 436 (1954).

Mg-intermetallics   G. Busch and V. Winkler, Physica **20**, 1067 (1954).

Gray tin   G. Busch, J. Wieland, and H. Zoller, in volume *Semiconducting materials*, pp. 188–197.

III–V compounds   H. Welker, Physica **20**, 893 (1954); Breckenridge *et al.*, Physica **20**, 1073 (1954).

LIFETIME AND RECOMBINATION

It is possible in semiconductors to obtain departures from the thermal equilibrium concentrations of electrons and holes in several ways: by injecting carriers into the sample through a metal contact or by the creation of electron-hole pairs by light or by charged particle bombardment. Once disturbed, the system tends to return to equilibrium by recombination of the excess electrons and holes. The recombination rate can be observed by measuring the time variation of the conductance[9] of the specimen after excitation or by detecting the drift[10] in an electric field of excess carriers produced at one point and detected at another point.

In the simplest case excess electrons and holes are produced in equal numbers and they recombine both at the same rate. Letting

Δn = excess electron concentration above value at thermal equilibrium;

Δp = excess hole concentration above value at thermal equilibrium;

we have by assumption $\Delta n = \Delta p$. At small concentrations of excess carriers the decay is usually exponential and characterized by a constant lifetime τ.[11] We have then

$$(13.44) \qquad \frac{dn}{dt} = -\frac{1}{\tau}\Delta n; \qquad \frac{dp}{dt} = -\frac{1}{\tau}\Delta p.$$

In practice it is often found that the decay of excess minority carrier concentration proceeds at different rates in n- and p-type material;

[9] Navon, Bray, and Fan, Proc. I.R.E. **40**, 1342 (1952); Gebbie, Nisenoff, and Fan, Phys. Rev. **91**, 230 (1953).

[10] Shockley, Pearson, and Haynes, Bell System Tech. J. **28**, 344 (1949); J. R. Haynes and W. C. Westphal, Phys. Rev. **85**, 680 (1952); see particularly Chapter 3 in the book by Shockley cited at the end of the chapter.

[11] It is standard practice, however unfortunate, that the same symbol τ should denote both relaxation time and lifetime.

thus we deal with a lifetime τ_n for excess electrons in p-type material and a lifetime τ_p for excess holes in n-type material.

The recombination mechanisms are still obscure, but it is known that direct radiative recombination of an electron and a hole with emission of a photon is relatively improbable in germanium and silicon. Shockley has calculated minority carrier lifetimes of the order of 1 sec for the radiative process in germanium at room temperature; overall observed lifetimes are reported to be of the order of 0.01 sec in unusually pure germanium crystals and are more typically of the order of 100 μsec in commercial material. The emission of radiation accompanying minority carrier injection has been observed experimentally.[12,13]

It has been found that recombination occurs both in the volume and on the surface of the crystal. The observed lifetime τ is composed of separate lifetimes for volume τ_v and surface τ_s recombination:

$$(13.45) \qquad \frac{1}{\tau} = \frac{1}{\tau_v} + \frac{1}{\tau_s}.$$

The two contributions are usually distinguished by measurements on filaments of varying dimensions and surface treatment. Both lifetimes may vary from crystal to crystal and also vary with temperature. The volume lifetime τ_v is particularly sensitive to small amounts of copper, iron, and nickel: a nickel contamination[14] of 10^{12} atoms/cm^3 may shorten the lifetime observably. The volume lifetime is also sensitive to lattice imperfections: quenching from an elevated temperature, plastic flow, and radiation damage have all been observed to reduce the lifetime drastically, in some instances to under 1 μsec.

The lifetime for surface recombination τ_s is particularly sensitive to the mechanical and chemical treatment of the surface. Because the carriers must diffuse to the surface before they can recombine there, the surface lifetime depends on the dimensions of the specimen. It is useful to deal with the surface velocity of recombination as this quantity does not depend on the specimen dimensions. The surface velocity of recombination s is defined by

s = (recombination rate per unit area)/(excess concentration just below the surface).

Values of s have been reported for germanium at room temperature between about 15 cm/sec and 10,000 cm/sec. The highest surface

[12,13] J. R. Haynes and H. B. Briggs, Phys. Rev. **86**, 647 (1952); R. Newman, Phys. Rev. **91**, 1313 (1953); P. Aigrain, Physica **20**, 1010 (1954).

[14] Burton, Hull, Morin, and Severiens, J. Phys. Chem. **57**, 853 (1953).

recombination velocities are found for sandblasted surfaces; the lowest velocities are found for surfaces polished smooth and then etched with empirical solutions. A certain amount of magic is thought to be involved in a good etch.

Shockley has derived equations relating τ_s, s, and the cross section dimensions for long rods of rectangular cross section $2B \times 2C$. He finds

$$(13.46) \qquad (s \to \infty) \qquad \frac{1}{\tau_s} = \frac{\pi^2 D}{4}\left(\frac{1}{B^2} + \frac{1}{C^2}\right);$$

$$(13.47) \qquad (s \to 0) \qquad \frac{1}{\tau_s} = s\left(\frac{1}{B} + \frac{1}{C}\right).$$

The first limit means that surface recombination is dominant; the second limit means that volume recombination is dominant. In (13.46) the quantity D is the diffusion constant for the minority carrier. The diffusion constant or diffusivity may be calculated from the mobility by the Einstein relation[15]

$$(13.48) \qquad\qquad \mu kT = eD.$$

In germanium at room temperature we have

$$D_n = 93 \text{ cm}^2/\text{sec}; \qquad D_p = 44 \text{ cm}^2/\text{sec}.$$

It will prove useful in connection with the discussion of p-n junctions in the next chapter to derive an expression for the average displacement distance of a carrier during its lifetime, considering for simplicity only volume recombination. In the steady state the general hydrodynamic equation of continuity as written for holes is

$$(13.49) \qquad \frac{\partial p}{\partial t} + \text{div } p\mathbf{v}_p = \text{(generation minus recombination) rate per}$$

unit volume.

Here $\mathbf{v}_p$ is the drift velocity of the holes. Now the diffusion equation is

$$(13.50) \qquad\qquad p\mathbf{v}_p = -D_p \text{ grad } p,$$

[15] This relation is easily proved. Suppose that the particles of charge e are in a constant electric field E. According to the Boltzmann distribution law the concentration of particles $n(x)$ at x is proportional to $\exp(-eEx/kT)$. The condition that in equilibrium no net current should flow is

$$\mu nE + D(dn/dx) = 0,$$

the definition of the diffusivity D being used as the net flux of particles per unit concentration gradient. From this equation we see that $n(x)$ is also proportional to $\exp(-\mu Ex/D)$; (13.48) follows on equating the exponents.

according to the definition of the diffusivity. Let us consider the steady-state flow of holes from a region in which they are generated to a region where they recombine at the rate p/τ_p, according to (13.44). In the steady state $\partial p/\partial t = 0$, and (13.49) and (13.50) reduce in the recombination region to

$$(13.51) \qquad D_p \nabla^2 p - (p/\tau_p) = 0.$$

For linear geometry we look for a solution of the form, for positive x,

$$(13.52) \qquad p = p_0 e^{-x/L_p};$$

it is supposed that the holes are generated in the region of negative x and recombine in the region of positive x. Substituting (13.52) in (13.51) we find we must have

$$(13.53) \qquad L_p = (D_p \tau_p)^{\frac{1}{2}}.$$

The length L_p is known as the *diffusion length* for holes; it is a measure of the length a hole diffuses in a lifetime. For electrons

$$(13.54) \qquad L_n = (D_n \tau_n)^{\frac{1}{2}}$$

by a parallel argument. In germanium at room temperature a hole with a lifetime of 10^{-3} sec has a diffusion length of

$$(13.55) \quad L_p = (44 \times 10^{-3})^{\frac{1}{2}}$$
$$\cong 0.2 \text{ cm.}$$

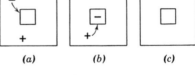

(a)   (b)   (c)

Fig. 13.11. A recombination center captures alternately an electron and a hole and thus catalyzes their recombination, as shown in parts (a), (b), and (c). (After Shockley.)

Shockley has suggested a mechanism whereby imperfections may catalyze recombination. As indicated in Fig. 13.11, an electron and hole are initially free at stage (a); in (b) an electron is captured by the recombination center; a hole is attracted electrostatically by the captured electron, and in (c) the electron has dropped into the hole, leaving the recombination center ready to repeat the process with another electron and hole.

MINORITY CARRIER TRANSPORT AND HOLE INJECTION

Haynes and Shockley[16] have developed an experiment which illustrates the participation of minority carriers in transport processes in solids and which provides a method for the direct measurement of diffusion and drift.

[16] J. R. Haynes and W. Shockley, Phys. Rev. **81**, 835 (1951); see also reference 10.

The experimental arrangement is illustrated diagrammatically in Fig. 13.12. The germanium is n-type as illustrated and is present as a rod. A sweeping field is applied from end to end of the rod by a battery. This field acts in such a direction as to draw electrons from right to left through the rod. If any holes were introduced in the rod, they would drift from left to right.

When the pulse generator at the left-hand point contact, or emitter point, operates, the emitter point is biased positive and causes holes to be injected into the rod. These holes are then drawn down the rod by the sweeping field. After a time they arrive in the neighborhood of the collector point, which, as the figure shows, is biased negative.

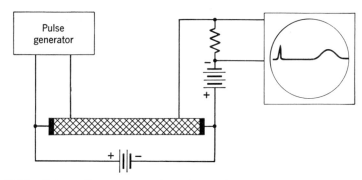

Fig. 13.12. Schematic representation of experiment to observe the drift and diffusion of injected holes in n-type germanium. (After Haynes and Shockley.)

It thus tends to attract holes, and some of the holes flow to the collector point and thus contribute to the current flowing in the collector circuit. This current flows through a resistor, and the voltage across the resistor is applied to the vertical plates of a cathode ray oscilloscope. At time t_1 the switch to the emitter point is closed for a brief moment; the time of closing is indicated by a "pick up" signal on the face of the oscilloscope. After this nothing happens until time t_2 when some of the holes arrive at the collector point; the concentration of holes builds up for a moment and then decays as the group of holes passes. The spread of time of arrival of the holes is a measure of the diffusion constant; the elapsed time $t_2 - t_1$ is a measure of the mobility, provided the minority carriers are not trapped and then released on the way between the emitter and collector. The evidence is that such trapping is not significant.

The experiment also demonstrates that it is possible to inject holes into a semiconductor at a suitable metal-semiconductor contact. The metal under positive bias voltage takes up electrons from the valence band of the semiconductor, thereby creating holes in the valence band. The process of hole injection is important in semiconductor applications, particularly in the point contact transistor.

CYCLOTRON RESONANCE EXPERIMENTS

In several substances it has proved possible to determine experimentally the form of the energy surfaces of the conduction and valence bands near the band edges; that is, the energy $E(\mathbf{k})$ is determined as a function of the wave vector $\mathbf{k}$. The determination of the energy surface is equivalent to a determination of the effective mass tensor, as we have seen that

(13.56)
$$\left(\frac{1}{m^*}\right)_{ij} = \hbar^{-2}\frac{\partial^2 E}{\partial k_i \, \partial k_j}.$$

The only direct determinations of the effective masses in semiconductors are provided by cyclotron resonance experiments, in which the current carriers in a solid are accelerated in spiral orbits about the axis of a static magnetic field H. The angular rotation frequency ω_c of the carriers is, according to the usual cyclotron equation,[17]

(13.57)
$$\omega_c = \pm eH/m^*c,$$

where m^* is an appropriate effective mass. Resonant absorption of energy from an r-f electric field perpendicular to the static magnetic field (Fig. 13.13) occurs when the frequency of the r-f field is equal to the cyclotron frequency $f_c = \omega_c/2\pi$. The $\pm$ choice of signs in (13.57) indicates that holes and electrons will rotate in opposite senses in a magnetic field.

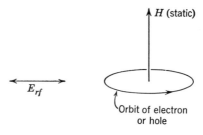

Fig. 13.13. Arrangement of fields in a cyclotron resonance experiment.

It is interesting to consider the order of magnitude of several physical quantities relevant to the experiment. We make the estimates using $m^*/m \cong 0.1$, which is not unrepresentative. For $f_c = 24{,}000$ mc/sec, or $\omega_c = 1.5 \times 10^{11}$ radians/sec, we have $H \cong 860$ oersteds at resonance. At 4°K the mean velocity for a Maxwellian distribution is 4×10^6 cm/sec, and so the radius of the orbit is $r = v/\omega_c \cong 3 \times$

---

[17] This equation is easily derived in an elementary way. The centrifugal force $m^*\omega_c^2 r$ is equal to the Lorentz force $\pm e\omega_c rH/c$, where r is the orbital radius. On canceling $\omega_c r$, we have $\omega_c = \pm eH/m^*c$. The $\pm$ signs are included to describe both electrons and holes.

10^{-5} cm. The line width is determined, as we shall see below, by the collision relaxation time τ, and it is necessary that $\omega_c \tau \geq 1$ in order to obtain a distinctive cyclotron resonance. In other words, the mean free path must be large enough to permit the average carrier to get $1/2\pi$ of the way around a circle between successive collisions. For $\omega_c = 1.5 \times 10^{11}$ sec^{-1}, we require $\tau = 10^{-11}$ sec or longer. At room temperature the relaxation times of carriers in crystals are commonly in the range 10^{-13} to 10^{-15} sec. It is usually necessary to work with high-purity crystals in the liquid hydrogen or liquid helium range to obtain relaxation times long enough to permit the observation of cyclotron resonance with K-band microwave equipment. These requirements may be relaxed significantly with the use of millimeter or infrared radiation.

We give now a brief classical discussion of cyclotron resonance absorption[18] by a carrier of isotropic effective mass. We review briefly the elementary classical theory of the process, assuming an isotropic effective mass m^* and an isotropic relaxation time τ, both independent of the velocity.

The equation of motion for the drift velocity is

$$(13.58) \qquad m^* \left(\frac{d\mathbf{v}}{dt} + \frac{1}{\tau} \mathbf{v} \right) = e \left(\mathbf{E} + \frac{\mathbf{v} \times \mathbf{H}}{c} \right).$$

We take H as the static field along the z axis and neglect the r-f magnetic field. For plane-polarized radiation E_x, we have

$$(13.59) \qquad m^* \left(i\omega + \frac{1}{\tau} \right) v_x = eE_x + \frac{e}{c} v_y H;$$

$$m^* \left(i\omega + \frac{1}{\tau} \right) v_y = -\frac{e}{c} v_x H.$$

We solve for v_x, finding for the complex conductivity,

$$(13.60) \quad \sigma = j_x/E_x = Nev_x/E_x = \sigma_0 \left[\frac{1 + i\omega\tau}{1 + (\omega_c{}^2 - \omega^2)\tau^2 + 2i\omega\tau} \right],$$

where

$$(13.61) \qquad \sigma_0 = Ne^2\tau/m^*$$

is the static conductivity; N is the carrier concentration. The losses are proportional to the real part of the conductivity if the specimen is

[18] References to early papers in the field are given by Dresselhaus, Kip, and Kittel, Phys. Rev. **98**, 368 (1955); this paper also contains an account of experimental methods.

thin in comparison with the skin depth and the wavelength. We express the result in convenient dimensionless form by writing $\nu = \omega\tau$, $\nu_c = \omega_c\tau$; the real part σ_R of σ is given by

$$(13.62) \qquad \sigma_R/\sigma_0 = \frac{1 + \nu^2 + \nu_c^2}{(1 + \nu_c^2 - \nu^2)^2 + 4\nu^2}.$$

This function is plotted in Fig. 13.14 for $\nu = 0.2$, 1, and 2; it is seen that the resonance is quite well defined for $\nu = 2$.

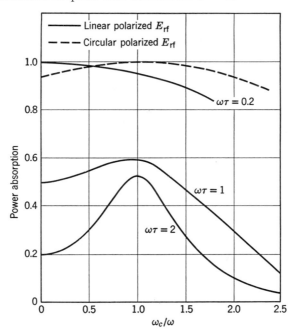

Fig. 13.14. Theoretical curves showing relative power absorption at constant frequency as a function of the static magnetic field intensity in units ω_c/ω, for various relaxation times in units $\omega\tau$. Curves are given for both linear polarization and circular polarization of the r-f field.

It is interesting to state in terms of the mobility the condition $\omega\tau > 1$ for the observation of cyclotron resonance. In esu, $\tau = m^*\mu/e$; to have $\omega\tau > 1$ requires $\mu > e/\omega m^*$. For $f = 24{,}000$ mc/sec, the condition on μ expressed in practical units is, approximately,

$$(13.63) \qquad (m^*/m)\mu > 11{,}000 \text{ cm}^2/\text{volt-sec}.$$

If $\nu = \nu_c \gg 1$, we have the condition for cyclotron resonance; from (13.62)

$$(13.64) \qquad \sigma_R/\sigma_0 = \tfrac{1}{2}.$$

Thus, at cyclotron resonance, the conductivity is one-half of the d-c conductivity. If we had taken circularly polarized radiation in place on plane-polarized radiation, the ratio would have been unity. The factor one-half represents the selective absorption of one of the two circular components of a plane wave; the other component passes freely in the limit considered. The component which is absorbed at cyclotron resonance remains in phase with the drift velocity throughout the motion, just as in ordinary d-c conductivity; hence the absorption of this component is identical with the d-c absorption.

The r-f conductivity at resonance is related to the r-f conductivity at zero magnetic field by the ratio

$$(13.65) \qquad \sigma_R(\text{res})/\sigma_R(H = 0) = \nu_c{}^2/2,$$

provided $\nu_c \gg 1$. For $\omega_c \tau \approx 10$, the ratio $\sigma_R(\text{res})/\sigma_R(H = 0)$ is of the order of 50.

We now consider the Q of the sample at cyclotron resonance. We suppose the specimen is located in the microwave cavity at a position of negligible r-f magnetic field. The stored energy density is $\epsilon \langle E^2 \rangle_{\text{Av}}/8\pi$; the energy dissipated per radian at resonance is $\sigma_R \langle E^2 \rangle_{\text{Av}}/\omega$; so

$$(13.66) \qquad Q_{\text{cycl}} = \epsilon \omega/8\pi\sigma_R = m^* \epsilon \omega/4\pi N e^2 \tau.$$

For the standard example described above

$$(13.67) \qquad Q_{\text{cycl}} \approx 10^{12}/N,$$

thus with sensitive equipment at klystron frequencies one might expect to detect $10^3 - 10^6$ carriers. It is of interest to note that (13.66) may be written

$$(13.68) \qquad Q_{\text{cycl}} = \omega/\omega_p{}^2 \tau,$$

where

$$(13.69) \qquad \omega_p = (4\pi N e^2/\epsilon m^*)^{\frac{1}{2}}$$

is often referred to as the *plasma* frequency.[19]

The half-width at half σ_R on the σ_R vs. ω curve is determined by the condition

$$\tau \, \Delta\omega = 1.$$

The neighborhood of the conduction band edge point in both germanium and silicon consists of a set of spheroidal energy surfaces located

---

[19] For a discussion of plasma resonance effects in semiconductor crystals, see Dresselhaus, Kip, and Kittel, Phys. Rev. **100**, 618 (1955); in this paper a more general definition of the plasma frequency is employed.

in equivalent positions in **k** space. By band edge point we mean the point of lowest energy in the conduction band and the point of highest energy in the valence band. We discuss now the theory of cyclotron resonance for spheroidal surfaces. We choose Cartesian coordinate axes with the z axis parallel to the figure axis of the spheroid, and we measure the wave vector components from the center of the spheroid. For points in **k** space sufficiently close to a band edge point, the energy is described by the equation

$$(13.70) \qquad E(\mathbf{k}) = \hbar^2 \left(\frac{k_x^2 + k_y^2}{2m_t} + \frac{k_z^2}{2m_l} \right).$$

Here m_l is the longitudinal mass parameter and m_t is the transverse mass parameter.

We wish now to discuss the energy levels in the presence of a uniform static field H. The usual procedure is to take the effective Hamiltonian,

$$(13.71) \qquad \mathfrak{3C}(\mathbf{P}) = \frac{P_x^2 + P_y^2}{2m_t} + \frac{P_z^2}{2m_l},$$

and solve the equations of motion

$$(13.72) \qquad \mathbf{v} = \nabla_P \mathfrak{3C}(\mathbf{P});$$

$$(13.73) \qquad d\mathbf{P}/dt = e[\mathbf{E} + (1/c)\mathbf{v} \times \mathbf{H}].$$

Here $\mathbf{P} = \mathbf{p} - e\mathbf{A}/c$, where $\mathbf{p}$ is the momentum and $\mathbf{A}$ the vector potential. A proof of the validity of this procedure in the present problem has been given by Luttinger and Kohn.[20]

Shockley[21] has given the solution of the cyclotron frequency problem for a general ellipsoidal energy surface. We indicate the method of solution here. For the spheroidal surface (13.71)

$$(13.74) \qquad \mathbf{v} = (P_x/m_t; P_y/m_t; P_z/m_l).$$

We take

$$(13.75) \qquad \mathbf{H} = H(\sin \theta; 0; \cos \theta).$$

Then Eq. (13.73) becomes, letting $\omega_t = eH/m_t c$ and $\omega_l = eH/m_l c$,

$$i\omega P_x - \omega_t P_y \cos \theta = 0;$$

$$(13.76) \qquad i\omega P_y - \omega_l P_z \sin \theta + \omega_t P_x \cos \theta = 0;$$

$$i\omega P_z + \omega_t P_y \sin \theta = 0.$$

[20] J. M. Luttinger and W. Kohn, Phys. Rev. **97**, 869 (1955).
[21] W. Shockley, Phys. Rev. **90**, 491 (1953).

The associated secular equation has the solution

$$(13.77) \qquad \omega^2 = \omega_t{}^2 \cos^2 \theta + \omega_t \omega_l \sin^2 \theta.$$

Thus, the effective mass determining the cyclotron frequency when the static magnetic field makes an angle θ with the longitudinal axis of the energy surface is

$$(13.78) \qquad \left(\frac{1}{m^*}\right)^2 = \frac{\cos^2 \theta}{m_t{}^2} + \frac{\sin^2 \theta}{m_t m_l}.$$

A typical cyclotron resonance run in germanium is shown in Fig. 13.15. In Fig. 13.16 we give a plot of the experimental points obtained

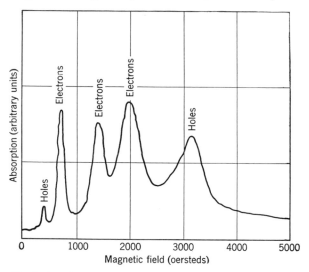

Fig. 13.15. Typical cyclotron resonance results in germanium near 24,000 mc/sec and 4°K: direct copy from a recorder trace of power absorption vs. static magnetic field in an orientation in a (110) plane at 60° from a [100] axis.

for electrons in germanium at 4°K as a function of the angle between the direction of the static magnetic field in a (110) plane and a [001] direction lying in the plane. The mass values derived from the theoretical fit to the experimental points are $m_l = (1.58 \pm 0.04)m$ and $m_t = (0.082 \pm 0.001)m$; we assume that there are a set of crystallographically equivalent energy spheroids oriented along the $\langle 111 \rangle$ directions in the Brillouin zone, as proposed originally by Lax[22] et al.

In silicon the energy surfaces near the band edge of the conduction band are spheroids[23] oriented along the equivalent $\langle 100 \rangle$ directions in

[22] Lax, Zeiger, Dexter, and Rosenblum, Phys. Rev. **93**, 1418 (1954).
[23] Dexter, Lax, Kip, and Dresselhaus, Phys. Rev. **96**, 222 (1954).

the Brillouin zone, with mass parameters $m_l = (0.97 \pm 0.02)m$ and $m_t = (0.19 \pm 0.01)m$. The surfaces of constant energy are drawn to scale in Fig. 13.17.

The structures of the valence band edges in germanium and silicon are complicated. The holes in these crystals are characterized by

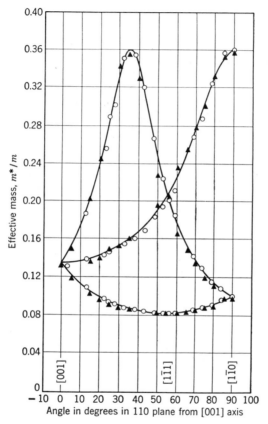

Fig. 13.16. Effective mass of electrons in germanium at 4°K for magnetic field directions in a (110) plane; the theoretical curves are calculated with $m_l = 1.58m$; $m_t = 0.082m$. (After Dresselhaus, Kip, and Kittel.)

two effective masses, and we speak of light and heavy holes. There is some anisotropy, easily apparent for the heavy hole (Fig. 13.18). The energy surfaces are of the form

$$(13.79) \quad E(k) = Ak^2 \pm [B^2k^4 + C^2(k_x^2 k_y^2 + k_y^2 k_z^2 + k_z^2 k_x^2)]^{1/2},$$

where the constants have the approximate values, in units $\hbar^2/2m$,

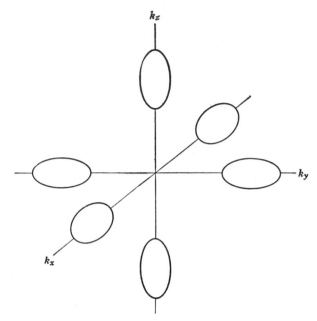

Fig. 13.17.   Constant energy ellipsoids for electrons in silicon, $m^*_l/m^*_t = 5$.

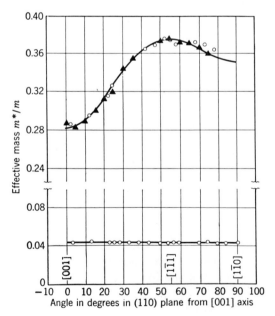

Fig. 13.18.   Effective mass of holes in germanium at 4°K for magnetic field directions in a (110) plane.

Si: $A = -4.1 \pm 0.2$; $|B| = 1.6 \pm 0.2$; $|C| = 3.3 \pm 0.5$;
Ge: $A = -13.0 \pm 0.2$; $|B| = 8.9 \pm 0.1$; $|C| = 10.3 \pm 0.2$.

The choice of sign in (13.79) distinguishes the two masses. Roughly speaking, the holes in germanium have masses $0.04m$ and $0.3m$; in silicon, $0.16m$ and $0.5m$.

The two hole masses arise in this way: at the center of the Brillouin zone ($\mathbf{k} = 0$) the bands formed from a p level of the isolated atoms have the three-fold orbital degeneracy characteristic of p states, so we might expect three valence bands coincident at $\mathbf{k} = 0$ and exhibiting three effective masses. However, we recall that in the isolated atom the spin-orbit interaction energy of the form $\mathbf{L} \cdot \mathbf{S}$ splits the p level into states $p_{3/2}$ and $p_{1/2}$ with total angular momentum $J = \frac{3}{2}$ and $\frac{1}{2}$, respectively, according to the relative orientation of the orbital and spin angular momenta. In the valence band the states associated with the $p_{3/2}$ level are uppermost and form the valence band edge. Of the three bands coincident at $\mathbf{k} = 0$ without spin-orbit interaction, two bands remain with the $p_{3/2}$ level, and one band connected with the $p_{1/2}$ level is lowered in energy by the amount of the spin-orbit interaction energy. In germanium the spin-orbit splitting of the valence band states is of the order of 0.2 ev. The two bands connected with the $p_{3/2}$ level give rise to the two hole masses observed.

In InSb the electron effective mass is isotropic and approximately equal to $0.014m$. The low value of the effective mass is a consequence, recalling (11.35), of the low value of the energy gap, which is only 0.18 ev. in InSb.

RADIATION DAMAGE IN SEMICONDUCTORS

Lattice defects are produced in crystals when they are irradiated by high energy particles. The principal effect of irradiation often is to displace atoms of the crystal from regular lattice positions to interstitial positions, creating in this way vacancies and interstitial atoms. Semiconductor crystals may be excellent vehicles for the study of the effects of radiation damage, as shown by the pioneer work of Lark-Horovitz and co-workers[24] using deuterons, alpha particles, fast neu-

[24] Lark-Horovitz, Bleuler, Davis, and Tendam, Phys. Rev. **73**, 1256 (1948); Davis, Johnson, Lark-Horovitz, and Siegel, Phys. Rev. **74**, 1255 (1948); Johnson and Lark-Horovitz, Phys. Rev. **76**, 442 (1949); Cleland, Crawford, Lark-Horovitz, Pigg, and Young, Phys. Rev. **83**, 312 (1951); E. Klontz and K. Lark-Horovitz, Phys. Rev. **82**, 763 (1951); Lark-Horovitz, Becker, Davis, and Fan, Phys. Rev. **78**, 334 (1950); Becker, Fan, and Lark-Horovitz, Phys. Rev. **85**, 730 (1952); H. Y. Fan and K. Lark-Horovitz, Proceedings of the Conference on Crystalline Solids. Bristol, 1954, pp. 232–245.

trons, and electrons. The electrical properties of semiconductors in the impurity (extrinsic) range are highly sensitive, as we have seen, to the concentration of donors and acceptors. It has been found that the effect of irradiation in germanium is dominated by the acceptors produced, so that it is possible to convert the conductivity type of an n-type specimen to p-type by a low concentration ($\sim 1:10^7$, depending on the specimen) of radiation-induced defects. In Fig. 13.19 we show

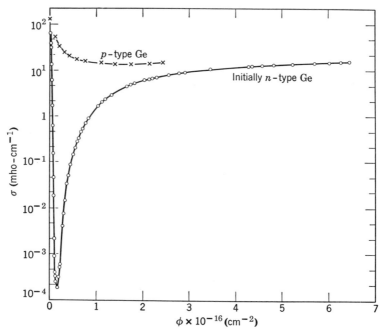

Fig. 13.19. Conductivity of germanium specimens originally n- and p-type as a function of the integrated deuteron flux to which the specimens have been exposed. (After Purdue group.)

the variation of conductivity of germanium specimens, one originally p-type and the other originally n-type, as a function of the integrated flux of deuterons to which the specimens have been exposed. The decrease of conductivity of the p-Ge is caused by the production of lattice defects which provide additional scattering. The variation of conductivity of the specimen initially n-type is attributed to the production of acceptors which gradually with increasing irradiation compensate the initial donor excess in the specimen, thereby converting the specimen to p-type. The conductivity minimum shown in the figure marks approximately the point of optimum compensation with $n \approx p$. Under further bombardment the specimen becomes more conducting as the total carrier concentration increases. Reference may be made to Problem 13.2.

Klontz and Lark-Horovitz have used electron irradiation to determine the threshold energy transfer to a germanium atom to produce an effect. They find 30 ev are required: this is compatible with estimates of the energy required to displace a germanium atom from its normal lattice position to an interstitial position. It is found in silicon that the majority carrier concentrations in both n- and p-type specimens decrease steadily with irradiation and become nearly intrinsic, with resistivity over 10^4 ohm-cm at room temperature. This behavior requires both donor and acceptor states to be produced, but the effect of the states depends on the position of the Fermi level. James and Lark-Horovitz[25] have proposed that each vacancy gives two acceptor levels and each interstitial atom gives two donor levels. Magnetic susceptibility measurements by Stevens[26] and co-workers show no detectable paramagnetic contribution in germanium following fast neutron irradiation, and it may be concluded that the acceptors active here are filled usually by pairs of carriers with antiparallel spin orientation.

PROBLEMS

13.1. Indium antimonide has $E_g = 0.18$ ev; $\epsilon = 17$; $m_e = 0.014m$. Calculate (a) the donor ionization energy; (b) the radius of the ground state orbit. (c) At what minimum donor concentration will appreciable overlap effects between the orbits of adjacent impurity atoms occur? (d) If $N_d = 1 \times 10^{14}$ cm^{-3} for a particular specimen, calculate the concentration of conduction electrons at 4°K. (e) For the same specimen, what temperature divides the region leading in the limit to (13.37) from the region leading in the limit to (13.40)?

13.2. (a) Discuss the phenomenon of impurity compensation, which is the reduction of carrier concentration and conductivity in a semiconductor initially of one conductivity type (n or p) by the addition of impurities of the other type.

(b) Suppose $N_d = 10^{17}$ cm^{-3} in a germanium specimen at room temperature; estimate n before and after adding $N_a = 10^{17}$ cm^{-3}. Assume $m_e = m_h$ and equal ionization energies for donors and acceptors.

(c) Does a nearly intrinsic resistivity prove the specimen is pure? Why?

13.3. The mobility of electrons is 3600 cm^2/v-sec and for holes 1600 cm^2/v-sec in a sample of germanium. This sample shows no Hall effect. What fraction of the current is carried by holes?

13.4. A semiconductor has 10^{18} acceptors per cubic centimeter. The energy level of these acceptors is 0.5 ev above the valence band of the crystal. If the mobility of holes in this band is 100 cm^2/v-sec, calculate the conductivity of the material at room temperature (300°K) and at the temperature of liquid oxygen (90°K).

[25] H. M. James and K. Lark-Horovitz, Z. phys. Chem. **198**, 107 (1951).

[26] D. K. Stevens, J. W. Cleland, J. H. Crawford, Jr., and H. C. Schweinler, Phys. Rev. **100**, 1084 (1955).

13.5. Show that, if N_a, N_d are comparable and both large in comparison with $n_+{}^0$, $n_-{}^0$, then

$$\frac{n}{p} \cong \left(\frac{m_e}{m_h}\right)^{3/2} \frac{N_d \ e^{-E_d/kT}}{N_a \ e^{-E_a/kT}},$$

where E_d, E_a are the donor and acceptor ionization energies, respectively.

13.6. Discuss the present interpretation of the conductivity of oxides of transition metals. (See the paper by E. J. W. Verwey in the book edited by Henisch cited in the References.)

13.7. Cuprous oxide, Cu_2O, is usually a p-type semiconductor in the impurity range. This circumstance is attributed to a stoichiometric deficiency of one of the components. (a) Which component must be missing in order to account for the conductivity type? Such a semiconductor is called a deficit semiconductor.

(b) Cuprous oxide in thin sections is red by transmitted light. Why?

13.8. Why do silicon and germanium look silvery and rather like metals to the eye, whereas diamond does not?

13.9. Discuss the phenomenon of plasma resonance.

REFERENCES

Battelle Memorial Institute, *Abstracts of the literature on semiconductor and luminescent materials and their applications*, 1953 issue, John Wiley & Sons, New York, 1955.

A. Coblenz and H. L. Owens, *Transistors: theory and applications*, McGraw-Hill, New York, 1955.

H. Y. Fan, "Valence semiconductors," *Solid state physics* **1**, 284 (1955).

R. H. Fowler, *Statistical mechanics*, Cambridge University Press, Cambridge 2nd ed., 1936, Chapter 11.

H. K. Henisch, editor, *Semiconducting materials*, Butterworths Scientific Publications, London, 1951.

International Conference on Semiconductors, Amsterdam, 1954, proceedings reprinted in Physica **20**, No. 11 (1954).

D. H. Menzel, editor, *Fundamental formulas of physics*, Prentice-Hall, New York, 1955: Chapter 25, "Solid State," C. Herring.

N. F. Mott and R. W. Gurney, *Electronic processes in ionic crystals*, Clarendon Press, Oxford, 2nd ed., 1950.

Present status of physics, American Association for the Advancement of Science, 1954: K. Lark-Horovitz, pp. 57–127; J. Bardeen, pp. 128–149. The paper by Lark-Horovitz contains an exceptionally full bibliography.

W. Shockley, *Electrons and holes in semiconductors*, Van Nostrand, New York, 1950.

E. Spenke, *Elektronische Halbleiter*, Springer, Wiesbaden, 1955.

Transistor Issue, Proc. I.R.E. **40**, No. 11 (November, 1952).

A. H. Wilson, *Semiconductors and metals; an introduction to the electron theory of metals*, Cambridge University Press, Cambridge, 1939.

14

Semiconductor Rectifiers and Transistors

In this chapter we discuss the physical principles of rectification and transistor action. The barrier layer rectifier is treated first, followed by the p-n junction rectifier and the point contact and junction transistors. The junction devices are in many respects easiest to discuss quantitatively, but the barrier rectifier and point contact transistor are of practical and historical importance. Thus, the development of the high-back-voltage germanium rectifier by S. Benzer at Purdue Universtity in 1942 was an important step toward the ultimate development of the transistor. We begin with a short section on the preparation of germanium crystals.

PREPARATION OF GERMANIUM CRYSTALS

Several semiconductor materials have been purified to a very high degree; high purification is required by the sensitivity of conductivity and lifetime to minute concentrations of certain impurity atoms. It has been said that the germanium used in transistor electronics is the purest of all chemical substances prepared in solid form. Such germanium is pure to one atom in 10^{10} with respect to a number of relevant impurities, including elements from columns III and V of the periodic table which act as acceptors or donors and elements such as Cu, Fe, and Ni which act as recombination centers. Other impurities may be present in higher concentrations. The figure quoted corresponds to a density of impurities of 10^{12} per cm^3; this density in a gas would give a pressure of less than 10^{-5} mm of mercury.

The most important process in the purification of germanium is that of zone purification, or zone melting, developed by Pfann.[1] We discuss this method because of the possible wide field of application to other crystals.

The application of the zone-melting process to germanium depends on the fact that most impurities in germanium prefer to remain in the

[1] W. G. Pfann, J. Metals **4,** 747, 861 (1952); C. H. L. Goodman, Science News, **39,** 26 (1956).

liquid phase rather than freeze into the solid phase. If we can progressively pass a melted section along an otherwise solid germanium rod the impurities will collect in the melted section. They will be swept along and concentrated in one end of the rod. A short section of this end is discarded when the process has been completed.

In the zone-melting process the ingot of germanium is placed in a carbon boat in an inert atmosphere. A short section of the ingot is melted by induction heating, using an r-f coil, as in Fig. 14.1. The boat is pulled through the coil at the rate of a few inches an hour, thus passing the molten section from one end of the ingot to the other, collecting impurities as it moves.

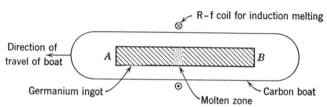

Fig. 14.1.   Molten zone purification of a germanium ingot.   The section near the r-f coil is molten.   Many impurities segregate preferentially in the molten material. A molten zone starting near *A* can be passed along to *B* by moving the boat to the left as indicated.   Impurities will then collect near *B*.

The zone-purified germanium is crystallized into single crystal ingots by a process called crystal pulling, otherwise known as the Czochralski technique. A germanium seed crystal is lowered into molten purified germanium in a crucible, as in Fig. 14.2. The seed is withdrawn slowly from the melt; the molten germanium adheres to the seed and on solidification forms a single crystal. The seed is usually rotated at about 100 rpm. The final crystal may weigh several pounds. For further details of the manufacture of transistor materials the reader is referred to Chapter 13 of the book by Coblenz and Owens listed at the end of the chapter and also to the two volumes entitled *Transistor technology*.

BARRIER RECTIFICATION

A rectifier[2] is a device which has a current-voltage characteristic asymmetrical with respect to voltage, as shown for example in Fig. 14.3. The rectification process requires a low conductivity barrier layer at the contact between two materials of different conductivity, usually a metal and a semiconductor. A rectifier is always of asymmetrical

    [2] For details on ordinary (non-junction) rectifiers, the book by Torrey and Whitmer listed at the end of the chapter is recommended.

Fig. 14.2.   Germanium crystal being pulled from a furnace.   (Courtesy of United
States Army, Signal Corps Engineering Laboratory.)

construction, whether by choice of materials, form of the contacts, or surface treatment.

It is easier to understand the physics of rectification by considering first an insulating barrier between two metals that differ in work function.   The contact is assembled as shown in Fig. 14.4.   The relative positions of the energy bands are determined after equilibrium has

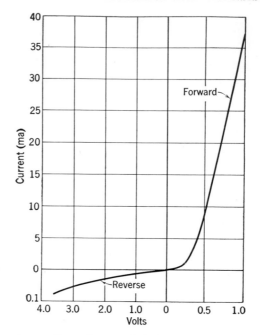

Fig. 14.3.   Current vs. voltage characteristic for a copper oxide rectifier; note the change of scale of the axes about the origin.

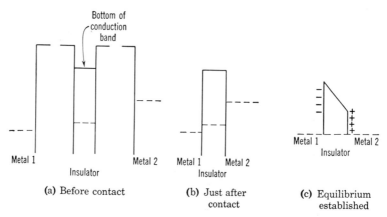

Fig. 14.4.   Formation of a rectifying barrier between two metals of different work function.   The broken line indicates the position of the Fermi level, which must be constant in thermal equilibrium when contact is established.

been established by the principle that *the Fermi levels must be equal for elements in contact.* This important result is derived in Appendix N.

Immediately after the contact is made in (b) of Fig. 14.4 electrons will flow over the top of the insulating barrier—that is, through the vacant conduction band of the insulator—preferentially in the direction $2 \rightarrow 1$ because the electrons in the conduction band of metal 2 are closer to the top of the barrier. The flow continues until a double layer of charge as shown in (c) is built up, bringing the Fermi levels of the two metals into coincidence. The positive charge in metal 2 results from the electron deficiency now existing there. When the Fermi levels are equal, there is no longer a net flow of electrons, and equilibrium obtains.

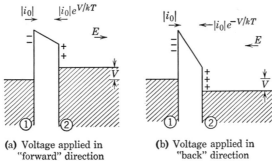

(a) Voltage applied in "forward" direction

(b) Voltage applied in "back" direction

Fig. 14.5. Effect of an applied voltage on the current flow through the contact of Fig. 14.4, exhibiting the origin of rectification. In (a) the electrons flow from 2 to 1 with low resistance; in (b) the electrons flow from 2 to 1 with high resistance; the resistance to electrons flowing from 1 to 2 is the same in both (a) and (b).

The effect of applying a voltage to the contact is shown in Fig. 14.5. In (a) the conduction band is raised on one side, favoring the emission of electrons from the metal of lower work function to the metal of higher work function. In (b) the voltage is reversed and the current flow is greatly reduced. To get significant rectification, $e \times$ the applied voltage must be comparable with kT, which is 0.026 ev at room temperature. It should be noted that the height of the barrier as viewed from metal 1 is independent of the applied voltage.

Many rectifiers are based on the rectifying barrier formed between a metal and a semiconductor, as shown in Fig. 14.6. The Fermi levels here are brought into coincidence in part by electrons flowing from donor impurity levels in the semiconductor to the metal and in part by surface state effects not considered here.[3] The positively

---

[3] We should note there is evidence that some semiconductors, including germanium and silicon, form a natural barrier layer as a result of surface states, even in

ionized impurity levels form an electrical double layer by attracting electrons in the metal toward the contact. The region in the semiconductor which is practically stripped of conduction electrons is known as the *barrier layer*. The conductivity of the barrier layer will be reduced by the removal of electrons, and it will have all the properties of an insulating barrier, as required for rectification.

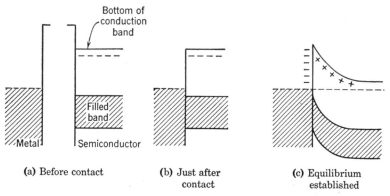

(a) Before contact   (b) Just after contact   (c) Equilibrium established

Fig. 14.6.   Rectifying barrier between a metal and an *n*-type semiconductor. The Fermi level is shown as a broken line.

Over most of the potential curve of the barrier layer $eV \gg kT$, so that the density of conduction electrons may be supposed to be zero in this region for the purpose of estimating the form of the potential variation.   Now

$$(14.1) \qquad \operatorname{div} D = 4\pi\rho,$$

or, for the potential ϕ, taking e as positive here,

$$(14.2) \qquad \frac{\partial^2 \phi}{\partial x^2} = \frac{4\pi N e}{\epsilon},$$

assuming N ionized donor atoms per unit volume in the barrier layer. As the solution of (14.2) is

$$(14.3) \qquad \phi = \frac{2\pi N e}{\epsilon} x^2,$$

the thickness D of the barrier layer for a potential drop of ϕ_0 is

$$(14.4) \qquad D = (\epsilon \phi_0 / 2\pi e N)^{\frac{1}{2}}.$$

the absence of a metallic contact; see J. Bardeen, Phys. Rev. **71**, 717 (1947).   The discussion here of the exhaustion layer theory of rectification is due to W. Schottky, Z. Physik **118**, 539 (1942).

Taking $N = 10^{18}$ cm^{-3}, $\epsilon = 12$, $\phi_0 = 0.5$ volt, we find $D \approx 3 \times 10^{-6}$ cm. The barrier layer thus formed plays the part of the insulating layer in Fig. 14.5; the greater part of any voltage drop across the contact takes place in the barrier.

The current-voltage relationship for the rectifying contact illustrated in Figs. 14.5 and 14.4 may be derived easily. If $\bar{v}$ is the average velocity of an electron, the number striking a unit area of the barrier from the left in unit time is $\frac{1}{4}N\bar{v}$, using a result of elementary kinetic theory. Here N is the electron concentration. The electric current density incident on the barrier from the left is then $\frac{1}{4}Ne\bar{v}$. The current crossing the barrier from left to right is just this quantity times $e^{-e\phi_0/kT}$, as this factor gives the probability that an electron will have energy in excess of the barrier energy $e\phi_0$. The current density across the barrier in the opposite direction, from right to left, is given by $\frac{1}{4}Ne\bar{v}e^{-e(\phi_0-V)/kT}$ when the voltage V is applied across the contact. The situation is made plain by the currents shown in Fig. 14.3. The net current density across the barrier is given by the difference between the separate currents, or

$$(14.5) \qquad j = \tfrac{1}{4}Ne\bar{v}e^{-e\phi_0/kT}(e^{eV/kT} - 1).$$

When eV is negative and larger in magnitude than kT, the current density is small and approximately equal to $\frac{1}{4}Ne\bar{v}e^{-e\phi_0/kT}$. This current in the back or reverse direction is substantially independent of the applied voltage in the assumed range. When eV is positive the current is given essentially by $\frac{1}{4}Ne\bar{v}e^{-e\phi_0/kT}e^{eV/kT}$. The forward current may be very large if $eV/kT \gg 1$. The expression (14.5) is of the general form of the experimental results; see, for example, Fig. 14.3.

p-n JUNCTION RECTIFICATION

It is possible to produce in several ways a germanium or silicon crystal in which there are both *p*-type and *n*-type regions, with a very thin interface between them. The interface between the different regions is called a *p-n* junction. Such junctions have important electrical properties,[4] including rectification and transistor action; the theory of the *p-n* junction is basic to a large amount of the development of transistor physics.

Suitable junctions in germanium have been prepared in several ways. They were first prepared by the crystal-pulling process[5] in which a

[4] W. Shockley, Bell System Tech. J. **28**, 435 (1949); Proc. I.R.E. **40**, 1289 (1952); Am. Scientist **42**, 41 (1954); see also L. Sosnowski, Phys. Rev. **72**, 641 (1947); B. Davydov, J. Tech. Phys. (U.S.S.R.) **5**, 87 (1938).

[5] G. K. Teal, M. Sparks, and E. Buehler, Phys. Rev. **81**, 637 (1951).

crystal is pulled slowly from a melt of molten germanium as the crystal is being grown.   If the melt initially has an excess of donor impurities the crystal will be n type.   At a certain stage of the process acceptor impurities are suddenly added to the melt, and the part of the crystal grown subsequently will be p type.   The acceptors are introduced in such concentration that they overcompensate the donors, as in Fig. 14.7.   The right half of the crystal shown contains donors; the left half contains both donors and acceptors with the acceptors present in greater abundance.   Most of the acceptors are un-ionized and are not shown in the figure.   In the alloy process for the produc-

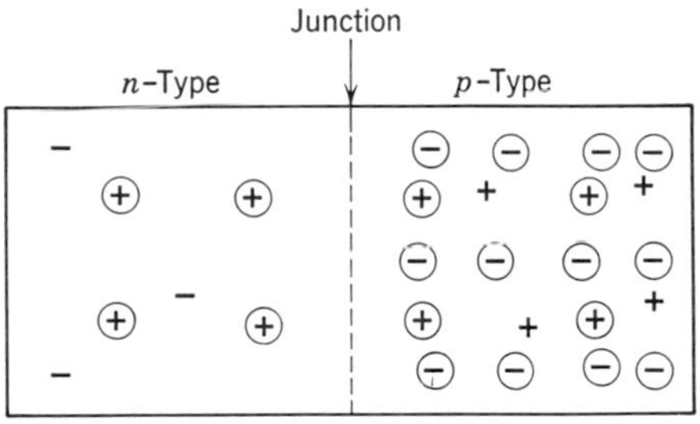

Fig. 14.7.   A p-n junction comprising a p-type region produced by overcompensation.   The circles indicate ionized impurity atoms; un-ionized impurity atoms are not shown.   (After Shockley.)

tion of junctions a small pellet of indium (for example) is placed on a crystal of n-type germanium.   On heating the indium melts and dissolves some germanium; on subsequent cooling most of the dissolved germanium precipitates on the main body of germanium forming a regrowth layer heavily doped with indium and consequently p type. A third process for the production of junctions is the rate-grown method[6] which depends on the circumstance that the solubility of antimony (particularly) in solid germanium increases with the rate of growth of the crystal.   When the crystal growth rate is large, the crystal is rich in antimony and is n type; when the growth rate is slow, the more soluble acceptor impurities are dominant and the crystal is p type.   Alternate regions of n- and p-type germanium may be produced by cycling the growth rate of the crystal.   A fourth method, known as the diffusion method, consists of heating a specimen in a gaseous atmosphere of donors or acceptors at high temperature so that the impurities from the atmosphere diffuse into the specimen.   The solar battery is made in silicon by this technique and is the most efficient converter of solar energy to electrical power [(electrical energy

[6] R. N. Hall, Phys. Rev. **88**, 139 (1952).

output) divided by (total incident solar energy) equals 12%] yet developed. The highest frequency transistors thus far made also use this method, in accordance with an invention made by Dacey, Lee, and Shockley to produce the base layer, and are known as diffused base transistors.

The actual thickness of the transition region between *n*- and *p*-type material should be small in comparison with the diffusion length, the distance that a carrier diffuses in a lifetime. We saw in (13.55) that the diffusion length L_p of holes in germanium at room temperature is 0.2 cm for a hole lifetime of 1 millisecond. If the lifetime were as low as 0.1 microsecond, the diffusion length would drop to the order of 10^{-3} cm and the device applications would suffer. We see, therefore, that there is a lower limit to the lifetime that carriers in a semiconductor may have if the material is to be made into *p-n* junctions or transistors.

We shall first give a qualitative description of the operation of a *p-n* junction as a rectifier before going into the quantitative details. In a crystal containing a *p-n* junction we expect that in thermal equilibrium the conduction electrons contributed by the donors will be found chiefly in the *n* region where the electrons neutralize the space charge of the donor ions, while similarly the holes contributed by the acceptor ions will be found chiefly in the *p* region. It is not possible for the electrons and holes to remain entirely separated in this way unless an electric field exists in the junction region of the crystal in equilibrium—without an electric field the electrons and holes would intermix by diffusion. If we suppose that initially there is no electric field across the junction, holes will diffuse in one direction leaving behind on one side of the junction negatively charged acceptor ions, while electrons will diffuse in the opposite direction leaving behind positively charged donor ions. This initial diffusion will therefore establish an electrostatic dipole layer at the junction, with an associated electric field in a sense which opposes further diffusion across the junction.

Because of the possibility of recombination of a hole and an electron, with the simultaneous emission of phonons or photons, there will be a small flow of holes from the *p* region into the *n* region, the holes ending their lives by recombination. This flow will be balanced by holes which are generated in the *n* region by thermal fluctuations and which diffuse to the *p* region. In equilibrium the recombination and thermal generation hole currents are equal and opposite, as shown in Fig. 14.8a.

We are now in a position to demonstrate the rectification action of a *p-n* junction. For reverse voltage bias (Fig. 14.8b), negative voltage

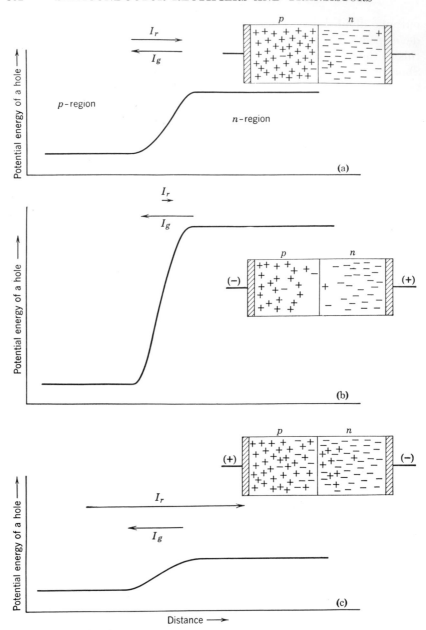

Fig. 14.8.   Dependence of recombination I_r and generation I_g hole currents across a p-n junction upon applied voltage bias.   The inserts show the distribution of current carriers.   (a) Thermal equilibrium, no bias.   (b) Reverse bias.   (c) Forward bias.   (After Shockley.)

is applied to the p region and positive to the n region, so that the potential difference between the two regions is increased. Now practically no holes can climb the potential hill, and the recombination current I_r drops to a very small value; I_g is not much affected by the reverse bias, as the distance a hole diffuses in its lifetime is large compared with the width of the dipole layer at the junction. When a forward bias V is applied (Fig. 14.8c), I_r increases according to the relation

(14.6) $$I_r = I_g e^{eV/kT}$$

from the Boltzmann distribution law; we note that for zero bias $I_r = I_g$, as required for equilibrium. The net current of holes from the p region to the n region is given by the difference (compare Eq. 14.5)

(14.7) $$I_r - I_g = I_g(e^{eV/kT} - 1).$$

This current is zero when $V = 0$, increases exponentially to large values for positive eV, and decreases when eV is negative toward a negative saturation value $-I_g$.

The electron current flowing across the junction behaves similarly. The applied voltage which lowers the height of the barrier for holes also lowers it for electrons, so that large numbers of electrons flow from the n region to the p region under the same voltage conditions that produce large hole currents in the opposite direction. We note that the electrical currents add; the total current, including the effects of both holes and electrons, is given by

(14.8) $$I = I_s(e^{eV/kT} - 1),$$

where I_s is the sum of the two generation currents. As shown in Fig. 14.9, this equation is well satisfied for p-n junctions in germanium. The diffusion theory of rectification in p-n junctions developed above has also been checked experimentally by photoelectric experiments by Goucher and co-workers.

We now estimate the value of the saturation or generation current I_s. A detailed analysis of the problem has been given by Shockley; the analysis supports a quite simple picture of events in the neighborhood of the barrier. Let us consider first the hole generation current density which we denote by j_{ps}. We assume the junction region is thin in comparison with the diffusion length, and so recombination within the junction proper may be neglected. The holes under consideration are generated in the n region (Fig. 14.8) and diffuse over to the p region. The current carried by these holes is equal approx-

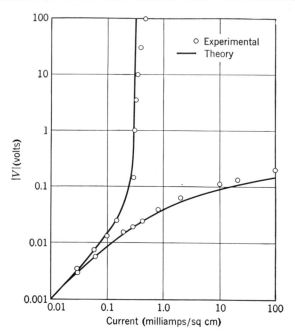

Fig. 14.9.   Rectification characteristic for a p-n junction in germanium.   (After Shockley.)

imately to the charge $|e|$ times the equilibrium hole density p_n in the n region times the mean diffusion velocity v_p, which we may take to be of the order of the diffusion length $L_p = (D_p\tau_p)^{\frac{1}{2}}$ divided by the lifetime τ_p.   Thus

$$(14.9) \qquad v_p = (D_p\tau_p)^{\frac{1}{2}}/\tau_p = D_p/L_p,$$

and may be of the order of 200 cm/sec for holes at room temperature in germanium having a lifetime of 10^{-3} sec.   The hole generation current density is then

$$(14.10) \qquad j_{ps} \approx p_n|e|D_p/L_p = p_n\mu_p kT/L_p,$$

using the Einstein relation $D = \mu kT/e$.

We can derive (14.10) from a slightly different viewpoint.   The equilibrium value p_n of the hole density in the n region holds nearly up to the edge of the n side of the junction region.   If now a potential V is applied across the barrier, the hole concentration just at the n side of the barrier becomes $p_n e^{eV/kT}$, which is an increase over the equilibrium value by the quantity

$$(14.11) \qquad p_0 = p_n(e^{eV/kT} - 1).$$

As we go farther into the n region the excess non-equilibrium hole concentration varies because of recombination as

(14.12) $$p = p_0 e^{-x/L_p},$$

according to (13.52). The diffusion current density is

(14.13) $$j_p = -|e| D_p \operatorname{grad} p = (|e| D_p/L_p)p,$$

which at the junction has the value

(14.14) $$j_p = (p_n |e| D_p/L_p)(e^{eV/kT} - 1).$$

Thus the net current density across the junction is

(14.15) $$j = j_n + j_p = [(p_n|e| D_p/L_p) + (n_p|e| D_n/L_n)](e^{eV/kT} - 1) \equiv j_s(e^{eV/kT} - 1),$$

in agreement with (14.8) and (14.10). It is seen that the current in the reverse direction is low if both diffusion lengths L_p and L_n are long. It should be noted that the current reaches its "saturation" value j_s when V is several times $kT/e = -0.026$ volt at room temperature, and that the rectification ratio is $e \cong 2.73$ for $V = \pm kT/e$. For somewhat smaller values of V, the junction is substantially an ohmic resistance. These characteristics, which actual p-n junctions possess quite precisely, are a consequence of the fact that the current carriers have a charge of one electron. In fact p-n junctions have as good rectification curves as it is possible to have for simple structures using carriers of one electron charge.

POINT CONTACT TRANSISTORS

The point contact transistor, discovered by Bardeen and Brattain,[7] is the first semiconductor device which performs the functions of a vacuum tube triode, such as amplification and modulation. It is now possible to build advanced types of electronic circuits entirely without vacuum tubes, using semiconductor rectifiers and triodes, with benefit from the absence of filament current, reduced size and weight, and increased life. Germanium is generally employed in transistors because the mobilities are higher in germanium than in any other common semiconductor; silicon is employed when stability over a wide range of temperature is required.

There are now a number of different types of transistors. We discuss first the original version of Bardeen and Brattain, known as type A. It consists of a small block of n-type germanium as shown in

[7] J. Bardeen and W. H. Brattain, Phys. Rev. **75**, 1208 (1949).

Fig. 14.10, with a large area base contact and with two closely spaced point contacts with a separation of the order of 0.01 cm.   The emitter point is normally biased in the forward (low resistance) direction of current flow, and the collector point is biased in the back (high resistance) direction.

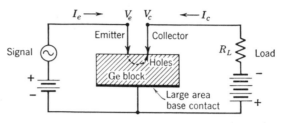

Fig. 14.10.   Schematic drawing of a point-contact transistor with a circuit for amplification of an a-c signal.   The convention regarding the signs of the currents is shown.   The normal bias is I_e, V_e positive; I_c, V_c negative.

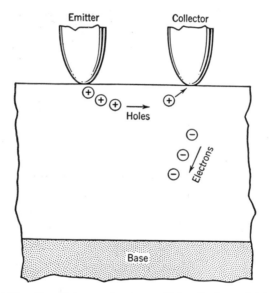

Fig. 14.11.   Transistor mechanism.   (After Ryder and Kircher.)

   Transistor action depends on the fact that the current from the emitter is composed largely of positive holes.   The holes are attracted to the collector point by the electric field in the germanium arising from the current flowing to the collector which has a strong negative voltage bias, as shown in Fig. 14.11.   While the holes are inside the rectifying barrier region next to the collector point they modify the barrier

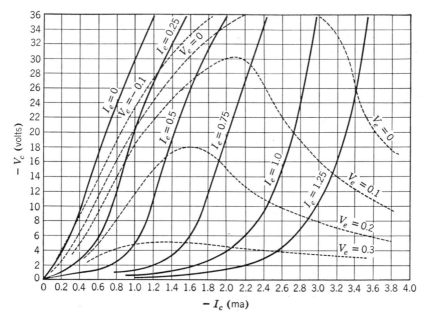

Fig. 14.12.   Characteristics of a type A experimental transistor.   (After Bardeen
and Brattain.)

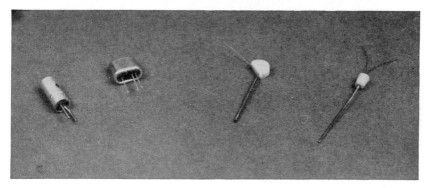

Fig. 14.13.   Point contact and junction transistors.   (Courtesy of the Bell
Telephone Laboratories, Inc.)

rectification properties.   Only a little hole current is required before
the concentration of holes near the collector becomes substantially
greater than the normal concentration of conduction electrons in
the germanium.   The modification of the collector barrier by the holes
injected by the emitter makes possible modulation of the collector
current by the emitter current.   The current amplification factor α is

defined by

$$(14.16) \qquad \alpha = -(\partial I_c/\partial I_e)_{V_c = \text{const}}$$

and is found to have values of the order of 2.   The power amplification may be quite large, of the order of 20 db or more, because the collector current flows in the high resistance direction.   Even without current amplification, it still is possible to have power amplification. Characteristics of a type A transistor are shown in Fig. 14.12.   Point contact and junction transistors are illustrated in Fig. 14.13.

JUNCTION TRANSISTORS

Shockley, Sparks, and Teal[8] have described an important type of transistor in which transistor action takes place within the germanium at the junctions between regions of n-type and p-type conductivity. Such junction transistor action had been predicted by Shockley[9] earlier on the basis of the diffusion theory of p-n junctions.   An n-p-n transistor is shown in Fig. 14.14.   When the unit is used as an amplifier, the junction J_c is biased in the "reverse" direction as shown in the figure; therefore electrons in the collector region are not encouraged to move to the base region; similarly holes are held in the base region.   Electrons in the emitter region may easily enter the base region and then may diffuse to the right p-n junction.   The flow over the potential barrier may be varied by applying a variable potential to the emitter while keeping the base at a constant potential.   The emitter region is made more highly conducting than the base region, so that most of the current across the left n-p junction consists of electrons moving to the right, rather than holes moving to the left. Under these conditions the behavior of the device is closely analogous to that of a vacuum tube: the emitter region corresponds to the cathode, the base to the region around the grid, and the collector to the plate.

When the collector electrode is biased positively with respect to the base electrode ("reverse" direction for collector p-n junction), only a small back current of electrons and holes will diffuse across the collector barrier.   If now the emitter n-p barrier is biased negatively (in the forward direction) with respect to the base, a relatively large forward current of electrons will flow across the reduced emitter barrier into the base region.   If the base region is sufficiently thin so that the electrons coming from the emitter do not recombine with holes in the

---

[8] Shockley, Sparks, and Teal, Phys. Rev. **83**, 151 (1951); see also R. L. Wallace, Jr., and W. J. Pietenpol, Bell System Tech. J. **30**, 530 (1951).

[9] W. Shockley, Bell Syst. Tech. J. **28**, 435 (1949).

p-type base region, the electrons will diffuse to the collector barrier. From here they are collected with the help of the collector field. Since the electrons were injected through the low forward impedance and collected through the high reverse impedance of bulk p-n junctions, high voltage amplification will result. Power gains are as high as 50 db. The detailed theory of the n-p-n transistor is given in reference

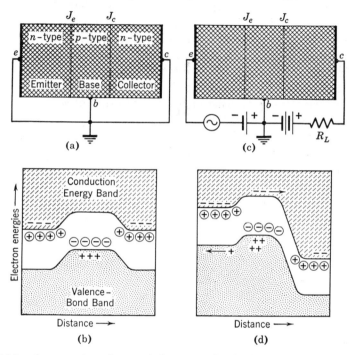

Fig. 14.14. An n-p-n transistor and the energy level scheme: (a) and (b) thermal equilibrium; (c) and (d) biased as an amplifier. The thickness of the base region must be much less than a diffusion length. (After Shockley, Sparks, and Teal.)

8. The theory is simpler than for the type A transistor, as the n-p-n problem is essentially one-dimensional.

In the same sense that a p-n junction is nearly a perfect rectifier at room temperature, a junction transistor is nearly a perfect electronic valve. To be more specific the current in a junction transistor depends on voltage to the maximum degree possible for a device using carriers of one electronic charge. The reason for this is that the current injected across the emitter junction varies with voltage through a Boltzmann factor $\exp (eV/kT)$ for the same reason that it does in a simple p-n junction. Consequently, for a transistor in the operating range at room temperature, the collector current increases by a factor of $e = 2.72$ for each increase of kT/e in the forward voltage across the emitter base junction and this is the highest sensitivity possible for a structure with singly charged current carriers controlled by a potential hill. The properties of p-n junctions permit junction transistors to operate at very low voltage. In fact, a voltage of one or two tenths of a volt across the collector junction will bring the collector current into the saturation range so that the pentode-like characteristic of very high collector impedance is obtained. This high impedance contributes greatly to the high gain of the junction transistor. The modest collector voltage requirement arises from the Boltzmann factor at the collection junction, which leads to saturation at a few times kT/e or a few tenths of a volt just as it does in a simple p-n junction.

The theory of p-n-p transistors is similar to that of n-p-n transistors, the roles of electrons and holes being reversed. The existence of transistors of opposite polarities gives a flexibility of circuit design not possible for vacuum tubes, and advantage has already been taken of this fact by electrical engineers in designing push-pull amplifiers, flip-flop circuits, and the like.

Junction transistors can operate down to very low power levels, of the order of a microwatt, and are therefore well adapted for miniaturization and for battery operation. They are much less noisy than point contact transistors and in many applications are superior to vacuum tubes. These characteristics have led to transistors being used in hearing aids since about 1953 and playing a major role in portable radios in 1956. Compared to point contact transistors, junction transistors enjoy freedom from short circuit instability; the input and output impedances are always positive whether the transistor is connected grounded-emitter, grounded-base, or grounded-collector. The gain is high: power gains of 40 to 50 db per stage are possible. The efficiency is high: in class A operation it is possible to obtain efficiencies of 48 or 49 percent of an ideal 50 percent. The small size of the unit (which is enclosed in a plastic bead $\frac{3}{16}$ inch in diameter) makes for ruggedness. In the audio-frequency range the junction devices are relatively free from microphonics. The power consumption is small: an audio-frequency oscillator may use microwatts of power from the supply, as contrasted with the watts required to heat the filament of an ordinary vacuum tube. The frequency response has been limited to below 1 mc, but the introduction of junctions such as p-n-i-p and n-p-i-n containing a region of intrinsic material makes it possible to extend the frequency range upwards. The reduction of base layer thickness in the diffused base transistor has led to oscillation and power gain at frequencies of several hundred megacycles.

PROBLEMS

14.1. The work function of two metals differs by 2 ev. If these metals are brought into contact, some electrons will flow from one into the other. This phenomenon is entirely limited to the surface of the metal, and it may be assumed that the electrons are displaced over a distance of 3×10^{-8} cm. How many electrons per square centimeter will be transferred?

14.2. Explain in detail the mechanism whereby a p-n junction when illuminated delivers electrical energy to a circuit. This is the principle of the silicon solar battery. [See W. G. Pfann and W. van Roosbroeck, J. Appl. Phys. **25**, 1422 (1954).]

14.3. Discuss and explain the statement, "The resistance of a p-n junction is much greater than the integrated resistivity of the material composing the junction" (Shockley).

14.4. Describe briefly the design and function of the following devices:

(a) Phototransistor.

(b) P-n-i-p junction transistor [see J. M. Early, Bell System Tech. J. **33**, 517 (1954)].

(c) Unipolar transistor [see W. Shockley, Proc. I.R.E. **40**, 1365 (1952); G. C. Dacey and I. M. Ross, Proc. I.R.E. **41**, 970 (1953)].

14.5. The rectification ratio is defined as the ratio of forward current to inverse current at voltages $+|V|$ and $-|V|$, respectively. Find an expression for this ratio for a p-n junction, and plot on semilog paper as a function of $|V|$. The Wagner relationship neglects the bulk resistance of the rectifier.

14.6. Suppose that the excess charge in the dipole layer of a p-n junction varies linearly from plus to minus on passing through the junction. Calculate the excess charge on one side of the junction as a function of the inverse potential V and of the barrier thickness L; show that the capacitance of the junction varies as $V^{-\frac{1}{3}}$.

14.7. Design a simple one-stage transistor amplifier for use in a hearing aid, using the characteristics of a commercial transistor.

REFERENCES

A. Coblenz and H. L. Owens, *Transistors: theory and applications*, McGraw-Hill, New York, 1955.

J. A. Morton, "Present status of transistor development," Bell System Tech. J. **31**, 411 (1952).

M. G. Say, editor, *Crystal rectifiers and transistors*, Newnes, London, 1954.

R. F. Shea, *Transistor circuits*, John Wiley & Sons, New York, 1953.

W. Shockley, *Electrons and holes in semiconductors*, Van Nostrand, New York, 1950.

M. J. O. Strutt, *Transistoren*, Hirzel, Zürich, 1954.

H. C. Torrey and C. A. Whitmer, *Crystal rectifiers*, McGraw-Hill, New York, 1948.

Transistor Issue, Proc. I.R.E. **40**, No. 11 (November, 1952).

Transistor technology, 2 vols., Bell Telephone Laboratories and Western Electric Co., 1952.

15

Ferromagnetism and Antiferromagnetism

We discuss first in this chapter the physical origin and properties of the saturation magnetization in ferromagnetics, and the interpretation of gyromagnetic and spin resonance experiments. The properties of ferromagnetic materials of interest in technical applications are closely related to the domain structure. We develop for simple situations the theory of ferromagnetic domains. An introduction to the behavior of antiferromagnetic substances and ferrites is presented.

CURIE POINT AND THE EXCHANGE INTEGRAL

We call a substance ferromagnetic if it possesses a spontaneous magnetic moment, that is, a magnetic moment even in the absence of an applied magnetic field. The saturation magnetization M_s is defined as the spontaneous magnetic moment per unit volume. In technical literature the saturation flux density $B_s = 4\pi M_s$ is often used. The Curie point T_c is the temperature above which the spontaneous moment vanishes.

If we could add to a paramagnetic substance an interaction tending to make the ionic and atomic magnetic moments line up the same way, we would have a ferromagnetic substance. Let us postulate such an interaction and call it the Weiss field.[1] The orienting effect of the Weiss field is opposed by the motion of thermal agitation of the elementary moments. We consider the Weiss field the equivalent of an effective magnetic field H_E acting on the electron spins. The interaction energy of a spin with the Weiss field must be of the order of magnitude of the thermal energy of a spin at the Curie point. Hence

(15.1)
$$gS\mu_B H_E \approx kT_c,$$

or

(15.2)
$$H_E \approx kT_c/gS\mu_B.$$

[1] Also called the molecular field or the exchange field; Weiss was the first to imagine such a field.

For iron we have $T_c \approx 1000°K$, $g \approx 2$, $S \approx 1$; therefore $H_E \approx 10^{-13}/$ $2 \times 10^{-20} = 5 \times 10^6$ oersteds.   This field is much stronger than that produced by the magnetic moments of the other ions in the crystal, as the magnetic interaction is only $\sim \mu_B/a^3 \sim 10^3$ oersteds, where a is the lattice constant.

Pierre Weiss (1907), inventor of this concept, showed that it will account for several important attributes of ferromagnetism provided that one assumes that the Weiss field H_E is proportional to the magnetization:

$$(15.3) \qquad\qquad H_E = \lambda M,$$

where λ stands for a constant called the Weiss field constant.   The susceptibility above the Curie point is deduced by postulating that the Curie law (9.15) holds if we take as the magnetic field the sum of the applied field H and the Weiss field H_E.   Then

$$(15.4) \qquad\qquad \frac{M}{H + \lambda M} = \frac{C}{T},$$

or

$$(15.5) \qquad\qquad \chi = \frac{M}{H} = \frac{C}{T - C\lambda}.$$

This gives a non-zero magnetization for zero applied field at the Curie point expressed by

$$(15.6) \qquad\qquad T_c = C\lambda,$$

and so

$$(15.7) \qquad\qquad \chi = \frac{C}{T - T_c}.$$

This expression, known as the Curie-Weiss law, describes quite well the observed susceptibility variation in the paramagnetic region above the Curie point.[2]   From (15.6) and the definition (9.15) and (9.23) of the Curie constant C we may determine the value of the Weiss field constant:

$$(15.8) \qquad \lambda^{-1} = C/T_c = Ng^2S(S + 1)\mu_B^2/3kT_c,$$

[2] Experimentally the susceptibility well above the Curie point is given quite accurately by $C/(T - \theta)$, where θ, called the paramagnetic Curie point, may be slightly greater than the actual transition temperature (ferromagnetic Curie point) T_c.

and so for iron, $\lambda \approx (4 \times 10^{-13})/(8 \times 10^{-17}) \approx 5000$, in agreement with the earlier estimate of H_E.

The physical origin of the Weiss field is in the quantum-mechanical exchange integral, as pointed out by Frenkel and Heisenberg. On certain assumptions it can be shown[3] that the energy of interaction of atoms i, j bearing spins S_i, S_j contains a term

$$(15.9) \qquad E_{ex} = -2J\mathbf{S}_i \cdot \mathbf{S}_j,$$

where J is the exchange integral and is related to the overlap of the charge distributions i, j. The exchange energy has no classical analogue, although it is of electrostatic origin. It expresses the difference in Coulomb interaction energy of the systems when the spins are parallel or antiparallel. It is a consequence of the Pauli exclusion principle that in quantum mechanics one cannot usually change the relative direction of two spins without making changes in the spatial charge distribution in the overlap region. The resulting changes in the coulomb energy of the system may conveniently be written in the form[4] (15.9), so that it appears *as if* there were a direct coupling between the spins $\mathbf{S}_i, \mathbf{S}_j$.

We establish an approximate connection between the exchange integral J and the Weiss field constant λ. Suppose that the atom under consideration has z nearest neighbors, each connected with the central atom by the interaction J; for more distant neighbors we take J as zero. Then the interaction energy may be written, neglecting components of $\mathbf{S}$ perpendicular to the average magnetization,

$$E_{ex} \cong -2Jz\bar{S}^2 = -g\bar{S}\mu_B H_E = -g\bar{S}\mu_B \lambda(g\bar{S}\mu_B \Omega^{-1}),$$

where the term in parentheses is equal to M_s; here Ω is the atomic volume. Then

$$(15.10) \qquad J = \lambda g^2 \mu_B{}^2 / 2z\Omega,$$

and, using (15.8) and recalling that $N = 1/\Omega$,

$$(15.11) \qquad J = \frac{3kT_c}{2zS(S+1)},$$

This is the connection, as given by the Weiss field theory, between the exchange integral and the Curie point. More exact quantum statistics

---

[3] This is shown in most texts on quantum theory; see also J. H. Van Vleck, Revs. Modern Phys. **17**, 27 (1945).

[4] Equation (15.9) is really an operator equation in the spin operators $\mathbf{S}_i, \mathbf{S}_j$, but for many purposes in ferromagnetism it is a good approximation to treat the spins as classical vectors.

give somewhat different results.   For a simple cubic lattice ($z = 6$) with $S = \frac{1}{2}$ various calculations give the results below.

	J/kT_c
P. Weiss theory (15.11)	0.333
Opechowski[5]	0.518
P. R. Weiss[6]	0.540

For a body-centered cubic lattice with spin 1, P. R. Weiss calculates $J/kT_c = 0.1502$; substituting $T_c = 1043°$K for iron, we have $J = 160k$.

TEMPERATURE DEPENDENCE OF THE SPONTANEOUS MAGNETIZATION

On the Weiss theory we must use the complete expression (9.21) for the magnetization in calculating the spontaneous magnetization

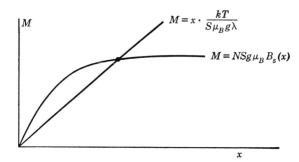

Fig. 15.1.   Method for finding the spontaneous magnetization at a temperature T, according to the Weiss theory.   The value of M_s is given by the intersection of the two curves.

as a function of temperature.   We have

$$(15.12) \qquad M_s = NSg\mu_B B_s(x),$$

where now in the absence of an applied magnetic field

$$(15.13) \qquad x = Sg\mu_B\lambda M_s/kT.$$

At a temperature $T < T_c$ we obtain M_s by plotting M_s vs. x as given by both (15.12) and (15.13) and looking for the intercept of the two curves, as shown in Fig. 15.1.   The Curie point is the highest tempera-

[5] W. Opechowski, Physica **4**, 181 (1937); **6**, 1112 (1939); V. Zehler, Z. Natur-forsch. **5A**, 344 (1950); H. A. Brown and J. M. Luttinger, Phys. Rev. **100**, 673 (1955).

[6] P. R. Weiss, Phys. Rev. **74**, 1493 (1948).

ture for which the curves have an intercept; as defined in this way it is consistent with the earlier result (15.6).

The curves of M_s vs. T obtained in this way reproduce the general features of the experimental results, as shown in Fig. 15.2 for nickel. At low temperatures, $T/T_c \ll 1$, a quantum treatment using the

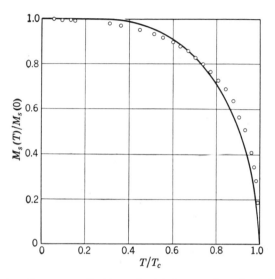

Fig. 15.2. Saturation magnetization of nickel as a function of temperature, together with the theoretical curve for $S = \frac{1}{2}$ on the Weiss theory. [Experimental values by P. Weiss and R. Forrer, Ann. phys. **5**, 153 (1926).]

method of spin waves[7] (Appendix O) predicts

$$(15.14) \qquad M_s(T) = M_s(0)[1 - CT^{3/2} - \cdots],$$

where, for a body-centered cubic structure and spin S,

$$(15.15) \qquad C = (0.0587/2S)(k/2SJ)^{3/2};$$

the constant C should not be confused with the Curie constant. For a face-centered cubic structure the right side of (15.15) is multiplied by $\frac{1}{2}$. Expression (15.14) is known as the Bloch $T^{3/2}$ law; it is in quite good agreement with observation in the very low temperature region. At somewhat higher temperatures a T^2 term is dominant, and it is

[7] Doubts recently expressed about the validity of spin wave theory at low temperatures have been laid to rest by a calculation by F. J. Dyson, Phys. Rev. **102**, 1217 (1956).

explained by Stoner[8] on a collective electron theory. Experimental
values[9] of C follow:

	J (P. R. Weiss		
Substance	C (deg$^{-3/2}$)	J (spin waves)	method)
Iron	3.5×10^{-6}	$205k$ $(S = 1)$	$160k$
Nickel	8.6×10^{-6}	$230k$ $(S = \frac{1}{2})$	....

SPONTANEOUS MAGNETIZATION AT ABSOLUTE ZERO

In Table 15.1 are representative values of the spontaneous magnetization, effective magneton number, and Curie point. The effective magneton number n_{eff} relates to the saturation magnetization,

TABLE 15.1. EFFECTIVE NUMBER n_{eff} OF BOHR MAGNETONS PER MAGNETIC
ATOM, AND DATA ON SATURATION MAGNETIZATION AND CURIE POINTS

(General reference: R. M. Bozorth, *Ferromagnetism*, Van Nostrand, New
York, 1951.)

| Substance | Saturation Magnetization M_s | | n_{eff} (0°K) | Ferromagnetic Curie Temperature (°K) |
	Room temperature	0°K		
Fe	1707	1752	2.221	1043
Co	1400	1446	1.716	1400
Ni	485	510	0.606	631
Gd	1090	1980	7.10	289
Dy	1830(80°K)	....	.....	105
MnBi	600	675	3.52	630
Cu$_2$MnAl	430	(580)	(4.0)	603
Cu$_2$MnIn	500	(600)	(4.0)	506
MnAs	670	870	3.40	318
MnB	147	....	.....	533
Mn$_4$N	183	....	0.24	745
MnSb	710	....	3.53	587
CrTe	240	....	2.39	336
CrO$_2$	(500)	....	2.07	390
MnOFe$_2$O$_3$	358	....	5.0†	783
FeOFe$_2$O$_3$	485	....	4.2†	848
CoOFe$_2$O$_3$	....	....	3.3†	793
NiOFe$_2$O$_3$	240	....	2.3†	863
CuOFe$_2$O$_3$	290	....	1.3†	728
MgOFe$_2$O$_3$	143	....	1.1†	583
UH$_3$	....	230	0.90	180

† Calculated per molecule MOFe$_2$O$_3$, where M is the bivalent cation.

[8] E. C. Stoner, Repts. Prog. Phys. **11**, 43 (1948); Proc. Roy. Soc. (London) **A165**,
372 (1938); see also C. Herring and C. Kittel, Phys. Rev. **81**, 869 (1951).

[9] M. Fallot, Ann. Phys. **6**, 305 (1936); see also E. Kondorski and L. N. Fedotor
Izvest. Akad. Nauk SSSR, Ser. Fiz., **16**, 432 (1952).

and must not be confused with the paramagnetic effective magneton number p defined by (9.24).   Observed magneton numbers are usually considerably smaller than the theoretical values calculated from the free ions and also are frequently non-integral.

It is possible to modify ionic models to account for the results by allowing mixtures of various ionicity.   However, perhaps the most natural way of accounting for the non-integral magneton numbers is

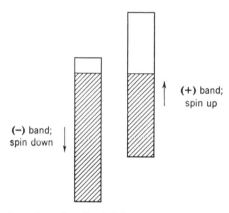

$(-)$ band; spin down

$(+)$ band; spin up

Fig. 15.3.   Schematic explanation (for $3d$ electrons) of non-integral magneton numbers, on the band model.   The $+$ and $-$ bands contain 5 states per atom each. The case of 7 electrons, 4.25 in one band and 2.75 in the other, is shown; the effective magneton number is 1.5.

to abandon the ionic model and to adopt instead a band or collective electron model[10] on which the $3d$ electrons, for example, are visualized as being in two energy bands, as in Fig. 15.3, one for electrons with spin up and the other for electrons with spin down.   The bands are separated in energy by the exchange interaction.   This topic is discussed in detail in Chapter 12.

GYROMAGNETIC AND SPIN RESONANCE EXPERIMENTS

GYROMAGNETIC EXPERIMENTS

Gyromagnetic experiments identify the magnetization in ferromagnetics as arising largely from the electron spin, rather than from the orbital moment.   The magnetomechanical ratio is defined as the

[10] J. C. Slater, Phys. Rev. **49**, 537 (1936); E. C. Stoner, Proc. Roy. Soc. (London) **A165**, 372 (1938); **A169**, 339 (1939); M. F. Manning, Phys. Rev. **63**, 190 (1943); for a recent attempt at an alternative explanation, see C. Zener, Phys. Rev. **81**, 440 (1951); **83**, 299 (1951); **85**, 324 (1952).

ratio of the magnetic moment to the angular momentum. It is useful to equate the ratio to $g'e/2mc$, where g' is called the *magnetomechanical factor*.[11] For an electron spin the magnetic moment is $\mu_B = e\hbar/2mc$, and the angular momentum is $\hbar/2$; the ratio is e/mc, so that $g_{\text{spin}}' = 2$. For orbital motion of an electron the magnetic moment z component is $L_z(e\hbar/2mc)$ and the angular momentum is $L_z\hbar$; therefore $g_{\text{orbit}}' = 1$. The experimental values of g' in ferromagnetic substances are usually between 1.85 and 2.0, showing that the major contribution comes from electron spin.

The two principal gyromagnetic methods are (1) the *Einstein-de Haas method*, in which one reverses the magnetization of a freely suspended specimen and observes the resulting rotation; and (2) the *Barnett method*, in which one rotates the specimen and observes the resulting magnetization.

We shall discuss the Einstein-de Haas method, which is illustrated in Fig. 15.4. If no external torques act on the system during magnetization reversal, and, if the system does not radiate, the total angular momentum change must be zero:

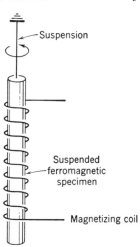

Fig. 15.4. Einstein-de Haas gyromagnetic experiment. When the current in the magnetizing coil is reversed, the magnetization in the specimen is reversed and the specimen rotates.

$$(15.16) \qquad \Delta \mathbf{J} = 0.$$

The total angular momentum is the sum of contributions from spin, orbit, and crystal lattice motions:

$$(15.17) \quad \mathbf{J} = \mathbf{J}_{\text{spin}} + \mathbf{J}_{\text{orbit}} + \mathbf{J}_{\text{lattice}}.$$

We actually observe $\Delta J_{\text{lattice}}$. The magnetic moment change is

$$(15.18) \qquad \Delta \mathfrak{M} = \Delta(\mathfrak{M}_{\text{spin}} + \mathfrak{M}_{\text{orbit}} + \mathfrak{M}_{\text{lattice}}),$$

but the lattice contribution here may be neglected because of the relatively large mass of the positive ions composing the lattice—the positive ions rotate too slowly to produce a significant magnetic moment. Thus what we measure in an experiment is

$$(15.19) \qquad \frac{g'e}{2mc} = \frac{\Delta(\mathfrak{M}_{\text{spin}} + \mathfrak{M}_{\text{orbit}})}{-\Delta J_{\text{lattice}}} = \frac{\Delta(\mathfrak{M}_{\text{spin}} + \mathfrak{M}_{\text{orbit}})}{\Delta(J_{\text{spin}} + J_{\text{orbit}})}$$

[11] This quantity, which is useful for comparison with the microwave resonance experiments, is sometimes called the gyromagnetic ratio, but strictly speaking the gyromagnetic ratio is the reciprocal of the magnetomechanical ratio.

from (15.16) and (15.17). If we suppose that

(15.20) $J_{\text{orbit}}/J_{\text{spin}} = 2\varepsilon,$

we must have

(15.21) $\mathfrak{M}_{\text{orbit}}/\mathfrak{M}_{\text{spin}} = \varepsilon,$

and so, for $\varepsilon \ll 1$,

(15.22) $g' \cong 2(1 - \varepsilon).$

We see that ε is a measure of the extent to which the orbital moment participates in the magnetization. If the orbital moment were completely quenched in the sense of Chapter 9, then $\varepsilon = 0$ and $g' = 2$. Experimental values of g' and ε are given in Table 15.2.

FERROMAGNETIC RESONANCE ABSORPTION

Spin resonance absorption experiments at microwave frequencies in ferromagnetic substances are closely similar in principle to the nuclear and electronic spin resonance experiments described in Chapter 9. The total magnetic moment of the specimen precesses about the direction of the static magnetic field, and energy is absorbed strongly from the r-f transverse field when its frequency is equal to the precessional frequency. We may equally well think of the macroscopic vector representing the total spin of the entire saturated ferromagnet as quantized in the large static field, with energy levels separated by the order of the usual Zeeman frequencies; the selection rule $\Delta m_s = \pm 1$ allows transitions only between adjacent levels.

TABLE 15.2. SUMMARY OF RESULTS OF GYROMAGNETIC EXPERIMENTS

[Reference: S. J. Barnett, Proc. Am. Acad. Arts Sci., **75**, 109 (1944); S. Brown, A. J. P. Meyer, and G. G. Scott, Compt. rend. **238**, 2502 (1954).

Substance	g'	ε (Eq. 15.22)
Iron	1.93	0.04
Cobalt	1.85	0.07
Nickel	1.84–1.92	0.04–0.08
Magnetite, Fe_3O_4	1.93	0.04
Heusler alloy, Cu_2MnAl	2.00	0.00
Permalloy, 78% Ni, 22% Fe	1.90	0.05
Supermalloy	1.91	0.05
FeNi	1.90	0.05

Ferromagnetic resonance was discovered first in experiments by Griffiths.[12] An unusually sharp resonance line (Fig. 15.5) was found

[12] J. H. E. Griffiths, Nature **158**, 670 (1946).

in the Ni-Fe alloy Supermalloy by Yager and Bozorth.[13]   A schematic experimental arrangement is shown in Fig. 15.6.   In the experiments it is found that the apparent g values are often very much higher than

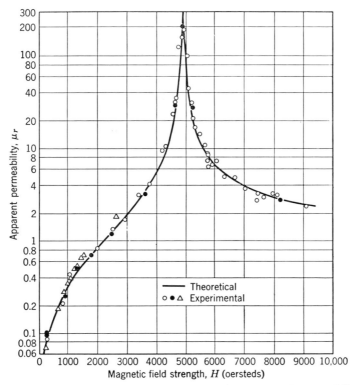

Fig. 15.5.   Resonance curve for Supermalloy, according to Yager and Bozorth; the apparent permeability is plotted on a logarithmic scale.

the free electron g value 2.00 when the results are interpreted in terms of the usual resonance relation (9.35):

$$(15.23) \qquad\qquad \omega = (ge/2mc)H.$$

It has been shown,[14] when all demagnetizing effects are included, that, with the usual experimental arrangement with metals—a thin disk specimen with the static field H parallel to the disk—the resonance relation becomes

$$(15.24) \qquad\qquad \omega = (ge/2mc)(BH)^{1/2},$$

[13] W. A. Yager and R. M. Bozorth, Phys. Rev. **72**, 80 (1947).
[14] C. Kittel, Phys. Rev. **71**, 270 (1947); **73**, 155 (1948).

where $B = H + 4\pi M_s$. Several g values obtained in this way are given in Table 15.3. The values are close to the free spin value and are independent of the frequency at which the experiments are performed, when the appropriate B and H values are used.

The derivation of (15.24) is straightforward. We start with (9.41):

$$dM/dt = \gamma \mathbf{M} \times \mathbf{H},$$

with $\gamma = ge/2mc$. If the sample is thin in the y direction, the demagnetizing factors are $N_x = 0$, $N_y = 4\pi$, $N_z = 0$. The components of

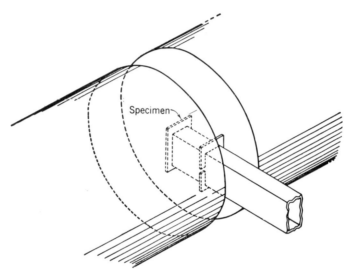

Specimen

Fig. 15.6.   Microwave cavity with ferromagnetic end wall in gap of electromagnet.

$\mathbf{H}$ are $(H_x, -4\pi M_y, H)$, where H_x is the r-f field; $H_y = -4\pi M_y$ is the demagnetizing field which arises when in the course of the precession the magnetization vector acquires a component M_y in the y direction; and H is the static field in the z direction. Then, for time dependence $e^{i\omega t}$ and neglecting squares and products of small quantities on the assumption $H_x, M_x, M_y \ll H_z$, we have

$$i\omega M_x = \gamma(M_y H + 4\pi M_y M_z);$$

(15.25) $$i\omega M_y = \gamma(M_z H_x - M_x H);$$

$$i\omega M_z \cong 0,$$

the last line referring to the time-dependent part of M_z. On substituting for M_y in the first equation, we find

(15.26) $$\chi_x = M_x/H_x = \frac{\chi_0}{1 - (\omega/\omega_0)^2},$$

where

$$\chi_0 = M_z/H.$$

The resonance frequency is

(15.27) $$\omega_0 = \gamma(BH)^{\frac{1}{2}},$$

with

(15.28) $$\gamma = ge/2mc,$$

and $B = H + 4\pi M_z$, where M_z may be taken as M_s.

The constant g as used here is called the *spectroscopic splitting factor;* it is quite similar to the Landé factor used in optical spectroscopy.   A

TABLE 15.3.   SUMMARY OF RESULTS OF FERROMAGNETIC RESONANCE
EXPERIMENTS

[For references see C. Kittel, J. phys. radium **12**, 291 (1951).]

Substance	g	ε (Eq. 15.30)
Iron	2.12–2.17	0.06–0.09
Cobalt	2.22	0.11
Nickel	2.2	0.1
Magnetite, Fe_3O_4	2.2	0.1
Heusler alloy, Cu_2MnAl	2.01	0.005
Permalloy, 78% Ni, 22% Fe	2.07–2.14	0.04–0.07
Supermalloy, 79% Ni, 5% Mn, 16% Fe	2.12–2.20	0.06–0.10
48 Ni 52 Fe	2.08	0.04

theoretical relationship[15] connects g and g', where g' is defined by (15.19) as the result of a gyromagnetic experiment:

(15.29) $$g - 2 \cong 2 - g',$$

as it can be shown (Appendix H) that

(15.30) $$g \cong 2(1 + \varepsilon)$$

where ε is defined by (15.21).   However, the values of ε given in Table 15.3 as determined by microwave experiments are appreciably higher than the values found in Table 15.2 from gyromagnetic experiments; the discrepancy is probably associated with the apparent tend-

[15] J. H. Van Vleck, Phys. Rev. **78**, 266 (1950); D. Polder, Phys. Rev. **73**, 1116 (1948); C. Kittel, Phys. Rev. **76**, 743 (1949); C. Kittel and A. H. Mitchell, Phys. Rev. **101**, 1611 (1956).

ency of the g values to decrease as the resonant frequency is increased,[16] and an explanation of this behavior has been proposed by Kittel and Mitchell.[15]

FERROMAGNETIC DOMAINS[17]

At temperatures well below the Curie point the electronic magnetic moments of a ferromagnetic specimen are essentially all lined up, when regarded on a microscopic scale.   Yet, looking at a specimen as a whole, the overall moment may be very much less than that corresponding

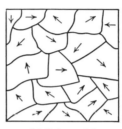

(a) Single crystal   (b) Polycrystal

Fig. 15.7.   Schematic domain arrangements for zero resultant magnetic moment in a single crystal (a) and in a polycrystalline specimen (b).   The domain structure of the polycrystalline specimen has been drawn for simplicity as if each crystallite contained only a single domain; this is not usually the case.   Domains can be larger than or smaller than a crystal grain, depending on the circumstances.

to saturation, and the application of an external magnetic field may be required to saturate the specimen.   The behavior observed in single crystals is similar to that in polycrystalline specimens.

Weiss explained this phenomenon, the existence of the technical magnetization curve, by assuming that actual specimens are composed of a number of small regions called domains, within each of which the local magnetization is saturated; the directions of magnetization of different domains need not necessarily be parallel, however.   A schematic arrangement of domains with zero resultant magnetic moment is shown in Fig. 15.7 for a single crystal and in a polycrystal.

The increase in the value of the resultant magnetic moment of the specimen under the action of an applied magnetic field may be imagined to take place, according to the domain theory, by two independent processes, as suggested by R. Becker: by an increase in the volume of domains which are favorably oriented with respect to the

[16] R. Hoskins and G. Wiener, Phys. Rev. **26**, 1153 (1954); Y. Kojima, Science Rpts. Tôhoku Univ. **A6**, 614 (1954).

[17] A 16-mm motion picture of actual domain movements, entitled "Action pictures of ferromagnetic domains," is available on loan from the Publications Department, Bell Telephone Laboratories, 463 West St., New York 14, N. Y.

field at the expense of unfavorably oriented domains; or by rotation of the directions of magnetization toward the direction of the field. These two methods by which the resultant magnetization may change are shown in Fig. 15.8.

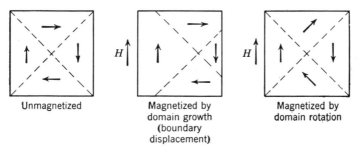

Unmagnetized   Magnetized by domain growth (boundary displacement)   Magnetized by domain rotation

Fig. 15.8. Fundamental magnetization processes.

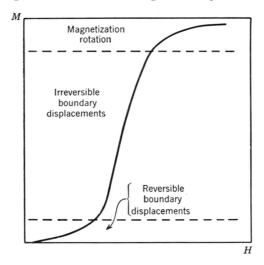

Fig. 15.9. Representative magnetization curve, showing the dominant magnetization processes in the different regions of the curve. In some sintered ferrites the regions appear to be divided up in another fashion, with reversible rotation effective at low H.

Closer examination reveals that in weak fields the magnetization changes usually proceed by means of domain boundary displacements, and so the domains change in size. In strong fields the magnetization usually changes by means of rotation of the direction of magnetization. A typical magnetization curve is shown in Fig. 15.9; the regions in which each process is dominant are designated. Technical terms are defined by Fig. 15.10.

The domain structure of ferromagnetic materials affects closely the technically important properties, which in a transformer core include high permeability, and in a permanent magnet include high coercive force.[18]   By suppressing the possibility of boundary displacement we may achieve a high coercivity; the suppression may be accomplished by using very fine powders or, as in Alnico V, by precipitating a second

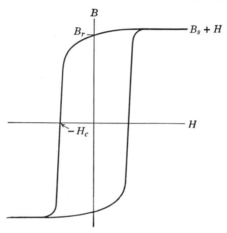

Fig. 15.10.   The technical magnetization curve.   The *coercive force* H_c is the reverse field necessary to bring the induction B to zero; the *remanence* B_r is the value of B at $H = 0$; the *saturation induction* B_s is defined as the limiting value of $(B - H)$ for large H.

metallurgical phase so that the specimen is heterogeneous on a very fine scale.   By making the material pure, homogeneous, and well-oriented we facilitate boundary displacement and thereby attain high permeability; values of the permeability up to 3.8×10^6 have been reported.[19]

ORIGIN OF DOMAINS

Now we shall show that domain structure is a natural consequence[20] of the various contributions to the energy—exchange, anisotropy, and

[18] The *coercive force* is defined as the reverse field needed to reduce the induction B or the magnetization M to zero, starting in a saturated condition.   Usually the definition is understood to refer to B, except in theoretical work.   When referred to M, one writes $_IH_c$ or $_MH_c$.

[19] M. Goertz, Phys. Rev. **82**, 340 (1951).

[20] L. Landau and E. Lifshitz, Physik. Z. Sowjetunion **8**, 153 (1935); L. Néel, J. Phys. radium, **5**, 241, 265 (1944), has extended the calculations to other geometries, and his results have been verified experimentally by L. F. Bates and F. E. Neale, Physica **15**, 220 (1949).

magnetic—of a ferromagnetic body. The existence of domains may be inferred from the character of the magnetization curve itself. But the most direct evidence of domain structure is furnished by photomicrographs of domain boundaries obtained by the technique of magnetic powder patterns. This method, applied originally by Bitter (1931), has, in the hands of W. C. Elmore and H. J. Williams and his collaborators, provided convincing proof that domains exist and behave

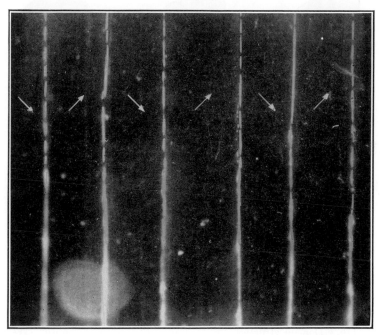

Fig. 15.11a. Simple domain structure in Si-Fe single crystal. [After Williams, Bozorth, and Shockley, Phys. Rev. **75,** 155 (1949).]

as expected theoretically. The powder pattern method consists in placing a drop of a colloidal suspension of finely divided ferromagnetic material, such as magnetite, on the carefully prepared surface of the ferromagnetic crystal under study. It is found on observation through a microscope that the colloid particles in the suspension become strongly concentrated about certain well-defined lines which represent the boundaries between domains magnetized in different directions. The reason why the colloid particles concentrate near these boundaries is that in their vicinity there exist very strong local magnetic fields which attract the magnetic particles. A photograph of a relatively simple domain structure in iron is shown in Fig. 15.11a, along with the interpretation derived from the photograph and from certain auxiliary experiments. In Fig. 15.11b are shown domain structures on a Si-iron crystal as viewed with polarized light; different stages of the magnetization curve are shown.

We may understand the origin of domains by considering the structures shown in Fig. 15.12, each representing a cross section through a

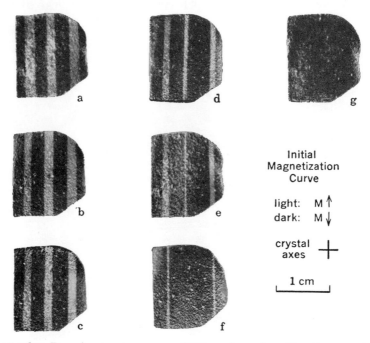

Fig. 15.11b. Domain structures on a (100) surface of a silicon-iron crystal as viewed by polarized light, after Fowler and Fryer. The external field is increased from the demagnetized condition (a) to the saturated condition (g). The changes in magnetization are shown clearly by the changes in the light and dark areas.

ferromagnetic single crystal. In (a) we have a saturated configuration consisting of a single domain; as a consequence of the magnetic "poles" formed on the surfaces of the crystal this configuration will have a high value of the magnetic energy $(1/8\pi) \int H^2 \, dV$. The magnetic energy for a square cross section will be of the order of $M_s{}^2 \approx 10^6$ ergs/cm^3; here M_s denotes the saturation magnetization.

In (b) the magnetic energy has been reduced by a factor of roughly one-half as a result of dividing the crystal into two domains magnetized in opposite directions. The subdivision process may be carried further as in (c): with N domains it turns out that the magnetic energy is reduced (because of the reduced spatial extension of the field) to approximately $1/N$ of the magnetic energy of the saturated configuration (a).

The subdivision process continues until the energy required to establish an additional boundary layer or interface, separating two domains magnetized oppositely, is greater than the reduction in magnetic field energy consequent on the finer subdivision. A boundary layer does have a certain amount of energy associated with it: on

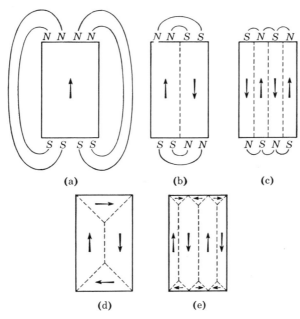

Fig. 15.12.   The origin of domains.

opposite sides of the boundary the magnetization is directed in antiparallel directions; as the exchange forces favor parallel and oppose antiparallel orientations of the magnetization, energy will be required to establish a boundary layer. Later we shall calculate this energy and we shall find that it is of the order of 1 erg/cm^2. If then we suppose tentatively that there are $N = 10^3$ domains/cm, the total boundary energy in a crystal cube 1 cm on each edge will be of the order of 10^3 ergs and the magnetic energy will also be of the order of 10^3 ergs. This situation represents approximately the equilibrium number of domains for the particular geometrical arrangement shown.

It is possible to devise domain arrangements such as (d) and (e) for which the magnetic energy is zero. Here the boundaries of the

triangular prism domains (termed "domains of closure") near the
end faces of the crystal make equal angles—45°—with the magnetization in the rectangular domains and with the magnetization in the
domains of closure: therefore the component of magnetization normal
to the boundary is continuous across the boundary, and no poles are
formed anywhere in the crystal. As there are no poles there is no
magnetic field associated with the magnetization, and we may speak of
the flux circuit being completed within the crystal—thus giving rise
to the phrase "domains of closure" for the domains near the surfaces
of the crystal which act to complete the flux circuit.

The energy required to form a domain of closure in a uniaxial crystal
such as cobalt comes principally from what is called the *crystalline*

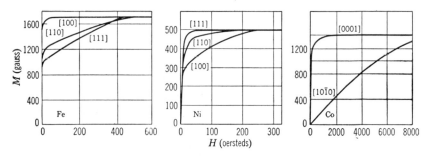

Fig. 15.13.   Magnetization curves for single crystals of iron, nickel, and cobalt.
(After Honda and Kaya.)

anisotropy energy.   The anisotropy energy tends to make the magnetization of a domain line up along certain crystallographic axes.
The axes thus favored are known as preferred axes, or axes of easy
magnetization.   Such axes are well established experimentally, and
it is known that a considerably larger amount of energy may be
required to saturate a specimen along an arbitrary axis than along one
of the preferred axes.   In cobalt the hexagonal axis of the crystal
is the only preferred axis, and cobalt is accordingly referred to as
uniaxial.   In iron, which is cubic, the preferred axes are the cube
edges; in nickel, which is also cubic, the preferred axes are the body
diagonals.   Figure 15.13 shows magnetization curves for iron, nickel,
and cobalt in directions of easy and hard magnetization.

In cobalt, if the basic rectangular domains are magnetized along the
easy axis of magnetization, the domains of closure will by necessity be
magnetized in hard directions.   In a cubic crystal such as iron it is
possible for both the basic domains and the closure domains to be
magnetized along different easy axes.   The energy expenditure in this

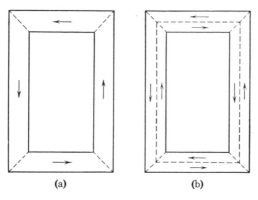

(a)   (b)

Fig. 15.14.   Simple domain structures in single crystal of iron in form of rectangular loop, with legs parallel to [001] and [010] axes.

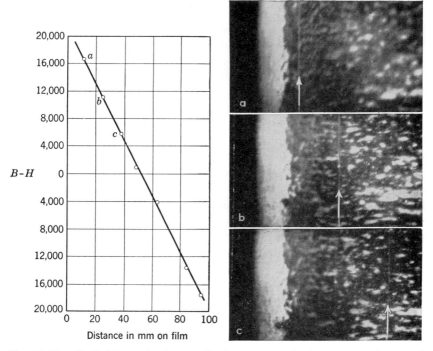

Fig. 15.15.   (*Left*) Magnetization vs. displacement of the domain boundary, and
(*right*) patterns showing the domain boundary in three different positions.   (After
Williams and Shockley.)

case arises from magnetostriction: since the closure domains are magnetized along different axes from the basic domains, they will tend to be elongated by magnetostriction along different axes, and in order to fit the various domains together in the crystal structure we have to do work against elastic forces.   Magnetostriction is the change of length with magnetization direction.

The termination structures revealed by powder patterns are often more complicated than the simple cases we have discussed, but *domain structure always has its origin in the possibility of lowering the energy of a system by going from a saturated configuration with high magnetic energy to a domain configuration with a lower energy.*

A particularly simple type of domain structure is shown in Fig. 15.14; this structure has been obtained by Williams and Shockley[21] with a single crystal of silicon iron which was cut to the form of a hollow rectangle with legs accurately parallel to [001] and [010] crystal axes.   When the crystal is saturated entirely in one sense the domain boundaries are the 45° lines shown in (a); when part of the crystal is magnetized clockwise and part counterclockwise, the square-shaped boundary in (b) is formed in addition.   Magnetization changes are then found to take place by the movement of the square-shaped boundary, the flux changes corresponding quantitatively to the displacements of the domain wall, as shown in Fig. 15.15.

COERCIVE FORCE AND HYSTERESIS

The coercive force is perhaps the most sensitive property of ferromagnetic materials which is subject to our control, and it is one of the most important criteria in the selection of ferromagnetic materials for practical application.   The essential difference between material for permanent magnets and material for transformer cores lies in the coercive force, which may range from the value of 600 oersteds in a loudspeaker magnet (Alnico V) and 20,000 in a special high stability magnet (Fe-Pt) to the value of 0.5 in a commercial power transformer (Si-Fe) or 0.004 in a pulse transformer (Supermalloy).   Thus the coercive force may be varied over a range of 5×10^6.

The problem of the theory is to interpret the observed values of the coercivity in terms of the physical state of the material.   A certain amount of progress has been made, although the problem is beset with the usual difficulty in determining quantitatively the relevant physical factors such as impurities, lattice imperfections, and internal strains. The saturation hysteresis loss at low frequencies is closely related to the coercive force, since the area enclosed by the hysteresis loop is

[21] H. J. Williams and W. Shockley, Phys. Rev. **75**, 178 (1949).

approximately given by the product of the saturation induction B_s and the coercive force.

The coercive force in "magnetically soft" (low H_c) materials may be understood from the following: The total energy of a given specimen may vary with the position of a domain boundary because of local variations in internal strains, impurities, crystallite dimensions, etc.; the variation is indicated schematically in Fig. 15.16. In the absence of an applied magnetic field the boundary will be situated at some minimum position such as A in the figure. In the presence of a field

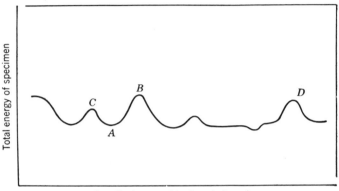

Fig. 15.16. Variation in energy of specimen as a function of the position of the boundary.

the boundary will be unable to make a large displacement to the extreme right (D) unless the energy is increased by a sufficient amount to enable the boundary to pass over the point B corresponding to the maximum boundary energy. The increase in energy must be furnished by the reorientation of the local magnetization M_s in the applied field H, and the value of H which suffices to reverse about one-half of the magnetization of the specimen will be the coercive field H_c.

Qualitatively this picture of the coercive process explains the fact that the coercive force diminishes as the precipitate or impurity content decreases and also as internal strains are removed through annealing (slow cooling); it also explains why it is that alloys containing a precipitated phase may be magnetically hard.

The coercive force of one type of magnetically hard material may be understood from a quite different picture; we refer to materials composed of very small grains or fine powders where each particle is always magnetized to saturation as a single domain. The fact that a sufficiently small particle, with diameter less than 10^{-4} or 10^{-5} cm, is composed of a single domain is a result of domain theory which has been confirmed by experiment. It can be shown[22] that with such very small particles the formation of a domain boundary is energetically unfavorable, frequently because too large a proportion of the volume of a small particle would be contained within the wall, the wall thickness being independent of the particle size.

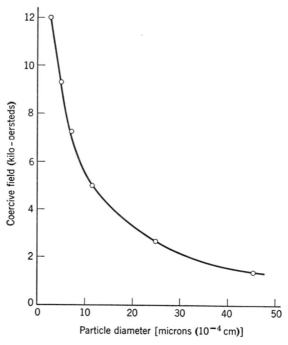

Fig. 15.17. Coercive force of fine particles of MnBi, as a function of particle size. (After Guillaud.)

If a small particle is constrained to remain as a single domain, it will not be possible for magnetization reversal to take place by means of the process of boundary displacement which usually requires relatively weak fields; instead the magnetization of the particle must rotate as a whole, a process which may require large fields depending on the anisotropy energy of the material or the shape of the particle: the reason is that we must rotate the magnetization over the energy hump corresponding to a direction of hard magnetization.

[22] C. Kittel, Phys. Rev. **70**, 965 (1946); E. C. Stoner and E. P. Wohlfarth, Trans. Roy. Soc. (London) **A240**, 599 (1948); L. Néel, Compt. rend. **224**, 1488 (1947).

The coercive force of fine iron particles is expected theoretically to be about 250 oersteds on the basis of rotation opposed by the crystalline anisotropy energy, and this is of the order of the value reported by several observers. Higher coercivities have been reported for elongated iron particles, the rotation here being opposed by the shape anisotropy of the demagnetization energy. Similarly the high coercivity of powders of MnBi ($_MH_c > 12,000$), according to Guillaud, seems to be in line with the rotation concept, with anisotropy energy as the factor opposing rotation. The transition to single domain behavior is shown in Fig. 15.17.

REVERSIBLE PERMEABILITY

The extent of the range of field strength over which the permeability is reversible is determined by the distance through which a domain

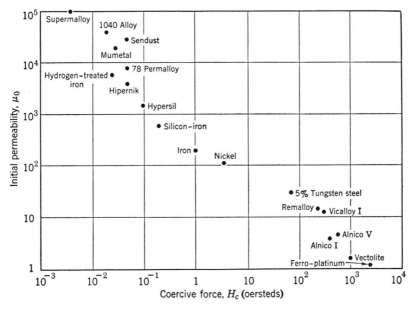

Fig. 15.18. Correlation between the initial permeability and coercive force of a wide range of magnetic materials.

boundary may move without passing over a peak in the curve of wall energy vs. distance; with reference to Fig. 15.16, one such region of reversible permeability is the region CAB; when the domain boundary leaves this region it moves irreversibly to the extreme right or extreme left of the figure.

The reversible permeability is determined by the irregularities of the

TABLE 15.4. DATA FOR MAGNETIC MATERIALS†

High-Permeability Materials

Material	Form	Approximate Percent Composition					Maximum Permeability	Saturation Flux Density B_s (gauss)	Coercive Force H_c (oersteds)
		Fe	Ni	Co	Mo	Other			
Cold-rolled steel	Sheet	98.5	....	....	..	......	2,000	21,000	1.8
Iron	Sheet	99.91	....	....	..	......	5,000	21,500	1.0
Purified iron	Sheet	99.95	....	....	..	......	180,000	21,500	0.05
4% silicon-iron	Sheet	96	....	....	..	4 Si	7,000	19,700	0.5
Grain oriented‡	Sheet	97	....	....	..	3 Si	30,000	20,000	0.15
Hipernik	Sheet	50	50	....	..	......	70,000	16,000	0.05
78 Permalloy	Sheet	21.2	78.5	....	..	0.3 Mn	100,000	10,700	0.05
Mu metal	Sheet	18	75	....	..	2Cr, 5Cu	100,000	6,500	0.05
Supermalloy	Sheet	15.7	79	....	5	0.3 Mn	800,000	8,000	0.002
Permendur	Sheet	49.7	....	50	..	0.3 Mn	5,000	24,500	2.0
Carbonyl iron	Insulated powder	99.9	....	....	..	......	132		
Ferroxcube III	Sintered powder	....	$MnFe_2O_4 + ZnFe_2O_4$				1,500	2,500	0.1

† From R. A. Chegwedden, *Metal Progr.* **54**, 705 (1948).
‡ Properties in direction of rolling.

TABLE 15.4 (*Continued*)

Permanent-Magnet Alloys

Material	Percent Composition (remainder Fe)	Coercive Force H_c (oersteds)	Residual Induction B_r (gauss)	Energy Product BH_{max} ($\times 10^{-6}$ ergs)
Carbon steel.	1 Mn, 0.9 C	50	10,000	0.20
Tungsten Steel	5 W, 0.3 Mn, 0.7 C	70	10,300	0.32
36% cobalt steel.	36 Co, 0.7 C, 4 Cr, 5 W	240	9,500	0.97
Remalloy or Comol.	17 Mo, 12 Co	250	10,500	1.1
Alnico II (sintered).	10 Al, 17 Ni, 2.5 Co, 6 Cu	520	6,900	1.4
Alnico V.	8 Al, 14 Ni, 24 Co, 3 Cu	550	12,500	4.5
Alnico VI.	8 Al, 15 Ni, 24 Co, 3 Cu, 1 Ti	750	10,000	3.5
Vicalloy II (wire).	52 Co, 14 V	510	10,000	3.5
Cunife (wire).	60 Cu, 20 Ni	550	5,400	1.5
Vectolite.	30 Fe_2O_2, 40 Fe_3O_4	1,000	1,600	0.60
Platinum-cobalt.	77 Pt, 23 Co	2,600	4,500	3.8
Hyflux.	Fine powder	390	6,000	0.97

curve of boundary energy vs. displacement, and thus is determined by essentially the same physical conditions as the coercive force. A comparison of the initial permeability μ_0 and the coercive force H_c for a wide range of magnetic materials is shown in Fig. 15.18. There is a very close correlation, materials with high coercivities having low permeabilities, and vice versa.

MAGNETIC MATERIALS

For reference purposes we give in Table 15.4 a summary of the properties of typical high-permeability magnetic materials and permanent-magnet alloys. The range of properties is a striking illustration of the sensitivity of domain processes to the state of stress and subdivision and to the values of the anisotropy and magnetostriction of the ferromagnetic material. In developing a high-permeability material we wish to make the domain boundaries move as freely as possible, free from trapping by strain centers, crystal boundaries, impurities, inclusions, and cavities; we look accordingly for highly purified, oriented, annealed materials of low anisotropy and low magnetostriction (low coupling with internal stresses). In developing a permanent-magnet alloy we wish to suppress completely the existence or motion of domain boundaries, leaving only the domain rotation processes, and these we wish to make as difficult as possible.

ANISOTROPY ENERGY

The anisotropy energy or, as it is sometimes called, the magneto-crystalline energy of a ferromagnetic crystal acts in such a way that the magnetization tends to be directed along certain definite crystallographic axes which, accordingly, are called directions of easy magnetization; the directions along which it is most difficult to magnetize the crystal are called hard directions. It is found experimentally to require the expenditure of a certain, and often considerable, amount of energy to magnetize a crystal to saturation in a hard direction, referred to the lower energy required to saturate along a direction of easy magnetization. The excess energy required in the hard direction is the anisotropy energy.

As an example of anisotropy energy we may consider cobalt, which is a hexagonal crystal. The direction of the hexagonal axis is the direction of easy magnetization (at room temperature), while all directions in the basal plane, normal to the axis, are hard directions. The magnetization curves of a single crystal of cobalt are shown in Fig. 15.13. The energy represented by the magnetization curve in the hard direction is given by $\int H\,dM$ per unit volume and amounts to an excess energy of about 5×10^6 ergs/cm^3 for the curve shown.

The origin of the anisotropy energy is illustrated schematically by Fig. 15.19. One important mechanism is believed to be the combined effect of spin-orbit interaction and the partial quenching of the orbital angular momentum in the solid. The magnetization of the crystal "sees" the crystal lattice through orbital overlap of the electrons: the spin interacts with the orbital motion by means of the spin orbit coupling, and the orbital motion in turn interacts with the crystal

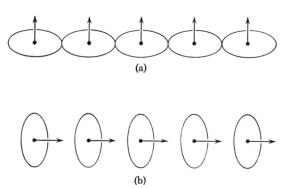

(a)

(b)

Fig. 15.19. Asymmetry of the overlap of electron distributions on neighboring ions as one mechanism causing magnetocrystalline anisotropy. Because of spin-orbit interaction the charge distribution may have the low symmetry shown. The asymmetry is tied to the direction of magnetization; thus changing the spin direction changes the overlap energy.

structure by means of the electrostatic fields and overlapping wave functions associated with neighboring atoms in the lattice. The theoretical position has been reviewed by Van Vleck.[23]

In cobalt it is found that a very good representation of the experimental observations is given by the two terms:

(15.31) $f_K = K_1' \sin^2 \theta + K_2' \sin^4 \theta,$

where θ is the angle the magnetization makes with the hexagonal axis. At room temperature

$$K_1' = 4.1 \times 10^6 \text{ ergs/cm}^3; \qquad K_2' = 1.0 \times 10^6 \text{ ergs/cm}^3.$$

Iron is a cubic crystal, and the magnetization curves (Fig. 15.13) show that the cube edges [100] and equivalent axes are the directions of

[23] J. H. Van Vleck, Quelques aspects de la théorie du magnétisme, Ann. inst. Henri Poincaré 10, 57 (1947); H. Brooks, Phys. Rev. 58, 909 (1940); G. C. Fletcher, Proc. Phys. Soc. (London) A67, 505 (1954); C. Zener, Phys. Rev. 96, 1335 (1954).

easy magnetization, while the body diagonals ([111] and equivalent axes) are hard directions. The excess work done in magnetizing along [111] is about 1.4×10^5 ergs/cm^3 room temperature.

In attempting to represent the anisotropy energy of iron in an arbitrary direction with direction cosines α_1, α_2, α_3 referred to the cube edges, we are guided by the restrictions imposed by cubic symmetry. For example, the expression for the anisotropy energy must be an even power of each α_i, and it must be invariant under interchanges of the α_i among themselves. The lowest order combination satisfying the symmetry requirements is $\alpha_1{}^2 + \alpha_2{}^2 + \alpha_3{}^2$, but this is identically

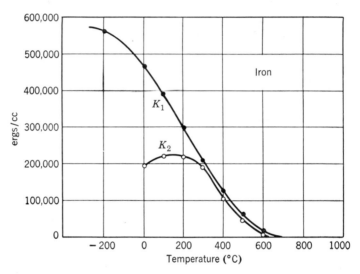

Fig. 15.20.   Temperature dependence of anisotropy constants of iron.

equal to unity and does not describe anisotropy effects. The next combination is of the fourth degree: $\alpha_1{}^2\alpha_2{}^2 + \alpha_1{}^2\alpha_3{}^2 + \alpha_3{}^2\alpha_2{}^2$, and then of the sixth degree: $\alpha_1{}^2\alpha_2{}^2\alpha_3{}^2$. As this is as far as one usually needs to go,

$$(15.32) \quad f_K = K_1(\alpha_1{}^2\alpha_2{}^2 + \alpha_2{}^2\alpha_3{}^2 + \alpha_3{}^2\alpha_1{}^2) + K_2\alpha_1{}^2\alpha_2{}^2\alpha_3{}^2,$$

where, at room temperature,

$$K_1 = 4.2 \times 10^5 \text{ ergs/cm}^3; \qquad K_2 = 1.5 \times 10^5 \text{ ergs/cm}^3.$$

Results for iron at other temperatures are shown in Fig. 15.20. For nickel at room temperature $K_1 = -5 \times 10^4$ ergs/cm^3. An excellent review of anisotropy data is included in the book by Bozorth cited at the end of the chapter.

MAGNETOSTRICTION

It is observed in ferromagnetic single crystals that the length of the crystal in a given direction relative to the crystal axes depends in general on the direction of the magnetization relative to the crystal axes. In cubic crystals the dimensional changes may be expressed approximately by the relation

$$(15.33) \quad \delta l/l = \tfrac{3}{2}\lambda_{100}(\alpha_1{}^2\beta_1{}^2 + \alpha_2{}^2\beta_2{}^2 + \alpha_3{}^2\beta_3{}^2 - \tfrac{1}{3})$$
$$+ 3\lambda_{111}(\alpha_1\alpha_2\beta_1\beta_2 + \alpha_2\alpha_3\beta_2\beta_3 + \alpha_3\alpha_1\beta_3\beta_1),$$

where α_1, α_2, α_3 are the direction cosines of the magnetization direction referred to the cubic axes, and β_1, β_2, β_3 are the direction cosines of the direction in which δl is measured; λ_{100} and λ_{111} are the saturation values of the longitudinal magnetostriction in the directions [100] and [111], respectively. It may be shown that λ_{100} and λ_{111} are simply related to the magnetoelastic coupling constants B_1 and B_2 introduced in Problem 15.2:

$$(15.34) \qquad\qquad \lambda_{100} = -\frac{2}{3}\frac{B_1}{c_{11} - c_{12}};$$

$$\lambda_{111} = -\frac{1}{3}\frac{B_2}{c_{44}}.$$

Experimental values are:

	$\lambda_{100} \times 10^6$	$\lambda_{111} \times 10^6$	$B_1 \times 10^6$ ergs/cm^3	$B_2 \times 10^6$ ergs/cm^3
Fe	19.5	−18.8	−29	64
Ni	−46	−25	62	90

For nickel, expression (15.33) does not give a very good fit to the observations, and an expression involving four parameters instead of two is often used, as discussed by Becker and Döring in the book cited at the end of the chapter.

Physically it is useful to think of magnetostriction as arising from the dependence of the crystalline anisotropy energy on the state of strain of the lattice: thus it may be energetically favorable for the crystal to deform slightly from the exactly cubic condition if doing so will lower the anisotropy energy by more than the elastic energy is raised.

In devising high-permeability materials an effort is often made to find an alloy composition with low magnetostriction (low coupling constants B_1, B_2) so that internal strains will not induce a local anisotropy energy. In Permalloy, for example, both the anisotropy energy and the magnetostriction are very low.

THE BLOCH WALL

The term "Bloch wall" denotes the transition layer which separates adjacent domains magnetized in different directions.

The essential idea of the Bloch wall is that the entire change in spin direction between domains magnetized in different directions does not occur in one discontinuous jump across a single atomic plane. Rather, the change of direction will take place in a gradual way over many atomic planes (Fig. 15.21). The reason for the gradual nature of the

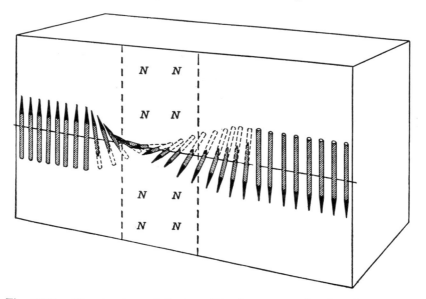

Fig. 15.21. The structure of the transition layer separating domains. In iron the thickness of the transition region is about 300 lattice constants.

change is the fact that for a given total change of spin direction the exchange energy is lower when the change is distributed over many spins than when the change occurs abruptly.

This behavior may be understood from the expression

$$(15.35) \qquad\qquad w_{ex} = JS^2\phi^2$$

for the exchange energy between two spins making a small angle ϕ with each other; here J is the exchange integral and S is the spin quantum number. We obtain this equation by interpreting (15.9) classically, and replacing $\cos\phi$ by $1 - \frac{1}{2}\phi^2$. Let the total desired change of angle be ϕ_0; if the change occurs in N equal steps, the angle change between neighboring spins is ϕ_0/N, and the exchange energy between each pair of neighboring atoms is

(15.36) $$w_{\text{ex}} = JS^2(\phi_0/N)^2.$$

The total exchange energy of the line of $N + 1$ atoms is thus

(15.37) $$E_{\text{ex}} = JS^2\phi_0{}^2/N.$$

If the total change of angle between domains is $\phi_0 = \pi$, corresponding to a reversal of magnetization direction on passing through the wall, the exchange energy of a line of atoms through a wall 100 atoms in thickness is of the order of $kT_c/100$, as compared with kT_c for a wall only one atom layer in thickness.

Since the exchange energy of a wall is inversely proportional to the thickness (15.37), the wall might spread out until it filled a sizable proportion of the crystal, were it not for the restraining effect of the anisotropy energy, which acts to limit the width of the transition layer. As the spins contained within the wall are largely directed away from the axes of easy magnetization, there is a certain amount of anisotropy energy associated with the wall, roughly proportional to the thickness.

The actual thickness and energy of the transition layer is the result of a balance between the competing claims of exchange energy and anisotropy energy, the former tending to increase the thickness and the latter tending to decrease the thickness.

We proceed to make a rough order-of-magnitude estimate of the thickness and energy of a Bloch wall. Let us consider a wall parallel to the cube face of a simple cubic lattice and separating domains magnetized in opposite directions. We wish to determine the thickness of the wall in terms of the number N of atomic planes contained within the wall, and also to determine the energy per unit surface area, σ_w.

The energy may be represented to a good approximation as the sum of contributions from exchange and anisotropy energies:

(15.38) $$\sigma_w = \sigma_{\text{ex}} + \sigma_{\text{anis}}.$$

The exchange energy is given approximately by (15.37) for each line of atoms through the wall and normal to the plane of the wall. There are $1/a^2$ such lines per unit area, where a is the lattice constant; whence

(15.39) $$\sigma_{\text{ex}} = \pi^2 JS^2/Na^2.$$

The anisotropy energy is of the order of the anisotropy constant times the volume, or

(15.40) $$\sigma_{\text{anis}} \approx KNa;$$

therefore

(15.41) $$\sigma_w \approx (\pi^2 J S^2 / N a^2) + K N a,$$

which is a minimum with respect to N when

(15.42) $$\partial \sigma_w / \partial N = 0 = -(\pi^2 J S^2 / N^2 a^2) + K a$$

or

(15.43) $$N = (\pi^2 J S^2 / K a^3)^{\frac{1}{2}}.$$

For order of magnitude, in iron,

$$N \approx (k T_c / K a^3)^{\frac{1}{2}} \approx (10^{-13} / 10^5 10^{-23})^{\frac{1}{2}} \approx 300 \text{ lattice constants}$$

$$\approx 1000 \text{ A.}$$

The total wall energy per unit area is

(15.44) $$\sigma_w = 2\pi (J K S^2 / a)^{\frac{1}{2}},$$

which in iron is of the order of magnitude

$$\sigma_w = (k T_c K / a)^{\frac{1}{2}} \approx 1 \text{ erg/cm}^2.$$

In the above estimate we have rather arbitrarily supposed that the total change in spin direction is shared equally by each of the N atoms on a line through the wall; we have also used a very rough estimate of the anisotropy energy of the spin system within the wall. More accurate calculation for a 180° wall in a (100) plane gives

(15.45) $$\sigma_w = 2(2 K_1 J S^2 / a)^{\frac{1}{2}},$$

which gives for iron 1.8 ergs/cm².

DOMAIN DIMENSIONS

We carry through, following the original treatment by Landau and Lifshitz, the calculation of the domain width for a flux-closure arrangement of domains (Fig. 15.22) in a uniaxial crystal. The wall energy per unit area of the crystal surface is approximately

$$w_{\text{wall}} = \sigma_w L / D.$$

The volume contained within the domains of closure is oriented in a direction of hard magnetization and involves an energy K per unit volume, where K is the anisotropy constant. Per unit area of crystal surface on one side, the volume in the domains of closure on both sides is $D/2$, and so

(15.46) $$w_{\text{anis}} = K D / 2.$$

The wall energy tends to increase the domain width, while the anisotropy energy tends to decrease the width.

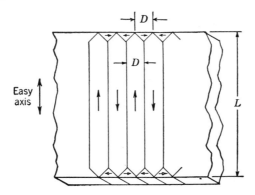

Fig. 15.22. Flux-closure domain configuration in a uniaxial crystal.

The total energy is

(15.47) $$w = (\sigma_w L/D) + (KD/2)$$

per unit area, and this is a minimum with respect to the domain width D when

$$\partial w/\partial D = -(\sigma_w L/D^2) + (K/2) = 0.$$

The condition for the minimum is then

(15.48) $$D = (2\sigma_w L/K)^{1/2},$$

and the corresponding energy per unit area is

(15.49) $$w = (2\sigma_w LK)^{1/2}.$$

The energy per unit volume is

(15.50) $$f_{\text{domain}} = (2\sigma_w K/L)^{1/2}.$$

If we arbitrarily substitute the approximate values of the constants for iron, and take the length L as 1 cm, we have

(15.51) $$D = [(2)(2)(1)/4 \times 10^5]^{1/2} \approx 3 \times 10^{-3} \text{ cm}$$

and

(15.52) $$f \approx 1.3 \times 10^3 \text{ ergs/cm}^3.$$

ANTIFERROMAGNETISM

The antiferromagnetic state is characterized by an ordered antiparallel arrangement of electron spins. When the exchange integral J

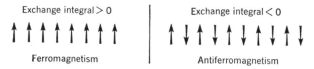

Fig. 15.23.   Comparison of spin ordering in the ferromagnetic and antiferromagnetic states.

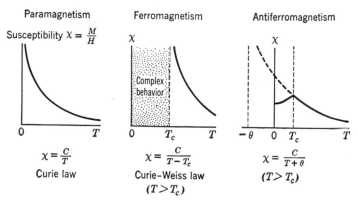

Fig. 15.24.   Distinguishing features of the temperature dependence of the magnetic susceptibility in paramagnetism, ferromagnetism, and antiferromagnetism.

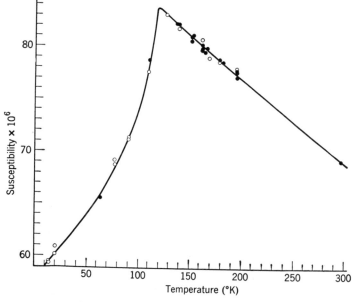

Fig. 15.25.   Magnetic susceptibility of MnO measured in a 5000-oersted field. (After Bizette, Squire, and Tsai.)

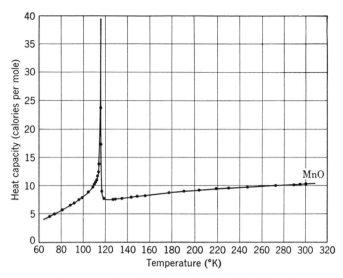

Fig. 15.26.   Molar heat capacity of MnO.   [After R. W. Millar, J. Am. Chem. Soc. **50**, 1875 (1928).]

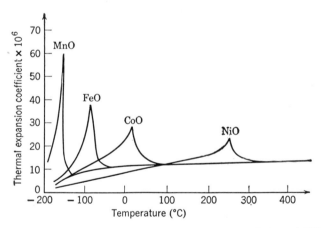

Fig. 15.27.   Thermal expansion coefficients of MnO, FeO, CoO, and NiO.   [After M. Foëx, Compt. rend. **227**, 193 (1948).]

in (15.9) is positive, we have ferromagnetism; when J is negative, we have antiferromagnetism. On passing below the Curie point of an antiferromagnetic the spins lock in (Fig. 15.23) with antiparallel orientations, and at the Curie point the susceptibility attains its maximum value, as shown in Figs. 15.24 and 15.25. We recognize antiferromagnetism by a well-defined kink in the susceptibility vs. temperature curve. The transition is also marked by anomalies in the heat capacity (Fig. 15.26) and thermal expansion coefficient (Fig. 15.27).

Bizette, Squire, and Tsai[24] in 1938 demonstrated that their data on MnO fitted certain predicted features of models of antiferromagnetism

TABLE 15.5. SUMMARY OF ANTIFERROMAGNETIC DATA

The Curie points often vary by considerable amounts between samples, and in some cases there is large thermal hysteresis. For a bibliography relating to experimental data on antiferromagnetic substances, see T. Nagamiya, K. Yosida, and R. Kubo, Advances in Physics **4**, 1–112 (1955); see especially Table 1. The value of θ is obtained by fitting an expression of the form $\chi = C/(T + \theta)$ to the susceptibility above the actual transition temperature T_c. In recent literature the transition temperature is sometimes referred to as the Néel temperature.

Substance	Paramagnetic Ion Lattice	Transition Temperature $T_c(^\circ \text{K})$	Curie-Weiss $\theta(^\circ \text{K})$	θ/T_c	$\dfrac{\chi(0)}{\chi(T_c)}$
MnO	fcc	122	610	5.0	$\frac{2}{3}$
MnS	fcc	165	528	3.2	0.82
MnSe	fcc	∼150(?)	∼ 435(?)	∼3	
MnTe	hex. layer	307			
MnF$_2$	bc rect.	72	113	1.57	0.76
FeF$_2$	bc rect.	79	117	1.48	0.72
FeCl$_2$	hex. layer	23.5	48	2.0	<0.2
FeO	fcc	198	570	2.9	0.8
CoCl$_2$	hex. layer	24.9	38.1	1.53	
CoO	fcc	291			
NiCl$_2$	hex. layer	49.6	68.2	1.37	
NiO	fcc	523			
α-Mn	complex	∼100			
Cr	bcc	475			
CrSb	hex. layer	725	∼1000	1.4	∼$\frac{1}{4}$
Cr$_2$O$_3$	complex	310			
TiCl$_3$	complex	∼100			
FeCO$_3$	complex	57			∼$\frac{1}{4}$

proposed by Néel[25] and Bitter.[26] Van Vleck[27] gave a detailed theoretical treatment.

Table 15.5 summarizes important data regarding antiferromagnetics. The effective magneton numbers, as deduced from the Curie constant C in the high temperature susceptibility, are not tabulated as the

[24] Bizette, Squire, and Tsai, Compt. rend. **207**, 449 (1938).
[25] L. Néel, Ann. phys. **18**, 5 (1932); **5**, 232 (1936).
[26] F. Bitter, Phys. Rev. **54**, 79 (1938).
[27] J. H. Van Vleck, J. Chem. Phys. **9**, 85 (1941).

values are generally in close agreement with the values obtaining in ordinary paramagnetic salts (Table 9.5). However, the moments for metallic manganese and chromium are much smaller than the free ion values; Shull finds by neutron diffraction that chromium has 0.4 μ_B and α-manganese 0.5 μ_B.

TWO-SUBLATTICE MODEL

The simplest situation in antiferromagnetism arises when the lattice of paramagnetic ions can be divided into two interpenetrating sub-lattices A, B such that all nearest neighbors of an ion on sublattice A lie on sublattice B. This condition is, for example, satisfied by the sc and bcc lattices, but not by the fcc lattice. If the only interactions are antiferromagnetic interactions between nearest neighbors, we may write for the magnetization above the Curie point on the Weiss field theory:

$$(15.53) \qquad TM_A = C'(H - \lambda M_B);$$

$$TM_B = C'(H - \lambda M_A).$$

Here C' is the Curie constant for one sublattice, and the effective field on sublattice A is written as $H - \lambda M_B$, which for positive λ corresponds to antiferromagnetic interactions between A and B. Adding,

$$(15.54) \qquad TM = T(M_A + M_B) = 2C'H - C'\lambda M,$$

and so

$$(15.55) \qquad \chi = \frac{2C'}{T + C'\lambda},$$

or

$$(15.56) \qquad \chi = \frac{C}{T + \theta}$$

with

$$(15.57) \qquad C = 2C'; \qquad \theta = C'\lambda.$$

The transition temperature is that below which each sublattice A and B possesses a magnetic moment even without a field. Below the Curie point it is not legitimate to treat the moment as a linear function of the effective field, but, as saturation is not important close to the Curie point, linearity may be assumed in the equations for the Curie point.

The transition temperature T_c is then the temperature at which equations (15.53) have a non-trivial solution for the magnetization when $H = 0$. The condition for this is that the determinant of the coefficients of the unknowns M_A, M_B should be zero:

$$\begin{vmatrix} T & \theta \\ \theta & T \end{vmatrix} = 0$$

or

(15.58) $$T_c = \theta.$$

On this model the transition temperature T_c should be equal to the constant θ in the Curie-Weiss law (15.56). The experimental values in Table 15.5 indicate that values of θ/T_c are usually of the order 1.5 to 5. Values of θ/T_c of the observed magnitude may be obtained when next nearest neighbor interactions[28] are provided for, and when more general kinds of sublattice arrangements[29] are considered. It is shown in Problem 15.5 that, if a molecular field constant $-\varepsilon$ is introduced to describe interactions within a sublattice, then

(15.59) $$\theta/T_c = (\lambda + \varepsilon)/(\lambda - \varepsilon).$$

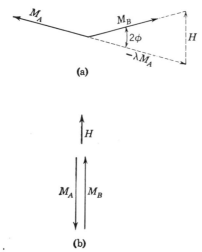

(a)

(b)

Fig. 15.28. Calculation of (a) perpendicular and (b) parallel susceptibilities at 0°K, on the molecular field theory.

SUSCEPTIBILITY BELOW THE CURIE POINT

We consider two cases on a two-sublattice model: first, with the applied magnetic field perpendicular to the axis of the spins; and, second, with the field parallel to the axis of the spins. At the Curie point the susceptibility is nearly independent of the direction of the field relative to the domain axis.

For $\mathbf{H} \perp \mathbf{M}_A$, $\mathbf{M}_B$ we can calculate the susceptibility on elementary considerations. If the spin systems A, B are turned by the field H so as to make an angle 2ϕ with each other (Fig. 15.28a), the component of the molecular field acting on B in a direction parallel to H will be, for small angles, $-2\lambda M_A \phi$, and at equilibrium this is equal to but opposite H. The total magnetization component parallel to H is

[28] L. Néel, Ann. phys. **3**, 137 (1948).

[29] P. W. Anderson, Phys. Rev. **79**, 350, 705 (1950); J. M. Luttinger, Phys. Rev. **81**, 1015 (1951).

$M\phi = (M_A + M_B)\phi = 2M_A\phi$, and so

(15.60) $$H = \lambda M,$$

or

(15.61) $$\chi_\perp = \frac{1}{\lambda} \qquad (T \le T_c).$$

Now, from (15.56), (15.57), and (15.58),

(15.62) $$\chi(T_c) = \frac{1}{\lambda},$$

and so

(15.63) $$\chi_\perp(0) = \chi(T_c).$$

On quantum-mechanical treatments $\chi_\perp(0)$ is somewhat larger than $\chi(T_c)$; therefore (15.61) need not hold.

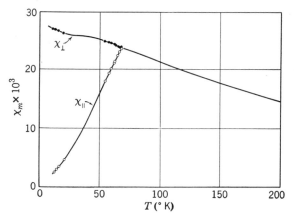

Fig. 15.29. Molar magnetic susceptibility of manganese fluoride, MnF_2, parallel and perpendicular to the c axis of the crystal. (After Griffel and Stout.) Recent measurements suggest $\chi_\perp$ is horizontal below T_c.

In the parallel orientation (Fig. 15.28b) the susceptibility at $T = 0°K$ is zero:

(15.64) $$\chi_\|(0) = 0;$$

the spins being at absolute zero all parallel or antiparallel to the field, no torque is exerted on them, and there is no net magnetization. Van Vleck's calculations show that the parallel susceptibility increases smoothly until it reaches the value

(15.65) $$\chi_\|(T_c) = \chi_\perp(T_c) = \chi(T_c).$$

Stout and Griffel[30] have verified the anisotropy of χ below the Curie point with measurements on a single crystal of manganese fluoride, as shown in Fig. 15.29.

In a polycrystalline specimen at $0°K$ the mean susceptibility is given by

$$(15.66) \qquad \overline{\chi(0)} = \overline{\sin^2 \theta}\, \chi_{\perp}(0) + \overline{\cos^2 \theta}\, \chi_{\parallel}(0) = \tfrac{2}{3}\chi(T_c),$$

assuming (15.63) and (15.64). The average of $\sin^2 \theta$ over a sphere is $\tfrac{2}{3}$. The factor $\tfrac{2}{3}$ is in fair agreement with some of the experimental ratios in Table 15.5. The calculated values will depend on the actual arrangement of the spin lattices.

ANTIFERROMAGNETIC RESONANCE

Spin resonance absorption in antiferromagnetic crystals at temperatures above the Curie point is similar to that observed in paramagnetic crystals, but below the Curie point there is a strong effective field leading to a zero field splitting of the resonance line. In the simplest situation at $0°K$ the effective field, apart from the applied magnetic field, is given by[31]

$$(15.67) \qquad H_{\text{eff}} = [H_A(2H_E + H_A)]^{1/2},$$

where H_A is the effective anisotropy field of one sublattice and H_E is the exchange field. For manganese fluoride the effective field amounts to 1.0×10^5 oersteds, corresponding to a zero field splitting of 1 mm wavelength. This has been observed by Johnson and Nethercot. Gorter and co-workers[32] have observed antiferromagnetic resonance in $CuCl_2 \cdot 2H_2O$ with a Curie point near $4°K$.

DETERMINATION OF SPIN LATTICES BY NEUTRON DIFFRACTION

Shull[33] and his collaborators have had remarkable success in the determination of the arrangement of spins into lattices in ferromagnetic and antiferromagnetic substances by neutron diffraction experi-

[30] J. W. Stout and M. Griffel, J. Chem. Phys. **18**, 1455 (1950).

[31] T. Nagamiya, Progr. Theoret. Phys. (Japan) **6**, 342 (1951); C. Kittel, Phys. Rev. **82**, 565 (1951); F. Keffer and C. Kittel, Phys. Rev. **85**, 329 (1952); F. Keffer, Phys. Rev. **87**, 608 (1952).

[32] Poulis, van den Handel, Ubbink, Poulis, and Gorter, Phys. Rev. **82**, 552 (1951); Ubbink, Poulis, Gerritsen, and Gorter, Physica **18**, 361 (1951).

[33] Shull, Strauser, and Wollan, Phys. Rev. **83**, 333 (1951); Shull, Wollan, and Koehler, Phys. Rev. **84**, 912 (1951). The first direct proof that antiferromagnetics contain ordered arrangements of antiparallel spins is due to C. G. Shull and J. S. Smart, Phys. Rev. **76**, 1256 (1949).

ments.   The experimental spin structure of manganese oxide in the antiferromagnetic state is shown in Fig. 15.30.   The most surprising feature about the observed spin lattice structure is that it suggests a strong next nearest neighbor interaction.   The strength of the next nearest neighbor interaction may be interpreted[29] on the Kramers[34]

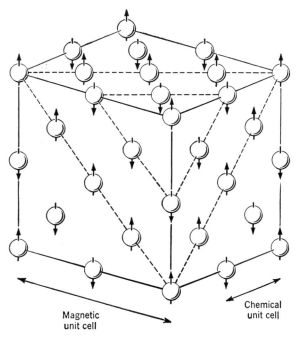

Fig. 15.30.   Arrangement of spins of the Mn^{2+} ions in manganese oxide, MnO, as determined by neutron diffraction methods by Shull, Strauser, and Wollan; see, however, Yin Yuan Li, Phys. Rev. **100**, 627 (1955).   More recent work indicates that the spin directions lie in the [111] planes.

picture of superexchange, according to which the possibility of excited paramagnetic states of the intervening anion (oxygen in this case) serves to carry the exchange interaction diametrically across the anion, thereby linking the spin systems of two Mn ions situated too far apart for direct exchange to be important.

MAGNETIC PROPERTIES OF FERRITES

The simplest ferrites of magnetic interest belong to the group of compounds of composition represented by the chemical formula $MOFe_2O_3$, where M is a divalent metal ion such as Mn, Co, Ni, Cu, Mg, Zn, Cd,

[34] H. A. Kramers, Physica **1**, 182 (1934).

Fe^{2+}, or a mixture of these ions.   These ferrites are cubic and have the spinel structure, after the mineral spinel ($MgAl_2O_4$).   Ferrites may be imagined as derived from magnetite, Fe_3O_4, by replacing the ferrous ions by the divalent ions listed above.

Ferrites have acquired great practical interest because their high electrical resistivities are useful in magnetic applications at high frequencies.   The resistivities of commercial ferrites are in the range 10^2 to 10^6 ohm-cm, as compared with 10^{-5} ohm-cm for iron.   The

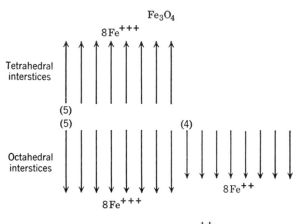

Fig. 15.31.   Schematic spin arrangements in magnetite, $FeO \cdot Fe_2O_3$, showing how the moments of the Fe^{+3} ions cancel out, leaving only the moments of the Fe^{+2} ions.

original commercial development is due to Snoek, Verwey, and others at the Philips Laboratories.   Ferroxcube 3 (Zn-Mn ferrite) and Ferroxcube 4 (Zn-Ni ferrite) are representative of the materials of interest.

The properties of ferrites are reviewed in the papers by Went and Gorter and by Fairweather et al., cited at the end of the chapter.   We mention here several aspects of the Néel theory[35] of the saturation magnetization of ferrites.   We note first from Table 15.1 that the value 485 for the saturation magnetization of Fe_3O_4 corresponds only to 4.2 Bohr magnetons per molecule Fe_3O_4, whereas the value expected if the one Fe^{2+} and two Fe^{3+} ions per molecule are lined up parallel to one another is about $14\mu_B$ per molecule.   Néel accounts for the experimental facts by supposing that the Fe^{3+} ions are antiparallel to each other and so the resultant moment arises only from the Fe^{2+} ion, as in Fig. 15.31.   This has a moment of $4\mu_B$ corresponding to a

[35] L. Néel, Ann. phys. **3**, 137 (1948).

spin of 2: the agreement with the observed moment of magnetite is quite satisfactory.   Néel terms a situation of this type *ferrimagnetism;* the basic idea was anticipated by the work of Guillaud on manganese compounds such as MnBi. The conditions are illustrated by Fig. 15.32.   Néel suggests that all the interactions in ferrites are antiferromagnetic, but shows that the condition of minimum free energy may often require, when two types of ions are involved, that the total magnetization be different from zero. Ferrimagnetics over their Curie point are characterized by a plot of $1/\chi$ vs. T which is concave downwards, as shown in Fig. 15.33 for magnetite.   Here χ is the susceptibility.

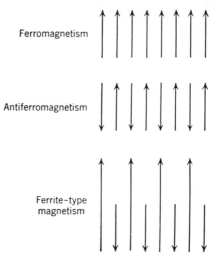

Fig. 15.32. Spin arrangements characterizing ferromagnetism, antiferromagnetism, and ferrite-type magnetism well below the Curie temperature.

The Néel theory accounts in a natural way for the variation with zinc content of the saturation magnetization curves shown in Fig. 15.34.   The moments for zero zinc content agree quite well with the

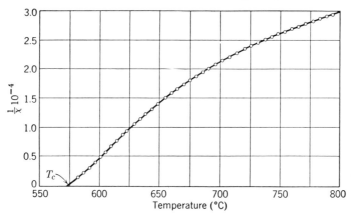

Fig. 15.33.   Reciprocal susceptibility of magnetite, $FeO \cdot Fe_2O_3$, above the Curie temperature.

idea that the Fe^{3+} ions do not contribute, and the trend of the moments toward zero for $ZnO \cdot Fe_2O_3$ is also plausible, as shown in Fig. 15.35.

In the intermediate region the zinc ions cause an unbalance in the system, increasing the total moment. The situation is discussed by Went and Gorter.

The spinel structure (Fig. 15.36) may be visualized as a cubic close packing of oxygen ions with the Fe^{3+} and M^{2+} ions distributed among

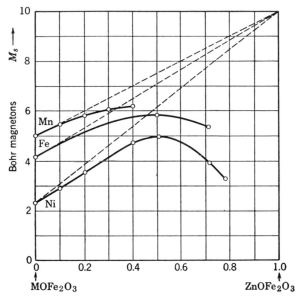

Fig. 15.34. Saturation magnetization of mixed Mn-Zn, Fe-Zn, and Ni-Zn ferrites, as a function of the zinc content. [After J. J. Went and E. W. Gorter, Philips Tech. Rev. **13**, 181 (1952).]

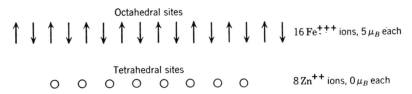

Fig. 15.35. Explanation of zero saturation magnetization in zinc ferrite; the zinc ions are diamagnetic and occupy the tetrahedral sites (Fig. 15.36). The antiferromagnetic interaction of the ferric ions on the octahedral sites controls the magnetic structure.

the various interstices between the O^{2-} ions. The unit cell is about 8.4 A on a side and contains 64 tetrahedral interstices (A) each with four O^{2-} nearest neighbors and 32 octahedral interstices (B) each with six O^{2-} nearest neighbors. Eight of the tetrahedral and sixteen of the octahedral sites are occupied, thus accommodating 24 metal ions in the unit cell. The exchange interactions $A - A$, $B - B$, and $A - B$ are all antiferromagnetic. The $A - B$ interaction is usually considerably the strongest, so the A and B lattices are individually ferromagnetic but with the magnetizations M_A, M_B oppositely directed. If, however, $M_A = 0$ as in zinc ferrite, the only effective exchange interaction is $B - B$; so the B ions will be antiferromagnetically ordered and $M_B = 0$.

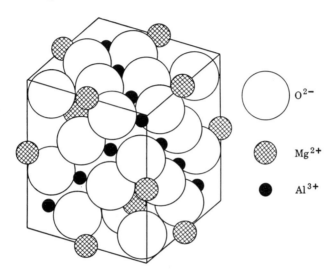

Fig. 15.36. Crystal structure of the mineral spinel ($MgAl_2O_4$); the Mg^{+2} ions occupy tetrahedral sites, each surrounded by four oxygen ions; the Al^{+3} ions occupy octahedral sites, each surrounded by six oxygen ions. This is a *normal* spinel arrangement.

The circumstance that three antiferromagnetic interactions can result in ferromagnetism is worth looking into more closely. The molecular fields acting on the A and B spin lattices may be written

(15.68)
$$\mathbf{H}_A = -\lambda \mathbf{M}_A - \mu \mathbf{M}_B;$$
$$\mathbf{H}_B = -\mu \mathbf{M}_A - \nu \mathbf{M}_B;$$

taking λ, μ, ν to be positive. The interaction energy is then

(15.69)
$$E = -\tfrac{1}{2}(\mathbf{H}_A \cdot \mathbf{M}_A + \mathbf{H}_B \cdot \mathbf{M}_B)$$
$$= \tfrac{1}{2}\lambda M_A{}^2 + \mu \mathbf{M}_A \cdot \mathbf{M}_B + \tfrac{1}{2}\nu M_B{}^2,$$

which is lower when M_A is antiparallel then when it is parallel to M_B. The energy when antiparallel must be compared with zero, the energy for $M_A = M_B = 0$. Thus when

(15.70) $$\mu M_A M_B > \tfrac{1}{2}(\lambda M_A{}^2 + \nu M_B{}^2)$$

the ground state will have M_A directed oppositely to M_B.

PROBLEMS

15.1. Show that the condition for ferromagnetic resonance in a general ellipsoid with demagnetizing factors N_x, N_y, N_z is

$$\omega = \gamma\{[H + (N_x - N_z)M][H + (N_y - N_z)M]\}^{1/2},$$

where the static field H is in the z direction. It is assumed that the ellipsoid is small in comparison with the wavelength and is made of an insulating ferromagnetic substance, such as a ferrite, so that eddy current effects may be neglected.

15.2. In a cubic crystal the elastic energy density is, according to (4.22),

$$U_e = \tfrac{1}{2}c_{11}(e_{xx}{}^2 + e_{yy}{}^2 + e_{zz}{}^2) + \tfrac{1}{2}c_{44}(e_{xy}{}^2 + e_{yz}{}^2 + e_{zz}{}^2)$$
$$+ c_{12}(e_{yy}e_{zz} + e_{xx}e_{zz} + e_{xx}e_{yy}),$$

and the magnetic anisotropy energy density is, from (15.32),

$$U_a \cong K(\alpha_1{}^2\alpha_2{}^2 + \alpha_2{}^2\alpha_3{}^2 + \alpha_3{}^2\alpha_1{}^2).$$

Coupling between elastic strain and magnetization direction may be taken formally into account by adding to the total energy density a term

$$U_c \cong B_1(\alpha_1{}^2 e_{xx} + \alpha_2{}^2 e_{yy} + \alpha_3{}^2 e_{zz}) + B_2(\alpha_1\alpha_2 e_{xy} + \alpha_2\alpha_3 e_{yz} + \alpha_3\alpha_1 e_{zz}),$$

which may be regarded as a first order correction to U_a arising from the strain dependence of U_a; here B_1 and B_2 are constants and are called *magnetoelastic coupling constants*. Show that the total energy is a minimum when

$$e_{ii} = B_1[c_{12} - \alpha_i{}^2(c_{11} + 2c_{12})]/[(c_{11} - c_{12})(c_{11} + 2c_{12})];$$

$$e_{ij} = -B_2\alpha_i\alpha_j/c_{44} \qquad (i \neq j).$$

This is a formal explanation of the origin of magnetostriction.

15.3. Show that the magnetic energy of a saturated sphere of diameter d is $\approx M_s{}^2 d^3$. The domain wall energy of an arrangement with appreciably less magnetic energy will be $\pi\sigma_w d^2/4$, where σ_w is the wall energy per unit area, and the wall is taken as passing through the center of the sphere. Estimate for cobalt the critical radius below which the particles are stable as single domains, taking JS^2/a as for iron.

15.4. Consider a small spherical single-domain particle. Show that the effective permeability for a weak field applied perpendicular to the easy axis is

$$\mu = 1 + 2\pi(M_s{}^2/K),$$

and show that $2K/M_s$ may be regarded as an effective anisotropy field. Show also that the reverse field along the axis required to reverse the magnetization is

$$H = 2K/M_s.$$

The coercive force for a single-domain particle is of this magnitude. Estimate H_c for iron single-domain particles.

15.5. Taking the effective fields on the two-sublattice model of an antiferro-magnetic is

$$H_A = H - \lambda M_B - \varepsilon M_A,$$

$$H_B = H - \lambda M_A - \varepsilon M_B,$$

show that

$$\theta/T_c = (\lambda + \varepsilon)/(\lambda - \varepsilon).$$

15.6.* Show that, for spins on a face-centered cubic lattice with antiferromag-netic nearest neighbor interactions only,

$$\theta/T_c = 3.$$

15.7. Explain in terms of domain magnetization processes the values of the magnetization at which the curves for nickel in Fig. 15.13 diverge from each other at low fields. Show that the turning points are given approximately by $M = M_s$, $M_s(2/3)^{1/2}$, $M_s/3^{1/2}$ for the [111], [110], and [100] directions, respectively.

15.8. Discuss the form of the variation of $1/\chi$ vs. T for a ferrimagnetic over the Curie point, assuming antiferromagnetic molecular field constants λ, ν, μ governing, respectively, interactions of the magnetization on sublattice A with itself, B with itself, and A with B.

15.9.* The theory of the microwave gyrator is discussed by C. L. Hogan, Bell System Tech. J. **31**, 1 (1952); applications are reviewed by J. H. Rowen, Bell System Tech. J. **32**, 1333 (1953). A plane-polarized electromagnetic wave is incident normally on a ferrite slab of thickness l. A static magnetic field H_0 is applied parallel to the propagation direction. Neglecting attenuation, show that the rotation θ of the plane of polarization in the ferrite is $\theta \cong \frac{1}{2}\varepsilon^{1/2}\omega_1 l$, where ε is the dielectric constant of the ferrite, $\omega_1 = 4\pi M\gamma \cong \gamma H_0$, where γ is defined by Eq. (9.40). The derivation proceeds most easily by substituting $\dot{M} = \gamma M \times H$ in the Maxwell equation for curl E, giving

$$c \text{ curl } E = -(\dot{H} + \omega_1 \times H).$$

Proceeding in the usual way, find a wave equation for H. Let $h^{\pm} = H_x \pm iH_y$, and look for solutions of the form $e^{i(\omega t - kz)}$. Assume $\omega_1 \ll \omega$.

REFERENCES

L. F. Bates, *Modern magnetism*, Cambridge University Press, Cambridge, 3rd ed., 1951.
R. Becker and W. Döring, *Ferromagnetismus*, J. Springer, Berlin, 1939.
R. M. Bozorth, *Ferromagnetism*, Van Nostrand, New York, 1951.
Fairweather, Roberts, and Welch, "Ferrites," Repts. Prog. Phys. **15**, 142 (1952).
C. Kittel, "Physical theory of ferromagnetic domains," Revs. Modern Phys. **21**, 541 (1949); C. Kittel and J. K. Galt, Solid State Physics, **3** (1956).
A. Lidiard, "Antiferromagnetism," Repts. Prog. Phys. **17**, 201–244 (1954).
U. M. Martius, "Ferromagnetism," Progress in Metal Physics **3**, 140–175 (1952).
T. Nagamiya, K. Yosida, and R. Kubo, "Antiferromagnetism," Advances in Physics **4**, 1–112 (1955).
ONR Maryland Magnetism Conference, Revs. Modern Phys. (January, 1953).
H. Reich, "Die Theorie des ferromagnetischen Resonanz und die Ergebnisse ihrer experimentellen Untersuchung," Z. angew. Physik **6**, 326–338 (1954).
M. G. Say, editor, *Magnetic alloys and ferrites*, Newnes, London, 1954.

J. S. Smart, The Néel theory of ferrimagnetism, Am. J. Phys. **23,** 356 (1955).

J. L. Snoek, *New developments in ferromagnetic materials*, Elsevier, Amsterdam, 2nd ed., 1949.

K. H. Stewart, Ferromagnetic domains, Cambridge University Press, Cambridge, 1954.

E. C. Stoner, "Ferromagnetism," Rept. Prog. Phys. **11,** 43 (1948); **13,** 83 (1950).

E. C. Stoner, *Magnetism and matter*, Methuen and Co., Ltd., London, 1934.

J. H. Van Vleck, "A survey of the theory of ferromagnetism," Revs. Modern Phys. **17,** 27 (1945).

J. H. Van Vleck, "Recent developments in the theory of antiferromagnetism," J. phys. radium **12,** 262 (1951).

J. J. Went and E. W. Gorter, "Magnetic and electrical properties of Ferroxcube materials," Philips Tech. Rev. **13,** 181 (1952).

16

Superconductivity

We first survey the central experimental facts concerning super-conductivity, and then discuss the theoretical situation and supplementary experiments bearing on the theory. There is not yet a satisfactory quantum theory of superconductivity, but we do have a fairly satisfactory macroscopic theory of the electrodynamics of superconductivity. The direction which the ultimate quantum theory may take is gradually becoming apparent.

EXPERIMENTAL SITUATION

Zero resistance. Superconductivity was discovered in 1911 when Kamerlingh Onnes observed at Leiden that the resistivity of mercury

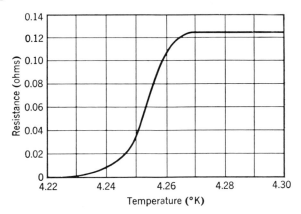

Fig. 16.1. Resistance of mercury as a function of temperature. (After Kamerlingh Onnes, 1911.)

(Fig. 16.1) vanished completely below 4.2°K, the transition from normal conductivity occurring over a very narrow range of temperature of the order of 0.05°K.

Persistent currents. A ring of superconducting material is cooled in a magnetic field from a temperature above the transition temperature T_c to below T_c; the field is then switched off, thereby inducing currents in the ring. The currents have been observed by the associated magnetic field to persist with undiminished strength for days. In experiments at Leiden[1] using a coil of 700 meters of lead wire wound non-inductively it was impossible in a run of about 12 hr to detect any decrease of the current. From the sensitivity of the apparatus and the decay formula $i \sim e^{-Rt/L}$ it was calculated that $R < 10^{-17}R_0$, where R_0 is the resistance at room temperature, or $R < 10^{-15}R_0'$,

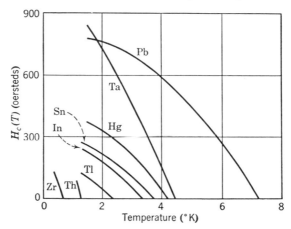

Fig. 16.2a.   Threshold field curves for several superconductors.   (From F. London, *Superfluids*, Vol. I, John Wiley & Sons, 1950.)

where R_0' is the extrapolated residual resistance at 0°K, extrapolated as if superconductivity did not set in.   In an unpublished experiment at M.I.T. it is reported that a lead ring has carried an induced current of several hundred amperes for over a year, with no change.

Effect of magnetic fields.   It is possible to destroy superconductivity by the application of a sufficiently strong magnetic field.   The threshold or critical value of the magnetic field for the destruction of superconductivity is denoted by $H_c(T)$ and is a function of the temperature; at $T = T_c$, $H_c = 0$.   The variation of the critical field with temperature for several superconducting elements is shown in Fig. 16.2a.   The threshold curves separate the superconducting state in the lower left region of the figure from the normal state in the uper right region.   The dependence of $H_c(0)$ on T_c is shown in Fig. 16.2b.

The original observation on destruction was made by Kamerlingh Onnes in 1913; he found that the passage of an electric current down a superconducting wire led to the destruction of superconductivity when a certain critical current was exceeded.   This circumstance prevents

[1] Unpublished; quoted by H. B. G. Casimir, Ann Arbor Lectures, 1948.

the use of superconducting electromagnets to produce intense magnetic fields. Silsbee (1916) suggested that the important factor in causing the transition back to the normal state was the magnetic field associated with the current, rather than the value of the current itself.

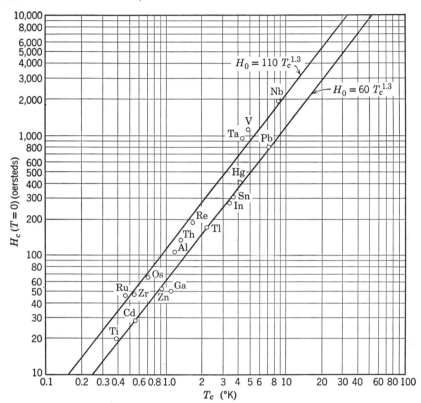

Fig. 16.2b. Log-log plot of critical field at $T = 0$ vs. transition temperature T_c, as given by H. W. Lewis, Phys. Rev. **101**, 939 (1956). This type of plot separates the hard and soft types of superconductors, or the transition and non-transition elements. [This particular graph was prepared by R. Glover from data in the book by Shoenberg and the review by J. Eisenstein, Revs. Mod. Phys. **26**, 277 (1954).]

Thus superconductivity in a long circular wire of radius a should be destroyed when the current I exceeds the value determined by the equation $H_c = 2I/a$ for the field at the surface of the wire. The Silsbee hypothesis has been confirmed experimentally for pure unstrained metallic elements; however, complex compounds and alloys, or impure and strained elements, do not satisfy the Silsbee relationship, and such specimens are termed *non-ideal*.

Flux exclusion. Meissner and Ochsenfeld[2] (1933) showed that, if a long superconductor is cooled in a longitudinal magnetic field from above the transition temperature, the lines of induction are pushed out (Fig. 16.3) at the transition. The Meissner effect shows that a superconductor behaves as if inside the specimen $B = 0$ or $\chi = -1/4\pi$; that is, a superconductor exhibits perfect diamagnetism. This very important result cannot be derived merely from the characterization of a superconductor as a medium of zero resistivity ρ: from $\mathbf{E} = \rho\mathbf{j}$ we

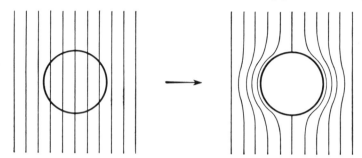

Fig. 16.3.   Meissner effect in a sphere cooled in a constant applied magnetic field; on passing below the transition temperature the lines of induction are ejected from the sphere.   (From F. London, *Superfluids*, Vol. I, John Wiley & Sons, 1950.)

see that, if ρ is zero while $\mathbf{j}$ is finite, then $\mathbf{E}$ must be zero and with it curl $\mathbf{E}$ must be zero.   Therefore from Maxwell's equations

$$(16.1) \qquad \frac{d\mathbf{B}}{dt} = -c \text{ curl } \mathbf{E} = 0,$$

so that the flux through the metal cannot change on cooling through the transition.   The Meissner effect contradicts this result and suggests that perfect diamagnetism and zero resistivity are two independent essential properties of the superconducting state.

Intermediate state. The magnetization curve for a *sphere* in the superconducting state (Fig. 16.4) shows that superconductivity is partially destroyed for $\tfrac{2}{3}H_c < H < H_c$. This region is called the intermediate state, although it is really a mixture of domains of normal and superconducting states. The magnetization curve for $H < \tfrac{2}{3}H_c$ is in good agreement with an apparent diamagnetic susceptibility $\chi = -(1/4\pi)$, provided that demagnetization effects are taken into account.

Entropy increase on going to normal state. There is a difference between the heat capacities in the normal and superconducting states

[2] W. Meissner and R. Ochsenfeld, Naturwiss. **21,** 787 (1933).

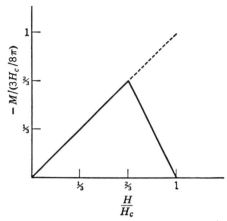

Fig. 16.4. Magnetization curve of a sphere below T_c, showing the onset of the intermediate state at $H/H_c = \frac{2}{3}$. The initial part of the curve is determined by the relations $H_i = H - (4\pi/3)M$; $B_i = 0 = H_i + 4\pi M = H + (8\pi/3)M$. (From F. London, *Superfluids*, Vol. I, John Wiley & Sons, 1950.)

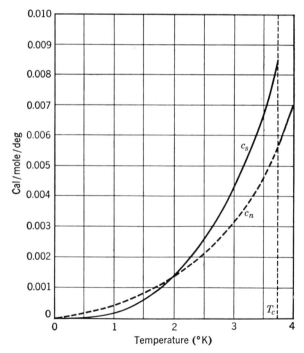

Fig. 16.5. Heat capacity of tin in the normal and superconducting states. [After Keesom and Van Laer, Physica **5**, 193 (1938).] The heat capacity in the normal state below T_c is measured in the presence of a magnetic field strong enough to destroy superconductivity.

(Fig. 16.5). Below the transition temperature there is an increase of entropy on going from the superconducting state to the normal state. That is, the superconducting state is more ordered than the normal state. The difference in entropy is of the order of $10^{-3} R$ per mole, instead of the order of R as in an ordinary transition of the second kind (such as in ferromagnetism). The small difference suggests that the rearrangement of the system on becoming superconducting is relatively small, so that only relatively few electrons are affected.

Frequency effects. In d-c measurements the resistivity in the superconducting state is zero. At infrared frequencies the resistivity is

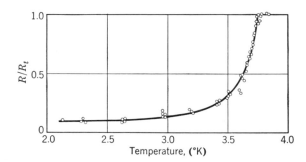

Fig. 16.6. Surface resistance of tin in the superconducting state, at 24,000 mc/sec. [After Maxwell, Marcus, and Slater, Phys. Rev. **76**, 1332 (1949).]

that of the normal state; that is, no change in the resistivity, as measured by the reflection coefficient, is observed on passing through the critical magnetic field. The transition between low frequency behavior and high frequency behavior occurs gradually, but is well along at microwave frequencies (Fig. 16.6). Measurements by Tinkham and Glover on lead indicate that the resistivity is that of the normal state at wavelengths below 100 microns.

Gyromagnetic ratio. Kikoin and Gubar[3] performed a gyromagnetic experiment on a superconductor and found the magnetomechanical factor (see Eq. 15.19) $g' = 1.0$, as expected if the superconducting currents are caused by the motion of electrons.

Isotope effect. It has been observed that the critical temperature of superconductors varies with isotopic mass. The observation was first made by Maxwell[4] and by Reynolds and co-workers,[5] who used mercury isotopes; the effect has since been found by workers using

[3] I. K. S. Kikoin and S. W. Gubar, J. Phys. (U.S.S.R.) **3**, 333 (1940); R. H. Pry, A. L. Lathrup, and W. V. Houston, Phys. Rev. **86**, 905 (1952).

[4] E. Maxwell, Phys. Rev. **78**, 477 (1950).

[5] Reynolds, Serin, Wright, and Nesbitt, Phys. Rev. **78**, 487 (1950).

tin[6] and lead[7] isotopes. To give an idea of the magnitude of the effect, for mercury T_c varies from 4.185°K to 4.146°K as the isotopic mass M varies from 199.5 to 203.4.

The experimental results are generally in agreement with a relation of the form

(16.2)
$$M^{\frac{1}{2}}T_c = \text{constant}$$

within each series of isotopes, as shown for mercury in Fig. 16.7. This

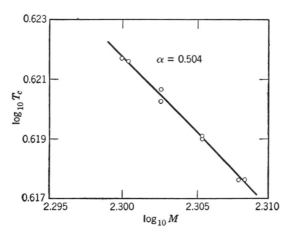

Fig. 16.7. Log-log plot of transition temperature vs. average mass number for separated isotopes of mercury. [After Reynolds, Serin, and Nesbitt, Phys. Rev. **84**, 691 (1951).] The line drawn is a fit of the equation $M^{\alpha}T_c = \text{constant}$; α as determined from these data by a least squares fit equals 0.504.

leads to the very suggestive relation

(16.3)
$$T_c/\Theta = \text{constant},$$

where Θ is the Debye temperature; (16.3) follows from (16.2) on observing that Θ is proportional to the sound velocity v, which in turn is proportional to $M^{-\frac{1}{2}}$. The constancy of T_c/Θ implies that lattice vibrations have an important bearing on superconductivity and gives a clear guide to theory by suggesting that electron lattice interactions must be taken into account.

[6] E. Maxwell, Phys. Rev. **79**, 173 (1950); **86**, 235 (1952); D. Shoenberg et al., Nature **166**, 1071 (1950); K. Mendelssohn et al., Nature **166**, 1071 (1950).

[7] M. Olsen, Nature **168**, 245 (1951); Serin, Reynolds and Lohman, Phys. Rev. **86**, 162 (1952).

TABLE 16.1. SUPERCONDUCTING ELEMENTS IN THE PERIODIC SYSTEM

(Transition temperatures given below superconductors)

H																	He
Li	Be											B	C	N	O	F	Ne
Na	Mg											Al 1.14°	Si	P	S	Cl	A
K	Ca	Sc	Ti 0.53°	V 5.1°	Cr	Mn	Fe	Co	Ni	Cu	Zn 0.79°	Ga 1.07°	Ge	As	Se	Br	Kr
Rb	Sr	Y	Zr 0.7°	Nb 9.22°	Mo	Tc 11.2°	Ru 0.47°	Rh	Pd	Ag	Cd 0.54°	In 3.37°	Sn† 3.73°	Sb	Te	I	Xe
Cs	Ba	La 4.71° Lu	Hf 0.35°	Ta 4.38°	W	Re 2.4°	Os 0.71°	Ir	Pt	Au	Hg 4.15°	Tl 2.38°	Pb 7.22°	Bi‡	Po	At	Rn
Fr	Ra	Ac	Th 1.32°	Pa	U 0.8°												

† White tin.

‡ Bismuth under pressure undergoes a crystallographic modification and becomes superconducting. It is also superconducting as an amorphous film.

Occurrence of superconductivity. The superconducting elements and their transition temperatures are listed in Table 16.1. The features to be noted are:

(a) Monovalent metals are not superconductors.

(b) The ferromagnetic and antiferromagnetic metals are not superconductors.

(c) Superconducting metals are not as good conductors at room temperature as the normal metals at room temperature. For example; titanium, zirconium, and hafnium have resistivities at room temperature of 89, 45, and 32 microhm-cm, respectively, while copper, silver, and gold have 1.6, 1.5, and 2.4 microhm-cm.

It is always possible that metals not reported as superconducting may become so at lower temperatures than attained during the tests, but in a number of cases runs have been made to $\sim$0.07°K without finding superconductivity. A negative result at low temperatures is conclusive only if the earth's magnetic field is compensated for, as emphasized by H. W. Lewis. The magnetic field of nuclear moments may also be effective.

Non-ideal superconductors. A number of chemical compounds are superconducting, including several compounds composed of elements none of which is superconducting, such as molybdenum carbide, MoC, with $T_c = 7.6 - 8.3$°K. The superconducting compounds and alloys are often characterized by a high transition temperature, high critical field, incomplete Meissner effect, breakdown of Silsbee's rule, and a broad transition region; because of these properties they are known as non-ideal or hard superconductors. The anomalous properties have not yet found a complete explanation. Transition elements which are superconducting are often "hard" in this sense. Absorbed gases may play a role in causing hardness. Data on compounds are given in Table 16.2. The intermetallic[8] compound Nb_3Sn has the highest transition temperature yet reported, 18.0°K. We may mention that Hilsch has reported that completely amorphous tin films have a superconducting transition at 4.5°K, compared with 3.7°K for bulk tin. The films were deposited on a substrate cooled by liquid helium. It would appear from this result that lattice order is not required for superconductivity. Films have been found superconducting down to nearly 10A in thickness.

Lasarew and Galkin[9] have shown that all the characteristic features of a superconductive alloy can be reproduced in a chemically pure

---

[8] Matthias, Geballe, Geller, and Corenzwit, Phys. Rev. **95**, 1435 (1954); B. T. Matthias, Phys. Rev. **92**, 874 (1953); **97**, 74 (1955).

[9] B. Lasarew and A. Galkin, J. Phys. (U.S.S.R.) **8**, 371 (1944).

specimen of a nominally ideal or soft superconductor by application of a severe inhomogeneous strain. They found that, for tin on going from the unstrained to the strained condition, T_c increased from 3.72° to 9.0°K, while H_c at 2°K increased from 210 to 15,000 oersteds; at the same time the critical current at 2°K dropped from 3.0 to 0.067 amp, demonstrating the breakdown of Silsbee's rule.

Superconductivity of small particles. The diamagnetic susceptibility of small particles is less than that of bulk superconductors. A large mercury sphere (Fig. 16.4) exhibits an effective volume susceptibility of $\chi_0 = -3/8\pi$, whereas Shoenberg[10] finds $\chi/\chi_0 < 0.005$ for mercury particles of diameter about 10^{-5} cm suspended in an albumen colloid. Mercury particles of diameter about 10^{-4} cm have $\chi/\chi_0 \approx 0.4$.

Thermoelectric effects. Daunt and Mendelssohn[11] found that the Thomson coefficient of superconductive lead was zero within their accuracy, which meant less than 2×10^{-3} of the Thomson coefficient just above the transition. It was concluded from this result that the entropy of the superconducting electrons is effectively zero.

TABLE 16.2. TRANSITION TEMPERATURES OF SUPERCONDUCTING COMPOUNDS

Results are variable from specimen to specimen, and in some cases the pure metal present as a precipitate may be responsible for the superconductivity. For data on alloys, see Shoenberg's book cited at the end of the chapter.

Compound	T_c(°K)	Compound	T_c(°K)
Pb_2Au	7.0	ZrB	2.8– 3.2
$PbTl_2$	3.8	CuS	1.6
Pb_5Na_2	7.2	TaSi	4.4
SnSb	3.9	MoC	7.6– 8.3
Sn_3Sb_2	4.0	Mo_2C	2.4– 3.2
Sn_2Au	2.5–2.75	MoB	4.4
Sn_4Au	2.5–2.75	Mo_2N	5
Tl_3Bi_5	6.4	MoN	12.0
Tl_2Hg_5	3.8	NbN	14.7
Tl_7Sb_2	5.2	NbB	6
Au_2Bi	1.7	NbC	10.1–10.5
WC	2.5–4.2	TaC	9.3– 9.5
ZrC	2.3	W_2C	2.0– 3.5
VN	1.5–3.2	ZrN	9.3– 9.6
PdSb	1.5°	$CoSi_2$	1.27

Thermal conductivity. Hulm, and Mendelssohn and Olsen,[12] have discussed results on thermal conductivity in superconductors. In ideal superconductors there is a marked drop in the thermal conduc-

[10] D. Shoenberg, Nature **143**, 434 (1939).

[11] J. G. Daunt and K. Mendelssohn, Proc. Soc. (London) **A185**, 225 (1946).

[12] K. Mendelssohn and J. L. Olsen, Proc. Phys. Soc. (London) **A63**, 2 (1950); J. K. Hulm, Proc. Roy. Soc. (London) **A204**, 98 (1950).

tivity when superconductivity sets in, suggesting that the electronic contribution drops, the superconducting electrons possibly playing no part in heat transfer. Results for a specimen of tin are given in Fig. 16.8. In impure or non-ideal superconductors an increase in thermal conductivity on becoming superconducting has been observed in a

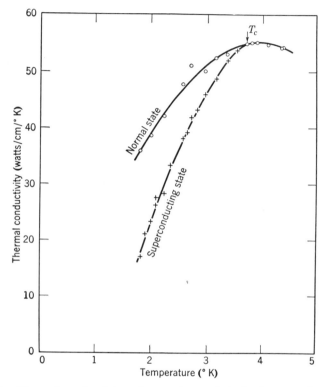

Fig. 16.8. Thermal conductivity of a specimen of tin in the normal and super-conducting states; results vary considerably among different specimens according to their purity. (After Hulm.)

few specimens. Hulm suggests that the increase is due to decreased scattering of lattice waves by electrons. Determinations of ultrasonic attenuation in superconductors indicate that only the normal electrons scatter phonons.

THEORETICAL SITUATION

There is at present no quantum theory of superconductivity which is generally accepted, although work by Fröhlich and Bardeen gives the impression that a period of progress may be close at hand. We first discuss several theoretical topics, including the London equations, which help define the problems requiring solution.

THERMODYNAMICS OF THE SUPERCONDUCTING TRANSITION

It has been demonstrated experimentally by van Laer and Keesom[13] that the transition between the normal and superconducting states is thermodynamically reversible, in the same sense that with slow evaporation the transition between liquid and vapor phases of a substance is reversible. The Meissner effect also suggests that the transition is reversible, which it would not be were the superconducting currents to die away with the production of Joule heat when superconductivity is destroyed. As the transition is reversible we may, following Gorter and Casimir,[14] apply thermodynamics to the transition, obtaining an expression for the entropy difference between normal and superconducting states in terms of the critical field curve H_c vs. T.

The Gibbs free energy per unit volume in a magnetic field is

$$(16.4) \qquad G = U - TS - HM;$$

here M is the magnetization and S the entropy; the pV term is neglected. We may verify (16.4) by observing that the internal energy density in the presence of a magnetic field is given, from Appendices F and R, by

$$(16.5) \qquad dU = T \, dS + H \, dM,$$

which may be compared with the familiar

$$(16.6) \qquad dU = T \, dS - p \, dV.$$

We see that the substitution

$$(16.7) \qquad p \to -H, \qquad V \to M$$

in the standard expression

$$(16.8) \qquad G = U - TS + pV$$

gives us (16.4) directly. Then, from (16.4) and (16.5),

$$(16.9) \qquad dG = -S \, dT - M \, dH.$$

---

[13] P. H. van Laer and W. H. Keesom, Physica **5**, 993 (1938).

[14] C. Gorter and H. B. G. Casimir, Physica **1**, 306 (1934); for a discussion of the "two-fluid" model of the superconducting state, see C. Gorter and H. B. G. Casimir, Physik. Z. **35**, 963 (1934).

Substituting $M = -H/4\pi$ and integrating (16.9), we have for the superconducting state

$$(16.10) \qquad G_s(H) = G_s(0) + \frac{1}{8\pi} H^2.$$

The central result of the thermodynamic theory of equilibria is that the Gibbs free energies must be equal for two phases to be in equilibrium (at constant T, P, H). Thus, along the critical field curve where the superconducting and normal states are in equilibrium,

$$(16.11) \qquad G_n = G_s(0) + \frac{1}{8\pi} H_c^2,$$

where G_n is the Gibbs free energy density of the normal state and is essentially independent of the magnetic field. From (16.9),

$$(16.12) \qquad (\partial G/\partial T)_H = -S,$$

and so (16.10) and (16.11) give the important result

$$(16.13) \qquad S_n - S_s = - \frac{H_c}{4\pi} \frac{dH_c}{dT},$$

where S_s is taken in zero field. As dH_c/dT is found to be always negative, the entropy of the normal state is always greater than the superconducting state.

The difference in heat capacity is given by

$$(16.14) \quad \Delta C = C_s - C_n = T \frac{d}{dT}(S_s - S_n) = \frac{TH_c}{4\pi} \frac{d^2H_c}{dT^2} + \frac{T}{4\pi}\left(\frac{dH_c}{dT}\right)^2,$$

per unit volume; at $T = T_c$, $H_c = 0$, and we have the Rutgers formula,

$$(16.15) \qquad \Delta C = \frac{T_c}{4\pi}\left(\frac{dH_c}{dT}\right)^2.$$

This relation is in satisfactory agreement with these experimental measurements:[15]

Substance	$T_c(°K)$	$(dH_c/dT)_{T=T_c}$ (oersteds/deg)	ΔC(calc) (cal/deg-mole)	ΔC(observed) (cal/deg-mole)
Tin	3.69	151.2	0.00229	0.0024
Thallium	2.38	137.4	0.00144	0.00148

We note from (16.13) that at the critical temperature there is no latent heat of transition ($\Delta S = 0$), but there is according to (16.15) a dis-

[15] The first work was by W. H. Keesom and J. A. Kok, Physica 1, 503, 595 (1934).

continuity in the heat capacity, so that the phase transition is of the second order. Below the critical temperature the transition in a magnetic field is accompanied by a latent heat.

THE BLOCH THEOREM

Before the discovery of the Meissner effect, discussions of the electrodynamics of superconductors were predicated on the assumption of free electrons moving with zero resistance, as this assumption accounts directly for the persistent currents and the zero resistivity. Attempts were made to set up quantum-mechanical models which would have the property that the lowest state of the system (or the state of lowest free energy) would exhibit a spontaneous current. Bloch, however, has proved the very important theorem that in general *the lowest state of a quantum-mechanical system in the absence of a magnetic field can carry no current*. The proof of the theorem is given in Appendix P. Bohm[16] has extended the result to show that states of finite current cannot be thermodynamically the most stable even if the temperature is different from zero. In a magnetic field, however, the most stable state *can* carry current.

THE LONDON EQUATIONS

We have explained the Meissner effect by taking $\chi = -1/4\pi$. This is a drastic assumption. An alternative approach is to modify the electrodynamic equations while leaving ϵ and μ unchanged. The assumption of zero resistivity leads to the acceleration equation

$$(16.16) \qquad e\mathbf{E} = m\dot{\mathbf{v}}$$

or, as $\mathbf{j} = Ne\mathbf{v}$,

$$(16.17) \qquad \mathbf{E} = \Lambda \, d\mathbf{j}/dt; \qquad \Lambda = m/Ne^2;$$

where N is the number of electrons per unit volume. Taking the curl of both sides, we have, as curl $\mathbf{E} = -\dot{\mathbf{H}}/c$,

$$(16.18) \qquad \text{curl } \Lambda \frac{d\mathbf{j}}{dt} = -\frac{1}{c}\dot{\mathbf{H}},$$

or, since $4\pi\mathbf{j}/c = $ curl $\mathbf{H}$,

$$(16.19) \qquad \frac{c}{4\pi}\text{curl curl }\Lambda\dot{\mathbf{H}} = \text{curl }\Lambda\frac{d\mathbf{j}}{dt} = -\frac{1}{c}\dot{\mathbf{H}}$$

[16] D. Bohm, Phys. Rev. **75**, 502 (1949).

We have, further, as div $\mathbf{H} = 0$,

(16.20)
$$\frac{\Lambda c^2}{4\pi} \nabla^2 \dot{\mathbf{H}} = \dot{\mathbf{H}}.$$

Integrating with respect to time, we have

(16.21)
$$\frac{\Lambda c^2}{4\pi} \nabla^2 (\mathbf{H} - \mathbf{H}_0) = \mathbf{H} - \mathbf{H}_0.$$

The result (16.21) admits the particular solution $H = H_0$, where H_0 is an arbitrary field existing at $t = 0$; but we know from the Meissner effect that we cannot have frozen-in fields. It is apparent that (16.21) has more general solutions than allowed by nature. We note that here the currents are considered the only internal source of field; no magnetization as such has been introduced. F. and H. London[17] therefore suggested that the acceleration equation be abandoned, and that we should take instead as the fundamental equation

(16.22)
$$c \text{ curl } \Lambda\mathbf{j} = -\mathbf{H},$$

which is postulated to replace Ohm's law in superconductors. We note that, if $\mathbf{H} = \text{curl } \mathbf{A}$, $\mathbf{j} = -\mathbf{A}/\Lambda c$. On taking curls in $4\pi\mathbf{j}/c = \text{curl } H$, we are led directly, using (16.22), to

(16.23)
$$\frac{\Lambda c^2}{4\pi} \nabla^2 \mathbf{H} = \mathbf{H},$$

which does not necessarily admit the former solution $H = H_0$. If we include the displacement current we have

(16.24)
$$\frac{\Lambda c^2}{4\pi} \left[\nabla^2 \mathbf{H} - \frac{1}{c^2} \ddot{\mathbf{H}} \right] = \mathbf{H}.$$

Equations (16.17) and (16.22), when applied to the superconducting electrons, are known as the London equations and are widely used, with considerable success, in macroscopic descriptions of the electrodynamic behavior of superconductors. London has shown that the usual thermodynamic treatment is consistent with his equations.

SUPERCONDUCTIVITY AT HIGH FREQUENCIES

We suppose that high frequency effects can be described by considering the current

(16.25)
$$\mathbf{j} = \mathbf{j}_n + \mathbf{j}_s$$

[17] F. London and H. London, Proc. Roy. Soc. (London) **A149**, 72 (1935); Physica **2**, 341 (1935); for earlier work leading to (16.21), see Becker, Sauter, and Heller, Z. Physik **85**, 772 (1933).

as the superposition of a normal (resistive) current given by

(16.26) $$\mathbf{j}_n = \sigma\mathbf{E}$$

and a superconductive current $\mathbf{j}_s$. Then

(16.27) $$c \text{ curl } \mathbf{H} = 4\pi(\sigma\mathbf{E} + \mathbf{j}_s) + \dot{\mathbf{E}},$$

and so

$$c \text{ curl curl } \mathbf{H} = -c\,\nabla^2\mathbf{H} = 4\pi(\sigma \text{ curl } \mathbf{E} + \text{ curl } \mathbf{j}_s) + \text{ curl } \dot{\mathbf{E}},$$

or, using (16.22) for curl $\mathbf{j}_s$,

(16.28) $$\nabla^2\mathbf{H} = \frac{4\pi\sigma}{c^2}\dot{\mathbf{H}} + \frac{4\pi}{\Lambda c^2}\mathbf{H} + \frac{\ddot{\mathbf{H}}}{c^2}.$$

We take $H \sim \exp\left[-i(\omega t - \mathbf{k}\cdot\mathbf{r})\right]$; so (16.28) gives

(16.29) $$k^2c^2 = 4\pi\sigma\omega i - (4\pi/\Lambda) + \omega^2,$$

the successive terms on the right representing the effects of the ordinary eddy current skin depth, the superconducting penetration depth, and the displacement current. This relation determines the propagation characteristics of the medium.

In the limit of low frequencies,

(16.30) $$k \cong i(4\pi/\Lambda c^2)^{\frac{1}{2}},$$

which represents a rapidly decreasing field penetration with H reduced by e^{-1} at the depth

(16.31) $$d = (\Lambda c^2/4\pi)^{\frac{1}{2}}.$$

Using the definition (16.17) of Λ,

(16.32) $$d = (mc^2/4\pi Ne^2)^{\frac{1}{2}}.$$

If we take $N \sim 10^{23}$ electrons/cm^3 as for a metal,

(16.33) $$\Lambda \sim 10^{-31} \text{ sec}^{-2},$$

and

(16.34) $$d \sim 10^{-5} \text{ cm}.$$

Thus at low frequencies the penetration of a magnetic field into a superconductor is severely limited by the superconducting properties of the substance as expressed by the constant Λ.

At frequencies in the infrared, taking $\sigma \approx 10^{20}$ esu (as for normal metals at low temperatures) and $\omega \approx 10^{13}$ sec^{-1}, we have from (16.29)

$$c^2k^2 \approx 10^{34}i - 10^{32} + 10^{26}.$$

We see that the eddy current term is dominant, and so in this range we may take

(16.35) $$k \cong i^{1/2}(4\pi\sigma\omega/c^2)^{1/2}.$$

This is just the usual eddy current result.   The superconducting properties of the material may be involved only through a change in the number of normal conduction electrons, which enters into σ.   At these frequencies $\hbar\omega \gg kT_c$, and electrons are probably raised out of superconducting states by radiation, thus explaining the "normal" behavior of superconductors with respect to reflection of infrared radiation.[18]

The transition between superconducting and normal behavior occurs when the first and second terms on the right in (16.29) become equal to each other, the third term being negligible in the region of validity of ordinary conductivity theory.   We see then that the transition in behavior occurs when the skin depth for eddy currents is equal to the London penetration depth (16.31).   The transition takes place when $\omega \approx 10^{11}$ sec^{-1}, or $f \approx 10^{10}$ cps, which is in the microwave region, in agreement with experiment.   The critical frequency is in fact given by, according to our definition,

(16.36) $$\omega_c = \frac{1}{\sigma\Lambda} = \frac{m}{N_n e^2 \tau}\frac{N_s e^2}{m} = \frac{1}{\tau}\frac{N_s}{N_n},$$

where N_s = density of superconducting electrons, N_n = density of effective normal electrons, and τ is the time of relaxation of the normal electrons as calculated in the ordinary theory of conductivity, entering by way of the relation

(16.37) $$\sigma = Ne^2\tau/m$$

according to (10.102).

Extensive microwave investigations[19] have been carried out to test the above theory.   It appears that the theory describes in a rough way the observed results, but closer examination reveals, according to Pippard, that the London equations should be generalized.   He has also shown that the dependence of Λ on magnetic field intensity is very weak, so that (16.23) is in fact approximately linear in H.

[18] See, for example, Daunt, Keeley, and Mendelssohn, Phil. Mag. **23**, 264 (1937); M. Tinkham and R. Glover, unpublished.

[19] H. London, Proc. Roy. Soc. (London), **A176** 522 (1940); A. B. Pippard, Proc. Roy. Soc. (London) **A191**, 370, 385, 399 (1947); **A203**, 98, 195, 210 (1950); Maxwell, Marcus, and Slater, Phys. Rev. **76**, 1332 (1949).

SUSCEPTIBILITY OF A SPHERE AND THE PARTICLE SIZE EFFECT

The magnetic field H_i within a sphere is

(16.38)
$$H_i = H - \frac{4\pi}{3} M,$$

as the demagnetizing field is $4\pi M/3$. If the sphere is very large in comparison with the penetration depth, we may write

(16.39)
$$M = \frac{\mu - 1}{4\pi} H_i,$$

or, as $\mu = 0$ for a bulk superconductor,

$$M = - \frac{1}{4\pi} H_i,$$

whence, using (16.38),

(16.40)
$$-\frac{8\pi}{3} M = H,$$

and so the effective susceptibility of a sphere is

(16.41)
$$\chi_0 = - \frac{3}{8\pi}.$$

We now give a more detailed theory of the magnetic moment of a sphere of arbitrary radius a (not necessarily large) in a uniform applied field H_0. We suppose that the sphere obeys the London equation (16.23), which, expressed in terms of the vector potential $\mathbf{A}$, is

(16.42)
$$\frac{\Lambda c^2}{4\pi} \nabla^2 \mathbf{A} = \mathbf{A}.$$

This is a standard boundary value problem.[20]

The vector potential of the uniform applied field is

(16.43)
$$\mathbf{A}_0 = \tfrac{1}{2} H_0 r \sin \theta \, \boldsymbol{\phi}$$

in spherical coordinates, where $\boldsymbol{\phi}$ is the unit longitude vector. The total potential external to the sphere is

$$\mathbf{A}_e = \left(\frac{1}{2} H_0 r \sin \theta + \frac{C}{r^2} \sin \theta \right) \boldsymbol{\phi},$$

[20] The problem is quite similar to that discussed on pp. 397–399 of W. R. Smythe, *Static and dynamic electricity*, McGraw-Hill Book Co., New York, 2nd ed., 1950.

while the solution within the sphere, from (16.42), is

$$\mathbf{A}_i = \frac{D}{r^{1/2}} I_{3/2}\{r[(4\pi/\Lambda c^2)^{1/2}]\} \sin\theta\,\boldsymbol{\phi},$$

where $I_{3/2}$ is a modified Bessel function. The boundary conditions which determine C and D are

$$\mathbf{A}_e = \mathbf{A}_i$$

and

$$\frac{\partial}{\partial r}(r\sin\theta\,\mathbf{A}_i) = \frac{\partial}{\partial r}(r\sin\theta\,\mathbf{A}_e),$$

at $r = a$ in both cases.

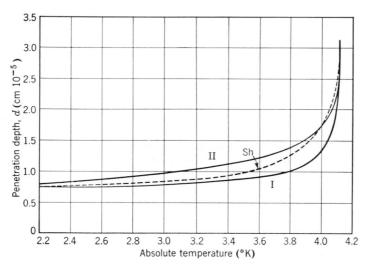

Fig. 16.9. Penetration depth in mercury. Curve Sh from magnetic susceptibility measurements on colloidal mercury [from D. Shoenberg, Nature **143**, 434 (1939)]; curves I and II from high-frequency resistance measurements [from A. B. Pippard, Proc. Roy. Soc. (London) **A191**, 370, 385, 399 (1947); Nature **162**, 68 (1948)].

On solving for C, it is easy to show that the sphere produces an external field as if it possessed a magnetic moment [writing $d = (\Lambda c^2/4\pi)^{1/2}$] of

$$\mathfrak{M} = -H_0\,\frac{a^3}{2}\,\frac{I_{5/2}(a/d)}{I_{1/2}(a/d)} = -H_0\,\frac{a^3}{2}\left[1 + 3\frac{d^2}{a^2} - 3\frac{d}{a}\coth\frac{d}{a}\right],$$

and so, writing $\chi_0 = -3/8\pi$,

(16.44)
$$\frac{\chi}{\chi_0} = \left[1 + 3\frac{d^2}{a^2} - 3\frac{d}{a}\coth\frac{a}{d}\right],$$

as given by F. London.[21]   For $d/a \ll 1$, $\chi = \chi_0$; for $d/a \gg 1$,

$$\frac{\chi}{\chi_0} \cong \frac{1}{15} \frac{a^2}{d^2}.$$

Equation (16.44) has been widely used to determine d experimentally,[22] and consistent values of d at a given temperature are obtained for colloidal particles of various sizes.   Results for mercury are shown in Fig. 16.9, where the penetration depths are compared with those obtained by Pippard from high frequency resistance measurements. Other values are given in Table 16.3.

TABLE 16.3. VALUES OF THE PENETRATION DEPTH EXTRAPOLATED TO 0°K

[Except for Hg, the values are from J. M. Lock, Proc. Roy. Soc. (London) **A208,** 391 (1951).]

Element	$10^6 \times d_0$(cm)
Hg	7
In	6.4 ± 0.3
Pb	3.9 ± 0.3
Sn	5.0 ± 0.1

INTERMEDIATE STATE AND DOMAIN STRUCTURE

At the edge of the equatorial plane of a sphere in an applied field H we apply the condition of continuity of the tangential component of H across the boundary, obtaining

(16.45) $H_i = H_{\text{ext}}$ (equator).

Now

$$H_i = H - \frac{4\pi}{3} M,$$

and for a sphere (16.40) gives us

(16.46) $M = -\frac{3}{8\pi} H,$

and so

(16.47) $H_i = \frac{3}{2} H.$

By consideration of the field pattern of a dipole we see that the maximum value of the tangential component of the external field is in

[21] F. London, Physica **3,** 450 (1936).
[22] D. Shoenberg, Nature **143,** 434 (1939).

the equatorial plane and has a value, by (16.47), of $\frac{3}{2}$ times the value of the uniform applied field. The field H_i will exceed the critical field H_c (as determined from measurements on a long wire in an axial field) when

$$(16.48) \qquad\qquad H > \frac{2}{3} H_c.$$

When this situation occurs we can avoid having the whole sphere become normal by having the material around the equator of the sphere become normal; the effective shape of the superconducting material will then become something like a prolate spheroid, thereby reducing the field in the interior. The material at the boundary between normal and superconducting regions will naturally be in the field H_c, but now the material outside the boundary, such as the material on the surface of the sphere, will see a field less than H_c and will become superconducting again. A stable state can only be attained by dividing the sphere up into many fine regions or domains, alternately normal and superconducting.

The effect of domain structure on the magnetic susceptibility of a sphere in the region of field intensities $\frac{2}{3}H_c < H < H_c$ may be discussed; the device of a fictitious "intermediate state" introduced by Peierls[23] and by London to describe the bulk properties of the mixture of superconducting and normal domains will assist in the discussion. The medium as a whole may be characterized by the average values

$$(16.49) \qquad\qquad H_i = H_c; \qquad B_i \neq 0.$$

The magnetization adjusts itself to make

$$H_c = H - \frac{4\pi}{3} M;$$

thus, for $\frac{2}{3}H_c < H < H_c$,

$$(16.50) \qquad\qquad \chi = \frac{3}{4\pi} \left(1 - \frac{H_c}{H} \right).$$

This is equal to $-(3/8\pi)$ for $H = \frac{2}{3}H_c$ and to 0 for $H = H_c$. The magnetization is a linear function of H:

$$(16.51) \qquad M = \frac{3}{4\pi} (H - H_c); \qquad \left(\frac{2}{3} H_c < H < H_c \right)$$

in agreement with measurements on spheres,[24] as sketched in Fig. 16.4.

[23] R. Peierls, Proc. Roy. Soc. (London) **A155**, 613 (1936).
[24] See, for example, D. Shoenberg, Proc. Roy. Soc. (London) **A152**, 10 (1935).

The nature and dimensions of the domain structure in superconductors have been discussed theoretically by Landau,[25] who finds that it is necessary to have a rather complicated branching structure in order to satisfy the boundary conditions within the material. A state with many thin domains is favorable from the standpoint of demagnetizing energy, but has a large area of boundary surface between normal and superconducting phases. The boundary surface energy

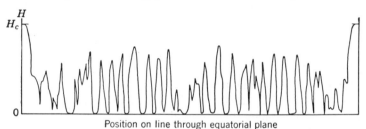

Position on line through equatorial plane

Fig. 16.10. Magnetic field distribution in the equatorial plane of a tin sphere in the intermediate state at 3.05°K, showing the domain structure. Regions of $H \sim H_c$ are associated with slabs of normal material. (After Meshkovsky and Shalnikov.)

density is of the order of

$$(16.52) \qquad\qquad \sigma \sim \frac{1}{8\pi} H_c{}^2 d,$$

where d is the penetration depth.

The supposed existence of a domain structure has several indirect consequences which have been confirmed experimentally. Direct experimental observation of domains has been reported by Meshkovsky and Shalnikov,[26] who explored with a fine bismuth strip probe the air gap between two hemispheres of superconductor spaced close together. The magnetoresistive effect of bismuth was used to measure magnetic field intensity as a function of the position of the probe in the plane of the gap; large irregular peaks of field intensity were found which are suggestive of a laminar domain structure (Fig. 16.10). The domains have also been observed by a powder pattern technique,[27] using a

[25] L. Landau, J. Phys. (U.S.S.R.)**7**, 99 (1943).

[26] A. Shalnikov, J. Phys. (U.S.S.R.) **9**, 202 (1945); A. Meshkovsky and A. Shalnikov, J. Phys. (U.S.S.R.) **11**, 1 (1947). A major revision of the London theory in order to include the boundary energy directly in the theory has been attempted by Landau and Ginsburg; a review is given by W. L. Ginsburg, Abhandl. sowjetischen Physik **2**, 135 (1951).

[27] A. L. Schawlow, B. T. Matthias, H. W. Lewis, and G. E. Devlin, Phys. Rev. **95**, 1344 (1954).

superconducting niobium powder on the surface of superconducting specimens of other metals in the intermediate state. The powder, being perfectly diamagnetic, collects preferentially on the regions of the surface where there is no field. A representative pattern is shown in Fig. 16.11.

In a superconducting wire of circular cross section in a transverse magnetic field H, the critical condition for the formation of domains is

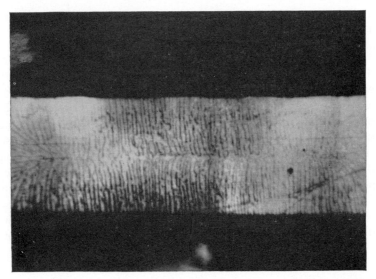

Fig. 16.11. Powder pattern of superconducting niobium powder on a plate of tin in the intermediate state. The laminar domains are easily visible. (After A. L. Schawlow.)

reached, by an analysis similar to that given for the sphere but using a demagnetizing factor of 2π, when

$$(16.53) \qquad\qquad H > \tfrac{1}{2}H_c.$$

The presence of layers of normal material suggests that the electrical resistance of the wire should begin to return when H exceeds $\tfrac{1}{2}H_c$; such an effect has in fact been observed. Detailed calculations and experiments relating to domain structure in superconducting cylinders in transverse magnetic fields have been made by Desirant and Shoenberg[28] and Andrew.[29]

[28] M. Desirant and D. Shoenberg, Proc. Roy. Soc. (London) **A194**, 63 (1948).
[29] E. R. Andrew, Proc. Roy. Soc. (London) **A194**, 80, 98 (1948).

QUANTUM THEORIES OF SUPERCONDUCTIVITY

There have been a number of attempts to give a quantum-mechanical explanation of superconductivity. We mention work by Heisenberg,[30] Tisza,[31] Slater,[32] Born and Cheng,[33] Fröhlich,[34] and Bardeen.[34] At the present time all these theories are highly controversial, and the difficulties do not lend themselves to analysis in an introductory textbook.

The discovery of the isotope effect, and in particular of the empirical relation (16.3),

$$T_c/\Theta = \text{constant},$$

for the various isotopes of a given element, suggests strongly that superconductivity arises from interactions between electrons and vibrations of the crystal lattice. This interaction enjoys a central role in the theories proposed by Fröhlich and Bardeen. The serious mathematical difficulties in discussing the electronic states in the presence of strong electron lattice interactions are pointed out in a review paper by Bardeen[34]. It is also not yet clear how the typical superconducting properties—infinite conductivity and perfect diamagnetism—follow from the models. In every theory the apparent contradiction between the Bloch theorem and the observed persistence of currents in a superconducting ring is explained by the presumed metastable nature of the current distribution.

The Fröhlich and Bardeen theories have the common feature that the superconducting state is realized when the interaction between electrons and the zero point lattice vibrations exceeds a certain value, which is nearly the same in the two theories. The condition can be expressed in terms of the electrical resistivity ρ at room temperature, a high resistivity at room temperature being propitious for superconductivity. In the Bardeen theory the criterion is, approximately,

(16.54) $n\rho > 10^6,$

where ρ is the resistivity at 20°C in esu, and n is the number of valence electrons per cubic centimeter. The comparison with experimental

---

[30] For a review of the Heisenberg theory, see H. Koppe, Ergeb. exak. Naturw. **23**, 283 (1950).

[31] L. Tisza, Phys. Rev. **80**, 717 (1950).

[32] J. C. Slater, Phys. Rev., **51**, 195 (1937); **52**, 214 (1937).

[33] M. Born and K. C. Cheng, J. Phys. radium **9**, 249 (1948).

[34] For references and a review of the Fröhlich and Bardeen theories, see J. Bardeen, Revs. Modern Phys. **23**, 261 (1951). The principal papers are H. Fröhlich, Phys. Rev. **79**, 845 (1950); J. Bardeen, Phys. Rev. **80**, 567 (1950).

results shows that the agreement is quite fair; for example, for sodium (which is not superconducting) $n\rho = 0.14 \times 10^6$, while for lead (which is superconducting) $n\rho = 3.1 \times 10^6$.

Note added in third printing: Bardeen, Cooper, and Schrieffer[35] have developed a remarkable theory which accounts in considerable detail for the essential aspects of superconductivity. The central interaction in the BCS theory is the coupling of two electrons by interaction with the lattice. The theory in particular predicts the existence of an energy gap $\Delta E \approx 4kT_c$ separating the superconducting state from the excited electronic states of the system. There is a large amount of evidence for such a gap from recent heat capacity and infrared transmission measurements. It is believed that the theory accounts for the Meissner effect and for persistent currents.

PROBLEMS

16.1. Often the threshold field curve is represented quite well by a parabola:

$$H_c(T) = H_0[1 - (T/T_c)^2].$$

Show that this relation leads to

$$S_n - S_s = \frac{H_0^2}{2\pi T_c}\left[\frac{T}{T_c} - \left(\frac{T}{T_c}\right)^3\right]$$

and

$$C_n - C_s = \frac{H_0^2}{2\pi T_c}\left[\frac{T}{T_c} - 3\left(\frac{T}{T_c}\right)^3\right]$$

for the entropy and heat capacity differences, per unit volume; n refers to the normal state and s to the superconducting state.

16.2. Obtain an expression (using the London equation) for the magnetic field H inside a superconducting plate of thickness D and infinite extent in a static field H_0 parallel to the plate.

16.3. Make a quantitative plot of effective susceptibility vs. the applied magnetic field for a long circular cylinder of a superconductor. The applied field is perpendicular to the cylinder axis.

16.4. The results of Problem 16.1 lead to a definite prediction in terms of H_0 and T_c for the coefficient of the linear term in C_n, supposing that the corresponding coefficient in C_s is zero (as seems to be true experimentally). Check this prediction approximately for two metals.

16.5. If C_s is of the form $C_s = Ae^{-bT_c/T}$, deduce the form of the critical field curve. This form of C_s, compatible with the existence of a finite energy gap separating normal and superconducting states, was reported for vanadium by Corak, Goodman, Satterthwaite, and Wexler, Phys. Rev. **96**, 1442 (1954).

[35] Bardeen, Cooper, and Schrieffer, Phys. Rev. **106**, 162 (1957); **108**, 1175 (1957).

16.6.* Give a theoretical discussion of the reason why the critical field may be much higher for thin films (thin in comparison with the penetration depth) than for bulk material.

REFERENCES

D. A. Buck, "Cryotron—a superconductive circuit element," Proc. I.R.E. **44**, 482 (1956).

F. London, *Superfluids*, John Wiley & Sons, New York, 1950, Vol. I.

W. Meissner, Handbuch der Experimentalphysik, **11/2** (1935), pp. 204–262.

K. Mendelssohn, Repts. Prog. Phys. **10**, 358 (1946); **12**, 270 (1949).

D. Shoenberg, *Superconductivity*, Cambridge University Press, Cambridge, 2nd ed., 1952.

F. E. Simon *et al.*, *Low temperature physics*, Academic Press, New York, 1952.

M. von Laue, *Theory of superconductivity*, Academic Press, New York, 1952.

17

Lattice Vacancies, Diffusion, and Color Centers

This is the first of three chapters devoted generally to the discussion of imperfections in solids. An imperfection is any deviation from a perfect regular lattice or structure. All actual crystals are in some respect imperfect, but the nature of the imperfections are better understood for some classes of solids than for others. One finds that a great deal of the work in this area is concerned with the alkali halides, the silver halides, germanium, silicon, copper, and tin. Research activity on the problems of imperfections represents today a large part of the total research effort in solid state physics. This condition may be explained by the observation that a number of the important properties of solids are controlled far more by the nature of the imperfections than by the nature of the host crystal, which may be only a vehicle for the imperfections. We have seen that the conductivity of semiconductors may be dictated entirely by trace amounts of chemical impurities. The color of many crystals arises from imperfections. The luminescence of crystals is nearly always connected with the presence of impurities. Diffusion through solids may be accelerated enormously by the presence of impurities or imperfections. The mechanical and plastic properties of solids are usually controlled by dislocations, a special type of imperfection. Under certain conditions crystals will not grow at an appreciable rate unless dislocations are present. In these chapters we shall be able only to sample the wealth of experimental and theoretical results in each area discussed; for a more complete picture the reader is directed to the references at the end of the chapters.

LATTICE VACANCIES

The simplest imperfection is a missing atom or lattice vacancy, indicated in diagrams and in chemical equations as a square (Fig. 17.1). Lattice vacancies are often known as Schottky defects. There will be a certain proportion of lattice vacancies in thermal equilibrium in an otherwise perfect crystal: the entropy is increased by the presence of disorder in the structure. We can treat very simply the statistics of the equilibrium state.

If E_s is the energy required to take an atom from a lattice site inside the crystal to a lattice site on the surface, nE_s is the increase in internal energy associated with the production of n isolated vacant

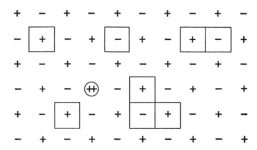

Fig. 17.1. Vacancies and vacancy clusters which play a prominent role in the theory of the alkali halides.   As displayed from upper left to lower right and reading across, the units are: positive-ion vacancy; negative-ion vacancy; coupled pair of vacancies of opposite sign; divalent ion present substitutionally with associated positive-ion vacancy; cluster of two positive-ion vacancies and one negative-ion vacancy.   It is believed that the coupled pair may diffuse faster than the isolated vacancies.   It is also possible that the triple cluster diffuses rapidly.   (After Seitz.)

sites.   The total number of ways in which we can pick n atoms from the crystal containing N atoms is

$$(17.1) \qquad \frac{N(N-1)\cdots(N-n+1)}{n!} = \frac{N!}{(N-n)!n!}.$$

Then $n!$ in the denominator occurs because the order in which the n vacancies are created is immaterial.   According to the Boltzmann formula, the increase in entropy on creating n vacancies is

$$(17.2) \qquad S = k \log \frac{N!}{(N-n)!n!}.$$

The change in the Helmholtz free energy is

$$(17.3) \qquad F = U - TS = nE_s - kT \log \frac{N!}{(N-n)!n!},$$

and in thermal equilibrium at constant volume must be a minimum with respect to changes in n.   The factorial terms may be simplified on using the Stirling approximation for large values of the argument:

$$(17.4) \qquad \log x! \cong x \log x - x,$$

and so

$$(17.5) \quad \log \frac{N!}{(N-n)!n!} \cong N \log N - N - (N - n) \log (N - n)$$
$$+ (N - n) - n \log n + n$$
$$= N \log N - (N - n) \log (N - n) - n \log n.$$

On differentiating,

$$(17.6) \qquad (\partial F / \partial n)_T = E_S - kT \log \frac{N - n}{n},$$

and in equilibrium

$$(17.7) \qquad \log \frac{n}{N - n} = -E_S/kT,$$

or, for $n \ll N$, we have the result

$$(17.8) \qquad n \cong Ne^{-E_S/kT}.$$

If $E_S \sim 1$ ev and $T \sim 1000°K$,

$$(17.9) \qquad n/N \sim e^{-12} \sim 10^{-5},$$

so that the proportion of vacancies for these numbers is the order of 0.001 percent.

Rather than the process just described, it is usually more favorable in ionic crystals to form a separated pair of positive and negative ion vacancies. The formation of pairs makes it possible to keep the surface of the crystal electrostatically neutral. The number of ways in which we can form n separated pairs is given by the square of (17.1). On following the exponent 2 through to the end of the above calculation, we obtain

$$(17.10) \qquad n \cong Ne^{-E_f/2kT}$$

for the number of pairs, where E_f is the energy of formation of a pair. In NaCl, $E_f = 2.02$ ev and at room temperature $n \sim 10^6$ cm^{-3}.

Another type of vacancy defect is the Frenkel defect (Fig. 17.2) in which an atom is transferred from a lattice site to an interstitial position. The calculation of the equilibrium number of Frenkel defects proceeds along familiar lines and is left to the student as Problem 17.1. If the number of Frenkel defects n is much smaller than the number of lattice sites N and the number of interstitial sites N', the result is

$$(17.11) \qquad n \cong (NN')^{1/2} e^{-E/2kT},$$

where E is the energy necessary to remove an atom from a lattice site to an interstitial position.

It is generally believed on the basis of ionic conductivity studies and density measurements that in pure alkali halides the most common lattice vacancies are Schottky defects while in pure silver halides the most common vacancies arise from Frenkel defects. We note that the production of Schottky defects lowers the density of the crystal because the net result of their production is an increase in the volume of the

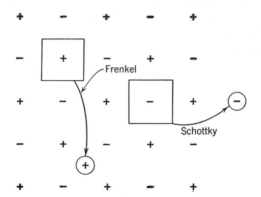

Fig. 17.2.   Schottky and Frenkel defects in an ionic crystal.   The arrows indicate the direction of displacement of the ions.

specimen with no increase in mass. The production of Frenkel defects does not, at least to the first order, change the volume of crystal, and so the density remains unchanged.

Perhaps the most convenient method of studying lattice vacancies is to study them in mixed crystals of alkali halides containing divalent additions.   If a crystal of KCl is grown containing controlled amounts of $CaCl_2$, it is found[1] that the density varies as if a K^+ lattice vacancy is formed for each Ca^{++} ion in the crystal.   The picture as shown in Fig. 17.3 is that the Ca^{++} enters the lattice in a normal cation site and the two Cl^- ions enter normal anion sites in the KCl crystal.   There is a net cation deficiency which is exhibited in the form of a vacant cation site.   As shown by the experimental results in Fig. 17.4, the addition of $CaCl_2$ lowers the density of the crystal.   If no vacancies were produced the density would be expected to increase, Ca^{++} being a heavier and smaller ion than K^+.

In the alkali and silver halides the electrical conductivity is usually electrolytic ionic conductivity up to the melting points of the crystals.

[1] H. Pick and H. Weber, Z. Physik **128**, 409 (1950).

This fact is established by comparing the transport of charge with the mass of the material plated out on the electrodes. It is found[2] that Faraday's law is well satisfied: this is a good test of whether the current is carried by ions or electrons.

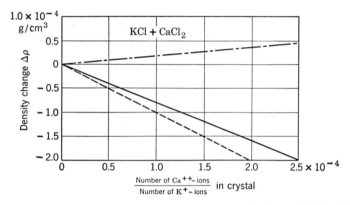

K^+	Cl^-	K^+	Cl^-	K^+	Cl^-
Cl^-	Ca^{++}	Cl^-	K^+	Cl^-	K^+
K^+	Cl^-	⊞	Cl^-	K^+	Cl^-
Cl^-	K^+	Cl^-	K^+	Cl^-	K^+

Fig. 17.3. Production of cation lattice vacancy by the solution of $CaCl_2$ in KCl: to ensure electrical neutrality a cation vacancy is introduced into the lattice with each divalent cation Ca^{++}.

Fig. 17.4. The change in density as a function of divalent addition for KCl containing controlled amounts of $CaCl_2$. The full line is the best fit of the experimental results; the lower dashed line represents the shift to be expected if the calcium ion plus vacancy occupied exactly the same volume as two potassium ions. The upper hyphenated curve represents the density to be expected if the densities of the two salts were purely additive.

The study of the ionic conductivity is the most important single tool in the investigation of the production and mobility of lattice defects. The work of Wagner, Maurer, Haven, Witt, and others[3] on

[2] See, for example, C. Tubandt and S. Eggert, Z. anorg. u. allgem. Chem. **110**, 196 (1920).

[3] E. Koch and C. Wagner, Z. physik. Chem. (B) **38**, 295 (1937); C. Wagner and P. Hantlemann, J. Chem. Phys. **18**, 72 (1950); H. W. Etzel and R. J. Maurer, J. Chem. Phys. **18**, 1003 (1950); I. Haven, Rec. trav. chim. **69**, 1259, 1471, 1505 (1950); H. Kelting and H. Witt, Z. Physik **126**, 697 (1949); J. Teltow, Z. physik. Chem. **195**, 197, 213 (1950); Ann. Physik **5**, 63 (1949).

alkali and silver halides containing known additions of divalent (Cd, Ca, Sr, Ba, Mg) halides (as in Fig. 17.5) leads us to several important conclusions:

1. At not too high temperatures, the ionic conductivity at a given temperature is directly proportional to the amount of divalent addition. As it is predominantly the monovalent cation which deposits at the cathode, rather than the divalent addition, we see that the cation lattice vacancies introduced (Fig. 17.3) with the divalent ions must

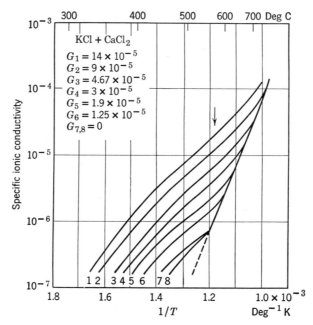

Fig. 17.5. The electrolytic conductivity of KCl crystals containing various amounts of $BaCl_2$. (After Witt.) The quantities G_i are the mole fractions of divalent addition. The steep straight lines on the right-hand side of the diagram represent the intrinsic conductivity. Curves 7 and 8 are for the same specimens of maximum available purity.

play a key part in the diffusion process, as shown in Fig. 17.6c. We note that the diffusion of a vacancy in one direction is equivalent to the diffusion of an atom in the opposite sense.

2. Above an elevated temperature which depends on the diavalent ion content, the conductivity becomes independent of the divalent content, suggesting that an intrinsic process has taken over. It is believed on the basis of density measurements that the intrinsic process in the alkali halides is diffusion of lattice vacancies generated thermally, whereas in the silver halides the intrinsic process is the diffusion of

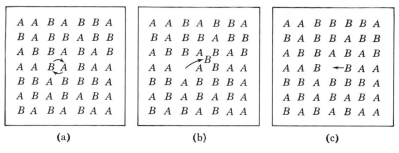

Fig. 17.6.   The three basic mechanisms of diffusion.   (a) Interchange by rotation about a midway point, forcing neighboring atoms apart.   (b) Migration through interstitial sites.   (c) Atoms exchange position with vacant lattice sites.   (From Seitz.)

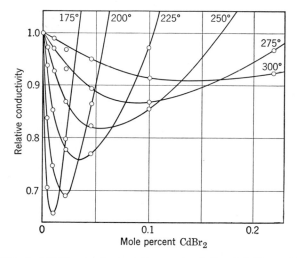

Fig. 17.7.   Effect of $CdBr_2$ content on the conductivity of AgBr crystals.   (After Teltow.)   Temperature in degrees C.   The decrease in conductivity for small amounts of cadmium is attributed to the consequent shift of the equilibrium concentration of interstitial silver ions.   For larger amounts of cadmium the conductivity increases as the vacancy diffusion mechanism becomes more important than interstitial diffusion of silver ions.

interstitial silver ions.   Jost first pointed out that large d shells make possible large van der Waals forces, favoring Frenkel rather than Schottky defects in the silver halides.   Teltow has shown (Fig. 17.7) that the addition of small quantities of divalent salts to silver halides reduces the ionic conductivity because, according to the law of mass action, the added vacancies shift downwards the equilibrium concentration of interstitial silver ions.

The energy of formation of lattice defects gives an extra contribution to the heat capacity of the crystal. Results for silver bromide are shown in Fig. 17.8 and are discussed in Problem 17.3. Breckenridge[4] has noted that an associated pair of vacancies of opposite sign should exhibit an electric dipole moment. He has observed contributions to the dielectric constant and dielectric loss in alkali halides which he attributes to pairs of vacancies. The dielectric relaxation time should

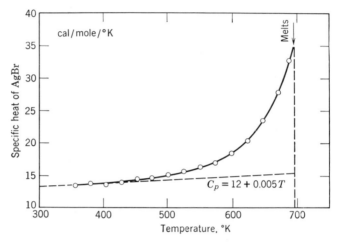

Fig. 17.8. Heat capacity of silver bromide at constant pressure, exhibiting an excess heat capacity from the formation of lattice defects. [After R. W. Christy and A. W. Lawson, J. Chem. Phys. **19**, 517 (1951).]

be a measure of the time required for one of the vacant sites to jump by one atomic position about the other. In sodium chloride the relaxation frequency occurs at 1000 cps at 85°C, with perhaps a 10 per-cent increase in the dielectric constant at lower frequencies.

DIFFUSION

The net flux J of atoms of one species in a solid is usually found to be related to the gradient of the concentration N of this species by Fick's law:

$$(17.12) \qquad J = -D \operatorname{grad} N,$$

where the constant of proportionality D is known as the diffusion con-stant or diffusivity and has the dimensions square centimeters per

---

[4] R. G. Breckenridge, J. Chem. Phys. **16**, 959 (1948); see also his paper in the book edited by Shockley *et al.* cited at the end of the chapter.

second in cgs units.   In a linear specimen,

(17.13) $J = -D(\partial N/\partial x)$.

While this statement of the law of diffusion is often adequate, it must be pointed out that it is shown in thermodynamics that the gradient of the chemical potential is rigorously the driving force for diffusion and not the concentration gradient alone.   For a thorough discussion the

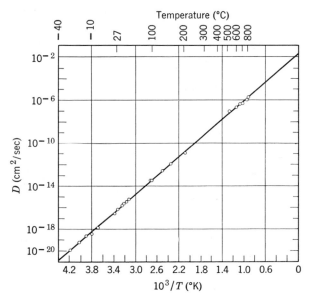

Fig. 17.9.   Diffusion coefficient of carbon in alpha iron.   (After Wert.)

reader is referred to the article by J. Bardeen and C. Herring entitled "Diffusion in alloys and the Kirkendall effect" in the volume *Imperfections in nearly perfect crystals* listed at the end of the chapter.

The diffusion constant is often found to vary with temperature as

(17.14) $D = D_0 e^{-H/kT}$;

here H is called the *activation energy* for the process.   Experimental results on the diffusion of carbon in alpha iron are shown in Fig. 17.9. The data are represented by $H = 20,100$ cal/mole; $D_0 = 0.020$ cm^2/sec.

Usually the diffusion process requires that an atom in changing position surmount a potential energy barrier.   If the barrier is of height E, the atom will have sufficient energy to pass over the barrier only a fraction exp $(-E/kT)$ of the time.[5] If ν is the atomic vibrational frequency, the probability r per unit time that the atom will get over the barrier is of the order

$$(17.15) \qquad\qquad r \sim \nu e^{-E/kT}.$$

We now consider two parallel planes of atoms, the planes separated by the lattice constant a. We suppose that a concentration gradient of interstitial atoms or vacancies exists, with concentration N at one plane and $(N + a\, dN/dx)$ at the other, the numbers associated with the planes being Na and $(N + a\, dN/dx)a$, respectively. The net number crossing unit area per unit time is of the order of

$$ra^2\, dN/dx,$$

so that the diffusion coefficient D_i of the interstitial ions may be taken as

$$(17.16) \qquad\qquad D_i \cong ra^2 \cong \nu a^2 e^{-E/kT},$$

to an order of magnitude. The gross diffusion coefficient D for the crystal is given by multiplying D_i by the fraction p of ions able to move, because they are adjacent to vacancies or are in interstitial positions:

$$(17.17) \qquad\qquad D = pD_i = (p\nu a^2)e^{-E/kT}.$$

On combining the Einstein relation $kT\mu = eD$ with the result (17.17) we have for the ionic mobility

$$(17.18) \qquad\qquad \mu = (ep\nu a^2/kT)e^{-E/kT},$$

and so the ionic conductivity is

$$\sigma = (N_0 e^2 p\nu a^2/kT)e^{-E/kT},$$

where N_0 is the total number of ions per unit volume of the appropriate species in the crystal.

We have now built up the background necessary for the further discussion of the conductivity measurements in ionic crystals. In the extrinsic range in which the number of vacancies is determined by the number of divalent cations[6] the quantity p giving the proportion of

---

[5] This argument is rather difficult to justify rigorously, but it may be taken as qualitatively reasonable. A careful discussion is given by C. Zener in the article entitled "Theory of diffusion" in the volume *Imperfections in nearly perfect crystals*.

[6] We neglect the association (binding) of vacancies and divalent ions at low temperatures; this subject is reviewed by F. Seitz, Rev. Modern Phys. **26**, 7 (1954), Sec. 6; an interesting application of nuclear resonance techniques to this problem was carried out by M. H. Cohen and F. Reif, reported in the volume *Defects in crystalline solids*.

vacancies is independent of temperature, and the slope of the plot of log σ vs. $1/kT$ gives essentially E_+, the barrier activitation energy for the jumping of positive ion vacancies. Representative values of E_+ are given in Table 17.1. If we express the jump frequency ν_+ as

$$(17.19) \qquad \nu_+ = \nu_{0+}e^{-E_+/kT},$$

it is found that ν_{0+} has a value close to 10^{14} sec^{-1} for NaCl and KCl. One expects atomic vibrational frequencies to be of this order of magnitude. At room temperature the jump frequency is of the order of 1 sec^{-1} and at 100°K of the order of 10^{-25} sec^{-1}.

TABLE 17.1. VALUES OF THE ACTIVATION ENERGY FOR MOTION OF POSITIVE ION VACANCIES

Values of the energy of formation of a vacancy pair, E_f, are also given. The numbers given in parentheses for the silver salts refer to interstitial silver ions.

Crystal	E_+(ev)	E_f(ev)	Workers
NaCl	0.86	2.02	Etzel and Maurer
LiF	0.65	2.68	Haven
LiCl	0.41	2.12	Haven
LiBr	0.31	1.80	Haven
LiI	0.38	1.34	Haven
KCl	0.89–0.9	2.1–2.4	Wagner; Kelting and Witt
AgCl	0.39 (0.10)	1.4†	Teltow
AgBr	0.25 (0.11)	1.1†	Compton

† For Frenkel defect.

In the intrinsic temperature range the proportion of vacancies in an ionic crystal will be given by

$$f \cong e^{-E_f/2kT},$$

according to (17.10) for Schottky defects and Problem (17.1) for Frenkel defects. Thus in the intrinsic range the slope of a plot of log σ vs. $1/kT$ is given approximately by $E_+ + \frac{1}{2}E_f$. The change of slope is obvious in Fig. 17.5. On combining measurements in the extrinsic and intrinsic ranges we can determine the energy of formation of a vacancy pair, E_f, as well as the jump activation energy already discussed. In this way the values of E_f given in Table 17.1 were determined.

Direct determinations of the diffusion constant have been carried out in ionic crystals, using radioactive tracer techniques in which the diffusion of a known initial distribution of radioactive ions is followed as a function of time or distance. It is possible to compare values of the diffusion constant determined directly by this method with values determined from observed conductivities with the use of the Einstein relation. It is found that the two sets of values do not usually agree within the experimental accuracy, suggesting that there may be present a diffusion mechanism which does not involve the transport of charge. The diffusion of pairs of positive and negative ion vacancies would provide such a unit and also the diffusion of an associated (divalent ion)-(vacancy) complex.

It has been pointed out[7] that for vacancy diffusion there is a small difference between the self-diffusion constant as measured by tagged (radioactive) atoms and as deduced from the ionic conductivity. Such differences were observed by Johnson.[8] According to the theory the diffusion constant is lower for a tracer atom than for a vacancy. The point is simple: suppose that a tracer atom has jumped forward by trading places with a vacancy. The tracer atom is not now in a random position with respect to the vacancy, but the vacancy is directly behind it and there is consequently a fair probability that while this relation persists the tracer atom will jump backwards. The probability is roughly of the order of $1/Z$, where Z is the number of nearest neighbor atoms. This result is explained by the consideration that there are Z neighbors which can jump into the vacancy; the tracer atom is only one of these Z atoms. We therefore expect the tracer diffusivities to be low by a fractional amount of the order of $1/Z$.

METALS

It is believed, speaking generally, that in metals self-diffusion usually proceeds by a vacancy mechanism, although ring interchange, direct interchange, and interstitial processes may be important in some instances. Careful theoretical calculations have been carried out for copper by Huntington, following earlier work by Huntington and Seitz. According to Huntington's calculations, the activation energy for self-diffusion is expected to be in the range 2.4–2.7 ev for the vacancy mechanism and 5.1–6.4 ev for the interstitial mechanism. Observed values are 1.7–2.1 ev. Kauffman and Koehler have measured at 80°K the resistivity of gold quenched from various temperatures, and they find results most easily explained by assuming a non-equilibrium concentration of vacancies is frozen in, with $E_f = 1.3$ ev as compared with the calculated $E_f = 1.5$–1.8 ev.

[7] For a full discussion see the paper by J. Bardeen and C. Herring in the volume *Imperfections in nearly perfect crystals*.

[8] W. A. Johnson, Trans. AIME **147**, 331 (1943).

Gutowsky and McGarvey[9] and others have determined activation energies in Li and Na from measurements of the temperature dependence of the nuclear resonance line width. They observe the onset of what is called motional narrowing of the resonance line as diffusion of neighboring atoms becomes rapid in comparison with the frequency corresponding to the static line width. In this way the values 13.2

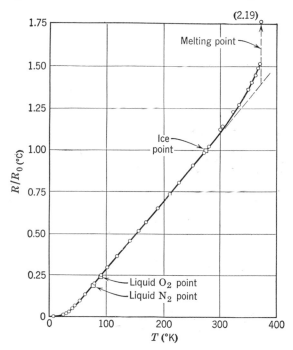

Fig. 17.10. Electrical resistance of sodium from 0°K to melting point. (After MacDonald.)

kcal/mole and 10.4 kcal/mole were determined for Li and Na, respectively, by Holcomb and Norberg. Self-diffusion measurements also give 10.4 kcal/mole for sodium.

MacDonald[10] has pointed out there is an apparent excess electric resistivity in Li, Na, and K as the melting point is approached. The excess is with respect to a linear increase of resistivity with temperature. Results for sodium are plotted in Fig. 17.10. MacDonald ascribes the excess resistivity to the formation of lattice vacancies; on

[9] H. S. Gutowsky and B. R. McGarvey, J. Chem. Phys. **20**, 1472 (1952); H. S. Gutowsky, Phys. Rev. **83**, 1073 (1951); D. F. Holcomb and R. E. Norberg, Phys. Rev. **93**, 919 (1954).

[10] D. K. C. MacDonald, J. Chem. Phys. **21**, 177, 2097 (1953).

plotting the log of the excess resistivity against $1/T$ he is able to determine from the slope the energy E_f for the formation of a lattice vacancy, finding the values 9.3 ± 0.5, 9.1 ± 0.1, and 9.1 ± 0.1 kcal/ mole for Li, Na, and K, respectively.

Interesting results on diffusion of radioactive Ag, Cd, In, Sn, and Sb each in metallic silver are reported by Slifkin and Tomizuka.[11] Substantial differences in activation energy were observed, ranging between 45.5 kcal/mole for self-diffusion of silver and 38.2 kcal/mole for Sb in Ag. The activation energy is a regular function of the atomic number; Lazarus[12] has carried out calculations suggesting that the effect may be attributed to the Coulomb screening of the ions by the conduction electrons.

Many of the older data on diffusion in metals are unreliable. Fisher and others have pointed out the important effect that diffusion along dislocations (Chapter 19) and grain boundaries can have in short-circuiting normal diffusion paths, especially at low temperatures.

KIRKENDALL EFFECT

A distinction between the interchange mechanism on the one hand and interstitial and vacancy mechanisms on the other hand is offered by the Kirkendall effect,[13] Fig. 17.11. Suppose that it is possible to regard the lattice framework of a crystal as a rigid frame of cells between which the atoms jump; on the interchange mechanism, pairs of atoms change places simultaneously, and there is no displacement of the assembly of atoms as a whole relative to the framework. However, in the case of vacancy or interstitial diffusion it is possible for the assembly to be displaced relative to the framework if there is a net flow of vacancies from one side to the other. This is possible if the specimen contains a concentration gradient allowing vacancies to enter one side more easily than the other. The vacancies may also be created or absorbed at edge dislocations and grain boundaries.

In the Kirkendall effect markers are placed at the interface between an alloy (CuZn) and a metal (copper). On heating to a temperature at which diffusion is possible, the markers are observed to move inwards, the opposite sets moving together. This is explained by saying that the zinc diffuses more rapidly than the copper and thus

[11] E. Sonder, L. Slifkin, and C. T. Tomizuka, Phys. Rev. **93,** 970 (1954); C. T. Tomizuka and L. Slifkin, Phys. Rev. **96,** 610 (1954).

[12] D. Lazarus, Phys. Rev. **93,** 973 (1954).

[13] A. D. Smigelskas and E. O. Kirkendall, Trans. Am. Inst. Mining Met. Engrs. **171,** 130 (1947). A review is given by J. Bardeen and C. Herring in the volume edited by Shockley et al. cited in the References.

diffuses out of the inner block. If diffusion were due to direct exchange of atoms, the diffusion coefficients of the two metals in the alloy would have to be equal. As this is not observed, we are inclined to suppose that the diffusion is due to the movement of vacancies and that a zinc atom changes place with a vacancy more easily than with a copper atom. This picture requires that sources and sinks of vacancies be present within the alloy. It is not unlikely that dislocations act to maintain the equilibrium concentration of vacancies. Pores are

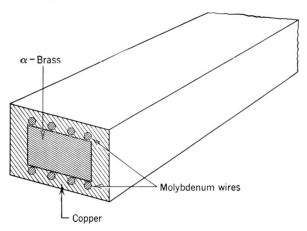

Fig. 17.11. The experiment of Smigelskas and Kirkendall. Molybdenum wires are located at the boundary between the inner CuZn block and the outer copper covering. After prolonged heating the markers are observed to move inward, suggesting that the zinc diffuses more rapidly than the copper and that the vacancies left behind as the zinc diffuses out may be largely annihilated, allowing the inner block to shrink. (After LeClaire, *Progress in metal physics* No. 1, Butterworths Scientific Publications, London, 1949.)

observed to form in the brass specimen as a result of the diffusion process.

COLOR CENTERS[14]

Pure alkali halide crystals are transparent throughout the visible region of the spectrum. The crystals are transparent even at elevated temperatures where there may be a substantial concentration of lattice vacancies in equilibrium, provided there is no chemical decomposition. It is possible to color the crystals in a number of ways. They may be colored by the introduction of suitable chemical impurities, such as transition element ions having excited energy levels separated from

[14] For a review of work on color centers in the alkali halides, see F. Seitz, Revs. Modern Phys. **18**, 384 (1946); **26**, 7 (1954).

the ground state by an optical frequency. That is, ions whose salts are normally colored may introduce color into alkali halide crystals. It has been known nearly one hundred years that it is also possible to color the crystals by introducing a stoichiometric excess of the cation, as by heating the crystal in the vapor of the alkali metal and then cooling the crystal quickly. When a sodium chloride crystal is heated in the presence of sodium vapor the crystal assumes a yellow color; KCl heated in potassium vapor assumes a magenta color, which may be quite deep according to the pressure of vapor employed. It is possible also to color or darken the crystals in other ways, including

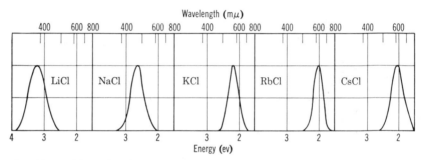

Fig. 17.12. The F bands for several alkali halides: optical absorption vs. wavelength.

x-ray and γ-ray radiation, neutron and electron bombardment, and electrolysis.

When the crystal is colored we say that it possesses *color centers*. A color center is then a lattice defect which absorbs light. The simplest type of color center is one called an F center, the name derived from the German word for color, *Farbe*. We produce F centers usually by heating in excess alkali vapor or by x-irradiation. The absorption bands associated with F centers in several alkali halides are shown in Fig. 17.12, and the quantum energies listed in Table 17.2. The center absorption band is referred to as the F band. The experimental properties of F centers have been investigated in detail, particularly by Pohl and his co-workers. Many types of centers other than F centers have been reported and to some extent their nature and composition understood. We shall discuss the F centers most fully.

TABLE 17.2. EXPERIMENTAL F CENTER ENERGIES (EV)

LiCl	3.1	LiBr	2.7	LiF	5.
NaCl	2.7	NaBr	2.3	NaF	3.6
KCl	2.2	KBr	2.0	KF	2.7
RbCl	2.0	RbBr	1.8		
CsCl	2.0				

F CENTERS

As it is believed that the excess alkali atoms fit into an alkali halide crystal in normal alkali ion lattice positions, a corresponding number of negative ion vacancies must be created in the process. A negative ion vacancy in an otherwise periodic lattice behaves electrostatically like a positive charge, so that an electron moving about a negative ion vacancy resembles qualitatively a hydrogen atom. We identify an F center with an electron bound to a negative ion vacancy, the electron being provided by the ionization of an alkali atom on entering the lattice. This model is due to de Boer. The F center is illustrated in Fig. 17.13.

A number of facts support this identification, among them:

(a) The F-band absorption is characteristic of the crystal and not of the alkali metal used in the vapor; that is, the band in potassium chloride is the same whether the crystal is heated in potassium or sodium vapor.

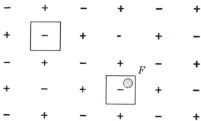

Fig. 17.13. Sketch showing an anion vacancy and an anion vacancy with an associated electron; the latter combination is identified as an F center.

(b) It is found by chemical analysis that crystals colored additively contain a stoichiometric excess of alkali metal atoms, the excess commonly being of the order of 10^{16} to 10^{19} per cubic centimeter. It is found further that the integrated absorption under the F band corresponds quantitatively to that expected theoretically based on the known amount of excess alkali metal.

(c) Colored crystals are less dense[15] than uncolored crystals, in agreement with the elementary picture than the introduction of vacancies should lower the density. This agreement is reasonable but not entirely conclusive. It would appear however to weigh against an interpretation of the F center as an electron bound to an interstitial alkali ion.

(d) Crystals with F centers can be bleached by illumination with light absorbed in the F band, and illumination in any part of the band bleaches the whole band. This proves that the F centers in any crystal are all similar. The bleaching is attributed to the ionization of the F center and is accompanied by photoconductivity; that is, the crystal

[15] Estermann, Leivo, and Stern, Phys. Rev. **75**, 627 (1949); H. Witt, Nachr. Akad. Wiss. Göttingen **1952**, 17.

becomes conducting during irradiation. The width of the band may be accounted for by the thermal motion of the ions.

(e) The paramagnetic susceptibility[16] of an F center corresponds closely to the spin contribution of one electron.

The interpretation of the results of electron spin resonance experiments[17] on F centers enable one to make a plausible picture of the wave function of the F center. It is convenient to think of the wave function as a linear combination of alkali atom functions centered about the six alkali metal ions neighboring the vacancy. The alkali functions are linear combinations of roughly equal parts of the lowest available s and p orbitals, the p contribution to take account of the atomic polarization induced by the presence of the adjacent vacancy. In a higher approximation the wave function will overlap somewhat the nearby halogen ions, but Coulomb repulsion effects are operative here. This model, and models similar to it, are supported by three main lines of evidence:

(a) It accounts[18] qualitatively for the shift in the g factor in KCl. The g factor determines the splitting of energy levels per unit magnetic field. The shift is $\Delta g = -0.007$ referred to the free electron value 2.0023. It is not possible to account for the g shift unless the atomic nature of the environment of an F center is taken explicitly into the model.

(b) The model accounts for the width and shape of the spin resonance line.[19] The width and shape are attributed to hyperfine interactions of the electron magnetic moment with the nuclear magnetic moments of the nuclei of the cations bordering the F center. It has been possible to change the width in KCl only by changing the isotopic composition of the potassium nuclei.

(c) The model is supported by detailed theoretical calculations[20] in the sense that the calculated properties of ground state wave functions of fairly general form are generally consistent with the model.

[16] P. Jensen, Ann. Physik **34**, 161 (1939); C. V. Heer and J. Rauch, Phys. Rev. **90**, 530 (1953).

[17] Early experiments are by C. A. Hutchison, Phys. Rev. **75**, 1769 (1949); C. A. Hutchison and G. A. Noble, Phys. Rev. **87**, 1125 (1952); M. Tinkham and A. F. Kip, Phys. Rev. **83**, 657 (1951); E. E. Schneider and T. S. England, Physica **17**, 221 (1951).

[18] A. H. Kahn and C. Kittel, Phys. Rev. **89**, 315 (1953).

[19] Kip, Kittel, Levy, and Portis, Phys. Rev. **91**, 1066 (1953); A. M. Portis, Phys. Rev. **91**, 1071 (1953).

[20] D. L. Dexter, Phys. Rev. **93**, 244 (1954); J. A. Krumhansl, Phys. Rev. **93**, 245 (1954).

OTHER ELECTRONIC CENTERS

There is evidence for a number of types of centers bearing trapped electrons; several of these are indicated in Fig. 17.14, and others are discussed in the review articles by Seitz listed at the end of the chapter.

The F' centers are produced by irradiating at not too high temperatures a crystal already colored by F centers with light that is absorbed by the F centers. A broad band on the red side of the F-band is produced in this way, and the intensity of the F band is decreased to a corresponding extent (Fig. 17.15). The new band is called the F'

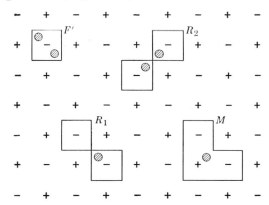

Fig. 17.14. Further units believed to give prominent optical absorption bands in alkali halide crystals. The F' center is obtained on adding a second electron to an F center. The R_1 center has one electron associated with two anion vacancies, and the R_2 center is obtained on adding a second electron to the R_1 center. The M center has one electron bound to two anion vacancies and one cation vacancy.

band. It is found that two F centers are destroyed for each incident quantum, suggesting that one F center is ionized by the incident radiation and the electron thus liberated is then captured by another F center to form an F' center consisting of an anion vacancy with two bound electrons. It is also found that the displacement range of the photoelectrons is inversely proportional to the concentration of F cen-. ters; this fact supports the assumption that the photoelectrons are trapped by F centers to produce F' centers. It is found further that F' centers may be destroyed by irradiating the crystal with light absorbed by the F' band, and the original F centers appear again in the process.

If crystals containing F centers are irradiated with light in the F band, there is a suitable temperature range in which coagulation occurs.

The final products of the coagulation are colloidal particles of alkali metal. The temperature range for NaCl and KCl includes room temperature and somewhat above. The first products[21] of coagulation

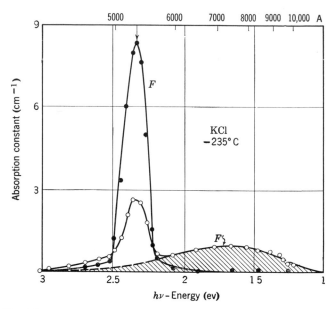

Fig. 17.15.   The F and the F' bands in KCl.   The F' band was produced by irradiating the crystal with light lying in the center of the F band.   (After Pick.)

are R_1, R_2, and M bands lying in the red and infrared.   It is believed that the centers associated with these bands are:

R_1	F center combined with a vacant anion site
R_2	Two F centers combined
M	F center combined with a pair of vacancies of opposite sign

The further steps leading to the formation of colloidal metal particles have been examined in a number of works, recently particularly by Scott[22] and his associates.

Large concentrations of F centers have been produced[23] by simultaneous evaporation of the salt and the metal, depositing the vapors on

[21] R. Ottmer, Z. Physik, **46**, 798 (1928); J. P. Molnar, unpublished; S. Petroff, Z. Physik, **127**, 443 (1950).

[22] A. B. Scott and L. P. Bupp, Phys. Rev. **79**, 341 (1950); F. E. Theisen and A. B. Scott, J. Chem. Phys. **20**, 529 (1952); A. B. Scott, J. Phys. Chem. **57**, 757 (1953).

[23] W. Buckel and R. Hilsch, Z. Physik, **131**, 420 (1952); R. Kaiser, Z. Physik, **132**, 482 (1952).

a cold surface. Densities of F centers of the order of 1 percent have been obtained in this way.

The photoconductive properties of colored crystals makes them applicable to determinations of the Hall coefficient, as have been carried out by Redfield[24] and by MacDonald.[25]

V CENTERS

It is a natural thought that by heating a crystal in halogen vapor to introduce a stoichiometric excess of halogen it should be possible

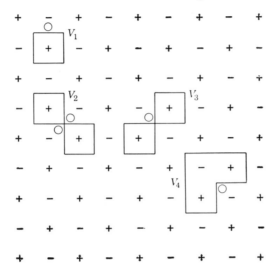

Fig. 17.16. Proposed models of V centers, after Seitz and Nagamiya. V_1 is assumed to be the antimorph of the F center. V_2, V_3 are antimorphs of the R centers, and V_4 the antimorph of the M center. The identification of the V_1 center above with the V_1 band is uncertain, as the spin resonance results of Kaenzig suggest that a center having the symmetry of the V_3 center produces the V_1 band.

to produce a whole new series of centers which are the antimorphs of the centers produced by excess alkali metal atoms. The new centers should contain holes instead of electrons, because a halogen atom has a deficit of one electron with respect to the ion; the hole will be attracted by a cation vacancy just as an excess electron is attracted to an anion vacancy.

Mollwo[26] showed it is possible to introduce excess halogen into KBr and KI, but not into KCl. A series of absorption bands in the ultra-

[24] A. Redfield, Phys. Rev. **91**, 244, 753 (1953).
[25] J. R. MacDonald, Phys. Rev. **91**, 412 (1953); **92**, 4 (1953).
[26] E. Mollwo, Ann. Physik, **29**, 394 (1937).

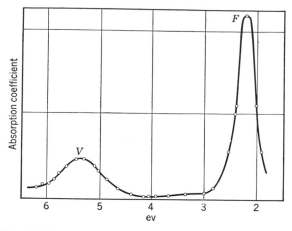

Fig. 17.17.   V and F bands in a potassium chloride crystal irradiated with 30-kev x-rays at 20°C.   [After H. Dorendorf and H. Pick, Z. Physik **128**, 106 (1950).]

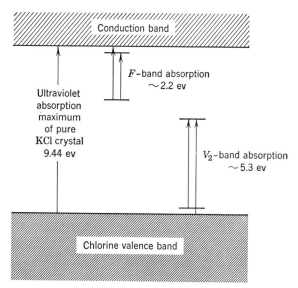

Fig. 17.18.   Energy level scheme of a potassium chloride crystal, as proposed by Dorendorf and Pick.

violet region is introduced in this way; the bands are known as *V* bands.   Tentative models of the several *V* centers are shown in Fig. 17.16.

The *V* bands may also be produced by x-ray or particle irradiation. It is clear from consideration of charge conservation that some type of hole center must be produced to accompany the *F* centers created by irradiation. In Fig. 17.17, a V_2 band is shown together with the F band; both were produced by irradiation at 20°C of a KCl crystal with 30-kev x-rays. A proposed energy level scheme to account for these particular results is shown in Fig. 17.18. Further structural details and the disappearance of the V_1 band in KCl on warming to

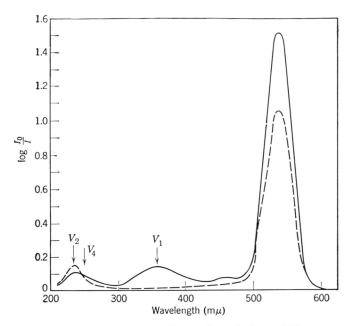

Fig. 17.19. The V_1 band produced by Casler, Pringsheim, and Yuster by irradiating KCl with x-rays at liquid nitrogen temperature (full curve). This vanishes when the specimen is warmed to room temperature (dashed curve). The intensity of the F band diminishes at the same time.

room temperature are shown in Fig. 17.19. Data on the V bands in KCl and KBr are summarized in Table 17.3.

At present the association of specific models of V centers with the appropriate absorption bands is in some doubt, particularly as electron

TABLE 17.3. POSITIONS OF THE PRINCIPAL V-BANDS IN KCl AND KBr

[After H. Dorendorf, Z. Physik **129**, 317 (1951)]

	V_1	V_2	V_3	V_4
KCl	3560 A	2300	2120	∼2540
	3.48 ev	5.37	5.83	∼4.87
KBr	4100 A	2650	2310	2750
	3.02 ev	4.67	5.35	4.50

spin resonance measurements by Kaenzig[27] show that the centers giving rise to the V_1 band have the symmetry properties of the V_3 centers: he finds the hole is closely associated with two halogen ions, the line joining the two halogens lying in a $\langle 110 \rangle$ direction in the crystal.

THE PHOTOGRAPHIC PROCESS[28]

There are three major stages in the basic photographic process. First, an emulsion containing microcrystals of AgBr or mixed Ag(Br, I) is exposed to light, with the formation of an invisible *latent image* in those microcrystals which have absorbed an adequate number of photons. Second, the emulsion is developed; in this stage the microcrystals containing a latent image are reduced to metallic silver by a suitable chemical agent. In the third stage the emulsion is fixed by the chemical conversion of the silver in grains without latent images so that these grains are no longer photosensitive.

The most interesting and critical stage is the first, the formation of the latent image. It is believed that the latent image is only a first step in a process called the print-out effect in which ultimately after long exposure but without chemical development a visible amount of metallic silver is formed in a grain.

The earliest discussion of the elements of the photographic process on an atomistic basis is that of Gurney and Mott. There is a great deal of experimental support[29] for their general model, although some details of the picture are not yet entirely agreed upon or worked out.

On the Gurney-Mott model a light quantum near 4500 A is absorbed in the crystal, forming a free electron and a hole (Fig. 17.20). The electron is then trapped, probably at the surface. An interstitial silver ion Ag^+ from a Frenkel defect is attracted to the trapped electron, joining it and forming a neutral silver atom. When a second quantum is absorbed in the crystal the electron thus freed wanders about and is in turn trapped by the neutral silver atom, forming an Ag^- ion. The Ag^- ion attracts another interstitial silver ion Ag^+, and the two combine to form a neutral Ag_2 molecule. This molecule appears to be the smallest stable unit and is known as a latent subimage. On further exposure the Ag_2 molecule collects further metallic

[27] W. Kaenzig, Phys. Rev. **99**, 1890 (1955); M. H. Cohen, Phys. Rev. **101**, 1432 (1956).

[28] R. W. Gurney and N. F. Mott, Proc. Roy. Soc. (London) **A164**, 151 (1938); F. Seitz, Revs. Modern Phys. **23**, 328 (1951); T. Evans, J. M. Hedges, and J. W. Mitchell, J. Photographic Science **3**, 73 (1955).

[29] See, for example, J. R. Haynes and W. Shockley, Phys. Rev. **82**, 935 (1951).

silver by the same process and grows in size, ultimately becoming a visible speck of silver, giving the print-out effect. Long before the speck is visible it will have reached a size, probably after about 50 quanta have been absorbed in the crystal, at which it can be developed

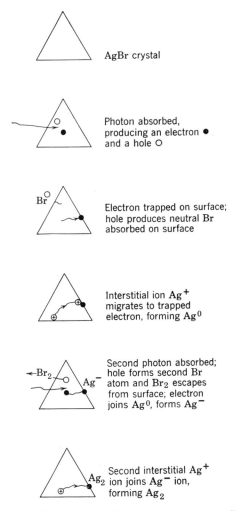

AgBr crystal

Photon absorbed, producing an electron ● and a hole ○

Electron trapped on surface; hole produces neutral Br absorbed on surface

Interstitial ion Ag^+ migrates to trapped electron, forming Ag^0

Second photon absorbed; hole forms second Br atom and Br_2 escapes from surface; electron joins Ag^0, forms Ag^-

Second interstitial Ag^+ ion joins Ag^- ion, forming Ag_2

Fig. 17.20. Formation of the latent subimage in AgBr, according to the Gurney-Mott theory.

chemically. When a crystal can be developed we say that it contains a latent image. The function of the developer is to give up further electrons to the latent image; eventually most of the silver in the grain may be deposited on the speck as metallic silver. The effect of dye sensitization[30] is to extend the spectral range in which the crystal may respond to light.

Mitchell and co-workers have carried out experiments which emphasize the importance of the internal and external surfaces of the crystal and the importance also of introducing chemical agents in the emulsion to remove the bromine produced before it can react with the metallic silver.

PROBLEMS

17.1. Show that the number n of Frenkel defects in equilibrium in a crystal having N lattice points and N' possible interstitial positions is given by

$$E = kT \log \left[(N - n)(N' - n)/n^2 \right],$$

whence, for $n \ll N,\ N'$

$$n \cong (NN')^{1/2} e^{-E/2kT}.$$

Here E is the energy necessary to remove an atom from a lattice site to an interstitial position.

17.2. Suppose that the energy required to remove a sodium atom from the inside of a sodium crystal to the boundary is 1 ev. (a) Calculate the number of Schottky vacancies at room temperature (300°K). (b) If a neighboring sodium atom has to move over a potential hill of 0.5 ev, and the atomic vibration frequency is 10^{12}, estimate the diffusion coefficient at room temperature for radioactive sodium in normal sodium. Repeat the calculation for 373°K.

17.3. From the data in Fig. 17.7, estimate the concentration of lattice defects in silver bromide just below the melting point.

17.4. (a) Treating an F center as a free electron of mass m moving in the field of a point charge $|e|$ in a medium of dielectric constant $\epsilon = n^2$, calculate the $1s$-$2p$ energy differences of F centers in NaCl, NaBr, and KCl.

(b) Compare the observed F-center energies in these crystals with the s-p energy differences of the free alkali atoms in the ground state.

17.5. Discuss the physical changes resulting from radiation damage in solids. Radiation damage is caused by the passage of neutrons or fast charged particles through the material. [See F. Seitz, Discussions Faraday Soc. No. 5, 271 (1949); Bristol Conference report, 1955; J. C. Slater, J. Appl. Phys. **22**, 237(1951); K. Lark-Horovitz, in H. K. Henisch, editor, *Semiconducting materials*, Butterworths Scientific Publications, London, 1951; E. G. H. Kinchin and R. S. Pease, Repts. Prog. Phys. **18**, 1 (1955)].

REFERENCES

R. M. Barrer, *Diffusion in and through solids*, Cambridge University Press, Cambridge, 1951.

Bristol Conference report, *Defects in crystalline solids*, Physical Society, London, 1955.

B. Chalmers, editor, *Progress in metal physics*, Butterworths Scientific Publications, London, 1949, vol. 1; and subsequent volumes.

[30] A mechanism for dye sensitization has been proposed by J. Franck and E. Teller, J. Chem. Phys. **6**, 861 (1938).

K. Hauffe, "Fehlordnungserscheinungen und Leitungsvorgänge in ionen- und elektronenleitenden festen Stoffen," Ergeb. exakt. Naturwiss. **25**, 193 (1951).

G. H. Kinchin and R. S. Pease, "Displacement of atoms in solids by radiation," Repts. Prog. Phys. **18**, 1 (1955).

C. E. K. Mees, *Theory of the photographic process*, Macmillan, New York, 1954.

J. W. Mitchell, editor, *Fundamental mechanisms of photographic sensitivity*, Butterworths Scientific Publications, London, 1951.

N. F. Mott and R. W. Gurney, *Electronic processes in ionic crystals*, Clarendon Press, Oxford, 2nd ed., 1950.

F. C. Nix and W. Shockley, "Order-disorder transformation in alloys," Revs. Modern Phys. **10**, 1 (1938).

Shockley, Hollomon, Maurer, and Seitz, editors, *Imperfections in nearly perfect crystals*, John Wiley & Sons, New York, 1952.

F. Seitz, "Color centers in alkali halide crystals," Revs. Modern Phys. **18**, 384 (1946); **26**, 7–94 (1954).

F. Seitz, "Speculation on the properties of silver halide crystals," Revs. Modern Phys **23**, 328 (1951).

18

Excitons, Photoconductivity, and Luminescence

The subjects of this chapter relate to optical phenomena in non-metallic crystals. We have already seen that an electron-hole pair is produced when photons of energy greater than the energy gap E_g are absorbed in a crystal. The electron and hole produced in this way are free and may move independently through the crystal, giving rise to photoconductivity. But because an electron and hole have an attractive Coulomb interaction it is possible for stable bound states of the two particles together to be formed, and the photon energy required for this purpose will be less than the gap energy. The bound electron-hole pair is known as an exciton; it may move through the crystal, transporting excitation energy but not transporting charge. Excitation energy may be stored by a crystal in various other ways, as by impurity atoms with partly-filled inner shells. The re-emission of excitation energy as visible or near visible radiation is known as luminescence.

EXCITONS[1]

An exciton is a neutral excited mobile state of a crystal: an exciton can travel through the crystal, giving up its energy of formation on recombination, but it is electrically neutral and therefore does not contribute directly to the electrical conductivity. It is possible to think of excitons in two different limiting approximations, one due to Frenkel, in which the exciton is considered as tightly bound, and a later approximation due to Mott and Wannier, in which the exciton is weakly bound, having an electron-hole interparticle distance large in comparison with an atomic radius. We discuss first the weakly bound model.

---

[1] J. Frenkel, Phys. Rev. **37**, 17, 1276 (1931); Physik. Zeit. Sowjetunion **9**, 158 (1936); R. Peierls, Ann. Physik **13**, 905 (1932); J. C. Slater and W. Shockley, Phys. Rev. **50**, 705 (1936); G. H. Wannier, Phys. Rev. **52**, 191 (1937); W. R. Heller and A. Marcus, Phys. Rev. **84**, 809 (1951); N. F. Mott, Trans. Faraday Soc. **34**, 500 (1938); D. L. Dexter and W. R. Heller, Phys. Rev. **84**, 377 (1951).

Let us consider an electron in the conduction band of a crystal and a hole in the valence band. The electron and hole are attracted to each other by the attractive Coulomb potential

(18.1) $$V = -e^2/\epsilon r,$$

where r is the distance between the particles and ϵ is the appropriate dielectric constant.[2] If ϵ is independent of r the potential is just the Coulomb potential reduced by the dielectric constant, and there will

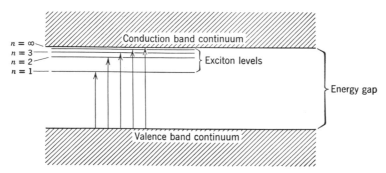

Fig. 18.1. Energy levels of an exciton whose center of mass is at rest. Optical transitions from the top of the valence band (assumed to be at $\mathbf{k} = 0$) are shown by the arrows, the longest of which corresponds to the ionization of the exciton and therefore to the energy gap between the edges of the conduction and valence bands. When one considers the translational motion of the center of mass of the exciton it is apparent that there is a continuum of levels associated with each exciton level shown here. In the allowed optical transitions the total translational energy does not change appreciably; thus sharp exciton lines are possible.

be bound states (Fig. 18.1) of the exciton system having total energies lower than the bottom of the conduction band. The problem is much like the hydrogen atom problem and the problem of donor and acceptor levels considered in Chapter 13. The energy levels referred to the bottom of the conduction band are given by the modified Rydberg formula

(18.2) $$E_n = \frac{\mu e^4}{2\hbar^2\epsilon^2 n^2}.$$

[2] The lattice polarization contribution to the dielectric constant usually should be subtracted off as the lattice will not respond at the frequency of motion of the exciton. It will usually be a reasonable procedure to take ϵ as the square of the refractive index measured near the frequency E_b/h, where E_b is the binding energy of the exciton. At very small r, less than an ionic radius, the dielectric constant should be allowed to approach unity.

Here n is the principal quantum number and μ is the reduced mass

$$(18.3) \qquad \frac{1}{\mu} = \frac{1}{m_e} + \frac{1}{m_h}$$

formed from the effective masses m_e, m_h of the electron and hole, respectively. If the energy surfaces are not spherical and non-degenerate the exciton problem is considerably more complicated, but there is little doubt that bound exciton states[3] exist for quite general energy surfaces.

The exciton ground state energy is obtained on setting $n = 1$ in (18.2); this energy corresponds to the ionization potential required

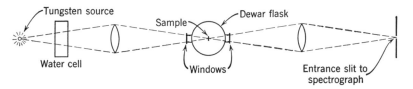

Fig. 18.2. Optical arrangement used to observe exciton absorption. (After Apfel and Hadley.)

to break up the exciton from its ground state. For $\epsilon = 5$, $\mu = 0.5m$, the ionization energy is about $\frac{1}{4}$ ev. It is difficult to produce excitons in sufficient concentration to observe directly the transitions among the exciton levels, but it is possible to observe the transitions between the valence band edge and an exciton level at the energies

$$(18.4) \qquad h\nu = E_g - E_n.$$

Here E_g is the energy gap, and E_n is the exciton energy referred to the conduction band edge.

One crystal is known whose exciton spectrum satisfies this relation with E_n given quite accurately by the Rydberg formula $E_n \propto 1/n^2$. Gross[4] and co-workers and others have observed optical absorption lines in cuprous oxide Cu_2O at low temperatures, with results for the spacing of the exciton levels in surprisingly good agreement with the Rydberg formula for $n > 2$. The experimental arrangement used by

---

[3] It may not always be possible to separate internal and center-of-mass coordinates, although this can be done for ellipsoidal energy surfaces.

[4] E. F. Gross, B. P. Zakharchenya, and N. M. Reinov, Doklady Akad. Nauk S.S.S.R. **92**, 265 (1953); **97**, 57, 221 (1954); **99**, 231, 527 (1954); S. Nikitine, G. Perny, and M. Sieskind, Compt. rend. (Paris) **238**, 67 (1954); J. H. Apfel and L. N. Hadley, Phys. Rev. **100**, 1689 (1955); A. G. Samoilovich and L. L. Kornblit, Doklady Akad. Nauk S.S.S.R. **100**, 43 (1955); for a review of work on several substances, see S. Nikitine, Helv. Phys. Acta **28**, 307 (1955).

Apfel and Hadley is shown in Fig. 18.2, and a recorder tracing of several absorption lines is shown in Fig. 18.3. The results of one run are given in Table 18.1. An empirical fit to the observed lines is obtained with the relation

(18.5) $\nu(\mathrm{cm}^{-1}) = 17{,}508 - (800/n^2).$

Taking $\epsilon = 10$, we have $\mu \cong 0.7m$ from the coefficient of $1/n^2$ in (18.5). As we have no adequate independent values of m_e and m_h, such a

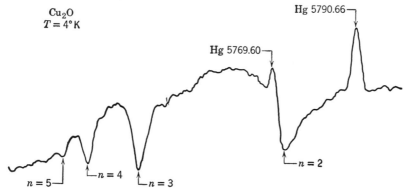

Fig. 18.3. Spectrometer record of exciton series in Cu_2O at a temperature of 4°K. The lines whose ordinal numbers are $n = 2$, 3, 4, and 5 are shown. The two mercury yellow lines are shown in emission for the purposes of calibration and to indicate instrumental band width. (After Apfel and Hadley.)

value for μ is entirely reasonable and is to a certain extent a check on the identification of the origin of the lines. Without a direct demonstration of the mobility of the excitons in Cu_2O one cannot be positive that we are correct in associating the transitions with the formation of excitons.

Gross has shown, using long photographic exposures and by studying the Stark effect, that there is a complex fine structure to the standard exciton lines in Cu_2O. It is possible that the fine structure reflects

TABLE 18.1.   EXCITON ABSORPTION LINES IN Cu_2O CRYSTAL AT A
TEMPERATURE BETWEEN 4°K AND 77°K

(After Apfel and Hadley)

n	λ_{exp} (A)	ν_{exp} (cm^{-1})	ν_{calc} (cm^{-1})
2	5777.7	17,308	17,308
3	5741.2	17,418	17,419
4	5728.2	17,457	17,458
5	5722.1	17,476	17,476
6	5718.9	17,486	17,486
7	5716.5	17,493	17,492

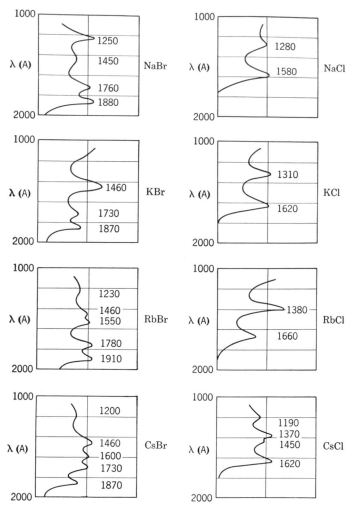

Fig. 18.4. Absorption spectra of alkali halides, observed by Schneider and O'Bryan, and Hilsch and Pohl.

the presumed degeneracy of the valence band edge. The Zeeman effect of one line was studied and can be accounted for[5] by a g value of approximately 2.

The absorption spectra of the alkali halides show considerable structure (Fig. 18.4). It is believed that the first one or two absorption peaks going from the visible to the ultraviolet are exciton lines; photo-

Another interpretation suggested by Gross appears to rest on a numerical

conductivity does not result until the crystal is irradiated with photons further in the ultraviolet. The exciton spectra are sharpened considerably on going to low temperatures, as shown in Fig. 18.5. We note that in Cu_2O Gross obtained better resolution near 1°K than at 4°K. It is likely that interest in the exciton field will develop considerably when more emphasis is placed on measurements at low temperatures.

Molecular crystals furnish examples of the Frenkel or tight-binding model of excitons. In molecular crystals the binding within a molecule

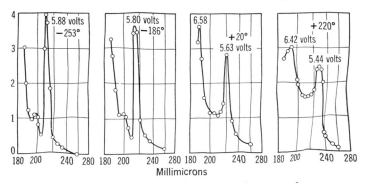

Fig. 18.5. Absorption spectra of KI; dependence of the first absorption band on temperature. (After Fesefeldt.)

is strong in comparison with the binding between molecules; the former is caused by covalent forces and the latter by van der Waals forces. Electronic excitation lines of an individual molecule will often appear in the crystalline solid with little change; at low temperatures the lines in the solid are quite sharp, although there may be more structure to the lines in the solid than in the molecule.[6] In solids of this type the exciton energies are much more closely related to the spectroscopic properties of the isolated molecule than to the hydrogenic model discussed earlier. The spectrum of crystalline phenanthrene $C_{14}H_{10}$ is shown in Fig. 18.6.

Apker and Taft[7] have carried out some very interesting optical and

[6] See, for example, the discussion of solid benzene by D. Fox and O. Schnepp, J. Chem. Phys. **23**, 767 (1955); the general theory is discussed by A. S. Davgdov, J. Exptl. Theoret. Phys. (U.S.S.R.) **18**, 210 (1948); H. Winston, J. Chem. Phys. **19**, 156 (1951). For a treatment of spin-orbit splitting effects in alkali-halide and other crystals, see A. W. Overhauser, Phys. Rev. **101**, 1702 (1956).

[7] L. Apker and E. Taft, Phys. Rev. **79**, 964 (1950); **81**, 698 (1951); **82**, 81 (1951); M. H. Hebb, Phys. Rev. **81**, 702 (1951). The scintillation counter work of W. Van Sciver and R. Hofstadter, Phys. Rev. **97**, 1181 (1955), is pertinent also W. Van Sciver thesis, Stanford Universtity, 1955.

photoelectric experiments on thin films of alkali halides; several of
their results are most naturally interpreted as caused by excitons.
When the yield of external photoelectrons is studied as a function of
photon energy in a film of alkali halide containing F centers, a broad

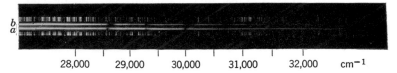

Fig. 18.6.   Portion of the absorption spectrum of crystalline phenanthrene;
crystal 1.4 μ thick; ab plane exposed.   (After D. S. McClure.)

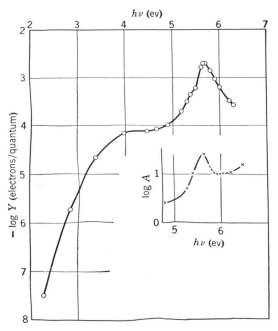

Fig. 18.7.   Evidence of the existence of excitons.   The photoelectric yield Y for
potassium iodide with F centers is similar in form near 5.6 ev to the optical absorption constant A (arbitrary units) for potassium iodide substantially without F
centers, suggesting that the excitons may ionize the F centers.   The hump in Y
occurs only if F centers are present.   [After L. Apker and E. Taft, Phys. Rev. **79**,
964 (1950).]

threshold is observed starting at about 2 ev photon energy.   The
broad ionization is attributed to direct ionization of F centers by the
incident photons, as no significant photocurrent is observed below 6
ev if the F centers are not present.   With the F centers present one

observes the broad excitation curve already mentioned and also a sharp peak, in KCl at about 5.6 ev, as shown in Fig. 18.7.

The sharp peak occurs at just the energy at which there is an optical absorption peak corresponding to the first exciton band. The inset in Fig. 18.7 shows the optical absorption vs. photon energy. The sharp peak in the photoelectric emission is found only in the colored

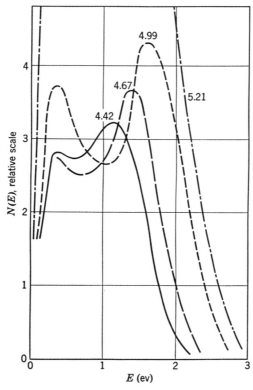

Fig. 18.8. The distribution in energy of photoelectrons in RbI produced with light quanta of the energies shown (in ev). The s and f components give separate peaks. The maximum of the f peak shifts to the right with increasing photon energy, whereas the maximum of the s peak does not change. (After Apker and Taft.)

crystals, while, of course, the optical absorption peak is observed in both colored and uncolored crystals. To explain the photoelectric peak we suppose that excitons are formed by photons in this energy region, and some of the excitons give up their energy to F centers, ejecting the F-center electron from the crystal.

This interpretation of the role of excitons is supported by experimental measurements of the distribution in energy of the photo-electrons, as shown for RbI in Fig. 18.8. There are two peaks visible, a high energy peak f which moves to higher energies as the photon energy is increased and a low energy peak s whose position does not change with photon energy. It is plausible to associate the peak f with photoelectrons emitted from F centers by the direct absorption of the incident photon; the peak s is associated with photoelectrons ejected from F centers by excitons. If the excitons have lost most of the kinetic energy with which they are formed before annihilating at F centers, we may then expect the peak s to be independent of the photon energy. Seitz has estimated that the excitons come to equilibrium with respect to translational energy in traveling about 1000 atom distances, and so it may be possible to infer that the Apker and Taft experiments give evidence of the motion of excitons. More direct evidence is demonstrated by the experiments of Van Sciver and Hofstadter[7] working with NaI crystals as scintillation counters. They identify with excitons radiation emitted at 0.3 μ in pure NaI; very small concentrations of added thallium quenches the 0.3 μ radiation. The Tl could not have much effect unless the excitons were mobile.

PHOTOCONDUCTIVITY IN INSULATING CRYSTALS

Photoconductivity is the increase in electrical conductivity of a crystal caused by radiation incident on the crystal. Much of the pioneering work in the field was done by Gudden and Pohl. The photoconductive effect finds considerable practical application in television cameras, infrared detectors, light meters, and indirectly in the photographic process. The direct effect of illumination is to increase the number of mobile charge carriers in the crystal. If the energy of the incident photon is higher than the energy difference between the lowest point of the vacant conduction band and the highest point of the filled valence band, then each photon absorbed in the crystal may have a high probability of producing a hole-electron pair. That is, the photon is absorbed by ionizing an electron originally in the valence band. In this circumstance both the hole in the valence band and the electron in the conduction band may contribute to the conductivity.

Ultimately the hole and electron will recombine with each other, but it is possible for them to have quite different histories before recombination, spending various amounts of time trapped on impurities and imperfections in the crystal. Because of the possible differing influence of traps on the two carrier types, it is not usual to find that holes and electrons make comparable contributions to the photoconductivity in a given specimen. Traps are of central importance in determining the photoconductive response of a crystal. At present the mechanisms of the atomic processes occurring in traps are not always well understood, but it is clear that we cannot understand much of photoconductivity without invoking the presence of traps.

If the energy of the incident photon is below the threshold for the production of pairs of holes and electrons, the photon may be able to cause ionization of impurity atoms (donor and acceptor atoms) and in this way produce mobile electrons or holes, according to the nature of the impurity.

Let us discuss first the simplest possible model of a photoconductor. There exist few, if any, realizations of this model in actual crystals,[8] but from the failure of our predictions to apply to real crystals we shall learn how to improve the model. The model (Fig. 18.9) supposes that hole-electron pairs are produced uniformly throughout the volume of the crystal by irradiation with an external light source. Recombination is postulated to occur by direct annihilation of electrons with holes. We suppose that electrons leaving the crystal at one electrode are replaced by electrons flowing in from the opposite electrode. It is convenient to suppose that the mobility of the holes may be neglected in comparison with the mobility of the electrons, but it is a trivial matter to generalize the result to include the hole current. It does happen in many photoconducting substances that the mobility of the holes may often be neglected.

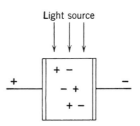

Fig. 18.9. Model of an ideal photoconductor: hole-electron pairs are produced uniformly through the volume of the crystal by an external light source. Recombination occurs by direct annihilation of electrons with holes. Electrons leaving at one electrode are replaced by others entering from the opposite electrode.

On this model the rate of change of the electron concentration n is given by

$$(18.6) \qquad \frac{dn}{dt} = L - Anp = L - An^2,$$

using $n = p$, with a similar expression for the hole concentration:

$$(18.7) \qquad \frac{dp}{dt} = L - Anp.$$

[8] A critical discussion of elementary photoconductive processes is given by A. Rose, RCA Review, **12**, 362 (1951); Phys. Rev. **97**, 322 (1955). Several elegant experiments demonstrating trapping and untrapping are described by J. A. Hornbeck and J. R. Haynes, Phys. Rev. **97**, 311(1955).

Here L is the number of photons absorbed per unit volume per unit time, and the term Anp gives a recombination rate proportional to the product of hole and electron concentrations, as is appropriate for bimolecular recombination. In the steady state we have

(18.8) $$n_0 = (L/A)^{\frac{1}{2}},$$

and the associated photoconductivity is

(18.9 $$\sigma = n_0 e\mu = (L/A)^{\frac{1}{2}} e\mu,$$

where μ is the electron mobility. This relation predicts that at a given voltage the photocurrent will vary as the light intensity to the power $\frac{1}{2}$. The exponents observed are usually between 0.5 and 1.0, with some crystals having higher exponents.

If the light is switched off suddenly the decay of carriers is described by

(18.10) $$\frac{dn}{dt} = -An^2,$$

which has the solution

$$n = \frac{n_0}{1 + Atn_0},$$

where n_0 is the concentration at $t = 0$ when the light was turned off. The carrier concentration should drop to $\frac{1}{2}n_0$ in the time

(18.11) $$t_0 = 1/An_0 = (LA)^{-\frac{1}{2}} = n_0/L.$$

Thus the elementary theory predicts that the response time t_0 should be directly proportional to the photoconductivity at a given illumination level: sensitive photoconductors should have long response times. The precise details of the predicted association of these properties is rarely observed in pravtice.

It is instructive to define a quantity called the sensitivity or gain factor G as the ratio of the number of carriers crossing the specimen to the number of photons absorbed in the specimen. If the thickness of the specimen is d and the cross-section area is unity, then the voltage V produces the particle current

(18.12) $$\frac{I}{e} = \frac{n_0\mu V}{d} = \frac{V\mu}{d^2(AL)^{\frac{1}{2}}} (Ld),$$

using (18.8), and so the gain is given by

(18.13) $$G = \frac{V\mu}{d^2(AL)^{\frac{1}{2}}}.$$

Now the transit time T_d of a carrier between the electrodes is given by

(18.14) $$T_d = d/(V\mu/d) = d^2/V\mu$$

and the lifetime T_e of an electron before recombination is given by

(18.15) $$T_e = (AL)^{-\frac{1}{2}},$$

according to (18.12). We see that the gain (18.13) may be expressed as

(18.16) $$G = T_e/T_d;$$

that is, the gain is equal to the ratio of the carrier lifetime to the transit time of a carrier between electrodes. A little reflection shows that this expression for the gain is quite general and is not limited to the specific model just discussed. If T_e is taken as the observed response time, it is found that the gains thus calculated from (18.16) are very much larger than those observed experimentally. In some instances the discrepancy amounts to a factor of 10^8. It is obvious that a new element must be added to our picture of the photoconductive process, and the element needed is the effect of traps.

TRAPS

A trap is an impurity atom or other imperfection in the crystal capable of capturing an electron or hole; the captured carrier may be re-emitted at a subsequent time. It is convenient to discuss models in which the holes are entirely trapped and a fraction of the electrons nominally in the conduction band are trapped at any instant. We shall discuss only very simple models; for a discussion of the properties of detailed and more realistic models the reader is referred to the paper by Rose.[8] We should note that there is an operational distinction between two types of traps. One type acts

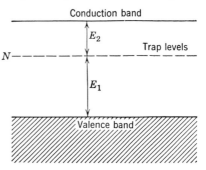

Fig. 18.10. Model for photoconductivity with electron traps in concentration N.

principally as a recombination center as discussed in Chapter 13, helping electrons and holes to recombine and thereby assisting in the restoration of thermal equilibrium. Another type of trap does not contribute directly in an important way to recombination, but affects principally the energy distribution and freedom of motion of charge carriers of one sign. It is this latter variety of trap which is of immediate concern to us here.

We consider first a crystal with N electron trap levels per unit volume (Fig. 18.10). We suppose that the temperature is sufficiently low in relation to the relevant ionization energies so that the concentration of thermal carriers may be neglected; this means the dark conductivity of the crystal is negligible. For simplicity we assume that the recombination coefficient A introduced in (18.6) is the same for electron-hole recombination as for electron-trap capture. Then

$$(18.17) \qquad \frac{dn}{dt} = L - An(n + N) + Bn_t,$$

where n is the electron concentration in the conduction band. The term Bn_t represents the rate of thermal evaporation of trapped carriers back into the conduction band; we shall neglect this term for the present. In the steady state

$$(18.18) \qquad n_0(n_0 + N) = L/A.$$

There are two limiting cases to be discussed. It is difficult to grow crystals with trap concentrations N much less than 10^{14} cm^{-3}. At low current levels the carrier concentration n_0 may be very much less than this, perhaps only 10^8 or 10^{10} cm^{-3}. In the limit $n_0 \ll N$ we have the result

$$(18.19) \qquad n_0 = L/AN,$$

so that the photocurrent is now directly proportional to the illumination L. At high levels of illumination if $n_0 \gg N$ the response is given by

$$(18.20) \qquad n_0 = (L/A)^{\frac{1}{2}},$$

just as found earlier in the absence of traps. The experimental results in Fig. 18.11 indicate a change in the response relation of this type.

The decay of the system on switching off the light is given by the solution of the rate equation (18.17):

$$(18.21) \qquad \log \frac{n + N}{n} - \log \frac{n_0 + N}{n_0} = NAt$$

If $N \gg n$, the solution reduces to

$$(18.22) \qquad n = n_0 e^{-NAt},$$

and so the time for the signal to fall to e^{-1} of its initial value is

$$(18.23) \qquad t_0 = 1/NA,$$

which may be contrasted with the earlier result (18.11) in the absence of traps. We see that the presence of traps reduces the conductivity and also reduces the response time on the present model. We note the model neglects the trap emptying time necessary to restore thermal equilibrium.

We estimate now the order of magnitude of the relevant quantities for the model discussed. The quantity A describing recombination has the dimensions of a volume times a reciprocal time and has a value

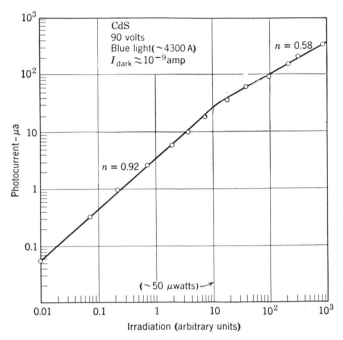

Fig. 18.11. Photoconductive response vs. illumination level for a CdS crystal. The exponent in the relation current $\propto$ (light intensity)^n varies between 0.92 at low levels and 0.58 at high levels of illumination. [After R. W. Smith, RCA Review **12**, 350 (1951).]

of the order of the cross section for capture σ times the thermal velocity u. Taking $\sigma \approx 10^{-16}$ cm^2 and $u \approx 10^7$ cm/sec, we have $A \sim 10^{-9}$ cm^3/sec. If the trap concentration N is of the order of 10^{15} cm^{-3}, we have for the response time $t_0 \approx 10^{-6}$ sec, using (18.23).

If $L = 10^{16}$ quanta/cm^3-sec, the power absorbed for quanta of energy 2 ev is $\approx 3 \times 10^4$ ergs/cm^3-sec, or 3 milliwatts/cm^3. From (18.19) we have $n_0 \approx 10^{16}10^{-6} = 10^{10}$ carriers/cm^3 in the steady state. For $\mu = 100$ cm^2/volt-sec $= 3 \times 10^4$ csu, we have $\sigma \approx 10^{10}(5 \times 10^{-10})(3 \times 10^4) = 1.5 \times 10^5$ esu, or $\rho \approx 10^7$ ohm-cm. If an electric field of 100 volts/cm is applied, the photocurrent density will be 10 μa/cm.^{2}

We do not yet have any feature in the model which will make the response time different from the carrier lifetime; thus far the sensitivity is directly proportional to the response time. Let us now improve the model, working in the approximation $n \ll N$. In Fig. 18.10 we now assume E_1, the height of the traps above the valence band, $\gg kT$, and E_2, the depth of the traps below the conduction band, not much larger than kT. We must then consider the process of thermal excitation of the trapped electrons back to the valence band; ultimately the trap population decays by recombination with holes permanently in lower traps. If $N \gg n_t \gg n$, where n_t is the concentration of electrons in traps, the rate equations are

$$\frac{dn}{dt} = L + Bn_t - ANn - Cnn_t$$

(18.24)

$$\frac{dn_t}{dt} = ANn - Bn_t.$$

The term Bn_t represents the thermal ionization rate of trapped carriers. The term in $-Cnn_t$ represents recombination of electrons with trapped holes, as the concentration of trapped holes is $n + n_t \cong n_t$ as long as $n_t \gg n$.

In the steady state under illumination we have

$$L = Cn_0n_t;$$

$$ANn_0 = Bn_t;$$

so

(18.25) $$n_0 = (BL/ANC)^{1/2}.$$

The quantity B is expected to be proportional to $e^{-E_i/kT}$, where E_i is related to the ionization energy of the traps. We can obtain an approximate value of a response time by supposing that after the light is cut off the system settles down approximately to a steady state with $ANn \cong Bn_t$, which is valid provided the term in C is characterized by a very long time constant in comparison with that of the terms in B and in AN. Then, letting

(18.26) $$\alpha = n_t/n = AN/B,$$

we have

(18.27) $$(1 + \alpha)\frac{dn}{dt} = -C\alpha n^2.$$

As $\alpha \gg 1$, the response time is approximately

$$(18.28) \qquad t_0 \cong \frac{1}{Cn_0} = \frac{n_0}{L}\frac{AN}{B},$$

using (18.25). Thus the response time is increased by the factor $AN/B \gg 1$ over the value predicted by the models we have discussed previously. This feature is in agreement with the experimental results, the observed response times being as much as 10^8 longer than expected from the relation $t_0 = n_0/L$.

PHOTOCONDUCTIVITY IN GERMANIUM

Tyler, Newman, and Woodbury[9] have carried out interesting studies of photoconductivity in germanium doped with transition element

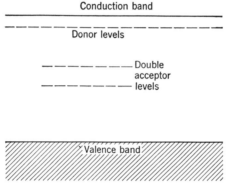

Fig. 18.12. Energy level scheme of germanium doped with a transition element impurity, such as Mn, which introduces two acceptor levels, and counterdoped to make the crystal n-type by the addition of a pentavalent impurity, such as As, giving shallow donor levels. The number of donor atoms is between 1 and 2 times the number of transition element atoms in the experiments described.

impurities. The photoconductive gain is particularly high in these experiments, values as high as 10^4 having been observed: that is, the absorption of one photon with the production of one hole-electron pair starts processes in train which allow as many as 10^4 electrons to pass through the specimen from one electrode to the other. We give here a brief account of their work.

The transition element impurities Mn, Fe, Co, Ni are believed to enter germanium substitutionally; two $4s$ electrons from each atom are available for bonding. As four electrons per atom are needed to form tetrahedral bonds, these elements are lacking two electrons and there-

[9] W. W. Tyler, R. Newman, and H. H. Woodbury, Phys. Rev. **97**, 669 (1955).

fore act as double acceptors with levels as shown in Fig. 18.12. The actual positions of the levels are known experimentally. In the work discussed the crystals were made n-type by counterdoping with donor impurities; so before light is allowed to fall on the crystal the acceptor levels are filled with electrons. Absorbed light produces hole-electron pairs. The acceptor atoms bearing two negative charges attract and capture one hole, leaving the acceptors with a single negative charge. This charge repels electrons, and there is little probability of a conduction electron recombining with a hole as long as the hole is trapped by such an acceptor atom. The probability of electron recombination with a free hole is found to be greater than the probability of recombination with a hole trapped on an acceptor atom if the latter combination bears a negative charge.

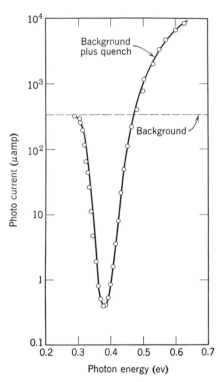

Fig. 18.13. Photoconductivity at 77°K in Mn-doped n-type germanium. (After Tyler.) The background photocurrent is produced by a constant illumination level at a wavelength 1.58 μ, or 0.78 ev. The photon energy plotted refers to the auxiliary or quench radiation. It is seen that radiation near 0.38 ev is highly effective in reducing the photocurrent produced by the primary radiation at 0.78 ev. It is known that 0.38 ev corresponds to the energy required to free one trapped hole from a Mn atom in germanium; so we may suppose that the release of holes to the valence band increases the recombination of the conduction electrons.

It is possible to produce the hole-electron pairs with approximately monochromatic radiation at a photon energy just over the gap energy: such excitation is called intrinsic. In Fig. 18.13 the background photocurrent is produced by a constant light level at 1.58 μ (0.78 ev). When a second light source of variable photon energy is applied to the crystal it is observed that there is a marked drop (by a factor of about 1000) in the photocurrent if the photon energy is such as to ionize the trapped holes from the Mn atoms, thereby making free holes available for recombination. We conclude that double acceptors which have trapped one hole are highly efficient in reducing the rate of recombination, and in this instance extrinsic excitation reduces the photocurrent caused by intrinsic excitation.

The measured mobility both with and without intrinsic excitation at 0.78 ev provides a further confirmation of the model proposed. Without light the mobility at low temperatures is dominated by scattering by the $Mn^=$ centers, acting as doubly ionized impurity centers; with high level intrinsic excitation the Mn centers can be kept saturated

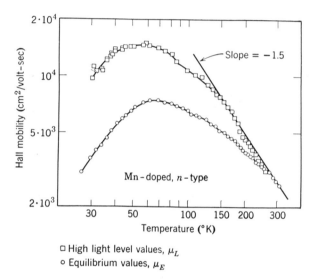

□ High light level values, μ_L
○ Equilibrium values, μ_E

Fig. 18.14.   Effect of high light level intrinsic excitation on the electron mobility in Mn-doped n-type germanium.   (After Tyler.)

with respect to one hole and act as singly ionized Mn^-, thereby reducing the ionized impurity scattering contribution as shown in Fig. 18.14.

SPACE CHARGE OR POLARIZATION EFFECTS

When the illumination is not uniform throughout the crystal or when the electrodes cannot supply or drain off charge carriers freely in the crystal, space charges build up which may reduce the photocurrents severely. Suppose that 300 volts is applied across a crystal slab 1 cm thick by electrodes not in contact with the crystal. This electric field is equivalent to that produced by about 2×10^8 carriers/cm^2 drawn to opposite faces of the slab, as

(18.29) $4\pi ne = E = 1$ statvolt/cm,

where n is the surface concentration of free charge. In this estimate we are taking the dielectric constant of the crystal as unity. Thus

$$n = 1/4\pi e \approx 2 \times 10^8 \text{ electrons/cm}^2.$$

This figure is comparable with the amount of charge piled up by a current density of 10 $\mu a/cm^2$ flowing for 3 μsec, as the reader may verify. After this amount of charge has collected on the crystal surfaces, the current will stop flowing because the electric field of the surface charges cancels the field applied by the electrodes. We observe that the currents and times involved are not large. Polarization effects are a major pitfall in measurements of the photoconductive and related properties of crystals. Pulse methods are often used to reduce the effects of space charge.

CRYSTAL COUNTERS[10]

The crystal counter is an instrument for the detection of single ionizing particles by means of the conductivity pulse accompanying

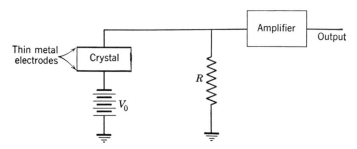

Fig. 18.15.   Schematic diagram of a crystal counter.

passage of a particle through a crystal slab across which a voltage is maintained. The first practical crystal counter was constructed by van Heerden[11] who detected beta rays passing through a silver chloride crystal. The basic circuit is illustrated in Fig. 18.15. The crystal counter is also a useful tool in the investigation of mobility and trapping in crystals.

The mechanism of counting is simple: the ionizing particle produces electron-hole pairs in the crystal. The charge carriers thus produced drift under the influence of the applied electric field until they reach the electrodes or are trapped. The net displacement of charge parallel

[10] For a review of work on crystal counters and further references, see R. Hofstadter, Nucleonics **4**, No. 4, 2 (1949); **4**, No. 5, 29 (1949); A. G. Chynoweth, Am. J. Phys. **20**, 218 (1952).

[11] P. J. van Heerden, *The crystal counter*, Utrecht Dissertation (1945).

to the electric field will induce a proportional charge on the electrodes. The electrode signal is then amplified. Among the materials in which counting effects have been observed are diamond, AgCl, AgBr, ZnS, CdS, TlBr, Tl(Br, I), liquid and solid argon, and sulfur.

We now give an analysis of the shape and magnitude of the voltage pulse induced by an alpha particle. The range of natural alpha particles in crystals is usually very small, of the order of 10^{-3} cm. We assume that n free electrons are produced by one alpha particle penetrating the negative electrode and stopping shortly thereafter. The contribution of the holes to the signal will be neglected, as they are swept up by the cathode near where they are produced. An electron moving a distance x across the crystal induces a charge

$$(18.30) \qquad\qquad q = ex/d$$

on the electrodes, where d is the thickness of the crystal. Electrons drifting toward the anode will be trapped along their path, with a trapping time T:

$$(18.31) \qquad\qquad n = n_0 e^{-t/T}.$$

Now

$$(18.32) \qquad\qquad x = \mu E t,$$

where μ is the mobility and E the electric field intensity. Thus

$$(18.33) \qquad\qquad n = n_0 e^{-x/\mu T E}.$$

The number trapped in dx at x is

$$(18.34) \qquad\qquad dn = (n_0/\mu E T)e^{-x/\mu E T}\, dx;$$

using (18.30) we see that the total charge appearing on the capacitance is

$$(18.35) \qquad q = \frac{n_0 e}{d\mu E t} \int_0^d x e^{-x/\mu E T}\, dx + n_0 e e^{-d/\mu E T}.$$

The second term on the right arises from electrons which get all the way across the crystal to the anode. On integrating we find for the pulse height

$$(18.36) \qquad q = (n_0 e \mu E T/d)(1 - e^{-d/\mu E T}).$$

The quantity

$$(18.37) \qquad\qquad \delta = \mu E T$$

is called the range (German *Schubweg*) of the carriers.   The charge is plotted as a function of δ/d in Fig. 18.16.

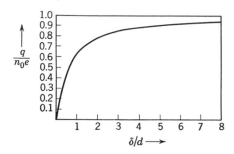

Fig. 18.16. Induced charge on electrodes for an alpha particle incident on a crystal counter as a function of the ratio of conduction electron range δ to crystal thickness d.

The charge dq induced in the time interval dt is readily seen from (18.30) and (18.31) to be

$$(18.38) \quad dq = (n_0 e \mu E/d)e^{-t/T}\, dt,$$

and so the total charge after a time t is

$$(18.39) \quad q(t) = (ne\delta/d)(1 - e^{-t/T}),$$

if the electrons have not reached the anode.   We see that measurements of the rise time give us the trapping time T, and measurements of the pulse height give us $\delta = \mu E T$; on combining the results we can determine the mobility.   This method has been applied to several crystals.

LUMINESCENCE[12]

Luminescence is a general term denoting the absorption in matter of energy and its re-emission as visible or near visible radiation.   The initial excitation may be by light, electron or positive ion bombardment, mechanical strain, chemical reaction, or heating.   If the emission occurs during excitation, or within 10^{-8} sec of excitation, the process is commonly called *fluorescence*.   The interval 10^{-8} sec is chosen as of the order of the lifetime of an atomic state for an allowed electric dipole transition in the visible region of the spectrum.   If the emission occurs after excitation has ceased, the process is called *phosphorescence* or *after-glow*.   The after-glow period may be of the order of microseconds to hours.

Many solids are luminescent with low efficiency for the conversion of other forms of energy into radiation.   The ability of a given material to luminesce with high efficiency is frequently related to *activator atoms*, which are special impurity atoms present in only small proportions; there are also a number of pure materials which luminesce efficiently.   Phosphorescent crystals may be divided into two classes: photoconductors of which Cu-activated ZnS is the prototype, and crystals in which the photoconductivity that may be present is incidental to the luminescent process; Tl-activated KCl is representative of the latter class.

Crystalline luminescent solids are known commonly as *phosphors*. Phosphors are used widely in fluorescent lamps, in cathode ray oscilloscope, radar, and television presentation, and in nucleon and radiation detectors. In the fluorescent lamp the problem is to convert the 2537 A mercury radiation into visible light, and for this purpose one may use a complex calcium halophosphate doubly activated with antimony (blue emission) and manganese (orange emission). In the cathode ray tube the kinetic energy of the electrons incident on the phosphor is converted partly into light with the aid usually of silver- or copper-activated zinc sulfide or mixed cadmium-zinc sulfide. In scintillation counters thallium-activated alkali halides and solid solutions of anthracene, napthalene, and terphenyl are used.

SULFIDE PHOSPHORS

Zinc and cadmium sulfides are characteristic sulfide phosphors, and we shall discuss them particularly in the forms ZnS:Ag, ZnS:Cu, and CdS:Ag. The notation indicates that silver and copper are the activators considered. Optimum concentrations of these activators are of the order of 0.01 atomic percent. Zinc sulfide occurs in both cubic (zinc blende) and hexagonal (wurtzite) modifications, with band gaps approximately equal to 3.64 ev (3410 A) for cubic ZnS and 3.70 ev (3350 A) for hexagonal ZnS. Probably because of crystalline imperfections it is possible to excite interband transitions with 3650 A radiation, and, of course, cathode rays are also effective. Cadmium sulfide is hexagonal; it has a band gap of 2.43 ev (5100 A). The luminescent processes in activated zinc or cadmium sulfide are not understood thoroughly at present. Work has been done in which a fairly satisfactory account is given of some of the principal features of the observed behavior, and we shall discuss some of this work below, as it provides a convenient framework for understanding a number of the salient experimental facts. Although the work discussed is not universally accepted, the discussion illustrates a typical line of reasoning in this field.

A model proposed by Lambe and Klick[13] for CdS:Ag reconciles in a simple way observations on luminescence and on photoconductivity,

[13] J. Lambe and C. C. Klick, Phys. Rev. **98**, 909 (1955); the model discussed by them is a development of models treated by M. Schön, Z. Physik **119**, 463 (1942), and H. A. Klasens, Nature **158**, 306 (1946); J. Electrochem. Soc. **100**, 72 (1953). For another interesting model, see the work of R. H. Bube, J. Chem. Phys. **21**, 5 (1953); **20**, 708 (1952); Phys. Rev. **90**, 70 (1953); **99**, 1105 (1955).

the two features being closely related in this material.   The model is shown in Fig. 18.17.   The mode of operation of the system is as follows:

(1) Light is absorbed producing a free hole and electron leading to conductivity.

(2) The hole and electron move about in their respective bands, and eventually the hole migrates near an impurity center (activator ion).

(3) The hole is captured by the impurity center, and luminescent emission occurs, leaving the center effectively neutral in charge.

(4) The electron wanders through the lattice until finally it comes near the center.

(5) The electron is captured by the center, resetting the center for the next cycle of operation.   In the capture a small amount of energy is given off as infrared radiation or as lattice phonons.

Let us discuss some features of the model:

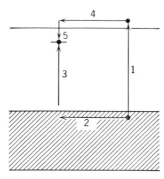

Fig. 18.17.   Lambe and Klick model for sulfides with monovalent activator: (1) excitation; (2) hole migration; (3) hole capture resulting in luminescence; (4) electron migration; (5) electron capture (non-radiative).

(1) The hole is captured first because the activator bears an effective negative charge.   If the activator is a Cu^+ or Ag^+ ion occupying a Zn^{++} or Cd^{++} lattice site substitutionally (Fig. 18.18), the activator will indeed act as negative with respect to the perfect crystal.   After capturing a hole the activator will act as neutral in the crystal and will now be able to capture the electron.

(2) It is found that the decay of luminescence is much more rapid than the decay of photoconductivity; in CdS:Ag at 77°K the luminescent decay time is one-hundredth of the photoconductive decay time. On our model the luminescent act occurs first and should occur much more rapidly than the decay of photoconductivity.   The hole sees an attractive Coulomb potential before capture by the activator, while the electron sees a repulsive potential from the activator before the hole is captured and a weak (neutral) potential thereafter.

(3) It is known from independent photoconductive experiments that holes are trapped in the sulfides much more rapidly than electrons. The photocurrent is known to be dominated by electrons.

(4) Neither silver nor copper in ZnS make the crystal paramagnetic[14]

[14] S. Larach and J. Turkevich, Phys. Rev. **98**, 1015 (1955); R. Bowers and N. T. Melamed, Phys. Rev. **99**, 1781 (1955).

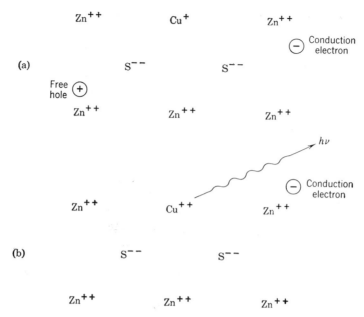

Fig. 18.18.   (a) ZnS:Cu with electron-hole pair produced by excitation.   (b) The hole is captured by the copper activator ion with the emission of a photon $h\nu$. Later the electron is also captured and the Cu^{++} ion reverts to Cu^+.

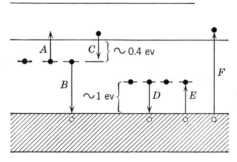

Fig. 18.19.   Specific model proposed for CdS:Ag by Lambe and Klick.   Levels $\sim$0.4 ev below conduction band result from silver activation.   Levels 1 ev above valence band are normally present in CdS. A: Infrared excitation of trapped electrons (3 μ region). B: Luminescent recombination of trapped electrons and free holes. C: Trapping of electrons. D: Trapping of holes. E: Freeing of trapped holes by excitation in 1 μ region. F: Excitation.

in the ground state: this negative result is consistent with the Ag^+ and Cu^+ valency assignment.

(5) On the specific model proposed for CdS:Ag in Fig. 18.19 the activator level is about 0.4 ev below the bottom of the conduction band.   There are also present levels from other traps, the levels being

about 1 ev above the top of the valence band; it is possible that these traps may be vacant Cd sites.   A vacant Cd^{++} site carries an effective single negative charge after the capture of a hole; thus electrons are repelled and will not recombine appreciably with holes trapped at such sites.   If a crystal is cooled to 77°K and irradiated with blue light, it is possible to populate these traps; the light is removed and the crystal irradiated at 1 ev, liberating the trapped holes which then are captured by the activator with the emission of orange light.

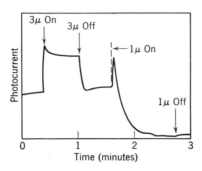

Fig. 18.20. Comparison of the action of 3 μ irradiation and 1 μ irradiation on photoconductivity of CdS:Ag at 77°K. (After Lambe and Klick.)

(6) Irradiation as above with 1 ev photons quenches the photo-current, as shown in Fig. 18.20.   Freeing the

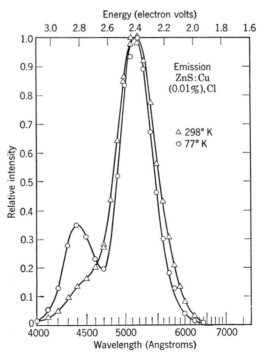

Fig. 18.21.   Emission spectrum of ZnS containing chloride and 0.01 percent copper. (After Bowers and Melamed.)

trapped holes makes them available for recombination with electrons via the activator ions.

Bowers and Melamed[14] and Kroger[15] have suggested identifications of the several types of traps associated with specific emission bands in $ZnS:Cu:Cl$ phosphors. Their identifications are based in part on the observation that all the unexcited traps in this system are diamagnetic. They associated a blue emission (Fig. 18.21) centered about 4400 A with the presence of Cl^- ions. According to the discussion of the last chapter the introduction of Cl^- substitutionally for $S^=$ must be accompanied by the creation of vacant Zn^{++} sites in order to maintain neutrality. One is thus led to consider either the Cl^- ion or the zinc vacancy as responsible for the blue emission. Because the same emission is found with other impurities such as Br^- and Al^{+++} which are also accompanied by zinc vacancies it is thought that the zinc vacancies are responsible.

When Cl^- and Cu^+ are present simultaneously a green emission is attributed to Cu^+ ions substituted for Zn^{++}. The presence of Cl^- simply makes it possible for Cu^+ to enter the lattice, by the familiar argument of charge neutrality.

The red emission at 6700 A is found when the only impurity present is copper. The copper is thought to be present as Cu^{++} in interstitial positions. The disposition of the two valence electrons is unclear.

THALLIUM-ACTIVATED POTASSIUM CHLORIDE

The thallium-activated alkali halide phosphors have been studied extensively by Williams[16] and co-workers and provide good examples of the class of non-photoconducting phosphors. The thallous ions Tl^+ are believed to occupy at random alkali metal sites in the lattice. The assumption that only those thallous ions isolated from other thallous ions are effective activators has been shown by Johnson and Williams to account for the concentration dependence of the luminescent intensity. The experimental situation is particularly simple for thallium concentrations of 0.01 percent or less.

The phosphor $KCl:Tl$ consists of an ionic lattice containing Tl^+ ions substituted for K^+ ions. Optical absorption of the host crystal begins at 1650 A and extends to shorter wavelengths. The thallium introduces two bell-shaped absorption bands centered about 1960 A and 2490 A and a broad emission band about 3050 A at 25°C. The absorption and emission bands are associated with excited states of

[15] F. A. Kroger, Brit. J. Appl. Phys. Suppl. No. 4, pp. 58–63 (1955).
[16] The work is reviewed by F. E. Williams, Advances in Electronics 5, 137 (1953); an early discussion was given by F. Seitz, J. Chem. Phys. 6, 150 (1938).

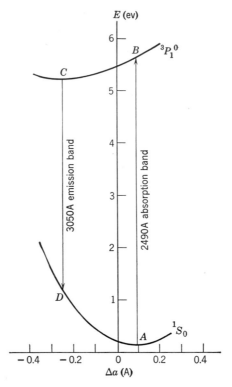

Fig. 18.22. Two energy levels of thallium ion in a potassium chloride lattice, as a function of configurational coordinate representing the symmetric displacement of the six chlorine ions around a thallium ion from the perfect potassium chloride lattice positions. The thallium ion in the ground state is close to point A, with some spread about this point caused by the thermal motion of the lattice. When irradiated with light near 2490 A, a transition $A \to B$ to the upper state may take place. According to the Franck-Condon principle the transition occurs with the lattice configuration characteristic of the ground state: thus the absorption occurs from A to B, rather than from A to C. After the transition a rearrangement of the neighboring ions takes place with the system ending up at the equilibrium position C, the energy difference $B - C$ being dissipated in lattice vibrations. From C the system emits light in a band around 3050 A, passing to D, and, after giving energy to the lattice, passes down to the equilibrium position A. (After F. E. Williams.)

the thallous ion. The configuration of the ground state of the Tl^- ion is $6s^2$, and the state is $^1S_0$. That is, the spins of the two s electrons are antiparallel. From spectroscopic studies of the free ion it is known that the lowest excited states arise from the configuration $6s6p$ and consist in order of increasing energy of $^3P_0{}^0$, $^3P_1{}^0$, $^3P_2{}^0$, and $^1P_1{}^0$, each separated by the order of 1 volt. The spectroscopic selection rule against transitions from $J = 0$ to $J' = 0$ suggests that the transition

$^1S_0 \leftrightarrow {}^3P_0{}^0$ does not occur, and the transition $^1S_0 \leftrightarrow {}^3P_2{}^0$ is excluded by the general selection rule $\Delta J = 0, \pm 1$. As the coupling is in part $j - j$, the selection rule $\Delta S = 0$ is not very effective and the transitions $^1S_0 \rightarrow {}^3P_1{}^0$ and $^1S_0 \rightarrow {}^1P_1{}^0$ have comparable intensities, the former leading to the 2490 A absorption band and the latter to the 1960 A absorption band. The emission at 3050 A is associated with the inverse transition $^3P_1{}^0 \rightarrow {}^1S_0$, as shown in Fig. 18.22.

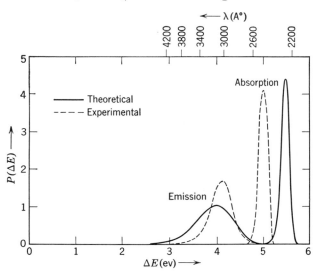

Fig. 18.23. Theoretical and experimental absorption and emission spectra of KCl:Tl. (After F. E. Williams.)

The general principles involved in this type of luminescence are evident in the figure drawn for the $^1S_0 \rightarrow {}^3P_1{}^0$ and inverse transitions. The absorption from the ground state occurs according to the Franck-Condon principle with the neighboring ions in the lattice roughly fixed in position. The width of the absorption band is accounted for by zero-point and thermal motions of the lattice; these motions cause transitions to occur over a certain spread of values of the configurational coordinate.[17] The lifetime of the excited state is long (by a factor of the order of 10^5) in comparison with the period of a lattice vibration, so that following absorption the system will come to thermal equilibrium for the $^3P_1{}^0$ state. Williams has calculated the position of the minimum energy point for this state, with the result shown in Fig. 18.22. Emission occurs in accordance with the Franck-Condon

[17] A configurational coordinate is a linear combination of the position vectors of the nuclei of ions in the neighborhood of interest. In our problem the symmetric displacement from the perfect KCl lattice positions of the six Cl⁻ ions bounding the Tl⁺ ion is defined as Δa.

principle from the $^3P_1{}^0$ state to the $^1S_0$ state at the value of the configuration coordinate corresponding to the minimum energy position of the excited state.   The rearrangement energy $B \rightarrow C$ and $D \rightarrow A$ is given to the lattice.   A comparison of the experimental and theoretical bands as calculated by Williams is given in Fig. 18.23.   It should be emphasized that the calculations are absolute in the sense that they are based on calculated wave functions and lattice energies.

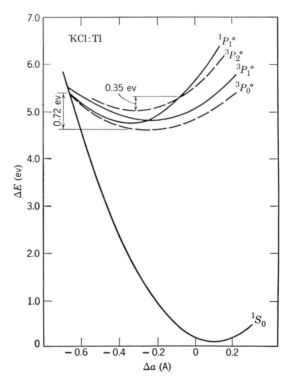

Fig. 18.24.   Configuration-coordinate model for ground state, emitting states, and trapping states of KCl:Tl.   (After Johnson and Williams.)

The configuration diagram for all four excited states considered is given in Fig. 18.24.   If by a fluctuation the configurational energy of the system in the excited $^3P_1{}^0$ state should exceed the activation energy of about 0.6 ev, it will be possible to make a radiationless transition to the ground state.   Once in the ground state, the system may descend to the position of minimum energy by the emission of phonons. The corresponding activation energy for the excited $^1P_1{}^0$ state is slightly less.   Excitation of KCl:Tl at low temperatures in the 1960 A absorption band gives emission preferentially at a band near 4750 A. The transitions are thought to be $^1S_0 \leftrightarrows {}^1P_1{}^0$.

The states $^3P_2{}^0$ and $^3P_0{}^0$ are not connected with the ground state by allowed electric dipole transitions, but there is enough transition probability to build up by optical excitation at low temperature an appreciable population in these states. The population is effectively trapped in these metastable states, but can be released by warming up and thereby providing enough thermal energy for the systems eventually to reach the crossover points indicated on Fig. 18.24. The effective trap depths of 0.35 and 0.72 ev are marked on the figure. The trap depths are measured by observing the thermoluminescence.

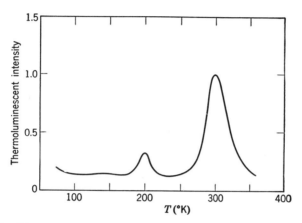

Fig. 18.25. Thermoluminescence of KCl:Tl. (After Johnson and Williams.)

This is accomplished by exciting the solid at a low temperature, removing the excitation, and then heating the solid slowly, measuring emission intensity and temperature. Glow peaks observed in this way are shown in Fig. 18.25. Each glow peak arises from the thermal emptying of a set of traps at a particular value of the trapping energy.

The luminescence of phosphors activated with divalent manganese is somewhat parallel to that of the thallium-activated phosphors. Divalent manganese is an efficient activator in many crystals and finds application in fluorescent lamps and oscilloscope screens.

ELECTROLUMINESCENCE

In electroluminescence[18] in the solid state, electrical energy is converted in a semiconductor directly into light. It is hoped that it may one day be possible to light a room by applying a voltage to electrodes

[18] G. Destriau, Phil. Mag. **38,** 700 (1947); O. Lossev, Phil. Mag. **6,** 1028 (1928); W. W. Piper and F. E. Williams, Phys. Rev. **87,** 151 (1952); D. Curie, J. phys. radium **13,** 317 (1952); K. Lehovec, C. A. Accardo, and E. Jamgochian, Phys. Rev. **83,** 603 (1951).

on a sheet covered with an appropriate semiconductor. There may also be applications to wall television.

Two basic mechanisms for the production of electroluminescence have been observed. One mechanism is photon emission in the act of electron-hole recombination. When current flows in the forward direction of a p-n junction (Chapter 14) electrons from the n region are swept into the p region and recombine with holes. The associated radiation has been observed in CdS, SiC, germanium, silicon, and several III-V type compounds. The second mechanism for electroluminescence is photon emission following electron impact excitation of an activator atom. This process has been observed in ZnS:Cu.

PROBLEMS

18.1. Derive an expression for the orbital g-factor of a simple exciton composed of an electron of effective mass m_e and a hole of effective mass m_h; show that the orbital magnetic moment vanishes if $m_e = m_h$.

18.2. Does an exciton in a triplet spin state ($S = 1$) have a spin magnetic moment? Compare in this respect an exciton and positronium.

18.3.* Taking $m_e = m_h = m$ and $\epsilon = 10$, estimate the electric field intensity required for an exciton to have a first order Stark splitting of 1 cm^{-1} in the level $n = 2$; compare this field with that required for atomic hydrogen.

18.4. A crystal slab of thickness d is uniformly irradiated and N mobile electrons are produced in unit time. Plane electrodes are in contact with the crystal surfaces but no charge is allowed to pass across the electrode-crystal interfaces. The holes are permanently trapped on formation, and the electrons are supposed to be trapped after a time such that a voltage V_0 is required to drive an electron across the crystal before trapping can occur.

(a) Show that the initial rate of charge of an electrode is

$$\frac{dQ}{dt} = \frac{NeV}{V_0}\left[1 - \frac{V}{2V_0}\right],$$

where V is the applied voltage.

(b) Derive an approximate expression for the time interval before the charging rate drops appreciably because of space charge effects.

18.5. You are given a crystal slab in which the photoconductivity is known to be associated with one carrier type, holes or electrons, but just which is not known. Describe an experiment (using light of a wavelength strongly absorbed in a short distance in the crystal) which will identify the carrier type, without utilizing the Hall effect.

18.6. The discussion in the text of the sulfide phosphors is stated in terms of ionic models. Indicate the translation of the principal statements to an energy band model.

18.7. Let the fractional concentration of Tl ions in KCl be c. Assuming only those Tl ions which do not have other Tl ions among their nearest cation neighbors are effective activators, derive and plot an expression for the variation in the concentration c^* of effective activators as a function of c.

REFERENCES

E. I. Adirowitsch, *Einige Fragen zur Theorie der Lumineszenz der Kristalle*, Akademie-Verlag, Berlin, 1953.

F. C. Champion, "Solid Conduction Counters," Prog. Nucl. Phys. **3**, 159 (1955).

M. Curie, *Fluorescence et phosphorescence*, Herman, Paris, 1946.

M. Curie and D. Curie, "Questions actuelles en luminescence cristalline," Cahiers physique **55, 56, 57–58** (1955).

G. Fonda and F. Seitz, editors, *Preparation and characteristics of solid luminescent materials*, John Wiley & Sons, New York, 1948.

G. F. J. Garlick, *Luminescent materials*, Clarendon Press, Oxford, 1949.

F. A. Kröger, *Some aspects of the luminescence of solids*, Elsevier, New York, 1948.

H. W. Leverenz, *Introduction to the luminescence of solids*, John Wiley & Sons, New York, 1950.

"Luminescence," supplement to Brit. J. Appl. Phys., No. 4, 1955.

G. A. Morton, "The scintillation counter," Advances in Electronics **4**, 69–107.

T. S. Moss, *Photoconductivity in the elements*, Butterworths, London, 1952.

N. F. Mott and R. W. Gurney, *Electronic processes in ionic crystals*, Clarendon Press, Oxford, 1940.

"Photoconductivity," September, 1951, issue of RCA Review.

Photoconductivity Conference, Breckenridge, Russell, and Hahn, editors, John Wiley & Sons, New York, 1956.

P. Pringsheim, *Fluorescence and phosphorescence*, Interscience Publishers, New York, 1949.

F. E. Williams, "Solid state luminescence," Advances in Electronics, **5**, 137 (1953).

19

Dislocations

The present chapter is concerned principally with the interpretation of the plastic properties of crystalline solids in terms of the theory of dislocations. We are rapidly gaining a basic qualitative understanding of many aspects of this field.

The plasticity of pure single crystals of many solids is a striking feature of their mechanical behavior. This fundamental weakness of crystals is exhibited in various ways depending on the crystal, but there appear to be few exceptions[1] to the rule that pure crystals are plastic and are not strong. Pure silver chloride melts at 455°C, yet at room temperature it has a cheese-like consistency and can be rolled into sheets. Pure aluminum crystals are elastic only to a strain of about 10^{-5}, after which they deform plastically. Theoretical estimates of the elastic limit of perfect crystals give values as much as 10^3 or 10^4 higher than the observed values, although it is more usual to find a factor of the order of 10^2.

SHEAR STRENGTH OF SINGLE CRYSTALS

Frenkel[2] gave a simple method of estimating the theoretical shear strength of a perfect crystal. Referring to Fig. 19.1, we consider the force needed to shear two planes of atoms past each other. In the region of small elastic strains the stress σ is related to the displacement x by

$$(19.1) \qquad \sigma = Gx/d,$$

where d is the interplanar spacing and G is the shear modulus, given by c_{44} for shear in a $\langle 100 \rangle$ direction on a $\{100\}$ plane in a cubic crystal.

---

[1] It seems that exceptions really exist; for example, crystals of highly purified germanium and silicon are not plastic at room temperature and fail only by fracture. Glass also fails only by fracture at room temperature, but it is not crystalline. The fracture of glass is believed to be caused by stress concentration at minute cracks, as proposed by A. A. Griffith, Phil. Trans. Roy. Soc. (London) **A221**, 163 (1921).

[2] J. Frenkel, Z. Physik **37**, 572 (1926).

When the displacement has proceeded to the point that atom A is directly over atom B in the figure, the planes of atoms are in a configuration of unstable equilibrium and the stress is zero. As a first approximation we may represent the stress-displacement relation by a sine function:

$$(19.2) \qquad \sigma = (Ga/2\pi d) \sin (2\pi x/a),$$

where a is the interatomic spacing in the direction of shear. For small x this relation reduces to (19.1). The critical shear stress σ_c at

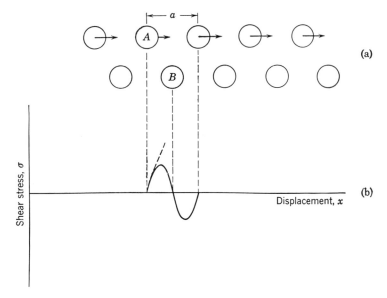

Fig. 19.1. (a) Relative shear of two planes of atoms (shown in cross section) in a uniformly strained crystal; (b) shear stress as a function of the relative displacement of the planes from their equilibrium position. The heavy broken line is drawn at the initial slope corresponding to the shear modulus G.

which the lattice becomes unstable is given by the maximum value of σ, or

$$(19.3) \qquad \sigma_c = Ga/2\pi d.$$

If $a \approx d$, $\sigma_c \approx G/2\pi$; the critical shear stress should be of the order of $\frac{1}{6}$ of the shear modulus.

Reference to the observations in Table 19.1 shows that the observed values of the elastic limit are much smaller than (19.3) would suggest. (We note for comparison with values tabulated in handbooks that a value given in kilograms per square millimeter is to be multiplied by approximately 0.98×10^8 to obtain dynes per square centimeter, and a value given in (long) tons per square inch is to be multiplied by 1.54×10^8 to obtain dynes per square centimeter.) The theoretical estimate may be improved by taking into account the actual form of the intermolecular forces and by consideration of other configurations of mechanical stability that the lattice may develop as it is sheared. Mackenzie has shown that these two effects may reduce the theoretical shear strength to about $G/30$, corresponding to a critical shear strain of about 2 degrees.[3]

TABLE 19.1. COMPARISON OF SHEAR MODULUS AND ELASTIC LIMIT
(After Mott)

	Shear Modulus G (dynes/cm^2)	Elastic Limit B (dynes/cm^2)	G/B
Sn, single crystal	1.9×10^{11}	1.3×10^7	15,000
Ag, single crystal	2.8×10^{11}	6×10^6	45,000
Al, single crystal	2.5×10^{11}	4×10^6	60,000
Al, pure, polycrystal	2.5×10^{11}	2.6×10^8	900
Al, commercial drawn	$\sim 2.5 \times 10^{11}$	9.9×10^8	250
Duralumin	$\sim 2.5 \times 10^{11}$	3.6×10^9	70
Fe, soft, polycrystal	7.7×10^{11}	1.5×10^9	500
Heat-treated carbon steel	$\sim 8 \times 10^{11}$	6.5×10^9	120
Nickel-chrome steel	$\sim 8 \times 10^{11}$	1.2×10^{10}	65

It is clear that the shear strength cannot be discussed simply by extending the theory of elasticity to large strains, but we must instead look for imperfections that can act as sources of mechanical weakness in real crystals. It is now known that special crystal imperfections called dislocations exist in almost all crystals, and their presence is responsible for slip at very low applied stresses.

In many crystals plastic deformation occurs by translational *slip*, as shown in Fig. 19.2. Here one part of the crystal slides as a unit across an adjacent part. The surface on which slip takes place is often a plane, which is known as the slip plane. The direction of motion is known as the slip direction. The visible intersection of a slip plane with the outer surface of the crystal is known as a slip band.

The great importance of lattice properties for plastic strain is indicated by the highly anisotropic nature of slip. Even in the cubic metals displacement takes place along well-defined crystallographic planes with a small set of Miller indices, such as the {111} planes in fcc metals and the {110}, {112}, and {123} planes in bcc metals.

[3] J. K. Mackenzie, thesis, Bristol, 1949. W. L. Bragg and W. M. Lomer, Proc. Roy. Soc. (London) **196,** 171 (1949) have shown that the observed shear strength of a perfect two-dimensional raft of bubbles is of this order.

Under most conditions the slip direction lies in the line of closest atomic packing, $\langle 110 \rangle$ in fcc metals, $\langle 111 \rangle$ in bcc metals, and $\langle 2\,\bar{1}\,\bar{1}\,0 \rangle$ in hcp metals.

Deformation by slip is inhomogeneous: large shear displacements occur on a few widely separated slip planes while parts of the crystal lying between slip planes remain essentially undeformed. A further property of slip is the Schmid law of the critical shear stress, which

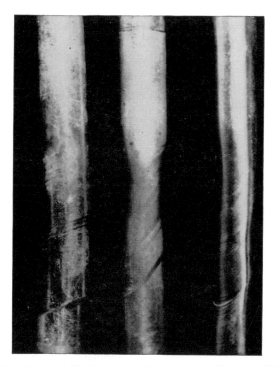

Fig. 19.2.   Translational slip in zinc single crystals.   (Courtesy E. R. Parker.)

states that slip takes place along a given slip plane and direction when the corresponding component of shear stress reaches a critical value.

A second mode of plastic deformation, called *twinning*, is observed in some crystals, particularly in hcp and bcc crystals. We saw that a considerable amount of displacement occurs on a few widely separated slip planes during the slip process. During twinning, on the other hand, a small amount of displacement (less than one lattice parameter) occurs successively on each of many neighboring crystallographic planes. After deformation, the deformed part of the crystal is converted to a mirror image of the undeformed part, accounting for the name of the process.   Although both slip and twinning are caused by the motion of dislocations, we shall be concerned primarily with slip.

DISLOCATIONS[4]

The low observed values of the critical shear stress can be explained in terms of the motion through the lattice of a particular type of imperfection known as a *dislocation*.   The idea that slip propagates over

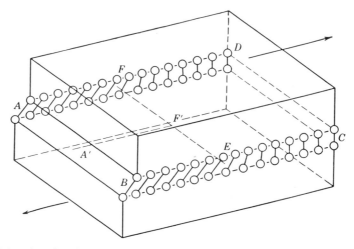

Fig. 19.3.   An edge dislocation, showing the glide plane *ABCD*, the slipped region *ABEF* in which the atoms have been displaced by more than half a lattice constant, and the unslipped region *FECD* with displacement less than half a lattice constant. The dislocation line is *EF* and the slip direction is *A'F'*.   (After Cottrell, *Progress in metal physics*, No. 1, Butterworths Scientific Publications, London, 1949.)

slip planes by the motion of dislocations was published in 1934 independently by Taylor, Orowan, and Polanyi; the concept of dislocations was introduced into physics somewhat earlier by Prandtl and Dehlinger.

We first describe an edge dislocation.   Figure 19.3 shows a simple cubic crystal in which slip of one atom distance has occurred over the left half of the slip plane but not over the right half.   The boundary between the slipped and unslipped regions is the dislocation.   It is a line imperfection, whose position is marked by the termination of an extra vertical half-plane of atoms crowded into the upper half of the crystal as shown in Fig. 19.4.   Near the dislocation the crystal is highly strained.   The simple edge dislocation extends indefinitely in

[4] Excellent discussions of dislocation theory are given in books by Cottrell and Read cited at the end of the chapter.

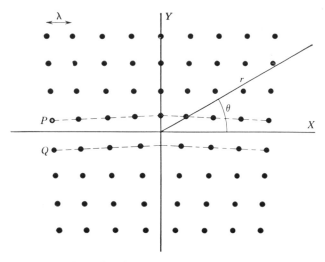

Fig. 19.4. Structure of an edge dislocation. The deformation may be thought of as caused by inserting an extra plane of atoms on the upper half of the y axis. Atoms in the upper half-crystal P are compressed and those in the lower half Q are extended. This is defined as a positive dislocation; if the extra plane is put in from below, the dislocation is negative. (After Cottrell.)

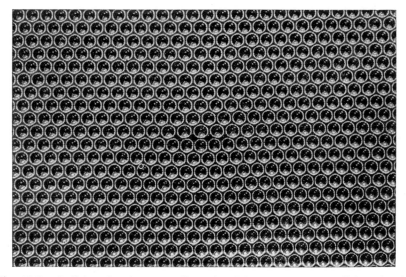

Fig. 19.5. A dislocation in a two-dimensional bubble raft. The dislocation is most easily seen by turning the page by 30° in its plane and sighting at a low angle. (Photograph courtesy of W. M. Lomer, after Bragg and Nye.)

the slip plane in a direction normal to the slip direction. Edge dislocations are called positive or negative according to the position of the extra plane of atoms above or below the slip plane. In Fig. 19.5 we show a photograph of a dislocation in a two-dimensional soap bubble raft obtained by the method of Bragg and Nye.[5]

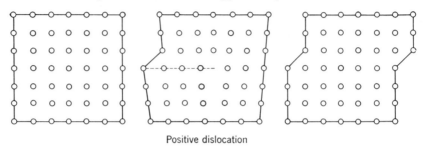

Positive dislocation

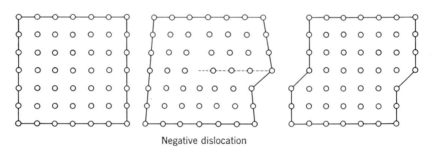

Negative dislocation

Fig. 19.6.   Motion of a dislocation under a shear tending to move the upper surface of the specimen to the right.   *Above*, a positive dislocation moves from left to right; *below*, a negative dislocation moves from right to left.   Note that the positive and negative dislocations leave the specimen on opposite sides.   (After Taylor.)

The mechanism responsible for the mobility of a dislocation and the attendant ease of slip is shown in Fig. 19.6.   When atoms on one side of the slip plane are moved with respect to those on the other side, part of the atoms at the slip plane will experience repulsive forces and part will experience attractive forces from their neighbors across the

[5] W. L. Bragg and J. F. Nye, Proc. Roy. Soc. (London) **A190,** 474 (1947); W. L. Bragg and W. M. Lomer, Proc. Roy. Soc. (London) **A196,** 171 (1949).   A film based on this work is distributed by Kodak Ltd., London, as "Cinegraph" 16-mm film No. 2015; see also the film "Bubble Model of a Metal Structure," commentary by Sir Lawrence Bragg, distributed by MacQueen Film Organization, West St., Bromley, Kent, England.

slip plane.   To a first approximation these forces cancel, and so the external stress required to move a dislocation will be quite small.   If the dislocation line is not straight, the cancellation will be even more

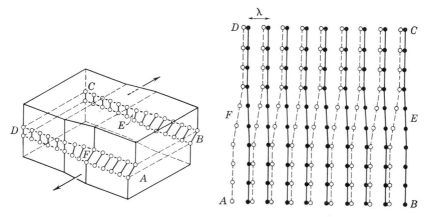

Fig. 19.7.   A screw dislocation.   A part *ABEF* of the slip plane has slipped in the direction parallel to the dislocation line *EF*.   A screw dislocation may be visualized as a spiral arrangement of lattice planes, such that we change planes on going completely around the dislocation line.   (After Cottrell.)

complete.   Calculations show that a dislocation in an otherwise perfect crystal can be made to move by very low stresses, probably below 10^5 dynes/cm^2.   Thus dislocations may make a crystal very plastic.

Passage of a dislocation through a crystal is equivalent to slip of usually one fundamental translation vector of the lattice.   The motion of an edge dislocation through a crystal is analogous to the passage of a ruck (wrinkle) across a rug: the ruck moves more easily than the whole rug, but passage of the ruck across the rug does amount to sliding the rug on the floor.

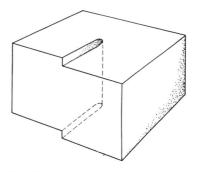

Fig. 19.8.   Another view of a screw dislocation.   The broken vertical line which marks the dislocation is surrounded by strained material.

The second simple type of dislocation is the screw dislocation, sketched in Figs. 19.7 and 19.8.   It marks a boundary between slipped and unslipped crystal.   The boundary parallels the slip direction, instead of lying perpendicular to it as with the edge dislocation.   The screw dislocation may be thought of as being produced by cutting the crystal part way through with a knife and shearing it one atom spacing parallel to the edge of the cut. We note that the presence of a screw dislocation transforms successive atom planes into the surface of a helix, accounting for the name of the dislocation.

Compound and ring dislocations may be formed from segments of edge and screw dislocations. Burgers has shown that the most general form of linear dislocation pattern in a crystal can be described as

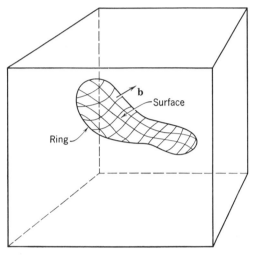

Fig. 19.9. General method of forming a dislocation ring in a medium. The medium is represented by the rectangular block. The ring is represented by the closed curve in the interior in the block. A cut is made along the surface bounded by the curve and indicated by the contoured area. The material on one side of the cut is displaced relative to that on the other by vector distance **b**, which may be arbitrarily oriented relative to the surface. Forces will be required to effect the displacement. The medium is filled in or cut away so as to be continuous after the displacement. It is then joined in the displaced state and the applied forces are relaxed. **b** is the Burgers vector of the dislocation. (After Seitz.)

shown in Fig. 19.9. We consider any closed curve not necessarily planar within a crystal, or an open curve terminating on the surface at both ends. Make a cut along any simple surface bounded by the line. Displace the material on one side of this surface by **b** relative to the other side; **b** is a fixed vector called the *Burgers vector*. In regions where **b** is not parallel to the cut surface this relative displacement will either produce a gap or cause the two halves to overlap. In these cases material is either added to fill the gap or is subtracted to prevent overlap. Then rejoin the material on both sides, leaving the strain displacement intact at the time of rewelding, but afterwards allowing the medium to come to internal equilibrium. The resulting strain pattern is that of the dislocation characterized jointly by the boundary curve and the Burgers vector. It is clear that the Burgers vector must be one of a discrete set of lattice vectors that will allow the rewelding process to maintain the crystallinity of the material.

The Burgers vector of a screw dislocation is parallel to the dislocation line, while that of an edge dislocation is perpendicular to the dislocation line and lies in the slip plane.

STRESS FIELDS OF DISLOCATIONS

The stress field of a screw dislocation is particularly simple. Figure 19.10 shows a shell of material surrounding an axial screw dislocation. It is evident that the shell has been sheared an amount b in a circumferential length $2\pi r$, giving a shear strain $e_{r\theta} = b/2\pi r$. If we treat the material as an elastic continuum, the corresponding shear stress is

$$(19.4) \qquad \sigma_{r\theta} = Ge_{r\theta} = Gb/2\pi r.$$

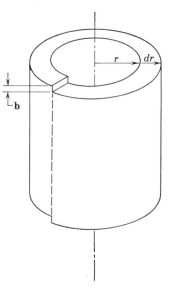

Fig. 19.10. Shell of elastically distorted crystal surrounding screw dislocation with Burgers vector b.

This expression cannot hold in the region immediately around the dislocation line, as the strains here are too large for linear elasticity theory to apply. The elastic energy of the shell in Fig. 19.10 is $dE_s = \frac{1}{2}Ge_{r\theta}{}^2\,dV = (Gb^2/4\pi)\,dr/r$ per unit length; so the total elastic energy per unit length of screw dislocation is

$$(19.5) \qquad E_s = (Gb^2/4\pi)\ln(R/r_0),$$

where R and r_0 are appropriate upper and lower limits for the variable r. It is clear that the proper value of r_0 is comparable to the magnitude b of the Burgers vector, and that the value of R cannot exceed the dimensions of the crystal. We shall see that in many applications R is considerably smaller than the dimensions of the crystal.

Consider as in Fig. 19.4 a positive edge dislocation at the origin of the coordinate system as shown. We let σ_{rr} and $\sigma_{\theta\theta}$ denote the normal stresses in the radial and circumferential directions, and let $\sigma_{r\theta}$ denote the shear stress. The reader will not be entirely surprised to learn that, if we treat the medium as an isotropic elastic continuum, σ_{rr} and $\sigma_{\theta\theta}$ are proportional to $(\sin\theta)/r$. We want a function falling off as $1/r$ that changes sign when y is replaced by $-y$. The shear stress $\sigma_{r\theta}$ is proportional to $(\cos \theta)/r$; considering the plane $y = 0$ we see from the figure that the shear stress is an odd function of x. We expect the constants of proportionality to be proportional to the shear modulus G and to the magnitude b of the Burgers vector. The result, which is derived in the books by Read and Cottrell, is

(19.6)
$$\sigma_{rr} = \sigma_{\theta\theta} = -\frac{Gb}{2\pi(1 - \nu)}\frac{\sin \theta}{r},$$

$$\sigma_{r\theta} = \frac{Gb}{2\pi(1 - \nu)}\frac{\cos \theta}{r},$$

where ν is the Poisson ratio ($\nu \approx 0.3$ for most crystals). The strain energy of a unit length of edge dislocation is

(19.7) $$E_e = [Gb^2/4\pi(1 - \nu)] \ln (R/r_0),$$

slightly larger than that of a screw dislocation.

Referring again to Fig. 19.4, we are interested in obtaining an expression for the shear stress component σ_{xy} on planes parallel to the slip plane. Taking components of σ_{rr}, $\sigma_{\theta\theta}$, and $\sigma_{r\theta}$ on the plane a distance y above the slip plane, we find

(19.8) $$\sigma_{xy} = \frac{Gb}{2\pi(1 - \nu)}\frac{\sin 4\theta}{4y}.$$

It is shown as an exercise in Problem 19.4 that the force per unit length of dislocation caused by a uniform shear stress σ is $F = b\sigma$. This holds also for the force that one dislocation exerts upon a unit length of another. As a result, the force that an edge dislocation at the origin exerts upon a similar one at the location (y, θ) is

(19.9) $$F = b\sigma_{xy} = \frac{Gb^2}{2\pi(1 - \nu)}\frac{\sin 4\theta}{4y}$$

per unit length.[6] This force is positive for θ less than $\pi/4$, showing that like edge dislocations repel each other when their separation in the x direction exceeds that in the y direction. The force is negative for θ between $\pi/4$ and $\pi/2$, and it becomes zero at $\pi/2$. A dislocation with $\pi/4 < \theta < \pi/2$ therefore will tend to glide to an equilibrium position at $\theta = \pi/2$, directly above the one at the origin. The force

[6] Strictly speaking, F is the component of force in the slip direction. There is another component of force perpendicular to the slip direction, but it is of no importance at low temperatures where the only possible motion of a dislocation is in the slip plane.

also is zero when $\theta = \pi/4$, but this position is unstable for dislocations of the same sign. If the two dislocations have opposite signs, the situation is reversed, the $\pi/4$ position being stable and the $\pi/2$ position unstable.

Pairs of parallel screw dislocations have no stable positions, because each can glide on any plane that contains it. Screw dislocations of like sign repel each other to infinity, and those of opposite sign attract each other until they annihilate.

LOW-ANGLE GRAIN BOUNDARIES

Burgers[7] suggested that low-angle grain boundaries in crystals consist of arrays of dislocations. A simple example of the Burgers model is shown in Fig. 19.11, in which the boundary occupies a (010) plane in a simple cubic lattice and divides two parts of the crystal that have a [001] axis in common. This is referred to as a pure tilt boundary, since the existing misorientation can be described by a small rotation (θ) of one part of the crystal relative to the other about the common [001] axis. The boundary is represented in Fig. 19.11 as an array of edge dislocations of the same sign having a spacing $D = b/\theta$, where b is the magnitude of the Burgers vector of the dislocations. It is clear from our discussion of the forces between edge dislocations that this configuration, with dislocations of like sign stacked up one above the other, is stable.

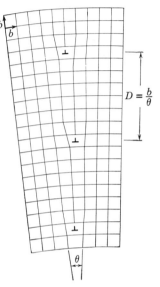

Fig. 19.11. Low-angle grain boundary. (After Burgers.) The inverted T denotes a positive edge dislocation, the vertical member of the T denoting an extra plane of atoms.

Developments have substantiated this model. Figure 19.12 shows clearly the distribution of dislocations along a grain boundary in a bubble raft, as photographed by C. S. Smith.[8] Read and Shockley[9] derived a theory of the interfacial energy as a function of the angle of tilt, in excellent agreement with the measurements of Dunn[10] and

[7] J. M. Burgers, Proc. Koninkl. Ned. Akad. Wetenschap. **42**, 293 (1939); Proc. Phys. Soc. (London) **52**, 23 (1940).

[8] C. S. Smith, Metal Progress **58**, 478 (1950).

[9] W. T. Read and W. Shockley, Phys. Rev. **78**, 275 (1950).

[10] C. G. Dunn and F. Lionetti, Trans. AIME **185**, 125 (1949).

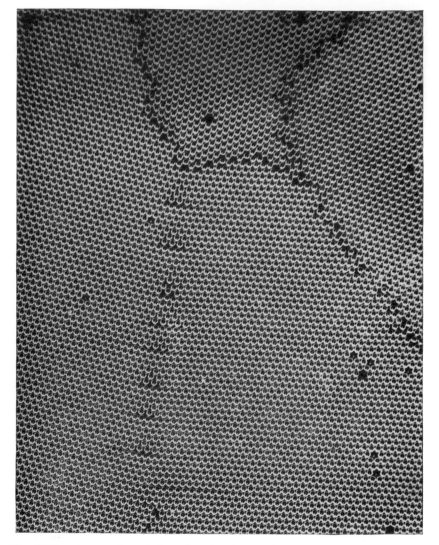

Fig. 19.12.   Low-angle grain boundary in a bubble raft, showing that it is made up
of dislocations.   (After C. S. Smith.[8])

of Aust and Chalmers.[11]   We may obtain their result by noting in
Fig. 19.12 that the region of elastic distortion near a grain boundary
does not extend very far into the two crystals: it is essentially confined
to a slab whose thickness equals the dislocation spacing D.   Each
dislocation is surrounded by its own strain field and by the strain fields

[11] K. T. Aust and B. Chalmers, Proc. Roy. Soc. (London), **A201**, 210 (1950).

of dislocations above and below it.   Since the latter strain fields nearly cancel each other, being equal in magnitude and opposite in sign, the strain energy near each dislocation results primarily from its own strain field.   With this approximation (19.7) gives the elastic strain energy per unit length of dislocation in the boundary as $[Gb^2/4\pi(1 - \nu)]$ ln $(\alpha D/b)$, where r_0 has been set equal to b and α is a number near 1.

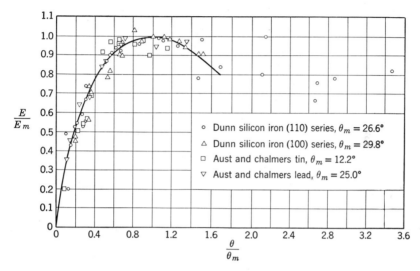

Fig. 19.13.   Comparison of theoretical curve with measurements of relative grain-boundary energy. The theoretical curve is given by $E/E_m = (\theta/\theta_m)[1 - \ln (\theta/\theta_m)]$; θ_m for each of the four sets of measurements is listed; the corresponding values of E_m are not known, since only relative energies are measured.   (By permission from *Dislocations in crystals*, by W. T. Read, Jr. Copyright, 1953. McGraw-Hill Book Company, Inc.)

Since there are $1/D$ dislocations per unit length of boundary, and setting $D = b/\theta$, the grain boundary energy is

(19.10) $\gamma = -[Gb/4\pi(1 - \nu)]\theta(\ln \theta + \ln \alpha).$

The grain boundary energy γ is zero when θ is zero, and rises with an initial vertical slope as θ increases.   With further increase in θ, γ reaches a maximum γ_m and begins to decline.   If we let θ_m be the value of θ for which $\gamma = \gamma_m$, (19.10) reduces to

(19.11) $\gamma/\gamma_m = (\theta/\theta_m)[1 - \ln (\theta/\theta_m)].$

This form of the equation may be compared with the experimental measurements of relative grain boundary energy as a function of θ as shown in Fig. 19.13.   The agreement is remarkably good, holding up to $\theta \geq 30°$, beyond the point where the dislocation model would be expected to apply.

If two portions of a crystal are rotated through a small angle about an axis perpendicular to the resulting grain boundary, instead of about

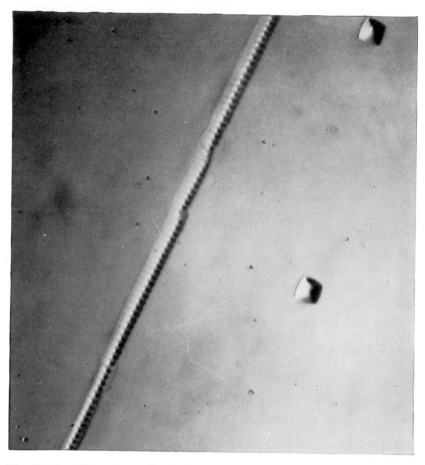

Fig. 19.14. Dislocation etch pits in low-angle boundary on (100) face of germanium; the angle of the boundary is 27.5 sec. The boundary lies in a (0 $\bar{1}$ 1) plane; the line of the dislocations is [100]. The Burgers vector is the shortest lattice translation vector, or $|\mathbf{b}| = \sqrt{2}\,a/2 = 4.0$ A. [After F. L. Vogel, Jr., Acta Metallurgica **3**, 245 (1955).]

an axis lying parallel to the grain boundary, a simple twist boundary is produced. It consists of two or more sets of screw dislocations forming a grid. The energy of this boundary, as well as of more general boundaries, is of the form (19.11).

A direct verification of the Burgers model is provided by the quantitative x-ray and optical studies of low-angle boundaries in germanium crystals by Vogel[12] and co-workers, following earlier semiquantitative studies of aluminum.[13, 14]   By counting etch pits along the intersection of a low-angle grain boundary with an etched germanium surface, Fig. 19.14, they determined the dislocation spacing D on the assumption that each etch pit marked the end of a dislocation.   They then

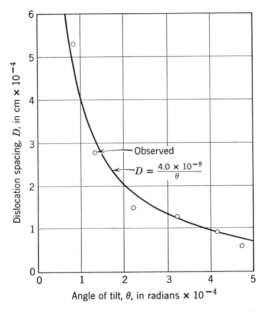

Fig. 19.15.   Plot of dislocation spacing calculated from angle of tilt vs. observed pit spacings.   Angles range from 17.5 to 85 sec.   (After Vogel.)

calculated the angle of tilt from the relation $\theta = b/D$, and compared it with the angle measured directly by means of x-rays.   The results are in excellent agreement, as shown in Fig. 19.15.

The interpretation of low-angle boundaries as arrays of dislocations is further supported by the fact that pure tilt boundaries can be made to move normal to themselves by the application of a stress.   The motion has been demonstrated in a beautiful experiment by Washburn

[12] F. L. Vogel, W. G. Pfann, H. E. Corey, and E. E. Thomas, Phys. Rev. **90**, 489 (1953); F. L. Vogel, Jr., Acta Met. **3**, 245 (1955).

[13] P. Lacombe, Report on Conference on Strength of Solids (The Physical Society, London, 1948).

[14] W. Shockley and W. T. Read, Phys. Rev. **75**, 692 (1949).

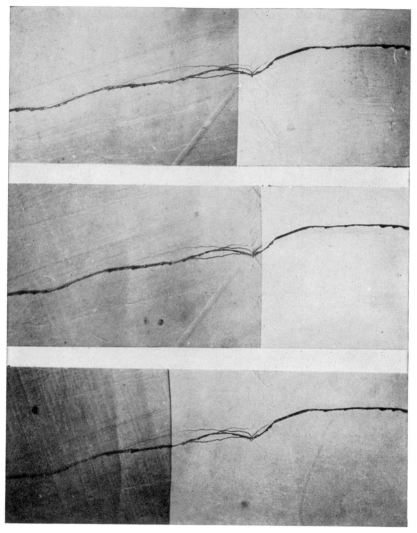

Fig. 19.16.   Motion of a small-angle grain boundary under stress.   The boundary
is the straight vertical line, and it is photographed under vertical illumination,
thereby making evident the 2° angular change in the cleavage surface of the zinc
crystal at the boundary.   The irregular horizontal line is a small step in the cleavage surface which serves as a reference mark.   The crystal is clamped at the left;
at the right it is subject to a force normal to the plane of the page.   *Top*, original
position of boundary; *center*, moved 0.1 mm to the right; *bottom*, moved back 0.4
mm.   (After J. Washburn and E. R. Parker, J. Metals, **4**, 1076 (1952).   A
motion picture showing these and related experiments has been prepared by
        Professor E. R. Parker, University of California, Berkeley, California.

and Parker.[15]   The nature of their results is exhibited in Fig. 19.16. The specimen consisted of a bicrystal of zinc containing a 2° tilt boundary.   The dislocations are about thirty atomic planes apart.   One side of the crystal was clamped, and a force was applied at a point on the opposite side of the boundary.   Motion of the boundary took place by cooperative motion of the dislocations in the array, each dislocation moving an equal distance in its own slip plane.   Opposite top and bottom intersections at the boundary with the surface moved approximately the same amount.   The motion was produced by stresses of the order of magnitude of the yield stress for zinc crystals, a fact that gives strong evidence that ordinary deformation results from the motion of dislocations.

It has been pointed out by a number of workers[16] that grain boundaries and dislocations offer relatively little resistance to diffusion in comparison with perfect crystalline material.   It is found that the enhanced diffusion parallel to the dislocations in a low-angle grain boundary is of the same order of magnitude as that produced by a large-angle incoherent grain boundary.   Diffusion at right angles to the dislocations in a low-angle boundary has been observed in one experiment to be 10 to 100 times slower[17] at 450°C, as compared with diffusion parallel to the dislocations.

Hoffman and Turnbull[18] find for self-diffusion in silver

$$D_B = 0.03 \exp\,(-20{,}200/RT)\;\text{cm}^2/\text{sec}$$

$$D_P = 0.14 \exp\,(-19{,}700/RT)\;\text{cm}^2/\text{sec}$$

$$D_I = 0.9 \exp\,(-40{,}000/RT)\;\text{cm}^2/\text{sec}$$

for the diffusion associated with incoherent grain boundaries (D_B), low-angle grain boundaries (D_P), and the interior of good crystal (D_I), respectively.   In order to compute D_B and D_P for grain-boundary diffusion, they consider an incoherent grain boundary to be a thin slab of low-resistance material, SA thick, of diffusivity D_B.   They similarly consider each dislocation in a low-angle grain boundary to be a rod of low-resistivity material with area $(SA)^2$ and diffusivity D_P.   Their experiments show that D_B and D_P are roughly equal.

[15] J. Washburn and E. R. Parker, J. Metals **4**, 1076 (1952); C. H. Li, E. H. Edwards, J. Washburn, and E. R. Parker, Acta Met. **1**, 223 (1953).

[16] For references to work in this area the reader may consult the papers by R. Smoluchowski and by D. Turnbull in the volume, *Defects in crystalline solids*, The Physical Society, London, 1955.

[17] R. E. Hoffman, private communication.

[18] R. E. Hoffman and D. Turnbull, J. Appl. Phys. **22**, 634 (1951); D. Turnbull and R. E. Hoffman, Acta Met. **2**, 419 (1954).

At 600°C to 700°C, D_B and D_P are larger than D_I by factors of the order of 10^5. It is therefore not surprising that diffusion should be accelerated in plastically deformed material with respect to annealed crystals. Turnbull[19] has shown that grain-boundary diffusion controls the rates of some precipitation reactions in solids: the precipitation of tin from lead-tin solutions at room temperature proceeds about 10^8 times faster than one would expect from lattice diffusion alone.

DISLOCATION DENSITIES

The density of dislocations is specified by giving the number of dislocation lines that intersect a unit area in the crystal. The density ranges from 10^2 to 10^3 dislocations/cm^2 in the best germanium and silicon crystals to as many as 10^{11} or 10^{12} dislocations/cm^2 in heavily deformed metal crystals.

The most precise dislocation density measurements have been made by counting the etch pits at the surfaces of polished and etched germanium and silicon crystals. Values of 10^2 to 10^3 etch pits/cm^2 are obtained with the best crystals, and a one-to-one correspondence between etch pits and dislocations has been established by the grain-boundary studies of Vogel[12] and co-workers. Cast metal crystals, and metal crystals that have been plastically deformed and then annealed, generally show about 10^5 to 10^9 dislocations/cm^2 by the etch pit technique.[20] A similar density is deduced from the extinction and breadth of x-ray lines,[21] which suggests that an annealed single crystal is usually composed of mosaic blocks perhaps 10^4 A on a side that are tilted with respect to one another by angles of the order of 10 min. This tilt corresponds to dislocations a few hundred atom distances apart in the boundaries of the blocks, giving about 10^9 dislocations/cm^2.

The actual dislocation configuration in cast or annealed crystals appears to correspond either to a group of low-angle grain boundaries or to a three-dimensional network of dislocations. Figure 19.17 shows an example of a three-dimensional network, photographed by Mitch-

[19] D. Turnbull and H. N. Treaftis, Acta Met. **3,** 43 (1955); D. Turnbull, Acta Met. **3,** 55 (1955).

[20] C. G. Dunn and W. R. Hibbard, Jr., Acta Met. **3,** 409 (1955); J. J. Gilman, private communication.

[21] The integrated intensity of x-ray reflections is often many times larger than calculated for a perfect crystal, and the lines may also be wider than calculated. For a discussion of intensity relations with reference to the role of mosaic structures in accounting for the observed intensities, the reader is referred to Chapter VI of R. W. James, *Optical principles of the diffraction of x-rays*, G. Bell and Sons, Ltd., London, 1950.)

ell[22] in a crystal of AgBr.   The dislocations were made visible by proper photographic development of the crystal.

The etch pit technique is not reliable for estimating the dislocation density in highly deformed crystals, as individual dislocations cannot

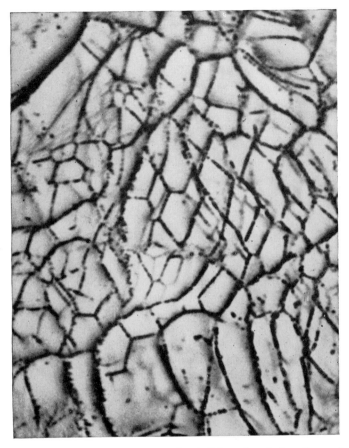

Fig. 19.17.   A three-dimensional network of dislocations below the surface of a single crystal of AgBr.   (After J. M. Hedges and J. W. Mitchell.)

be resolved when their spacing is less than about 10^{-4} cm.   However, we may estimate the dislocation density in deformed crystals from the increased internal energy that results from plastic deformation.   From (19.5) and (19.7), the energy per unit length of dislocation is about $(Gb^2/4\pi) \ln (R/r_0)$.   We take R comparable to the dislocation spacing and $r_0 \approx b$, and so $R/r_0 \approx 10^3$.   The dislocation energy then is about

[22] J. M. Hedges and J. W. Mitchell, Phil. Mag. **44**, 223 (1953).

5×10^{-4} erg/cm (about 8 ev per atom plane through which the dislocation passes).

The maximum energy stored in lattice distortions as a consequence of severe plastic deformation, as by twisting, filing, or compressing, has been measured thermally for several metals, with results given in Table 19.2. If the deformation is not too great, about 10 percent of the energy expended in plastic flow is stored in the lattice. Upon

TABLE 19.2.   MAXIMUM ENERGY STORED BY PLASTIC
              DEFORMATION (cal/g)

Aluminum	1.1
Copper	0.5
Iron	1.2
Nickel	0.8
Brass	0.5

continued plastic flow, however, the stored energy approaches a saturation value. The observed values of the stored energy in Table 19.2 correspond to about 2×10^8 ergs/cm^3. If the energy per unit length of dislocation is 5×10^{-4} erg/cm, there must be about 4×10^{11} cm of dislocation line per cubic centimeter of crystal, or about 10^{11} dislocations/cm^2 passing through the average unit area. This is about one dislocation per square 100 atoms on a side, which is also believed on other grounds to be the concentration of dislocations characteristic of severely deformed metals.

Analyses by Warren and Averbach[23] of the breadth of x-ray diffraction lines from plastically deformed brass yield a stored energy of 1.4 cal/g of the same order as the calorimetric value. From the shape of the lines they conclude that a major fraction of the strains are nonuniform over distances of several unit cell dimensions, as might be expected on a dislocation model.

We mention now other estimates of the density of dislocations in heavily deformed crystals. The electrical resistivity of metals increases with plastic deformation, the increase reaching 2 percent in copper at room temperature. Dexter[24] has worked out the theory of the resistivity change on a dislocation model, finding that of the order of 4×10^{12} dislocations/cm^2 will account for the observations on copper. This density probably is about 10 times too great, and it may be that the discrepancy is caused by the scattering of electron waves by lattice vacancies. From magnetic saturation measurements

[23] B. L. Averbach and B. E. Warren, J. Appl. Phys. **20**, 1066 (1949); B. E. Warren and B. L. Averbach, J. Appl. Phys. **21**, 595 (1950).
[24] D. L. Dexter, Phys. Rev. **86**, 770 (1952).

in nickel, Brown[25] estimates 3×10^{11} dislocations/cm^2 for severe plastic deformation.

A problem is posed by the presence of dislocations in cast and annealed crystals. No dislocations can be present in thermal equilibrium, because their energy is much too great in comparison with the increase in entropy that they produce. They must therefore be introduced in a non-equilibrium manner during the solidification of crystals from the melt, and they must remain even during the most careful annealing. The mechanism of their introduction during solidification is not known, although it is thought to be associated with the precipitation of lattice vacancies, which can occur at edge dislocations as the crystal cools. If an edge dislocation is present, lattice vacancies precipitating along its length will eat away a portion of the extra half-plane of atoms and cause the dislocation to *climb*, or move at right angles to its slip direction. If no edge dislocations are present, the crystal will become supersaturated with lattice vacancies, whose precipitation in penny-shaped vacancy plates may be followed by collapse of the plates and formation of dislocation rings which grow with further vacancy precipitation.

A second problem is posed by the very great increase in dislocation density that is caused by plastic deformation. Dislocation density measurements show an increase from about 10^8 to about 10^{11} dislocations/cm^2 during deformation, a 1000-fold increase. Equally striking is the fact that, if a dislocation were to move completely across its slip plane, an offset of only one atom spacing would be produced, whereas offsets of as much as 100 to 1000 atom spacings are actually observed. Frank and Read[26] showed how the required dislocation multiplication could occur, and we discuss it in the following paragraphs.

DISLOCATION MULTIPLICATION AND SLIP

Consider a closed circular dislocation loop of radius r surrounding a slipped area of the same radius. The loop will be partly edge, partly screw, and mostly intermediate in character. Because the strain energy of the dislocation of loop increases in proportion to its circumference, the loop will tend to shrink. However, if a shear stress σ that favors slip is acting, the sloop will tend to expand. We seek the relationship between stress and loop radius for which the loop is in (metastable) equilibrium. To simplify the calculation, the strain energy per unit length of dislocation (19.5 or 19.7) is taken as $(Gb^2/4\pi) \ln (R/r_0)$ for edge, screw, and intermediate dislocations alike. In addition, the

[25] W. F. Brown, Jr., Phys. Rev. **60**, 139 (1941).
[26] F. C. Frank and W. T. Read, Phys. Rev. **79**, 722 (1950).

term $\ln (R/r_0)$, which is approximately $\ln (R/b)$ for a dislocation loop of radius r, will be approximated by 2π, to which it is roughly equal for r/b in the range 10^2 to 10^5. With these approximations the energy per unit length of dislocation is $Gb^2/2$.

The elastic energy of a dislocation loop of radius r is $2\pi r$ times its energy per unit length, or $\pi r Gb^2$. If the loop is formed in the presence of a shear stress σ, the energy of the crystal will decrease by the product of σb and the area of the loop, $\pi r^2 \sigma b$. The net energy change on introducing the loop is

$$(19.12) \qquad \Delta E = \pi r Gb^2 - \pi r^2 \sigma b.$$

The value of ΔE passes through a maximum when $d\,\Delta E/dr = 0$, or when

$$(19.13) \qquad 2r/b = G/\sigma,$$

showing that the ratio of the diameter of the critical loop to the magnitude of the Burgers vector equals the ratio of the shear modulus to the shear stress. Since this latter ratio is of the order 10^3 or 10^4 for the yielding of most crystals, the ratio $2r/b$ is about the same, as assumed in making the approximation $\ln (r/b) \approx 2\pi$.

Loops smaller than the critical loop will contract spontaneously, and those larger than critical will expand spontaneously. The energy of the critical loop is $\Delta E_c = \pi G^2 b^3/4\sigma$, which is so large in comparison with kT (for $G/\sigma = 10^3$ and $T = 300°K$ the ratio is $\Delta E_c/kT = 3 \times 10^5$) that thermal activation cannot be responsible for their creation, and we are led again to the necessity of pre-existing dislocations for initiating slip, and to purely mechanical processes for generating new lengths of dislocation.

Frank and Read[26] pointed out that dislocations rarely lie entirely in one slip plane, and that instead they jog from one slip plane to another until they meet the surface of the crystal or join others at a dislocation node. A segment of dislocation lying in a slip plane may be considered as pinned at its ends where it leaves the plane. When an external stress is applied, the segment cannot glide as a whole because its ends are fixed, and the only possible motion is to bend into an arc of a circle. We already have calculated the equilibrium radius of this arc (19.13) to be $2r/b = G/\sigma$. As long as $2r > L$, where L is the initial length of the segment, the configuration is stable, because further motion of the dislocation then decreases its radius. Whenever the stress rises beyond the point where $L/b = G/\sigma$, however, there is no stable equilibrium, and the dislocation arc expands indefinitely as a growing partial loop. This process not only multiplies an original segment of length L into a large partial loop but also allows the partial loop to complete itself while regenerating a new segment that can repeat the whole process, as sketched in Fig. 19.18. A dislocation segment pinned at each end is called a *Frank-Read source,* and we have seen how it can lead to the generation of a large number of concentric dislocation loops on a single slip plane. This type of dislocation multiplication gives rise to slip and to the increased density of dislocations during plastic deformation.

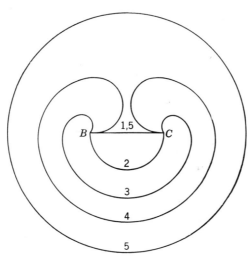

Fig. 19.18. Frank-Read mechanism for multiplication of dislocations, showing successive stages in the generation of a dislocation loop by the segment BC of a dislocation line. A photograph is given on the cover of J. Appl. Phys., Nov., 1956.

STRENGTH OF ALLOYS

Pure crystals tend to be very plastic, and to yield at very low stresses. There appear to be four important ways of increasing the yield strength of an alloy so that it will withstand shear stresses as high as $10^{-2}G$. They are mechanical blocking of dislocation motion, pinning of dislocations by solute atoms, impeding dislocation motion by short-range order, and increasing the dislocation density so that tangling of dislocations results. All four of these strengthening mechanisms depend for their success upon impeding dislocation motion. A fifth mechanism, that of removing all dislocations from the crystal, may operate for certain fine hair-like crystals that are discussed in the section on crystal growth.

Mechanical blocking of dislocation motion can be produced most directly by introducing tiny particles of a second phase into a crystal.

This process is followed in the hardening of steel, where particles of iron carbide are precipitated into iron, and in hardening aluminum, where particles of Al_2Cu are precipitated. If L is the mean spacing of particles on a slip plane, the stress necessary to force a dislocation between particles should be approximately

$$(19.14) \qquad\qquad \sigma/G = b/L,$$

which is (19.13) rewritten. The smaller the spacing L, the higher is the yield stress σ. Orowan[27] has discussed this mechanism of precipitation hardening. He points out that, before particles precipitate, L is large and the strength is low. Immediately after precipitation is complete and many small particles are present, L is a minimum and the strength is a maximum. If the alloy is held at a high temperature where some particles grow at the expense of others, L increases and the strength drops. Mechanical blocking also can be caused by the grain boundaries in polycrystalline materials, and by the microscopic stress fields that sometimes surround precipitated particles.

The strength of dilute solid solutions appears to result from the pinning of dislocations by solute atoms. Cottrell has pointed out that the solubility of a foreign atom will be greater in the neighborhood of a dislocation than elsewhere in a crystal. For example, an atom that tends to expand the crystal will dissolve preferentially in the expanded region near an edge dislocation. As a result of the affinity of solute atoms for dislocations, each dislocation will collect a cloud of associated solute atoms during solidification or annealing when the mobility of solute atoms is high. On cooling to lower temperatures, where diffusion of solute atoms effectively ceases, the solute atom cloud becomes fixed in the crystal. When a dislocation moves, leaving its solute cloud behind, the energy of the crystal must increase. The increase in energy can come only from an increased stress acting on the dislocation as it pulls away from the solute atom cloud, and so the presence of the cloud strengthens the crystal.

In pure crystals, the passage of a dislocation across a slip plane does not alter the binding energy across the plane after the dislocation is gone. The internal energy of the crystal remains unaffected. The same is true for random solid solutions, because the solution is equally random across a slip plane after slip. Most solid solutions, however, contain short-range order. Atoms of different species are not arranged at random on the lattice sites, but tend to have an excess or a deficiency

[27] E. Orowan, Discussion, "Symposium on internal stresses," Institute of Metals, London, 1947, p. 451.

of pairs of unlike atoms. Fisher[28] has pointed out that, whatever its nature, short-range order is partially destroyed by the motion of a dislocation: the internal energy across the slip plane is increased, the slip plane is increased, and the slip plane is transformed into an internal surface having a specific surface energy γ. It is easy to see that a shear stress

$$(19.15) \qquad\qquad\qquad \sigma = \gamma/b$$

is required to cause dislocation motion under these circumstances. Estimates of γ for brass and for copper-gold alloys, based upon the thermodynamics of the alloys, give order of magnitude agreement with the observed strengths of these alloys.

It is well known that the strength of a crystalline material increases with plastic deformation. The phenomenon is called *work-hardening*. The strength is believed to increase because of the increased density of dislocations and the greater difficulty of moving a given dislocation across a slip plane that is threaded by many others. The difficulty is particularly acute when one screw dislocation tries to cross another, and it is possible that lattice vacancies and interstitial atoms may be generated in the process. Work-hardening frequently is employed in the strengthening of materials, but its usefulness is limited to low enough temperatures for annealing not to occur.

Each of the four mechanisms of strengthening crystals can raise the yield strength to the order of $10^{-3}G$ to $10^{-2}G$. In combination they can give about $10^{-2}G$. Unfortunately, all four mechanisms begin to break down at temperatures where diffusion can occur at an appreciable rate. Precipitated particles begin to dissolve; solute clouds begin, by diffusion, to drift along with dislocations as they glide; short-range order repairs itself behind slowly moving dislocations; and dislocation climb and annealing tend to decrease the dislocation density. The resulting time-dependent deformation is called *creep*. The search for superalloys for use at very high temperatures is therefore a search for alloys with reduced diffusion rates, where the four strengthening mechanisms will survive to higher temperatures.

DISLOCATIONS AND CRYSTAL GROWTH

It has been shown by Frank[29] and his collaborators that in some cases dislocations may be the controlling factor in crystal growth.

[28] J. C. Fisher, Acta Met. **2,** 9 (1954).

[29] For a full review of this field see F. C. Frank, Advances in Physics **1,** 91 (1952); detailed calculations are given by Burton, Cabrera, and Frank, Trans. Roy. Soc. (London) **A243,** 299 (1951). A motion picture in color on the growth of crystals has been prepared by J. B. Newkirk of the General Electric Research Laboratory, Schenectady, N.Y.

When crystals are grown in conditions of low supersaturation, of the order of 1 percent, it has been observed that the growth rate is faster than that calculated for an ideal crystal by a factor, in one case, of the order of e^{3000}. The actual growth rate is explained by Frank in terms of the effect of dislocations on growth.

The theory of growth of ideal crystals, due to Gibbs, Volmer, Becker, and others, predicts that in crystal growth from vapor a supersaturation (pressure/equilibrium vapor pressure) of the order of 10 is required to nucleate new crystals, of the order of 5 to form liquid drops, and of of 1.5 to form a two-dimensional monolayer of molecules on the face of a perfect crystal. Actually Volmer and Schultze observed growth of iodine crystals at vapor supersaturations down to less than 1 percent, where the growth rate should have been down by e^{-3000} from the rate defined as the minimum observable growth. This has been referred to as an all-time record for disagreement between observation and theory.

Frank pointed out that the large factor just mentioned expresses the difficulty of nucleating a new monolayer on a completed surface of the crystal and that if there is a screw dislocation present as in Fig. 19.19 it is never necessary to nucleate a new layer, as the crystal will grow in helical fashion at the edge of the discontinuity shown. The calculated growth rates for this mechanism are in good agreement with observation. We therefore expect that nearly all crystals in nature grown at low supersaturation will contain dislocations, as otherwise they could not have grown. The growth mechanism is shown in greater detail in Fig. 19.20, for both spiral (a) and closed loop (b) growth.

Griffin and others, using optical and electron microscopes, have observed spiral growth patterns[30] on a large number of crystals. Their photographs are convincing evidence of the reality of dislocations. A beautiful example of the growth pattern from a single screw dislocation is given in Fig. 19.21a. If the growth rate were independent of direction in the plane of the surface, the growth pattern would be an Archimedes spiral,

(19.16) $r = a\theta,$

where a is a constant, with a limiting minimum radius of curvature near the dislocation determined by the supersaturation. If the radius of curvature is too small, atoms on the curved edge evaporate until the equilibrium curvature is attained. Away from the origin each part of

[30] A beautiful collection of photographs of spiral growth is given in the book by Ajit Ram Verma cited at the end of the chapter.

the step acquires new atoms at a constant rate, so that

(19.17) $dr/dt = $ const.

The spiral appears to rotate with uniform angular velocity during growth, for, if $d\theta/dt$ is constant, dr/dt will appear to be constant, as required for uniform deposition by (19.17).

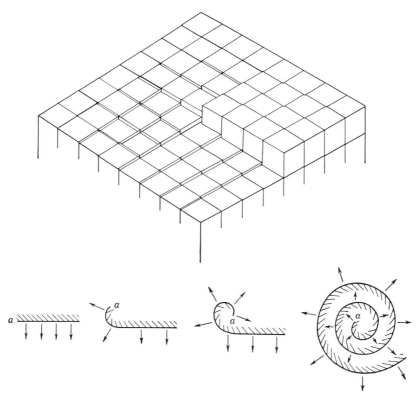

Fig. 19.19.   Development of a spiral step produced by intersection of a screw dislocation with the surface of a crystal.   Each cube represents a molecule.   (After F. C. Frank.)

Dawson and Vand,[31] working with the straight chain hydrocarbon $C_{36}H_{74}$, find a step height of 43 $\pm$ 5 A, in suitable agreement with the x-ray cell height 47.5 A.   The ledge widths were in the range 1000 to 4000 A.   For their crystals the number of dislocations N was correlated empirically with the total area A of the (001) face of the crystal by the relation, with A in cm^2,

(19.18) $N = 1.6 \times (2 \times 10^6)A$

[31] I. M. Dawson and V. Vand, Proc. Roy. Soc. (London) **A206**, 555 (1951).

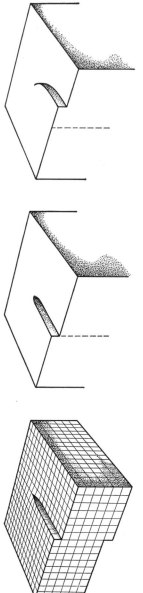

Fig. 19.20. (a) SCREW DISLOCATION, illustrated at left, produces its spiral growth steps in the manner indicated by the succeeding diagrams. A screw dislocation is the type of imperfection that would result if a cut were made part way through a crystal and the two sides slipped over one another. The result is a permanent step extending across a portion of the crystal face and anchored at the boundary of the cut.

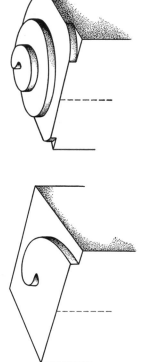

Molecules depositing on the surface from a vapor would lodge against the step, causing it to advance. Since one end is fixed, the step would pivot around that point, with the outer points falling behind the inner, producing a never-ending spiral layer on the surface.

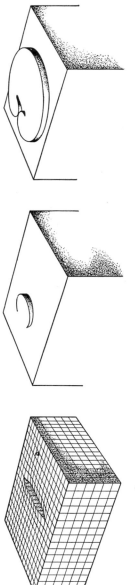

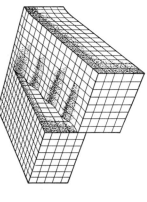

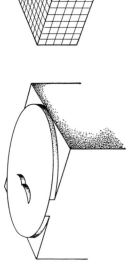

grow only by bulging. The second drawing shows the bulging step just beginning to turn back on itself. In the next figure its parts have met behind its original position. Finally the inner section detaches from

(After *Scientific American*)

(b) CLOSED GROWTH LOOPS can arise from a step which begins and ends within the surface (*left*) connecting a right-handed screw dislocation with a left-handed one. This step is anchored at both ends and can

the completed layer and shrinks inward until it becomes a new straight step located on top of the growth loop first formed.

FOUR-LAYERED STEP is formed by four closely spaced dislocations of the same kind. Larger groups give many-layered steps.

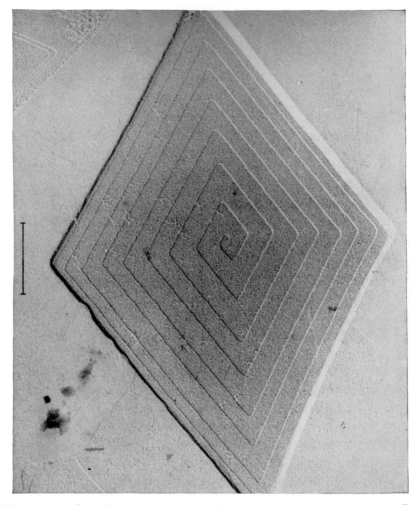

Fig. 19.21a. Growth pattern from single dislocation on single crystal of paraffin n-$C_{36}H_{74}$. [Electron micrograph courtesy of H. F. Kay and B. J. Appelbe, after Dawson and Vand, Proc. Roy. Soc. (London) **A206**, 555 (1951).]

suggesting that there are on the average 1.6 dislocations present in the nucleus from which growth takes place, and that there are $\sim 2 \times 10^6$ dislocations/cm^2 in a large crystal grown under their conditions.

A revealing study of the early stages of crystal growth from solution has been carried out by Newkirk.[32] He worked with cadmium iodide

[32] J. B. Newkirk, Acta Met. **3**, 121 (1955); the mechanisms studied were proposed by J. C. Fisher, R. L. Fullman, and G. W. Sears, Acta Met. **2**, 346 (1954).

because it had been shown by Firtz that CdI forms crystals having growth steps which are clearly visible at low magnification.   In stage one, small perfect platelets having three-fold symmetry are formed from an aqueous solution at 30°C initially saturated at 85°C.   After a certain number of platelets have grown, the supersaturation will have decreased to a point where further thickening of the platelets by the uniform deposition of a new atomic layer is not possible.   It appears

Fig. 19.21b.   Growth spiral on a crystal of cadmium iodide.   (After J. B. New-kirk.)

that the binding energy is greater at the edges of the crystals, as the crystals continue to grow edgewise at constant thickness.   When, however, the edges of two crystals come in contact forming a low-angle twist boundary, screw dislocations are produced and the crystals grow in thickness.   Both single growth spirals and closed loops, resulting from the interaction of two dislocations of opposite sign, are observed. A growth spiral on CdI is shown in Fig. 19.12b.

Fine hair-like crystals have been observed to grow under conditions of high supersaturation without the necessity for more than perhaps one dislocation. It may be that these crystals contain a single axial screw dislocation that aids their essentially one-dimensional growth. From the absence of dislocations we would expect these crystal whiskers to have high yield strengths, of the order of the calculated value $G/30$ discussed earlier in this chapter.   A single axial screw dislocation, if present, could not cause yielding because it is not subjected to a shear stress parallel to its Burgers vector.   Herring and Galt[33] have observed in this connection that whiskers of tin (radius $\sim 10^{-4}$ cm) have elastic

Fig. 19.22.   Iron wiskers grown from the vapor by hydrogen reduction of ferrous bromide at 710°C in an iron boat. (Courtesy of S. Brenner and Miss D. Kontoleon.)

properties near those expected from theoretically perfect crystals. They observed yield strains of the order of 10^{-2}, which correspond to shear stresses of order $10^{-2}G$, about 1000 times greater than in bulk tin, confirming the early estimates of perfect crystal strength.

Iron whiskers[34] grown from the vapor are shown in Fig. 19.22. They are of the order of 15 μ in thickness, and are bcc iron bounded by four {100} planes parallel to the long axis.   The largest elastic strain observed for iron was 1.4 percent, which is close to the theoretical limit.

Theoretical perfect crystal elastic properties have been observed for a number of materials, including Cu (Fig. 19.23), CdS, p-toluidine,

[33] C. Herring and J. K. Galt, Phys. Rev. **85**, 1060 (1952); W. W. Piper and W. L. Roth, Phys. Rev. **92**, 503 (1953).

[34] G. W. Sears, A. Gatti, and R. L. Fullman, Acta Met. **2**, 727 (1954).

Fig. 19.23.   Copper whisker strained 1.5 percent.   (Courtesy S. S. Brenner.)

and the potassium halides.   The mechanism of whisker growth has
been studied in detail by Sears and his co-workers,[35] among others.

PROBLEMS

19.1. Show that the lines of closest atomic packing are $\langle 110 \rangle$ in fcc structures,
$\langle 111 \rangle$ in bcc structures, and $\langle 2\,\bar{1}\,\bar{1}\,0 \rangle$ in hcp structures.

19.2. A cylindrical crystal of cross section A is under a tension T.   Find the
expression of the Schmid law of the critical shear stress in terms of the angle λ
between the slip direction and the axis of tension and the angle θ between the
normal to the slip plane and the axis of tension.

19.3. (a) Find a pair of dislocations equivalent to a row of lattice vacancies;
(b) find a pair of dislocations equivalent to a row of interstitial atoms.

19.4. Consider a crystal in the form of a cube of side L containing an edge dislocation of Burgers vector $\mathbf{b}$.   If the crystal is subjected to a shear stress σ on the
upper and lower faces in the direction of slip, show by considering energy balance
that the force acting on the dislocation is $F = b\sigma$ per unit length.

REFERENCES

C. S. Barrett, *Structure of metals: crystallographic methods, principles, data*, McGraw-
Hill Book Company, New York, 2nd ed., 1952.

W. Boas, *An introduction to the physics of metals and alloys*, John Wiley & Sons,
New York, 1948.

M. Cohen, editor, *Dislocations in metals*, American Institute of Mining and Metallurgical Engineers, New York, 1954.

[35] G. W. Sears, Acta Met. **1**, 457 (1953); Acta Met. (in press); S. S. Brenner and
G. W. Sears, Acta Met. (in press).

A. H. Cottrell, *Dislocations and plastic flow in crystals*, Clarendon Press, Oxford, 1953.

Defects in crystalline solids, Physical Society (London) 1955.

F. Frank, "Crystal growth and dislocations," Advances in Physics **1**, 91 (1952).

N. F. Mott, "Mechanical properties of metals," Proc. Phys. Soc. (London) **B64**, 729 (1951).

W. T. Read, *Dislocations in crystals*, McGraw-Hill Book Company, New York, 1953.

Report of a conference on the strength of solids, University of Bristol, Physical Society, London, 1948.

F. Seitz, *Physics of metals*, McGraw-Hill Book Co. New York, 1943.

Shockley, Hollomon, Maurer, and Seitz, editors, *Imperfections in nearly perfect crystals*, John Wiley and Sons, New York, 1952.

Ajit Ram Verma, *Crystal growth and dislocations*, Academic Press, New York, 1953.

C. Zener, *Elasticity and anelasticity of metals*, University of Chicago Press, Chicago, 1948.

Appendix

A. EWALD METHOD FOR CALCULATING LATTICE SUMS

The Ewald[1] calculation is developed here by a method which is simpler than the original derivation. The present form is due to Ewald and to Shockley. The problem is to calculate the electrostatic potential experienced by one ion in the presence of all the other ions in the crystal. We shall consider a lattice made up of ions with positive or negative charges and shall assume that the ions are spherical and do not overlap.

We compute the total potential

$$(A.1) \qquad \psi = \psi_1 + \psi_2$$

at an ion as the sum of two distinct but related potentials. The potential ψ_1 is that of a structure with a Gaussian distribution of charge situated at each ion site, with signs the same as those of the real ions. According to the definition of the Madelung constant, the charge distribution on the reference point is not considered to contribute to the potential ψ_1 or ψ_2 (Fig. A.1a). We therefore calculate the potential ψ_1 as the difference

$$(A.2) \qquad \psi_1 = \psi_a - \psi_b$$

of two potentials, ψ_a being the potential of a continuous series of Gaussian distributions and ψ_b being the potential of the single Gaussian distribution on the reference point. The potential ψ_2 is that of a lattice of point charges with an additional Gaussian distribution of opposite sign superposed upon the point charges (Fig. A.1b).

The point of splitting the problem into the two parts ψ_1 and ψ_2 is that by a suitable choice of the parameter determining the width of each Gaussian peak we can get very good convergence of both parts at the same time. The Gaussian distributions drop out completely on taking the sum of the separate charge distributions giving rise to ψ_1 and ψ_2, so that the value of the total potential ψ is independent of the width parameter, but the rapidity of convergence depends on the value chosen for the parameter.

We calculate first the potential ψ_a of a continuous Gaussian distribution. We expand ψ_a and the charge density ρ in Fourier series:

$$(A.3) \qquad \psi_a = \sum_G c_G e^{iG \cdot r};$$

$$(A.4) \qquad \rho = \sum_G \rho_G e^{iG \cdot r},$$

[1] P. P. Ewald, Ann. Physik **64**, 253 (1921).

where **G** is 2π times a vector in the reciprocal lattice.   The Poisson
equation is

$$\nabla^2 \psi_a = -4\pi\rho,$$

or

$$\Sigma\, G^2 c_G e^{i\mathbf{G}\cdot\mathbf{r}} = 4\pi\,\Sigma\,\rho_G e^{i\mathbf{G}\cdot\mathbf{r}},$$

so that

(A.5) $c_G = 4\pi\rho_G/G^2.$

We suppose in finding ρ_G that that there is associated with each
lattice point of the Bravais lattice a basis containing ions of charge

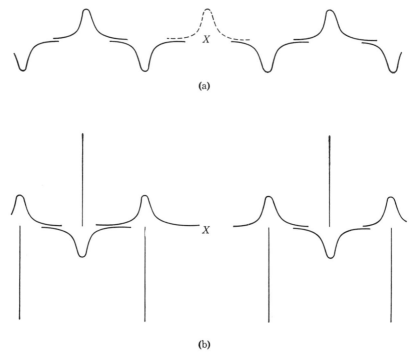

(a)

(b)

Fig. A.1.   (a) Charge distribution used for computing potential ψ_1; the potential
ψ_a is computed (it includes the dashed curve at the reference point), while ψ_b is the
potential of the dashed curve alone.   (b) Charge distribution for potential ψ_2.
The reference point is denoted by an X.

q_t at positions $\mathbf{r}_t$ relative to the lattice point.   Each ion point is therefore the center of a Gaussian charge distribution of density

(A.6) $\rho(\mathbf{r}) = q_t(\eta/\pi)^{3/2} e^{-\eta r^2},$

where the factor in front of the exponential ensures that the total
charge associated with the ion is q_t; the range parameter η is to be

chosen judiciously to ensure rapid convergence of the result (A.13), which is in value independent of η. We would normally evaluate ρ_G by multiplying both sides of (A.4) by $e^{-i\mathbf{G}\cdot\mathbf{r}}$ and integrating over the volume Δ of one cell, in which case the charge distribution to be considered is that originating on the ion points within the cell and also that of the tails of the distributions originating in all other cells. It is easy to see, however, that the integral of the total charge density times $e^{-i\mathbf{G}\cdot\mathbf{r}}$ over a single cell is equal to the integral of the charge density originating in a single cell times $e^{-i\mathbf{G}\cdot\mathbf{r}}$ over all space.

We have therefore

$$(A.7)\qquad \rho_G \int_{\substack{\text{one}\\\text{cell}}} e^{i\mathbf{G}\cdot\mathbf{r}}e^{-i\mathbf{G}\cdot\mathbf{r}}\,d\mathbf{r} = \rho_G\Delta = \int_{\substack{\text{all}\\\text{space}}} \sum_t q_t(\eta/\pi)^{3/2}e^{-\eta(r-r_t)^2}e^{-i\mathbf{G}\cdot\mathbf{r}}\,d\mathbf{r}.$$

This expression is readily evaluated:

$$\rho_G\Delta = \sum_t q_t e^{-i\mathbf{G}\cdot\mathbf{r}_t}(\eta/\pi)^{3/2}\int_{\substack{\text{all}\\\text{space}}} e^{-(i\mathbf{G}\cdot\boldsymbol{\xi}+\eta\xi^2)}\,d\boldsymbol{\xi}$$

$$= \left(\sum_t q_t e^{-i\mathbf{G}\cdot\mathbf{r}_t}\right) e^{-G^2/4\eta} = S(\mathbf{G})e^{-G^2/4\eta},$$

where $S(\mathbf{G}) = \sum_t q_t e^{-i\mathbf{G}\cdot\mathbf{r}_t}$ is just the structure factor (Chapter 2) in appropriate units. Using (A.3) and (A.5),

$$(A.8)\qquad \psi_a = \frac{4\pi}{\Delta}\sum_\mathbf{G} S(\mathbf{G})G^{-2}e^{i\mathbf{G}\cdot\mathbf{r}-(G^2/4\eta)}.$$

At the origin $\mathbf{r} = 0$ we have

$$(A.9)\qquad \psi_a = \frac{4\pi}{\Delta}\sum_\mathbf{G} S(\mathbf{G})G^{-2}e^{-G^2/4\eta}.$$

The potential ψ_b at the reference ion point i due to the central Gaussian distribution is

$$(A.10)\qquad \psi_b = \int_0^\infty (4\pi r^2\,dr)(\rho/r) = 2q_i(\eta/\pi)^{1/2},$$

and so

$$(A.11)\qquad \psi_1(i) = \frac{4\pi}{\Delta}\sum_\mathbf{G} S(\mathbf{G})G^{-2}e^{-G^2/4\eta} - 2q_i(\eta/\pi)^{1/2}.$$

The potential ψ_2 is to be evaluated at the reference point, and it differs from zero as a result of the fact that other ions have the tails of their Gaussian distributions overlapping the reference point. The potential is due to three contributions from each ion point:

$$q_l \left[\frac{1}{r_l} - \frac{1}{r_l} \int_0^{r_l} \rho(\mathbf{r}) \, d\mathbf{r} - \int_{r_l}^{\infty} \frac{\rho(\mathbf{r})}{r} \, d\mathbf{r} \right],$$

where the terms are from the point charge, from the part of the Gaussian distribution lying inside a sphere of radius r_l about the lth ion point, and from that part lying outside the sphere, respectively. On substituting for $\rho(\mathbf{r})$ and carrying out elementary manipulations, we have

$$(A.12) \qquad\qquad \psi_2 = \sum_l \frac{q_l}{r_l} F(\eta^{\frac{1}{2}} r_l),$$

where

$$F(x) = (2/\pi^{\frac{1}{2}}) \int_x^{\infty} e^{-s^2} \, ds.$$

Finally,

$$(A.13) \quad \psi(i) = \frac{4\pi}{\Delta} \sum_{\mathbf{G}} \mathbb{S}(\mathbf{G}) G^{-2} e^{-G^2/4\eta} - 2q_i(\eta/\pi)^{\frac{1}{2}} + \sum_l \frac{q_l}{r_l} F(\eta^{\frac{1}{2}} r_l)$$

is the desired total potential of the reference ion i in the field of all the other ions in the crystal. In the application of the Ewald method the trick is to choose η such that both sums in (A.13) converge rapidly.

EWALD-KORNFELD METHOD FOR LATTICE SUMS FOR DIPOLE ARRAYS

Kornfeld[2] has extended the Ewald method to dipolar and quadrupolar arrays. We discuss here the field of a dipole array at a point which is not a lattice point. According to (A.8) and (A.12) the potential at a point $\mathbf{r}$ in a lattice of positive unit point charges is

$$(A.14) \quad \psi = (4\pi/\Delta) \sum_{\mathbf{G}} \mathbb{S}(\mathbf{G}) G^{-2} \exp\left[i\mathbf{G} \cdot \mathbf{r} - (G^2/4\eta) \right]$$

$$+ \sum_l F(\sqrt{\eta} \, r_l)/r_l,$$

where r_l is the distance from $\mathbf{r}$ to the lattice point l. The first term on the right gives the potential of the charge distribution $\rho = (\eta/\pi)^{\frac{3}{2}} e^{-\eta r^2}$ about each lattice point. By a well-known relation in electrostatics we obtain the potential of an array of unit dipoles pointing in the z direction by taking $-d/dz$ of the above potential. The term under discussion contributes

$$(A.15) \qquad -(4\pi i/\Delta) \sum_{\mathbf{G}} \mathbb{S}(\mathbf{G})(G_z/G^2) \exp\left[i\mathbf{G} \cdot \mathbf{r} - G^2/4\eta \right],$$

[2] H. Kornfeld, Z. Physik **22**, 27 (1924).

and the z component of the electric field from this term is $E_z = \partial^2\psi/\partial z^2$, or

(A.16) $\qquad -(4\pi/\Delta) \sum_{\mathbf{G}} \mathcal{S}(\mathbf{G})(G_z{}^2/G^2) \exp [i\mathbf{G}\cdot\mathbf{r} - G^2/4\eta].$

The second term on the right of (A.14) on one differentiation gives

(A.17) $\qquad -\sum_{l} z_l[(F(\sqrt{\eta}r_l)/r_l{}^3) + (2/r_l{}^2)(\eta/\pi)^{\frac{1}{2}} \exp (-\eta r_l{}^2)],$

and the z component of this part of the field is

(A.18) $\qquad \sum_{l} \{z_l{}^2[(3F(\sqrt{\eta}r_l)/r_l{}^5) + (6/r_l{}^4)(\eta/\pi)^{\frac{1}{2}} \exp (-\eta r_l{}^2)$

$\qquad\qquad + (4/r_l{}^2)(\eta^3/\pi)^{\frac{1}{2}} \exp (-\eta r_l{}^2)] - [(F(\sqrt{\eta}r_l)/r_l{}^3)$

$\qquad\qquad\qquad\qquad\qquad\qquad + (2/r_l{}^2)(\eta/\pi)^{\frac{1}{2}} \exp (-\eta r_l{}^2)]\}.$

The total E_z is given by the sum of (A.16) and (A.18). The effects of any number of lattices may be added.

B. QUANTUM-MECHANICAL EXPRESSION FOR THE POLARIZABILITY

We compute the energy of interaction of an atomic system with an applied static electric field and set this equal to the macroscopic expression for the energy, which is

(B.1) $\qquad\qquad\qquad \Delta E = -\int E\, dP = -\tfrac{1}{2}\alpha\mathcal{E}^2.$

The result of second order perturbation theory is

(B.2) $\qquad\qquad\qquad \Delta E = -\sum_{j} \frac{e^2|x_{ij}|^2\mathcal{E}^2}{\hbar\omega_{ij}}$

when the perturbing energy is $e\mathcal{E}x$ and $\hbar\omega_{ij} = E_j - E_i$. Therefore

(B.3) $\qquad\qquad\qquad \alpha = \sum_{j} 2e^2|x_{ij}|^2/\hbar\omega_{ij},$

which is the expression to which (7.16) reduces when $\omega = 0$. The association of the polarizability with the second order perturbation energy of a single atomic level i depends for its validity on the condition $\hbar\omega_{ij} \gg kT$; that is, only the ground state i is significantly populated at the temperature considered.

C. ONSAGER THEORY OF THE DIELECTRIC CONSTANT OF POLAR SUBSTANCES

The Lorentz treatment of the local field assumes explicitly that the dipole moments of all the atoms are parallel, and this is clearly a valid assumption for the induced moments in sufficiently symmetrical structures. The assumption is not valid, however, for permanent dipole moments which are oriented more or less at random. Onsager has carried out an approximate treatment of the latter situation by considering a very small spherical cavity, just large enough to contain one molecule. If we consider this cavity real, we may ask what is the value of the field inside it, when the boundary condition is that the field at large distances from the cavity is uniform and equal to E_0. We consider the potential ϕ such that $\mathbf{E} = -\nabla\phi$. Outside the cavity the potential may be written as

$$(C.1) \qquad \phi = -\left(\frac{A}{r^2} + E_0 r\right)\cos\theta,$$

while inside the cavity

$$(C.2) \qquad \phi = -E_{\text{loc}}\, r\cos\theta.$$

The boundary conditions at the surface of the sphere $r = a$ are that the normal component of D and the tangential component of E should be continuous across the interface, so that, taking the dielectric constant of the medium as ϵ and of the cavity as unity,

$$\epsilon(-2A + E_0 a^3) = E_{\text{loc}} a^3;$$
$$A + E_0 a^3 = E_{\text{loc}} a^3;$$

whence

$$(C.3) \qquad E_{\text{loc}} = \frac{3\epsilon}{2\epsilon + 1} E_0.$$

The polarization is given by (7.27):

$$P = Np^2 E_{\text{loc}}/3kT = x E_{\text{loc}}/4\pi,$$

where we have written $x = 4\pi Np^2/3kT$. Then

$$(C.4) \qquad \epsilon E_0 = E_0 + \frac{3\epsilon x}{2\epsilon + 1} E_0,$$

which may be solved for ϵ:

$$(C.5) \qquad \epsilon = \tfrac{1}{4}[1 + 3x + 3(1 + \tfrac{2}{3}x + x^2)^{1/2}],$$

which is Onsager's result. This probably overestimates the correction which must be applied to the Lorentz field in dipolar media.

Pirenne[3] has suggested that the Onsager theory will lead to a Curie

[3] J. Pirenne, Helv. Phys. Acta **22**, 479 (1949).

point when non-linear effects are considered, although the Curie point is at about 0.2 of that predicted by the Lorentz expression.

D. QUANTUM THEORY OF DIAMAGNETISM OF MONONUCLEAR SYSTEMS

The magnetic vector potential $\mathbf{A}$ is defined by the relation $\mathbf{H} = \text{curl } \mathbf{A}$. In a magnetic field the generalized momentum $\mathbf{p}$ of a particle of charge e is

(D.1) $$\mathbf{p} = \mathbf{p}_{\text{kin}} + \mathbf{p}_{\text{pot}} = m\dot{\mathbf{r}} + e\mathbf{A}/c;$$

so the kinetic energy is

(D.2) $$T = \frac{1}{2}m\dot{r}^2 = \frac{1}{2m}\left(\mathbf{p} - \frac{e}{c}\mathbf{A}\right)^2$$

$$= \frac{1}{2m}p^2 - \frac{e}{mc}\mathbf{p}\cdot\mathbf{A} + \frac{e^2}{2mc^2}A^2.$$

In quantum mechanics in the Schrödinger coordinate representation the momentum $\mathbf{p}$ is the operator $-i\hbar\nabla$; therefore the effect of a magnetic field is to add to the Hamiltonian the terms

(D.3) $$\mathcal{3C}' = \frac{ie\hbar}{2mc}(\nabla\cdot\mathbf{A} + \mathbf{A}\cdot\nabla) + \frac{e^2}{2mc^2}A^2,$$

which may usually be treated as a small perturbation. If the magnetic field is uniform and in the z direction, we may write

$$A_x = -\tfrac{1}{2}yH, \qquad A_y = \tfrac{1}{2}xH, \qquad A_z = 0,$$

and (D.3) becomes

(D.4) $$\mathcal{3C}' = \frac{ie\hbar H}{2mc}\left(x\frac{\partial}{\partial y} - y\frac{\partial}{\partial x}\right) + \frac{e^2 H^2}{8mc^2}(x^2 + y^2).$$

The first term on the right is proportional to the orbital angular momentum component L_z if $\mathbf{r}$ is measured from the nucleus, and in mononuclear systems gives rise only to paramagnetism. The second term gives for a spherically symmetric system a diamagnetic contribution

(D.5) $$E' = \frac{e^2 H^2}{12mc^2}\overline{r^2}$$

to the perturbation energy, and the associated magnetic moment is

(D.6) $$\mu = -\partial E'/\partial H = -(e^2\overline{r^2}/6mc^2)H,$$

in agreement with the classical result (9.5).   For further details of the derivation the book by Van Vleck may be consulted.

E. VAN VLECK TEMPERATURE-INDEPENDENT PARAMAGNETISM

We consider a molecular system which has no magnetic moment in the ground state, by which we mean that the diagonal matrix element of the magnetic moment operator μ_z is zero.

Suppose that there is a non-diagonal matrix element $(n|\mu_z|0)$ of the magnetic moment operator, connecting the ground state 0 with the excited state n of energy $\Delta = E_n - E_0$ above the ground state. Then by standard perturbation theory we see that the wave function of the ground state in a small field ($\mu_z H \ll \Delta$) becomes

$$(E.1) \qquad \psi_0' = \psi_0 + \frac{H(n|\mu_z|0)}{\Delta} \psi_n;$$

and the wave function of the excited state becomes

$$(E.2) \qquad \psi_n' = \psi_n - \frac{H(0|\mu_z|n)}{\Delta} \psi_0.$$

The ground state now has a moment

$$(E.3) \qquad (0'|\mu_z|0') = 2H|(n|\mu_z|0)|^2/\Delta,$$

and the upper state has a moment

$$(E.4) \qquad -2H|(n|\mu_z|0)|^2/\Delta.$$

There are two interesting cases to consider:

Case (a). $\Delta \ll kT$ (*low frequency matrix elements*).   The surplus population [see derivation of (9.19)] in the ground state is approximately equal to $N\Delta/2kT$, so that the resultant magnetization is

$$M = (2H|(n|\mu_z|0)|^2/\Delta)(N\Delta/2kT),$$

which gives for the susceptibility

$$(E.5) \qquad \chi = \frac{N \Sigma |(n|\mu_z|0)|^2}{kT}.$$

This contribution is of the usual Curie form, although the mechanism of magnetization here is through polarization of the states of the system, whereas with free spins the mechanism of magnetization is the redistribution of ions among the spin states.   We note that the splitting Δ does not enter in (E.5), on the assumption $\Delta \ll kT$.

Case (b). $\Delta \gg kT$ *(high frequency matrix elements).*   Now the population is nearly all in the ground state, so that

$$M = 2NH_z|(n|\mu_z|0)|^2/\Delta,$$

and the susceptibility is, summed over all suitable states n,

(E.6) $$\chi = 2N \sum_n \frac{|(n|\mu_z|0)|^2}{E_n - E_0}$$

independent of temperature.   This type of contribution is known as Van Vleck paramagnetism.

F. MAGNETIC AND ELECTROSTATIC ENERGY

We shall consider explicit only magnetic energy, as the corresponding expressions for electric energy are obtained by appropriate transcription.   Our treatment is simple and rather naive, but it leads to the correct results.

PERMANENT MOMENT μ IN EXTERNAL FIELD H

If we consider the effects of the moment μ $(=2ma)$ as reproduced by N and S poles $\pm m$ separated by a distance $2a$, it is apparent by symmetry that it is reasonable to take the zero point, from which we shall measure changes in energy, as the state with $\mathbf{\mu} \perp \mathbf{H}$.   If we turn the magnet toward the field by an angle θ, we change the potential of the N pole by $-m(a \sin \theta)H$, and the potential of the S pole by the same amount; so the interaction energy of the magnet with the field may be written

(F.1) $$E = -2maH \sin \theta = -\mathbf{\mu} \cdot \mathbf{H}.$$

If the external field is produced by a coil, the work done in turning the magnet goes into the electrical circuit keeping the value of H constant; if the external field is produced by a permanent magnet, the work done serves to increase the potential energy of the permanent magnet.

INTERACTION ENERGY OF AN ASSEMBLY OF PERMANENT MAGNETS

The energy is

(F.2) $$E = \sum_{i<j} r_{ij}^{-5}[r_{ij}^2\mathbf{\mu}_i \cdot \mathbf{\mu}_j - 3(\mathbf{\mu}_i \cdot \mathbf{r}_{ij})(\mathbf{\mu}_j \cdot \mathbf{r}_{ij})] = -\tfrac{1}{2}\sum_i \mathbf{\mu}_i \cdot \mathbf{H}_i,$$

where $\mathbf{H}_i$ is the field at magnet i caused by all the other magnets in the assembly.   If the assembly is in the form of an ellipsoid magnetized along one of the principal axes, the self-field is given by $H = -NM$, where N is the demagnetization factor as discussed in Chapter 7.

Then

(F.3) $$E = \tfrac{1}{2}NM^2V,$$

where M is the magnetization and V the volume.

ENERGY OF INDUCED MAGNETIZATION

From the Maxwell equations,

$$c \operatorname{curl} \mathbf{H} = 4\pi\mathbf{j};$$

$$c \operatorname{curl} \boldsymbol{\varepsilon} = -d\mathbf{B}/dt;$$

we have on multiplication by appropriate factors

$$4\pi\mathbf{j} \cdot \boldsymbol{\varepsilon}\, dV = c\, (\operatorname{curl} \mathbf{H}) \cdot \boldsymbol{\varepsilon}\, dV;$$

$$(d\mathbf{B}/dt) \cdot \mathbf{H}\, dV = -c\, (\operatorname{curl} \boldsymbol{\varepsilon}) \cdot \mathbf{H}\, dV;$$

here dV is an element of volume. It follows that

$$\int dV \mathbf{H} \cdot (d\mathbf{B}/dt) + 4\pi \int dV \boldsymbol{\varepsilon} \cdot \mathbf{j} = c \int dV (\boldsymbol{\varepsilon} \cdot \operatorname{curl} \mathbf{H} - \mathbf{H} \cdot \operatorname{curl} \boldsymbol{\varepsilon}).$$

The integral on the right is equal to div $\mathbf{H} \times \boldsymbol{\varepsilon}$, by a vector identity. If, as is usually true in our problems, $\mathbf{H} \times \boldsymbol{\varepsilon}$ approaches zero for large r faster than r^{-2}, then by the Gauss theorem the integral on the right vanishes. Hence we have

$$-\int dV \boldsymbol{\varepsilon} \cdot \mathbf{j}\, \delta t = \frac{1}{4\pi} \int dV \mathbf{H} \cdot \delta\mathbf{H} + \int dV \mathbf{H} \cdot \delta\mathbf{M}.$$

The term on the left is the work done in the coils of the system during the interval δt, supposing that the coils are resistanceless. The work done in the coils appears in the terms on the right. The first term on the right may be considered the work done in building up the magnetic field, and the second term the work done in building up the magnetization. Thus the energy of magnetization E_m is

(F.4) $$E_m = \int dV \int \mathbf{H} \cdot d\mathbf{M};$$

the corresponding result for the energy of dielectric polarization comes out by a similar argument to be

(F.5) $$E_e = \int dV \int \boldsymbol{\varepsilon} \cdot d\mathbf{P}.$$

If $M = \chi H$ and χ is independent of H,

(F.6) $$E_m = \tfrac{1}{2}\chi H^2 V.$$

A good general discussion of magnetic and electrostatic energy is given by E. A. Guggenheim, Proc. Roy. Soc. (London) **A155,** 49 (1936);

see also R. Becker and W. Döring, *Ferromagnetismus*, J. Springer, Berlin, 1939, pp. 53–66.

G. QUENCHING OF THE ORBITAL ANGULAR MOMENTUM BY CRYSTALLINE ELECTRIC FIELDS

The easiest way to understand quenching of the orbital moment is to consider the behavior of a simple model. We consider a single electron with orbital quantum number $L = 1$ moving about a nucleus, the whole being placed in an inhomogeneous crystalline electric field. We omit electron spin from the problem, as we are concerned here only with what happens to the orbital motion.

We suppose that the ion is embedded in a crystal of orthorhombic symmetry; then the charges on neighboring ions located along the x, y, z axes will produce an electrostatic potential V about the nucleus of the form

$$(G.1) \qquad eV = Ax^2 + By^2 - (A + B)z^2,$$

where A and B are constants. This expression is the lowest degree polynomial in x, y, z which is a solution of the Laplace equation $\nabla^2 V = 0$ and which is compatible with the symmetry of the crystal; that is, invariance under the operations $x \to -x$; $y \to -y$; $z \to -z$.

Let us now consider what will be the effect of the crystal field on the energy levels of the model. The ground state has $L = 1$, and in free space this level is three-fold degenerate; that is, it consists of the $2L + 1$ magnetic sublevels which are associated with the magnetic quantum numbers $M_L = 1, 0, -1$. In a magnetic field these levels are split by energies proportional to the field H, and it is this field-proportional splitting which is responsible for the normal paramagnetic susceptibility of the ion. In the crystal field the picture may, however, be quite different. Let us take as the three wave functions associated with the unperturbed ground state of the ion the following:

$$U_x = xf(r);$$

$$(G.2) \qquad U_y = yf(r);$$

$$U_z = zf(r).$$

These wave functions are orthogonal, and we suppose that they are normalized. We may confirm that each of the U's has the property

$$(G.3) \qquad \mathcal{L}^2 U_i = L(L + 1)U_i = 2U_i,$$

where $\mathcal{L}^2$ is the operator for the square of the orbital angular momentum, in units of $\hbar$. The result (G.3) confirms that the selected wave functions are in fact p functions, having $L = 1$.

We observe now that the U's are diagonal with respect to the perturbation (G.1), as by symmetry the non-diagonal elements vanish:

(G.4) $(U_x|eV|U_y) = (U_x|eV|U_z) = (U_y|eV|U_z) = 0.$

Consider for example

(G.5) $(U_x|eV|U_y) = \int xy|f(r)|^2\{Ax^2 + By^2 - (A + B)z^2\}\ dx\ dy\ dz;$

the integrand is an odd function of x (and also of y) and therefore the integral must be zero. The energy levels are then given by the diagonal matrix elements:

(G.6) $(U_x|eV|U_x) = \int |f(r)|^2\{Ax^4 + By^2x^2 - (A + B)z^2x^2\}\ dx\ dy\ dz$

$= A(I_1 - I_2),$

where

(G.7)
$$I_1 = \int |f(r)|^2 x^4\ dx\ dy\ dz;$$
$$I_2 = \int |f(r)|^2 x^2 y^2\ dx\ dy\ dz.$$

In addition,

(G.8)
$$(U_y|eV|U_y) = B(I_1 - I_2);$$
$$(U_z|eV|U_z) = -(A + B)(I_1 - I_2).$$

We note that the three eigenstates in the crystal field are p functions with their angular lobes directed along each of the x, y, z axes, respectively.

The orbital moment of each of the levels is zero, since

$$(U_x|L_z|U_x) = (U_y|L_z|U_y) = (U_z|L_z|U_z) = 0.$$

This is what is known as *quenching*. The level still has a definite total angular momentum, since $\mathcal{L}^2$ is diagonal and gives $L = 1$, but the spatial components of the angular momentum are not constants of the motion and their time average is zero in the first approximation. Therefore the orbital magnetic moment also vanishes in the same approximation. The role of the crystal field in the quenching process is to split the originally degenerate levels into "non-magnetic" levels separated by energies $\gg \mu H$, so that the magnetic field is a small perturbation in comparison with the crystal field.

Bethe[4] has treated thoroughly the splitting of levels in crystalline fields of various symmetries.

H. SPECTROSCOPIC SPLITTING FACTOR
g IN PARAMAGNETIC SALTS

We refer to Appendix G and suppose for convenience that the crystal field constants, A, B are such that $U_x = xf(r)$ is the orbital wave

[4] H. A. Bethe, Ann. Physik **3**, 133 (1929).

function of the ground state of the atom in the crystal. For a spin $S = \frac{1}{2}$ there are two possible spin states $S_z = \pm\frac{1}{2}$ represented by the spin functions α, β, which in the absence of a magnetic field are degenerate in the zeroth approximation. The problem is to take into account the spin-orbit interaction energy $\lambda \mathbf{L} \cdot \mathbf{S}$.

If the ground state function is $\psi_0 = U_x\alpha = xf(r)\alpha$ in the zeroth approximation, then in the first approximation, considering the $\lambda \mathbf{L} \cdot \mathbf{S}$ interaction by standard perturbation theory, we have

(H.1) $$\psi = [U_x - i(\lambda/2\Delta_1)U_y]\alpha - i(\lambda/2\Delta_2)U_z\beta,$$

where Δ_1 is the energy difference between the U_x and U_y states, and Δ_2 is the difference between the U_x and U_z states. The term in $U_z\beta$ actually has only a second order effect on the result and may be discarded. The expectation value of the orbital angular momentum to the first order is given directly by

(H.2) $$(\psi|L_z|\psi) = -\lambda/\Delta_1,$$

and the magnetic moment of the state as measured in the z direction is

(H.3) $$\mu_B(\psi|L_z + 2S_z|\psi) = [-(\lambda/\Delta_1) + 1]\mu_B.$$

As the separation between the levels $S_z = \pm\frac{1}{2}$ in a field H is

(H.4) $$\Delta E = g\mu_B H = 2[1 - (\lambda/\Delta_1)]\mu_B H,$$

the g value or spectroscopic splitting factor in the z direction is

(H.5) $$g = 2[1 - (\lambda_1/\Delta_1)].$$

If, following (15.20), we define

(H.6) $$2\varepsilon = \overline{L_z}/\overline{S_z},$$

we have

(H.7) $$\varepsilon \cong -\lambda/\Delta_1,$$

and

(H.8) $$g = 2(1 + \varepsilon).$$

I. PERTURBATION OF NEARLY FREE ELECTRONS BY A PERIODIC POTENTIAL

Let the perturbation due to the crystal lattice be written as a Fourier series:

(I.1) $$H' = \sum_{-\infty}^{\infty} V_n e^{-2\pi inx/a}; \qquad (V_0 = 0).$$

For example, if the perturbation is simply $V_1 \cos(2\pi x/a)$, then

$$H' = (V_1/2)(e^{2\pi ix/a} + e^{-2\pi ix/a}).$$

The matrix elements of H' in a plane wave representation are

(I.2) $\qquad (k'|H'|k) = \sum_n (V_n/L) \int_0^L e^{-ik'x} e^{-2\pi inx/a} e^{ikx}\, dx;$

the integral is zero unless

(I.3) $\qquad\qquad\qquad\qquad k' = k - 2\pi n/a,$

in which case the matrix element is equal to the appropriate V_n.   The first order wave function is

(I.4) $\qquad \psi_k = \dfrac{1}{L^{1/2}} \left[e^{ikx} + \sum_{k'} \dfrac{(k'|H'|k)}{E_k - E_{k'}} e^{ik'x} \right]$

$$= \frac{1}{L^{1/2}} e^{ikx} \left[1 + \sum_n \frac{V_n}{E_k - E_{k'}} e^{-2\pi inx/a} \right],$$

subject to $k' = k - 2\pi n/a$.   The solution (I.4) is of the Bloch form as required.   We have $E_{k'} = \hbar^2 k'^2/2m$.   The energy to the second order is

(I.5) $\qquad\qquad E_k = (\hbar^2 k^2/2m) + \sum_n \dfrac{|V_n|^2}{E_k - E_{k'}}.$

The assumption on which this calculation is based is that the denominator

$$E_k - E_{k'} = \frac{\hbar^2}{2m} \left[k^2 - \left(k - \frac{2\pi n}{a} \right)^2 \right]$$

is not very small.   The denominator will, however, vanish for $k = \pi n/a$.   In this case we must do a more careful calculation.

When k is close to $\pi n/a$, we may take the wave function as

(I.6) $\qquad\qquad\qquad \psi = e^{ikx}(A_0 + A_n e^{-2\pi inx/a}),$

because the other Fourier coefficients will be small.   The coefficients A_0, A_n are determined by minimizing the energy

(I.7) $\qquad E = [E_0 A_0^2 + E_n A_n^2 + 2V_n A_0 A_n]/[A_0^2 + A_n^2];$

here $\qquad\quad E_0 = \hbar^2 k^2/2m; \qquad E_n = \hbar^2(k - 2\pi n/a)^2/2m,$

and the mean value of V is taken to be zero; we have supposed that $V^*_n = V_n$.

At the minimum we have, by taking variations δA_0 and δA_n,

$$2A_0(E - E_0) - 2V_n A_n = 0;$$

$$-2V_n A_0 + 2A_n(E - E_n) = 0.$$

These equations have solutions for A_0, A_n only if

$$(E - E_0)(E - E_n) + V_n^2 = 0$$

or

(I.8) $$E = \tfrac{1}{2}\{E_0 + E_n \pm [(E_0 - E_n)^2 + 4V_n^2]^{1/2}\}.$$

The most interesting feature of this result is the discontinuity in energy for $k = \pi n/a$; we have at this point

(I.9) $$\Delta E = 2|V_n|,$$

so that energies lying between

$$(\hbar^2/2m)(n\pi/a)^2 \pm |V_n|$$

are forbidden. We note that the Bragg condition for reflection is also $k = \pi n/a$, and this condition also marks the boundaries on the Kronig-Penney model. At the boundary the wave functions are standing waves which do not carry current.

For k just above the first gap we find on expanding (I.8) to the first order in $(E_0 - E_n)^2$ that, letting $k' = k - \pi/a$,

(I.10) $$E \cong \frac{\hbar^2}{2m}\left[\left(\frac{\pi}{a}\right)^2 + k'^2\left(1 + \frac{4E_a}{\Delta E}\right)\right] + \Delta E/2,$$

E_a being the energy at the gap, so that as far as dependence on k' is concerned

(I.11) $$E - E_a = \frac{\hbar^2}{2m}\alpha k'^2; \qquad \alpha = 1 + \frac{4E_a}{\Delta E},$$

which suggests that the electron behaves as if it had a mass

(I.12) $$m^* = m/\alpha.$$

THREE DIMENSIONS

In a three-dimensional simple cubic lattice

$$H' = \sum_{\mathbf{G}} V_{\mathbf{G}} e^{i\mathbf{G}\cdot\mathbf{r}}$$

and the condition for non-vanishing matrix elements is

$$\mathbf{k}' = \mathbf{k} + \mathbf{G}.$$

A forbidden zone occurs when

(I.13) $$k^2 = (\mathbf{k} + \mathbf{G})^2,$$

or

(I.14) $$2\mathbf{k} \cdot \mathbf{G} + G^2 = 0$$

or

(I.15) $$k_x n_1 + k_y n_2 + k_z n_3 = \pi(n_1{}^2 + n_2{}^2 + n_3{}^2)/a,$$

where n_1, n_2, n_3 are positive or negative integers.

J. TIGHT BINDING APPROXIMATION FOR METALLIC ELECTRONS

Suppose that the ground state of an electron moving in the potential $V(r)$ of an isolated atom is $\phi(r)$ and that the energy is E_0; suppose further that ϕ is an s state. The treatment of bands arising from degenerate $(p, d, \cdot \cdot \cdot)$ atomic levels is more complicated. If the influence of one atom on another is small, we get a zero order wave function for one electron in the whole crystal by taking

(J.1) $$\psi_k(\mathbf{r}) = \sum_j C_{kj} \phi(\mathbf{r} - \mathbf{r}_j),$$

where the sum is over all lattice points. This function is of the Bloch form if we take $C_{kj} = e^{i(\mathbf{k} \cdot \mathbf{r}_j)}$, which gives

(J.2) $$\psi_k(\mathbf{r}) = \sum_j e^{i(\mathbf{k} \cdot \mathbf{r}_j)} \phi(\mathbf{r} - \mathbf{r}_j).$$

We prove it is of the Bloch form by considering the effect of a translation by a vector $\mathbf{g}$ connecting two lattice points:

(J.3) $$\psi_k(\mathbf{r} + \mathbf{g}) = \Sigma \, e^{i(\mathbf{k} \cdot \mathbf{r}_j)} \phi(\mathbf{r} + \mathbf{g} - \mathbf{r}_j)$$
$$= e^{i(\mathbf{k} \cdot \mathbf{g})} \Sigma \, e^{i\mathbf{k} \cdot (\mathbf{r}_j - \mathbf{g})} \phi[\mathbf{r} - (\mathbf{r}_j - \mathbf{g})]$$
$$= e^{i(\mathbf{k} \cdot \mathbf{g})} \psi_k(\mathbf{r})$$

and so the Bloch requirement is satisfied.

We get the first order energy by calculating the diagonal matrix elements of the perturbation $H'(r)$ expressing the difference between the potential in the crystal near an ion and the potential of an individual atom. We have

(J.4) $$(\mathbf{k}|H'|\mathbf{k}) = \sum_j \sum_m e^{i\mathbf{k} \cdot (\mathbf{r}_j - \mathbf{r}_m)} (\phi_m|H'|\phi_j);$$

writing $\varrho_m = \mathbf{r}_m - \mathbf{r}_j$ and treating all lattice points as equivalent,

(J.5) $\qquad (\mathbf{k}|H'|\mathbf{k}) = N \sum_m e^{-i\mathbf{k}\cdot\varrho_m} \int \phi(\mathbf{r} - \varrho_m) H' \phi(\mathbf{r}) \, dV.$

If now we neglect all integrals except those between nearest neighbors connected by ϱ and write, for a crystal of N atoms,

(J.6) $\qquad\qquad \int \phi^*(\mathbf{r}) H' \phi(\mathbf{r}) \, dV = -\alpha/N;$

(J.7) $\qquad\qquad \int \phi^*(\mathbf{r} - \varrho) H' \phi(\mathbf{r}) \, dV = -\gamma/N;$

we get

$$(\mathbf{k}|H'|\mathbf{k}) = -\alpha - \gamma \sum_m e^{-i\mathbf{k}\cdot\varrho_m},$$

and so the first order energy is given by

(J.8) $\qquad\qquad E = E_0 - \alpha - \gamma \Sigma\, e^{i(\mathbf{k}\cdot\varrho_m)}.$

For a simple cubic lattice the nearest neighbor atoms are at the positions

(J.9) $\qquad \varrho_m = (\pm a, 0, 0); \qquad (0, \pm a, 0); \qquad (0, 0, \pm a)$

and

(J.10) $\qquad E = E_0 - \alpha - 2\gamma(\cos k_x a + \cos k_y a + \cos k_z a),$

so that the energies are confined to a band with limits $\pm 6\gamma$. For small k,

(J.11) $\qquad\qquad E \cong E_0 - \alpha - 6\gamma + \gamma k^2 a^2.$

The energy at the bottom of the band is independent of the direction of motion. The effective mass is

(J.12) $\qquad\qquad m^* = \hbar^2/2\gamma a^2.$

We see that for every state of an electron in the free atom there exists a band of energies in the crystal. We have considered here one state of the free atom and have obtained one band. The number of states in the zone which corresponds to a non-degenerate atomic level is equal to $2N$, where N is the number of atoms. We see this directly: (J.10) is periodic in $\mathbf{k}$, and thus only values of $\mathbf{k}$ lying within a certain polyhedron in $\mathbf{k}$-space will define independent wave functions. In the simple cubic case the polyhedron is defined by $-\pi/a < k_x < \pi/a$, etc. The volume of the polyhedron is $8\pi^3/a^3$; now the number of states (counting both spin orientations) per unit volume of $\mathbf{k}$ space is $1/4\pi^3$, so the number of states is $2/a^3 = 2N$.

K. ELECTRICAL CONDUCTIVITY AT LOW TEMPERATURES

At low temperatures the electrons may be scattered only through small angles; so the number of scattering processes needed to reduce the average forward momentum by a given fraction is increased.

The scattering angle at low temperatures is necessarily small because the phonon momentum available for transfer to the electron is small at low temperatures. The momentum of the electron is changed in the scattering process, and the difference appears as a change of momentum of an elastic wave. The phonon momentum P is of the order of kT/v_s, where $v_s \approx a\omega_{max}$ is the velocity of sound. The electron momentum at the top of the Fermi distribution is $p \approx \hbar/a$, so that

$$(K.1) \qquad\qquad P \approx (T/\Theta)p,$$

as $\Theta = \hbar\omega_{max}/k$. Thus for $T \ll \Theta$ we must have $\Delta p \cong P \ll p$. This means that the angle of scattering is $\approx T/\Theta$. The number of collisions in a time equal to the relaxation time is ≈ 1 for $T \gg \Theta$, as here the collisions may be nearly spherically symmetric, but for $T \ll \Theta$ there are $\approx (\Theta/T)^2$ collisions in a relaxation time as $(1 - \cos\phi)$ is the measure of the loss of forward momentum in a collision with scattering angle ϕ.

The number of phonons at low temperatures is proportional to T^3 on the Debye theory. The combined effect of the T^3 temperature dependence of the number of phonons and the T^2 dependence of the scattering angle factor makes the conductivity proportional to T^5.

L. MOBILITY IN INTRINSIC SEMICONDUCTORS

At first sight we might expect the effect of lattice scattering on mobility in semiconductors to be given by expression (11.89) for the electrical conductivity, where p^2 now would be taken as a suitable average over the Maxwellian velocity distribution of the electrons excited to the conduction band. However, in calculating the conductivity in Chapter 11 we made a tacit assumption which is quite good for the fast electrons at the top of the Fermi distribution in a metal, but which is a poor assumption for the electrons near the bottom of the conduction band in a semiconductor. In arriving at (11.83) we performed an operation equivalent to taking

$$(L.1) \qquad\qquad \text{grad } \psi = i\mathbf{k}\psi,$$

as for a plane wave. For the Bloch function

$$(L.2) \qquad\qquad \psi = u_\mathbf{k}(\mathbf{r})e^{i\mathbf{k}\cdot\mathbf{r}}$$

we actually have

(L.3)
$$\text{grad } \psi = \left[i\mathbf{k} + \frac{1}{u} \text{ grad } u \right] \psi,$$

and so for the small values of k $(ka \ll 1)$ of importance in the semi-conductor problem it is a better approximation to take

(L.4)
$$\text{grad } \psi \cong \left[\frac{1}{u} \text{ grad } u \right] \psi.$$

On redefining ψ_i in (11.77) and ψ_s in (11.78), and making other appropriate changes in the previous derivation, we may expect to replace (11.85) by a relation of the form

(L.5)
$$\overline{Q_d} = G^2 d^2 \overline{Q_s},$$

where G is a factor involving something like $|\text{grad } u|^2$. The result (13.17) obtained by more accurate quantum-mechanical methods is more or less consistent with this expression for $\overline{Q_d}$.

M. DERIVATION OF THE CONWELL-WEISSKOPF FORMULA

In the standard derivation of the Rutherford scattering formula it is shown that the angle θ through which the particle is deflected in a Coulomb potential $e/\epsilon r$ is given in terms of the collision parameter b by the relation

(M.1)
$$b = (e^2/\epsilon m v^2) \cot (\theta/2),$$

where v is the velocity of the incident particle of charge e. The collision parameter b is the distance of the nucleus from the line which would be followed by the particle if there were no Coulomb force. We are interested in the quantity $1 - \cos \theta$ as a measure of the loss of forward momentum on collision. By a trigonometric identity we have

(M.2)
$$1 - \cos \theta = 2/[1 + (\epsilon m v^2 b/e^2)^2].$$

We suppose that the effective range of the interaction of an electron with a single ion is d, where d is related to the concentration N_e of ionized impurity atoms by

(M.3)
$$d = \tfrac{1}{2} N_e^{-\frac{1}{3}}.$$

We are in effect saying here that the impurities are arranged on a simple cubic lattice of spacing $2d$ and that each impurity atom dominates the scattering within a sphere of radius d.

The probability that the collision parameter will have a value between b and $b + db$ is $2\pi bdb/\pi d^2$, so that the average value of $1 - \cos \theta$ is

(M.4)
$$\overline{1 - \cos \theta} = (1/\pi d^2) \int_0^d (1 - \cos \theta)2\pi bdb$$
$$= 2(e^2/\epsilon dmv^2)^2 \log [1 + (\epsilon dmv^2/e^2)^2].$$

The mean free path is approximately

(M.5)
$$\Lambda \approx 2d/\overline{(1 - \cos \theta)}.$$

The mobility (13.41), apart from a constant of the order of unity, follows from (M.4) and (M.5) after averaging over a Maxwellian distribution and making certain minor approximations.

N. FERMI LEVEL AND THE CHEMICAL POTENTIAL

Using the Boltzmann definition of the entropy,

(N.1)
$$S = k \log W,$$

the variational equation leading to the Fermi-Dirac distribution function may be written as

(N.2)
$$\delta\left(\frac{S}{k} - \alpha N - \beta U\right) = 0,$$

so that

(N.3)
$$\alpha = \frac{1}{k}\left(\frac{\partial S}{\partial N}\right)_{U,V}.$$

Now the *chemical potential* μ is defined through

(N.4)
$$dU = T\, dS - p\, dV + \mu\, dN$$

for a system in which the number of particles is allowed to vary. From (N.4),

(N.5)
$$T\, dS = dU + p\, dV - \mu\, dN,$$

and

(N.6)
$$\left(\frac{\partial S}{\partial N}\right)_{U,V} = -\frac{\mu}{T}.$$

Comparing (N.3) with (N.6), we have

(N.7)
$$\alpha = -\mu/kT.$$

Now on looking back at the derivation of the Fermi-Dirac distribution function in Chapter 10 we see that $\alpha = -E_F/kT$.   Therefore

(N.8) $\mu = E_F;$

the chemical potential is equal to the Fermi energy.

It is a well-known thermodynamic result[5] that the condition for two phases to be in equilibrium with respect to any chemical species (in this case the electrons) is that the chemical potential of that species should have the same value in the two phases.   This result follows on considering the change of the Helmholtz free energy

(N.9) $dF = -p \, dV - S \, dT - \Sigma \, \mu \, dn$

on transferring dn particles from phase i to phase j at constant volume and temperature:

(N.10) $dF = -\mu_j \, dn + \mu_i \, dn.$

For equilibrium $dF = 0$, whence we have the stated result

$$\mu_j = \mu_i.$$

This result has an important application to contact potential problems, for it tells us that in equilibrium the Fermi level must have a constant value in all conductors in contact.

O. SEMICLASSICAL DISCUSSION OF FERROMAGNETIC SPIN WAVES

The Hamiltonian of the system is

(O.1) $H' = -2J \, \Sigma \, \mathbf{S}_i \cdot \mathbf{S}_j,$

where $\mathbf{S}_i$ is the spin operator in units of $\hbar$ for the ith atom.   Each atom has $2S_0$ resultant electron spins.   The quantum equation of motion for $\mathbf{S}_m$ is

$$i\hbar\dot{\mathbf{S}}_m = [\mathbf{S}_m, H'] = 2J[(\Sigma \, \mathbf{S}_i \cdot \mathbf{S}_j)\mathbf{S}_m - \mathbf{S}_m(\Sigma \, \mathbf{S}_i \cdot \mathbf{S}_j)]$$

$$= 2J \sum_j [(\mathbf{S}_m \cdot \mathbf{S}_j)\mathbf{S}_m - \mathbf{S}_m(\mathbf{S}_m \cdot \mathbf{S}_j)] = -2J \sum_j \mathbf{S}_j \times [\mathbf{S}_m \times \mathbf{S}_m],$$

which becomes, upon using the commutation relation $\mathbf{S} \times \mathbf{S} = i\mathbf{S}$,

(O.2) $\hbar\dot{\mathbf{S}}_m = 2J\mathbf{S}_m \times \Sigma \, \mathbf{S}_j.$

For a simple cubic lattice with lattice constant a we have, by series expansion, treating $\mathbf{S}_m$ as the center and counting only nearest neigh-

---

[5] See, for example, M. W. Zemansky, *Heat and thermodynamics*, McGraw-Hill Book Co., New York, 3rd ed., 1951, pp. 391, 444.

bor interactions,

(O.3) $$\sum_j \mathbf{S}_j = 6\mathbf{S}_m + a^2 \nabla^2 \mathbf{S}_m + \cdots,$$

where the $\mathbf{S}$'s are now considered *classical* vectors, and not as quantum operators. For small distortions we neglect higher order terms in the

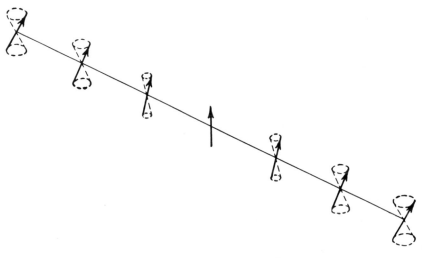

Fig. O.1.   Spin wave on a line of atoms.

series expansion; thus we have the equation of motion

(O.4) $$\hbar \dot{\mathbf{S}} = 2Ja^2 [\mathbf{S} \times \nabla^2 \mathbf{S}]$$

for the spin considered a classical quantity.

Let

(O.5) $$\mathbf{S} = \mathbf{S}_0 + \boldsymbol{\varepsilon}$$

where $\mathbf{S}_0$ is the unperturbed spin vector, and $\boldsymbol{\varepsilon}$ represents a spin wave of small amplitude. We look for solutions of the form

(O.6) $$\varepsilon_x = \varepsilon_0 \sin \omega t \sin k_x x \sin k_y y \sin k_z z;$$

(O.7) $$\varepsilon_y = \varepsilon_0 \cos \omega t \sin k_x x \sin k_y y \sin k_z z.$$

Then, from (O.4),

(O.8) $$\hbar \omega = 2S_0 Ja^2 k^2.$$

This is the fundamental relation between the frequency and the wave number of a spin wave. A drawing of a spin wave is shown in Fig. O.1.

The energy of a spin wave is

$$(O.9) \qquad E = Ja^2 \Sigma \, |\nabla \mathbf{S}_m|^2,$$

using (O.1) and (O.3), taking care not to count interactions twice. Using our standing spin waves in a rectangular enclosure we have, after replacing $a^3 \Sigma$ by $\int$,

$$(O.10) \qquad E = Jk^2 a^2 \varepsilon_0^2 \int \sin^2 k_x x \, \sin^2 k_y y \, \sin^2 k_z z \, dV/a^3,$$

or, finally,

$$(O.11) \qquad E = Jk^2 \varepsilon_0^2 V/8a,$$

where V is the volume of the specimen. The energy is also equal to $n\hbar\omega$, where n is the excitational quantum number. Therefore

$$(O.12) \qquad \varepsilon_0^2 = (8an/JV)(\hbar\omega/k^2) = 16S_0 a^3 n/V.$$

The next thing to do is to relate the spin wave amplitude to the change in intrinsic magnetization M of the specimen. If the specimen is saturated along the z axis in the absence of spin waves, the component of magnetization along this axis will be reduced by the excitation of spin waves. By geometry

$$(O.13) \qquad M^2 = M_0^2 (1 - \overline{(\varepsilon/S_0)^2}),$$

which gives

$$(O.14) \qquad \Delta M/M_0 = \overline{\varepsilon^2}/2S_0^2 = \varepsilon_0^2/16S_0^2,$$

after the spatial average is carried out. Using (O.12),

$$(O.15) \qquad V \, \Delta M = a^3 n M_0/S_0 = 2n\mu_B.$$

This result shows that the change in magnetic moment of the specimen, as a consequence of the excitation of a spin wave with excitation quantum number n, corresponds to the reversal of n electrons. This is in agreement with the more rigorous quantum theory treatment.

BLOCH $T^{3/2}$ LAW

For thermal equilibrium the average value of the quantum number n for a wave of frequency ω is given by

$$(O.16) \qquad \bar{n} = (\Sigma \, ne^{-n\beta})/\Sigma \, e^{-n\beta} = 1/(e^\beta - 1),$$

where $\beta = \hbar\omega/kT$. We now want the sum of $\bar{n}$ over all allowed states. The number of states with wave number less than k is, per unit volume, $(1/2\pi)^3(4\pi/3)k^3$, whence the number of states with energy in dE at E is $(1/2\pi^2)k^2(dk/dE)\,dE$, which is equal to $(1/4\pi^2)E^{\frac{1}{2}}(2S_0Ja^2)^{-\frac{3}{2}}\,dE$. Thus the sum of $\bar{n}$ over all states is, per unit volume,

$$(O.17) \qquad \Sigma\,\bar{n} \cong (N/4\pi^2)(2S_0J)^{-\frac{3}{2}}\int_0^\infty \frac{E^{\frac{1}{2}}\,dE}{e^{E/kT}-1}$$

$$= (N/4\pi^2)(kT/2S_0J)^{\frac{3}{2}}\int_0^\infty \frac{x^{\frac{1}{2}}\,dx}{e^x-1}.$$

Here $N = 1/a^3$ is the number of atoms per unit volume. Now by series expansion

$$(O.18) \qquad \frac{1}{4\pi^2}\int_0^\infty \frac{x^{\frac{1}{2}}\,dx}{e^x-1} = 0.0587,$$

so that

$$(O.19) \qquad \Sigma\,\bar{n} = 0.0587N(kT/2S_0J)^{\frac{3}{2}}.$$

Therefore

$$(O.20) \qquad \frac{\Delta M}{M_0} = (0.0587/S_0)(kT/2S_0J)^{\frac{3}{2}}.$$

This expresses the well-known Bloch $T^{\frac{3}{2}}$ law in the form obtained by Moller for atoms with spin quantum number S_0. For a body-centered cubic lattice,

$$(O.21) \qquad \frac{\Delta M}{M_0} = (0.0587/2S)(kT/2S_0J)^{\frac{3}{2}}.$$

If we had included the zero-point motion of the spin system by increasing $\bar{n}$ in (J.16) by adding $\frac{1}{2}$, we should have found that, at $0°K$, $\Delta M/M_0 = \{[S(S+1)]^{\frac{1}{2}} - S\}/S$. This expresses the fact that the maximum spin component in quantum theory is S, whereas the magnitude of the spin is $[S(S+1)]^{\frac{1}{2}}$. The transverse spin components appear in spin wave theory as a zero-point motion of the spin wave system.

P. THE BLOCH THEOREM

We now prove that the lowest state of a quantum-mechanical system in the absence of a magnetic field can carry no current, even when interelectronic interactions are taken into account.

The Hamiltonian is, in the absence of a magnetic field,

$$(\text{P.1}) \qquad \mathcal{3C} = \sum_n \left[V(X_n) - \frac{\hbar^2}{2m} \nabla_n{}^2 \right] + \frac{1}{2} \sum_{m \neq n} V(X_{nm}),$$

where $V(X_n)$ is the potential of the nth electron in the field of the ion lattice and $V(X_{nm})$ is the Coulomb interaction energy of electrons n and m. The total current $\mathbf{j}$ is related to the total electronic momentum by $\mathbf{j} = e\mathbf{P}/m$.

Suppose that the lowest state carries a momentum $\mathbf{P}_0$, and that $\psi(X_1, X_2, X_3, \cdot \cdot \cdot)$ is the exact wave function for this state. Consider the wave function

$$(\text{P.2}) \qquad \phi = e^{i(\delta\mathbf{P}/\hbar) \cdot \mathbf{\Sigma}\mathbf{X}_r}\psi,$$

where $\delta\mathbf{P}$ is very small; this corresponds to a state in which each electron has been given an additional momentum $\delta\mathbf{P}$. Then the total momentum in the state ϕ is

$$(\text{P.3}) \qquad \mathbf{P} = \mathbf{P}_0 + N\delta\mathbf{P},$$

N being the total number of electrons.

The potential energy for ϕ is the same as for ψ, since $\phi^*\phi = \psi^*\psi$. The kinetic energy is, however, changed:

$$(\text{P.4}) \qquad T = T_0 + \frac{(\mathbf{P}_0 \cdot \delta\mathbf{P})}{m} + \frac{N(\delta P)^2}{2m}$$

$$= T_0 + \frac{m}{Ne^2} \mathbf{j}_0 \cdot \delta\mathbf{j} + \frac{m}{2Ne^2} (\delta j)^2.$$

We can choose $\delta\mathbf{P}$ opposite in sign to $\mathbf{P}_0$, so that $\mathbf{P}_0 \cdot \delta\mathbf{P}$ is negative. If $\delta\mathbf{P}$ is small enough, the term involving $(\delta P)^2$ can be neglected. Thus the total energy of the state ϕ is less than that of the state ψ; but ψ is the exact ground state wave function and any other function must have a higher energy. Therefore $\mathbf{P}_0$ (and $\mathbf{j}_0$) must be zero for the ground state. This means that at absolute zero the system cannot have a spontaneous current.

Bohm has attempted to show that for *each* state with a non-vanishing current there exists another solution with a lower current and a lower energy. Thus, if we have a group of states carrying some current $\mathbf{j}_i$, they cannot have a minimum free energy, because there is always another group of states with the same statistical weight, but with a lower energy and hence with a lower free energy. It is important to note, however, that in the presence of a magnetic field the state of lowest free energy *can* carry current. This observation is central to recent theoretical work in superconductivity.

Q. IMPORTANT CONVERSION FACTORS

(Approximate—velocity of light taken as 3×10^{10} cm/sec)

To obtain result in	Multiply number of	by
gauss	webers/meter^2	10^4
webers/m^2	gauss	10^{-4}
oersteds	ampere-turns/meter	$4\pi \times 10^{-3}$
ampere-turns/meter	oersteds	$10^3/4\pi$
statvolts	volts	$1/300$
volts	statvolts	300
amps	abamps	10
amps	statamps	$1/(3 \times 10^9)$
esu resistivity	ohm-cm	$1/(9 \times 10^{11})$
ohm-cm	esu resistivity	9×10^{11}
mho/cm	esu conductivity	$1/(9 \times 10^{11})$
esu conductivity	mho/cm	9×10^{11}
mho/meter	esu conductivity	9×10^9
esu charge/cm^2	coulomb/meter^2	3×10^5
coulomb/meter^2	esu charge/cm^2	$\frac{1}{3} \times 10^{-5}$
volt-cm/amp	statvolt-cm/statamp	9×10^{11}

R. SUMMARY OF RESULTS OF THERMODYNAMICS AND STATISTICAL MECHANICS

We review here some of the central results of thermodynamics and statistical mechanics; for further reading there are a number of specialized texts. We mention among the more elementary texts those by Zemansky[6] and by Gurney.[7]

The first and second laws of thermodynamics lead to the relation

(R.1) $$dU = T\, dS + dE,$$

for a reversible process, that is, for a process occurring sufficiently slowly that there is always equilibrium between the system and its surroundings. For a reversible process $T\, dS$ is equal to dQ, the heat flow into the system; here S is the entropy. In (R.1), dU is the increase in internal energy of the system and dE is the work done on the system by an external agency.

If the work is done mechanically by the pressure p, we have

(R.2) $$dE = -p\, dV;$$

if the work is done by a magnetic field (Appendix F) we have, per unit volume,

(R.3) $$dE = \mathbf{H} \cdot d\mathbf{M},$$

[6] M. W. Zemansky, *Heat and thermodynamics*, McGraw-Hill Book Co., New York, 3rd ed., 1951.

[7] R. W. Gurney, *Introduction to statistical mechanics*, McGraw-Hill Book Co., New York, 1949.

while for an electric field

(R.4) $$dE = \mathcal{E} \cdot d\mathbf{P}.$$

In what follows we shall use the connection (R.2), as the appropriate changes for the electric and magnetic problems may always be easily made.

It is useful to consider the Helmholtz free energy defined by

(R.5) $$F = U - TS,$$

and the Gibbs free energy defined by

(R.6) $$G = U - TS + pV.$$

Using (R.1) and (R.2), we have

(R.7) $$dF = -S\,dT - p\,dV;$$

(R.8) $$dG = -S\,dT + V\,dp.$$

Thus, in an isothermal reversible change ($dT = 0$) at constant volume

(R.9) $$dF = 0,$$

and at constant pressure

(R.10) $$dG = 0.$$

These conditions for equilibrium are frequently the basis of the applications of thermodynamics to solid state problems.

The central result of statistical mechanics is that in thermal equilibrium the probability of finding a system in a state i is proportional to $e^{-E_i/kT}$, where E_i is the energy of the state. Thus the average value of a quantity x is given by

(R.11) $$\bar{x} = \sum_i x_i e^{-E_i/kT} \Big/ \sum_i e^{-E_i/kT},$$

where x_i is the value of x when the system is in the state i, and the sum is over all states.

Defining the partition function Z as

(R.12) $$Z = \sum_i e^{-E_i/kT},$$

the Helmholtz free energy F is given by

(R.13) $$e^{-F/kT} = Z.$$

This result follows from the definition of F and from (R.11).

Using the celebrated Boltzmann definition of the entropy is the best way to get physical insight into the significance of entropy. Boltzmann shows that

(R.14) $S = k \log w,$

where w is the number of possible independent arrangements of the particles in the system.   Thus a system of spins all lined up has zero entropy, but in random orientations may have a high entropy, as in (9.29).

S. VALUES OF GENERAL PHYSICAL CONSTANTS

Source: J. W. M. Du Mond and E. R. Cohen, "A least squares adjustment of the atomic constants, as of Dec. 1950," published by the National Research Council, Washington, D.C., 1951.

Quantity	Value
Avogadro's number, L	$(6.025438 \pm 0.000107) \times 10^{23}$ g mol^{-1} (phys.)
Electronic charge, e	$-(4.802233 \pm 0.000071) \times 10^{-10}$ esu
Electron rest mass, m	$(9.107208 \pm 0.000246) \times 10^{-28}$ grams
Planck's constant, h	$(6.623773 \pm 0.000180) \times 10^{-27}$ erg sec
(h-"bar"), $\hbar$	$(1.054206 \pm 0.000028) \times 10^{-27}$ erg sec
Velocity of light, c	(299790.22 ± 0.86) km sec^{-1}
Faraday constant, $F = Ne$	$(2.893556 \pm 0.000021) \times 10^{13}$ esu g mol^{-1} (phys.)
Specific charge of the electron, e/m	$(1.758897 \pm 0.000032) \times 10^{7}$ emu g^{-1}
Compton radian length of the electron, $\lambda_{ce} = \hbar/mc$	$(3.8612050 \pm 0.0000516) \times 10^{-11}$ cm
First Bohr radius, $a_0 = \hbar^2/me^2$	$(5.291508 \pm 0.000035) \times 10^{-9}$ cm
Classical radius of the electron, $r_0 = e^2/mc^2$	$(2.817515 \pm 0.000056) \times 10^{-13}$ cm
Atomic weight of hydrogen	1.0081284 (phys.) ± 0.0000030
Ratio proton mass to electron mass	1836.1388 ± 0.0339
Boltzmann's constant, k	$(1.3802565 \pm 0.0000615) \times 10^{-16}$ erg deg^{-1}
Bohr magneton, $\mu_B = e\hbar/2mc$	$-(0.92712031 \pm 0.0000219) \times 10^{-20}$ erg gauss^{-1}
Wavelength associated with 1 ev, λ_0	$(12396.44 \pm 0.174) \times 10^{-8}$ cm
Frequency associated with 1 ev, ν_0	$(2.418357 \pm 0.000032) \times 10^{14}$ sec^{-1}
Wave number associated with 1 ev, k_0	(8066.832 ± 0.113) cm^{-1}
Energy associated with 1 ev	$(1.601864 \pm 0.000024) \times 10^{-12}$ erg
Energy associated with unit wave number	$(1.985742 \pm 0.000054) \times 10^{-16}$ erg
Energy associated with 1 rydberg	13.60353 ± 0.00210 ev
Speed of 1-ev electron	$(5.931099 \pm 0.000055) \times 10^{7}$ cm sec^{-1}
Energy associated with 1° Kelvin	$(8.616562 \pm 0.000357) \times 10^{-5}$ ev
"Temperature" associated with 1 ev	(11605.556 ± 0.480)°K
Loschmidt's number, n_0	$(2.687444 \pm 0.000067) \times 10^{19}$ cm^{-3}

Author Index

Subject Index

INTRODUCTION TO
SOLID STATE PHYSICS

WILEY SERIES ON THE SCIENCE AND TECHNOLOGY OF MATERIALS

Advisory Editors: J. H. Hollomon, J. E. Burke, B. Chalmers, R. L. Sproull, A. V. Tobolsky

MECHANICAL PROPERTIES OF METALS
  D. McLean

THE METALLURGY OF WELDING
  D. Séférian—Translated by E. Bishop

THERMODYNAMICS OF SOLIDS
  Richard A. Swalin

TRANSMISSION ELECTRON MICROSCOPY OF METALS
  Gareth Thomas

PLASTICITY AND CREEP OF METALS
  J. D. Lubahn and R. P. Felgar

INTRODUCTION TO CERAMICS
  W. D. Kingery

PROPERTIES AND STRUCTURE OF POLYMERS
  Arthur V. Tobolsky

MAGNESIUM AND ITS ALLOYS
  C. Sheldon Roberts

PHYSICAL METALLURGY
  Bruce Chalmers

FERRITES
  J. Smit and H. P. J. Wijn

ZONE MELTING
  William G. Pfann

THE METALLURGY OF VANADIUM
  William Rostoker

INTRODUCTION TO SOLID STATE PHYSICS, SECOND EDITION
  Charles Kittel